Louis Cumberbatch

Radiate Science knowledge with CGP...

OK, so there's a lot to learn in GCSE Combined Science — it is worth two GCSEs, after all.

Not to worry. This chunky CGP book explains all the facts, theory and practical skills you'll need, with essential exam practice questions on every page. It's a beautiful thing.

How to access your free Online Edition

This book includes a free Online Edition to read on your PC, Mac or tablet. To access it, just go to **cgpbooks.co.uk/extras** and enter this code...

2016 7640 2707 7075

By the way, this code only works for one person. If somebody else has used this book before you, they might have already claimed the Online Edition.

CGP — still the best! ☺

Our sole aim here at CGP is to produce the highest quality books — carefully written, immaculately presented and dangerously close to being funny.

Then we work our socks off to get them out to you — at the cheapest possible prices.

Contents

Published by CGP.
From original material by Richard Parsons.

Editors: Katie Braid, Charlotte Burrows, Katherine Faudemer, Robin Flello, Emily Howe, Chris McGarry, Ciara McGlade, Sarah Pattison, Frances Rooney, Hayley Thompson, Charlotte Whiteley, Sarah Williams and Jonathan Wray.
Contributors: Michael Bossart and Paddy Gannon.

With thanks to Sophie Scott and Karen Wells for the proofreading.

With thanks to Ana Pungartnik for the copyright research.

Printed by Elanders Ltd, Newcastle upon Tyne.
Clipart from Corel®

The Scientific Method

This section isn't about how to 'do' science — but it does show you the way most scientists work.

Scientists Come Up With Hypotheses — Then Test Them

1) Scientists try to explain things. They start by observing something they don't understand.
2) They then come up with a hypothesis — a possible explanation for what they've observed.
3) The next step is to test whether the hypothesis might be right or not. This involves making a prediction based on the hypothesis and testing it by gathering evidence (i.e. data) from investigations. If evidence from experiments backs up a prediction, you're a step closer to figuring out if the hypothesis is true.

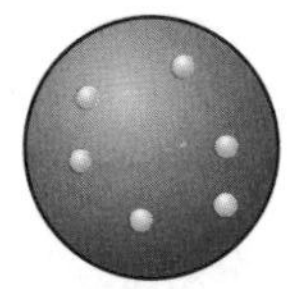

About 100 years ago, scientists hypothesised that atoms looked like this.

Several Scientists Will Test a Hypothesis

1) Normally, scientists share their findings in peer-reviewed journals, or at conferences.
2) Peer-review is where other scientists check results and scientific explanations to make sure they're 'scientific' (e.g. that experiments have been done in a sensible way) before they're published. It helps to detect false claims, but it doesn't mean that findings are correct — just that they're not wrong in any obvious way.
3) Once other scientists have found out about a hypothesis, they'll start basing their own predictions on it and carry out their own experiments. They'll also try to reproduce the original experiments to check the results — and if all the experiments in the world back up the hypothesis, then scientists start to think the hypothesis is true.
4) However, if a scientist does an experiment that doesn't fit with the hypothesis (and other scientists can reproduce the results) then the hypothesis may need to be modified or scrapped altogether.

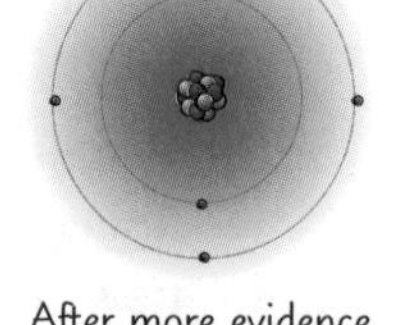

After more evidence was gathered, scientists changed their hypothesis to this.

If All the Evidence Supports a Hypothesis, It's Accepted — For Now

1) Accepted hypotheses are often referred to as theories. Our currently accepted theories are the ones that have survived this 'trial by evidence' — they've been tested many times over the years and survived.
2) However, theories never become totally indisputable fact. If new evidence comes along that can't be explained using the existing theory, then the hypothesising and testing is likely to start all over again.

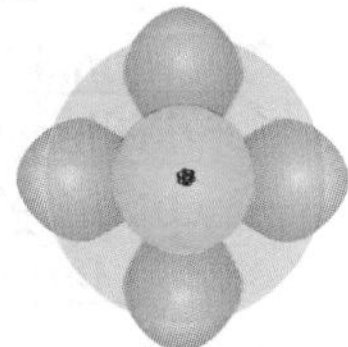

Now we think it's more like this.

Theories Can Involve Different Types of Models

1) A representational model is a simplified description or picture of what's going on in real life. Like all models, it can be used to explain observations and make predictions. E.g. the Bohr model of an atom is a simplified way of showing the arrangement of electrons in an atom (see p.103). It can be used to explain trends down groups in the periodic table.
2) Computational models use computers to make simulations of complex real-life processes, such as climate change. They're used when there are a lot of different variables (factors that change) to consider, and because you can easily change their design to take into account new data.
3) All models have limitations on what they can explain or predict. E.g. ball and stick models (a type of spatial model) can be used to show how ions are arranged in an ionic compound. One of their limitations is that they don't show the relative sizes of the ions (see p.114).

Scientists test models by carrying out experiments to check that the predictions made by the model happen as expected.

I'm off to the zoo to test my hippo-thesis...

The scientific method has developed over time, and many people have helped to develop it. From Aristotle to modern day scientists, lots of people have contributed. And many more are likely to contribute in the future.

Communication & Issues Created by Science

Scientific developments can be great, but they can sometimes raise more questions than they answer...

It's Important to Communicate Scientific Discoveries to the General Public

Some scientific discoveries show that people should change their habits, or they might provide ideas that could be developed into new technology. So scientists need to tell the world about their discoveries.

Gene technologies are used in genetic engineering to produce genetically modified crops. Information about these crops needs to be communicated to farmers who might benefit from growing them and to the general public, so they can make informed decisions about the food they buy and eat.

Scientific Evidence can be Presented in a Biased Way

1) Reports about scientific discoveries in the media (e.g. newspapers or television) aren't peer-reviewed.
2) This means that, even though news stories are often based on data that has been peer-reviewed, the data might be presented in a way that is over-simplified or inaccurate, making it open to misinterpretation.
3) People who want to make a point can sometimes present data in a biased way. (Sometimes without knowing they're doing it.) For example, a scientist might overemphasise a relationship in the data, or a newspaper article might describe details of data supporting an idea without giving any evidence against it.

Scientific Developments are Great, but they can Raise Issues

Scientific knowledge is increased by doing experiments. And this knowledge leads to scientific developments, e.g. new technologies or new advice. These developments can create issues though. For example:

Economic issues: Society can't always afford to do things scientists recommend (e.g. investing in alternative energy sources) without cutting back elsewhere.

Personal issues: Some decisions will affect individuals. For example, someone might support alternative energy, but object if a wind farm is built next to their house.

Social issues: Decisions based on scientific evidence affect people — e.g. should fossil fuels be taxed more highly? Would the effect on people's lifestyles be acceptable...

Environmental issues: Human activity often affects the natural environment. For example, building a dam to produce electricity will change the local habitat so some species might be displaced. But it will also reduce our need for fossil fuels, so will help to reduce climate change.

Science Can't Answer Every Question — Especially Ethical Ones

1) We don't understand everything. We're always finding out more, but we'll never know all the answers.
2) In order to answer scientific questions, scientists need data to provide evidence for their hypotheses.
3) Some questions can't be answered yet because the data can't currently be collected, or because there's not enough data to support a theory.
4) Eventually, as we get more evidence, we'll answer some of the questions that currently can't be answered, e.g. what the impact of global warming on sea levels will be. But there will always be the "Should we be doing this at all?"-type questions that experiments can't help us to answer...

Think about new drugs which can be taken to boost your 'brain power'.

- Some people think they're good as they could improve concentration or memory. New drugs could let people think in ways beyond the powers of normal brains.
- Other people say they're bad — they could give you an unfair advantage in exams. And people might be pressured into taking them so that they could work more effectively, and for longer hours.

Tea to milk or milk to tea? — Totally unanswerable by science...

Science can't tell you whether or not you should do something. That's for you and society to decide. But there are tons of questions science might be able to answer, like where life came from and where my superhero socks are.

Risk

By reading this page you are agreeing to the risk of a paper cut or severe drowsiness...

Nothing is Completely Risk-Free

1) A hazard is something that could potentially cause harm.
2) All hazards have a risk attached to them — this is the chance that the hazard will cause harm.
3) The risks of some things seem pretty obvious, or we've known about them for a while, like the risk of causing acid rain by polluting the atmosphere, or of having a car accident when you're travelling in a car.
4) New technology arising from scientific advances can bring new risks, e.g. scientists are unsure whether nanoparticles that are being used in cosmetics and suncream might be harming the cells in our bodies. These risks need to be considered alongside the benefits of the technology, e.g. improved sun protection.
5) You can estimate the size of a risk based on how many times something happens in a big sample (e.g. 100 000 people) over a given period (e.g. a year). For example, you could assess the risk of a driver crashing by recording how many people in a group of 100 000 drivers crashed their cars over a year.
6) To make decisions about activities that involve hazards, we need to take into account the chance of the hazard causing harm, and how serious the consequences would be if it did. If an activity involves a hazard that's very likely to cause harm, with serious consequences if it does, it's considered high risk.

People Make Their Own Decisions About Risk

1) Not all risks have the same consequences, e.g. if you chop veg with a sharp knife you risk cutting your finger, but if you go scuba-diving you risk death. You're much more likely to cut your finger during half an hour of chopping than to die during half an hour of scuba-diving. But most people are happier to accept a higher probability of an accident if the consequences are short-lived and fairly minor.
2) People tend to be more willing to accept a risk if they choose to do something (e.g. go scuba diving), compared to having the risk imposed on them (e.g. having a nuclear power station built next door).
3) People's perception of risk (how risky they think something is) isn't always accurate. They tend to view familiar activities as low-risk and unfamiliar activities as high-risk — even if that's not the case. For example, cycling on roads is often high-risk, but many people are happy to do it because it's a familiar activity. Air travel is actually pretty safe, but a lot of people perceive it as high-risk.
4) People may underestimate the risk of things with long-term or invisible effects, e.g. using tanning beds.

Investigations Can be Hazardous

1) Hazards from science experiments might include:
   - Microorganisms, e.g. some bacteria can make you ill.
   - Chemicals, e.g. sulfuric acid can burn your skin and alcohols catch fire easily.
   - Fire, e.g. an unattended Bunsen burner is a fire hazard.
   - Electricity, e.g. faulty electrical equipment could give you a shock.

Hmm... Where did my bacteria sample go?

2) Part of planning an investigation is making sure that it's safe.
3) You should always make sure that you identify all the hazards that you might encounter. Then you should think of ways of reducing the risks from the hazards you've identified. For example:
   - If you're working with sulfuric acid, always wear gloves and safety goggles. This will reduce the risk of the acid coming into contact with your skin and eyes.
   - If you're using a Bunsen burner, stand it on a heat proof mat. This will reduce the risk of starting a fire.

You can find out about potential hazards by looking in textbooks, doing some Internet research, or asking your teacher.

Not revising — an unacceptable exam hazard...

The world's a dangerous place, but if you can recognise hazards, decide how to reduce their risks, and be happy to accept some risks, you can still have fun. Just maybe don't go skydiving with a great white shark on Friday 13th.

Designing Investigations

Dig out your lab coat and dust down your badly-scratched safety goggles... it's investigation time.

Investigations Produce Evidence to Support or Disprove a Hypothesis

1) Scientists observe things and come up with hypotheses to explain them (see p.1). You need to be able to do the same. For example:

   Observation: People have big feet and spots. Hypothesis: Having big feet causes spots.

2) To determine whether or not a hypothesis is right, you need to do an investigation to gather evidence. To do this, you need to use your hypothesis to make a prediction — something you think will happen that you can test. E.g. people who have bigger feet will have more spots.
3) Investigations are used to see if there are patterns or relationships between two variables, e.g. to see if there's a pattern or relationship between the variables 'number of spots' and 'size of feet'.

Evidence Needs to be Repeatable, Reproducible and Valid

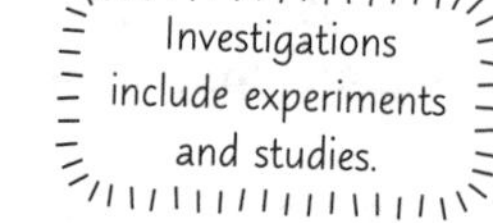

1) Repeatable means that if the same person does an experiment again using the same methods and equipment, they'll get similar results.
2) Reproducible means that if someone else does the experiment, or a different method or piece of equipment is used, the results will still be similar.
3) If data is repeatable and reproducible, it's reliable and scientists are more likely to have confidence in it.
4) Valid results are both repeatable and reproducible AND they answer the original question. They come from experiments that were designed to be a FAIR TEST...

To Make an Investigation a Fair Test You Have to Control the Variables

1) In a lab experiment you usually change one variable and measure how it affects another variable.
2) To make it a fair test, everything else that could affect the results should stay the same — otherwise you can't tell if the thing you're changing is causing the results or not.
3) The variable you CHANGE is called the INDEPENDENT variable.
4) The variable you MEASURE when you change the independent variable is the DEPENDENT variable.
5) The variables that you KEEP THE SAME are called CONTROL variables.

   You could find how temperature affects the rate of an enzyme-controlled reaction. The independent variable is the temperature. The dependent variable is the rate of reaction. Control variables include the concentration and amounts of reactants, pH, the time period you measure, etc.

6) Because you can't always control all the variables, you often need to use a control experiment. This is an experiment that's kept under the same conditions as the rest of the investigation, but doesn't have anything done to it. This is so that you can see what happens when you don't change anything at all.

The Bigger the Sample Size the Better

1) Data based on small samples isn't as good as data based on large samples. A sample should represent the whole population (i.e. it should share as many of the characteristics in the population as possible) — a small sample can't do that as well. It's also harder to spot anomalies if your sample size is too small.
2) The bigger the sample size the better, but scientists have to be realistic when choosing how big. For example, if you were studying the effects of living near a nuclear power plant, it'd be great to study everyone who lived near a nuclear power plant (a huge sample), but it'd take ages and cost a bomb. It's more realistic to study a thousand people, with a range of ages, gender, and race.

This is no high street survey — it's a designer investigation...

Not only do you need to be able to plan your own investigations, you should also be able to look at someone else's plan and decide whether or not it needs improving. Those examiners aren't half demanding.

Collecting Data

You've designed the perfect investigation — now it's time to get your hands mucky and collect some data.

Your Data Should be Repeatable, Reproducible, Accurate and Precise

1) To check repeatability you need to repeat the readings and check that the results are similar. You need to repeat each reading at least three times.
2) To make sure your results are reproducible you can cross check them by taking a second set of readings with another instrument (or a different observer).
3) Your data also needs to be ACCURATE. Really accurate results are those that are really close to the true answer. The accuracy of your results usually depends on your method — you need to make sure you're measuring the right thing and that you don't miss anything that should be included in the measurements. E.g. estimating the amount of gas released from a reaction by counting the bubbles isn't very accurate because you might miss some of the bubbles and they might have different volumes. It's more accurate to measure the volume of gas released using a gas syringe (see p.232).
4) Your data also needs to be PRECISE. Precise results are ones where the data is all really close to the mean (average) of your repeated results (i.e. not spread out).

Brian's result was a curate.

Repeat	Data set 1	Data set 2
1	12	11
2	14	17
3	13	14
Mean	13	14

Data set 1 is more precise than data set 2.

Your Equipment has to be Right for the Job

1) The measuring equipment you use has to be sensitive enough to measure the changes you're looking for. For example, if you need to measure changes of 1 cm^3 you need to use a measuring cylinder or burette that can measure in 1 cm^3 steps — it'd be no good trying with one that only measures 10 cm^3 steps.
2) The smallest change a measuring instrument can detect is called its RESOLUTION. E.g. some mass balances have a resolution of 1 g, some have a resolution of 0.1 g, and some are even more sensitive.
3) Also, equipment needs to be calibrated by measuring a known value. If there's a difference between the measured and known value, you can use this to correct the inaccuracy of the equipment.

You Need to Look out for Errors and Anomalous Results

1) The results of your experiment will always vary a bit because of RANDOM ERRORS — unpredictable differences caused by things like human errors in measuring. The errors when you make a reading from a ruler are random. You have to estimate or round the distance when it's between two marks — so sometimes your figure will be a bit above the real one, and sometimes it will be a bit below.
2) You can reduce the effect of random errors by taking repeat readings and finding the mean. This will make your results more precise.
3) If a measurement is wrong by the same amount every time, it's called a SYSTEMATIC ERROR. For example, if you measured from the very end of your ruler instead of from the 0 cm mark every time, all your measurements would be a bit small. Repeating the experiment in the exact same way and calculating a mean won't correct a systematic error.
4) Just to make things more complicated, if a systematic error is caused by using equipment that isn't zeroed properly, it's called a ZERO ERROR. For example, if a mass balance always reads 1 gram before you put anything on it, all your measurements will be 1 gram too heavy.
5) You can compensate for some systematic errors if you know about them though, e.g. if your mass balance always reads 1 gram before you put anything on it you can subtract 1 gram from all your results.
6) Sometimes you get a result that doesn't fit in with the rest at all. This is called an ANOMALOUS RESULT. You should investigate it and try to work out what happened. If you can work out what happened (e.g. you measured something totally wrong) you can ignore it when processing your results.

If there's no systematic error, then doing repeats and calculating a mean can make your results more accurate.

Watch what you say to that mass balance — it's very sensitive...

Weirdly, data can be really precise but not very accurate. For example, a fancy piece of lab equipment might give results that are really precise, but if it's not been calibrated properly those results won't be accurate.

Processing and Presenting Data

Processing your data means doing some calculations with it to make it more useful. Once you've done that, you can present your results in a nice chart or graph to help you spot any patterns in your data.

Data Needs to be Organised

Tables are dead useful for organising data. When you draw a table use a ruler and make sure each column has a heading (including the units).

You Might Have to Process Your Data

1) When you've done repeats of an experiment you should always calculate the mean (a type of average). To do this add together all the data values and divide by the total number of values in the sample.
2) You might also need to calculate the range (how spread out the data is). To do this find the largest number and subtract the smallest number from it.

Ignore anomalous results when calculating these.

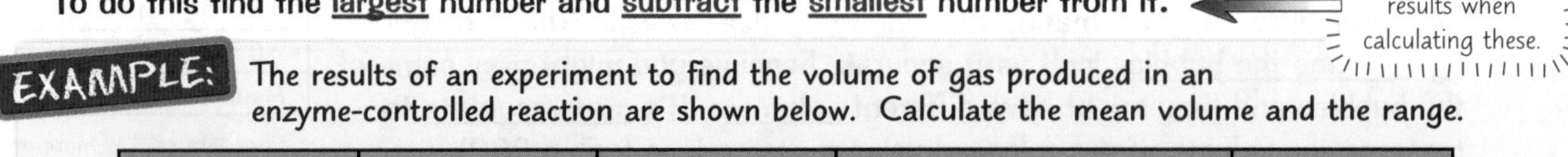

EXAMPLE: The results of an experiment to find the volume of gas produced in an enzyme-controlled reaction are shown below. Calculate the mean volume and the range.

Repeat 1 (cm^3)	Repeat 2 (cm^3)	Repeat 3 (cm^3)	Mean (cm^3)	Range (cm^3)
28	37	32	$(28 + 37 + 32) \div 3 = 32$	$37 - 28 = 9$

3) You might also need to calculate the median or mode (two more types of average). To calculate the median, put all your data in numerical order — the median is the middle value. The number that appears most often in a data set is the mode.

E.g. If you have the data set: 1 2 1 1 3 4 2
The median is: 1 1 1 2 2 3 4. The mode is 1 because 1 appears most often.

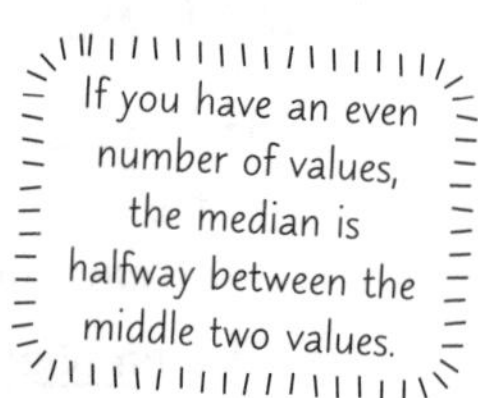

Round to the Lowest Number of Significant Figures

The first significant figure of a number is the first digit that's not zero. The second and third significant figures come straight after (even if they're zeros). You should be aware of significant figures in calculations.

1) In any calculation, you should round the answer to the lowest number of significant figures (s.f.) given.
2) Remember to write down how many significant figures you've rounded to after your answer.
3) If your calculation has multiple steps, only round the final answer, or it won't be as accurate.

The mass of a solid is 0.24 g and its volume is 0.715 cm^3. Calculate the density of the solid.

Density = 0.24 g ÷ 0.715 cm^3 = 0.33566... = 0.34 g/cm^3 (2 s.f.)

2 s.f. — 3 s.f. — Final answer should be rounded to 2 s.f.

If Your Data Comes in Categories, Present It in a Bar Chart

1) If the independent variable is categoric (comes in distinct categories, e.g. flower colour, blood group) you should use a bar chart to display the data.
2) You also use them if the independent variable is discrete (the data can be counted in chunks, where there's no in-between value, e.g. number of protons is discrete because you can't have half a proton).
3) There are some golden rules you need to follow for drawing bar charts:

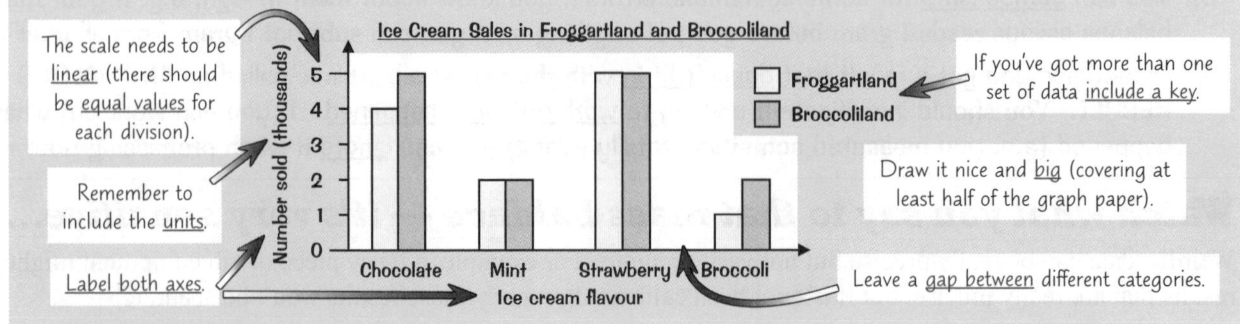

If Your Data is Continuous, Plot a Graph

If both variables are continuous (numerical data that can have any value within a range, e.g. length, volume, temperature) you should use a graph to display the data.

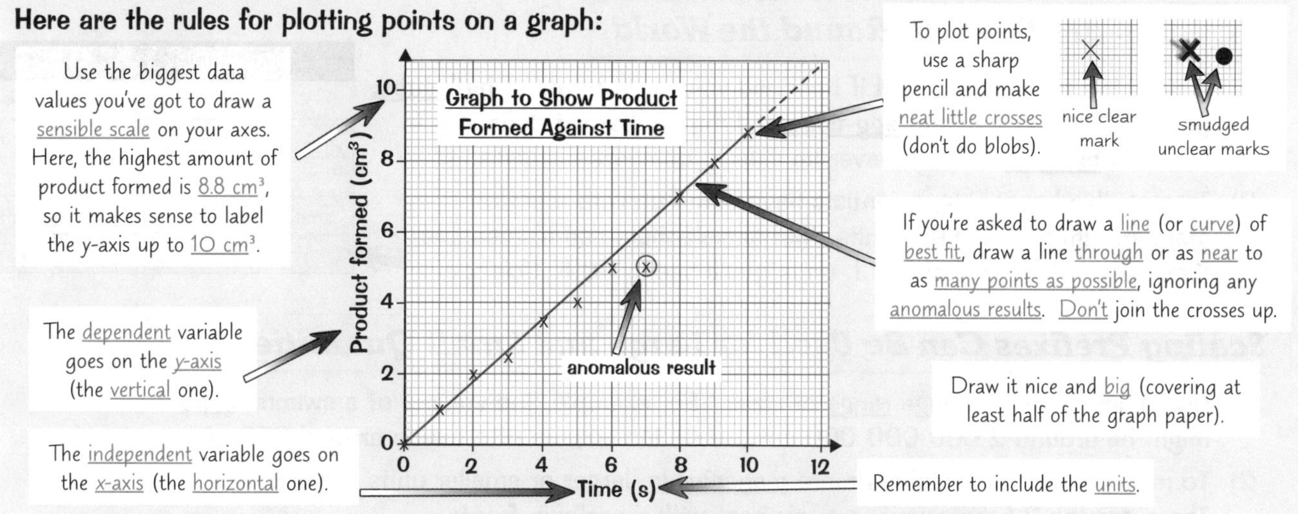

Graphs Can Give You a Lot of Information About Your Data

1) **The gradient (slope) of a graph tells you how quickly the dependent variable changes if you change the independent variable.**

$$\text{gradient} = \frac{\text{change in } y}{\text{change in } x}$$

This graph shows the volume of gas produced in a reaction against time. The graph is linear (it's a straight line graph), so you can simply calculate the gradient of the line to find out the rate of reaction.

1) **To calculate the gradient, pick two points on the line that are easy to read and a good distance apart.**
2) **Draw a line down from one of the points and a line across from the other to make a triangle. The line drawn down the side of the triangle is the change in y and the line across the bottom is the change in x.**

Change in y = 6.8 – 2.0 = 4.8 cm³   Change in x = 5.2 – 1.6 = 3.6 s

$$\text{Rate} = \text{gradient} = \frac{\text{change in } y}{\text{change in } x} = \frac{4.8\text{ cm}^3}{3.6\text{ s}} = 1.3\text{ cm}^3/\text{s}$$

The units of the gradient are (units of y)/(units of x). cm³/s can also be written as cm^3s^{-1}.

You can use this method to calculate other rates from a graph, not just the rate of a reaction. Just remember that a rate is how much something changes over time, so x needs to be the time.

2) **To find the gradient of a curve at a certain point, draw a tangent to the curve at that point and then find the gradient of the tangent.** **See page 146 for details on how to do this.**
3) **The intercept of a graph is where the line of best fit crosses one of the axes. The x-intercept is where the line of best fit crosses the x-axis and the y-intercept is where it crosses the y-axis.**

Graphs Show the Relationship Between Two Variables

1) **You can get three types of correlation (relationship) between variables:**
2) **Just because there's correlation, it doesn't mean the change in one variable is causing the change in the other — there might be other factors involved (see page 9).**

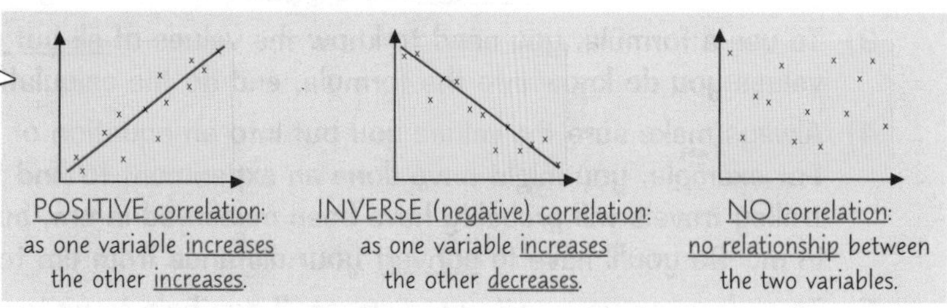

I love eating apples — I call it core elation...

Science is all about finding relationships between things. And I don't mean that scientists gather together in corners to discuss whether or not Devini and Sebastian might be a couple... though they probably do that too.

Units and Equations

Graphs and maths skills are all very well, but the numbers don't mean much if you can't get the units right.

S.I. Units Are Used All Round the World

1) It wouldn't be all that useful if I defined volume in terms of bath tubs, you defined it in terms of egg-cups and my pal Sarwat defined it in terms of balloons — we'd never be able to compare our data.
2) To stop this happening, scientists have come up with a set of standard units, called S.I. units, that all scientists use to measure their data. Here are some S.I. units you'll see in GCSE Science:

Quantity	S.I. Base Unit
mass	kilogram, kg
length	metre, m
time	second, s
amount of a substance	mole, mol
temperature	kelvin, K

Scaling Prefixes Can Be Used for Large and Small Quantities

1) Quantities come in a huge range of sizes. For example, the volume of a swimming pool might be around 2 000 000 000 cm³, while the volume of a cup is around 250 cm³.
2) To make the size of numbers more manageable, larger or smaller units are used. These are the S.I. base unit (e.g. metres) with a prefix in front:

prefix	tera (T)	giga (G)	mega (M)	kilo (k)	deci (d)	centi (c)	milli (m)	micro (μ)	nano (n)
multiple of unit	10^{12}	10^{9}	1 000 000 (10^{6})	1000	0.1	0.01	0.001	0.000001 (10^{-6})	10^{-9}

3) These prefixes tell you how much bigger or smaller a unit is than the base unit. So one kilometre is one thousand metres.

The conversion factor is the number of times the smaller unit goes into the larger unit.

4) To swap from one unit to another, all you need to know is what number you have to divide or multiply by to get from the original unit to the new unit — this is called the conversion factor.

- To go from a bigger unit (like m) to a smaller unit (like cm), you multiply by the conversion factor.
- To go from a smaller unit (like g) to a bigger unit (like kg), you divide by the conversion factor.

5) Here are some conversions that'll be useful for GCSE Science:

Mass can have units of kg and g.

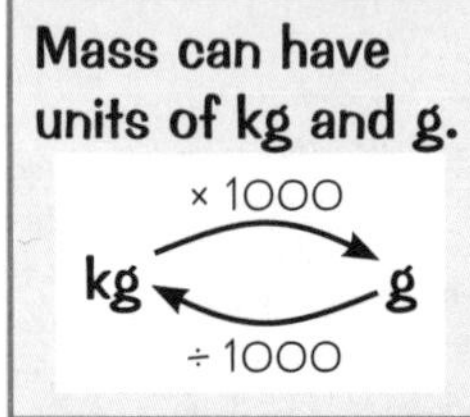

Energy can have units of J and kJ.

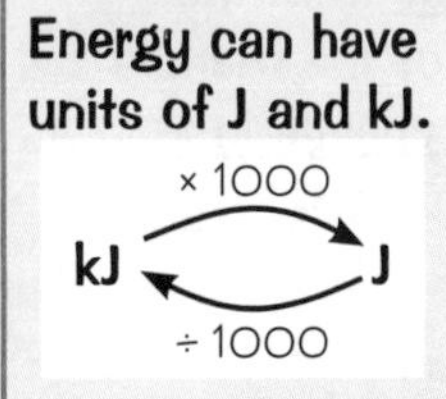

Volume can have units of m³, dm³ and cm³.

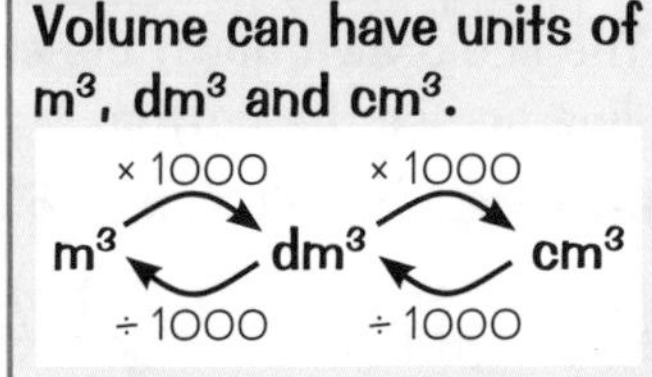

Length can have lots of units, including mm, μm and nm.

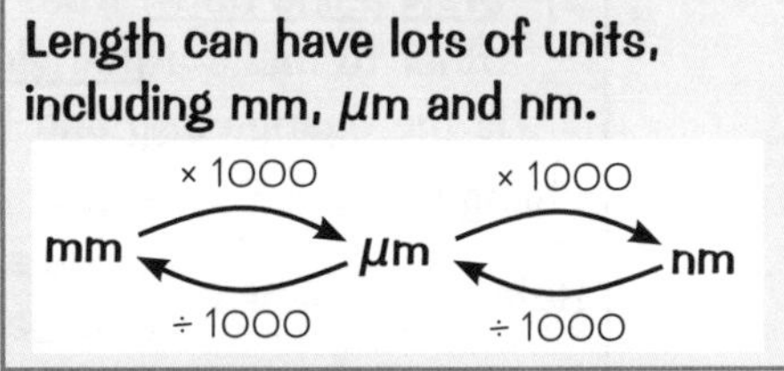

Always Check The Values Used in Equations Have the Right Units

1) Formulas and equations show relationships between variables.
2) To rearrange an equation, make sure that whatever you do to one side of the equation you also do to the other side.

You can find the speed of a wave using the equation: wave speed = frequency × wavelength. You can rearrange this equation to find the frequency by dividing each side by wavelength to give: frequency = wave speed ÷ wavelength.

3) To use a formula, you need to know the values of all but one of the variables. Substitute the values you do know into the formula, and do the calculation to work out the final variable.
4) Always make sure the values you put into an equation or formula have the right units. For example, you might have done an experiment to find the speed of a trolley. The distance the trolley travels will probably have been measured in cm, but the equation to find speed uses distance in m. So you'll have to convert your distance from cm to m before you put it into the equation.
5) To make sure your units are correct, it can help to write down the units on each line of your calculation.

I wasn't sure I liked units, but now I'm converted...

It's easy to get in a muddle when converting between units, but there's a handy way to check you've done it right. If you're moving from a smaller unit to a larger unit (e.g. g to kg) the number should get smaller, and vice versa.

Drawing Conclusions

Congratulations — you're nearly at the end of a gruelling investigation, time to draw conclusions.

You Can Only Conclude What the Data Shows and NO MORE

1) Drawing conclusions might seem pretty straightforward — you just look at your data and say what pattern or relationship you see between the dependent and independent variables.

The table on the right shows the rate of a reaction in the presence of two different catalysts:

Catalyst	Rate of reaction (cm³/s)
A	13.5
B	19.5
No catalyst	5.5

CONCLUSION: Catalyst B makes this reaction go faster than catalyst A.

2) But you've got to be really careful that your conclusion matches the data you've got and doesn't go any further.

You can't conclude that catalyst B increases the rate of any other reaction more than catalyst A — the results might be completely different.

3) You also need to be able to use your results to justify your conclusion (i.e. back up your conclusion with some specific data).

The rate of this reaction was 6 cm³/s faster using catalyst B compared with catalyst A.

4) When writing a conclusion you need to refer back to the original hypothesis and say whether the data supports it or not:

The hypothesis for this experiment might have been that catalyst B would make the reaction go quicker than catalyst A. If so, the data supports the hypothesis.

Correlation DOES NOT Mean Cause

If two things are correlated (i.e. there's a relationship between them) it doesn't necessarily mean a change in one variable is causing the change in the other — this is REALLY IMPORTANT — DON'T FORGET IT. There are three possible reasons for a correlation:

1) CHANCE: It might seem strange, but two things can show a correlation purely due to chance.

For example, one study might find a correlation between people's hair colour and how good they are at frisbee. But other scientists don't get a correlation when they investigate it — the results of the first study are just a fluke.

2) LINKED BY A 3RD VARIABLE: A lot of the time it may look as if a change in one variable is causing a change in the other, but it isn't — a third variable links the two things.

For example, there's a correlation between water temperature and shark attacks. This isn't because warmer water makes sharks crazy. Instead, they're linked by a third variable — the number of people swimming (more people swim when the water's hotter, and with more people in the water you get more shark attacks).

3) CAUSE: Sometimes a change in one variable does cause a change in the other. You can only conclude that a correlation is due to cause when you've controlled all the variables that could, just could, be affecting the result.

For example, there's a correlation between smoking and lung cancer. This is because chemicals in tobacco smoke cause lung cancer. This conclusion was only made once other variables (such as age and exposure to other things that cause cancer) had been controlled and shown not to affect people's risk of getting lung cancer.

I conclude that this page is a bit dull...

...although, just because I find it dull doesn't mean that I can conclude it's dull (you might think it's the most interesting thing since that kid got his head stuck in the railings near school). In the exams you could be given a conclusion and asked whether some data supports it — so make sure you understand how far conclusions can go.

Uncertainties and Evaluations

Hurrah! The end of another investigation. Well, now you have to work out all the things you did wrong.

Uncertainty is the Amount of Error Your Measurements Might Have

1) When you repeat a measurement, you often get a slightly different figure each time you do it due to random error. This means that each result has some uncertainty to it.
2) The measurements you make will also have some uncertainty in them due to limits in the resolution of the equipment you use (see page 5).
3) This all means that the mean of a set of results will also have some uncertainty to it. You can calculate the uncertainty of a mean result using the equation:
4) The larger the range, the less precise your results are and the more uncertainty there will be in your results. Uncertainties are shown using the '±' symbol.

The range is the largest value minus the smallest value (p.6).

The table below shows the results of a respiration experiment to determine the volume of carbon dioxide produced. Calculate the uncertainty of the mean.

Repeat	1	2	3	mean
Volume of CO_2 produced (cm^3)	20.1	19.8	20.0	20.0

1) First work out the range:
Range = 20.1 − 19.8
= 0.300 cm^3

2) Use the range to find the uncertainty:
Uncertainty = range ÷ 2 = 0.300 ÷ 2 = 0.150 cm^3. So the uncertainty of the mean = 20.0 ± 0.150 cm^3

5) Measuring a greater amount of something helps to reduce uncertainty. For example, in a rate of reaction experiment, measuring the amount of product formed over a longer period compared to a shorter period will reduce the percentage uncertainty in your results.

Evaluations — Describe How it Could be Improved

An evaluation is a critical analysis of the whole investigation.

1) You should comment on the method — was it valid? Did you control all the other variables to make it a fair test?
2) Comment on the quality of the results — was there enough evidence to reach a valid conclusion? Were the results repeatable, reproducible, accurate and precise?
3) Were there any anomalous results? If there were none then say so. If there were any, try to explain them — were they caused by errors in measurement? Were there any other variables that could have affected the results? You should comment on the level of uncertainty in your results too.
4) All this analysis will allow you to say how confident you are that your conclusion is right.
5) Then you can suggest any changes to the method that would improve the quality of the results, so that you could have more confidence in your conclusion. For example, you might suggest changing the way you controlled a variable, or increasing the number of measurements you took. Taking more measurements at narrower intervals could give you a more accurate result. For example:

Enzymes have an optimum temperature (a temperature at which they work best). Say you do an experiment to find an enzyme's optimum temperature and take measurements at 10 °C, 20 °C, 30 °C, 40 °C and 50 °C. The results of this experiment tell you the optimum is 40 °C. You could then repeat the experiment, taking more measurements around 40 °C to a get a more accurate value for the optimum.

6) You could also make more predictions based on your conclusion, then further experiments could be carried out to test them.

When suggesting improvements to the investigation, always make sure that you say why you think this would make the results better.

Evaluation — next time, I'll make sure I don't burn the lab down...

So there you have it — Working Scientifically. Make sure you know this stuff like the back of your hand. It's not just in the lab that you'll need to know how to work scientifically. You can be asked about it in the exams as well.

Cells

When someone first peered down a microscope at a slice of cork and drew the boxes they saw, little did they know that they'd seen the building blocks of every organism on the planet...

Organisms can be Prokaryotes or Eukaryotes

1) All living things are made of cells.
2) Cells can be either prokaryotic or eukaryotic. Eukaryotic cells are complex and include all animal and plant cells. Prokaryotic cells are smaller and simpler, e.g. bacteria (see below).
3) Eukaryotes are organisms that are made up of eukaryotic cells.
4) A prokaryote is a prokaryotic cell (it's a single-celled organism).

Plant and Animal Cells have Similarities and Differences

The different parts of a cell are called subcellular structures.
Most animal cells have the following subcellular structures — make sure you know them all:

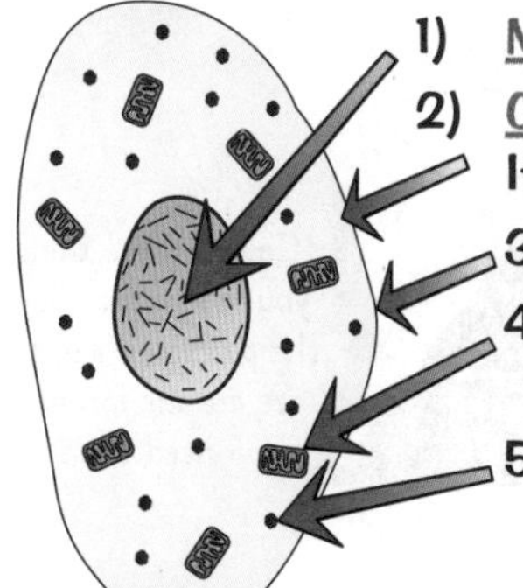

1) Nucleus — contains genetic material that controls the activities of the cell.
2) Cytoplasm — gel-like substance where most of the chemical reactions happen. It contains enzymes (see page 25) that control these chemical reactions.
3) Cell membrane — holds the cell together and controls what goes in and out.
4) Mitochondria — these are where most of the reactions for aerobic respiration take place (see page 55). Respiration transfers energy that the cell needs to work.
5) Ribosomes — these are where proteins are made in the cell.

Plant cells usually have all the bits that animal cells have, plus a few extra things that animal cells don't have:

1) Rigid cell wall — made of cellulose. It supports the cell and strengthens it.
2) Permanent vacuole — contains cell sap, a weak solution of sugar and salts.
3) Chloroplasts — these are where photosynthesis occurs, which makes food for the plant (see page 50). They contain a green substance called chlorophyll, which absorbs the light needed for photosynthesis.

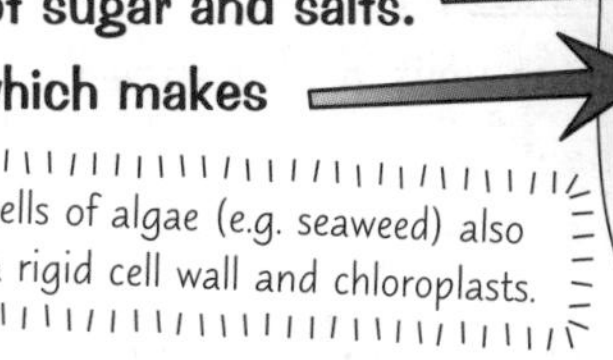

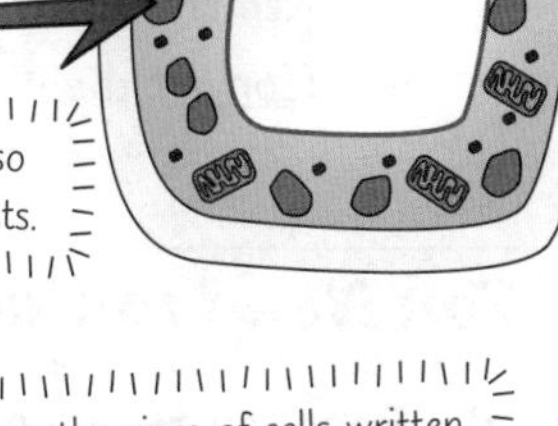

Bacterial Cells Are Much Smaller

You might see the sizes of cells written in standard form (see the next page).

Bacteria are prokaryotes. Here's what a bacterial cell might look like:

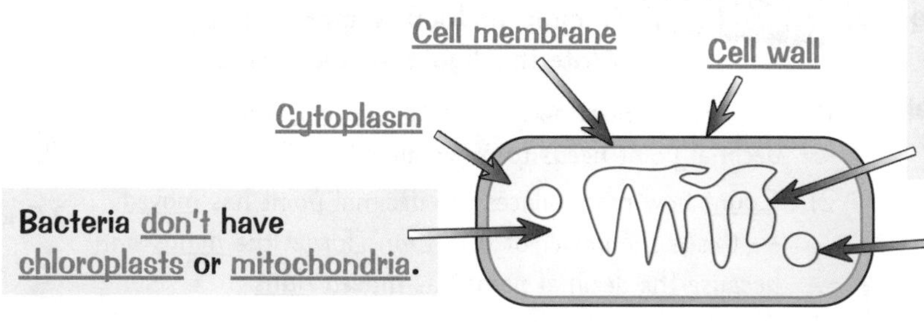

Bacterial cells don't have a 'true' nucleus — instead they have a single circular strand of DNA that floats freely in the cytoplasm.

They may also contain one or more small rings of DNA called plasmids.

Cell structures — become an estate agent...

You could get asked to estimate the area of a subcellular structure in your exam. If you do, treat it as a regular shape. For example, if it's close to a rectangle, use the area formula 'area = length × width'.

Q1 Give two differences in structure between prokaryotic and eukaryotic cells. [2 marks]

Microscopy

Microscopes are pretty important for biology. So here's a couple of pages all about them...

Cells are Studied Using Microscopes

1) Microscopes let us see things that we can't see with the naked eye. The microscopy techniques we can use have developed over the years as technology and knowledge have improved.
2) Light microscopes use light and lenses to form an image of a specimen and magnify it (make it look bigger). They let us see individual cells and large subcellular structures, like nuclei.
3) Electron microscopes use electrons instead of light to form an image. They have a much higher magnification than light microscopes.
4) They also have a higher resolution. (Resolution is the ability to distinguish between two points, so a higher resolution gives a sharper image.)
5) Electron microscopes let us see much smaller things in more detail, like the internal structure of mitochondria and chloroplasts. They even let us see tinier things like ribosomes and plasmids.

See the next page for how to use a light microscope.

You Need to be Able to Use the Formula for Magnification

You can calculate the magnification of an image using this formula:

$$\text{magnification} = \frac{\text{image size}}{\text{real size}}$$

Image size and real size should have the same units. If they don't, you'll need to convert them first (see page 8).

If you want to work out the image size or the real size of the object, you can rearrange the equation using this formula triangle:

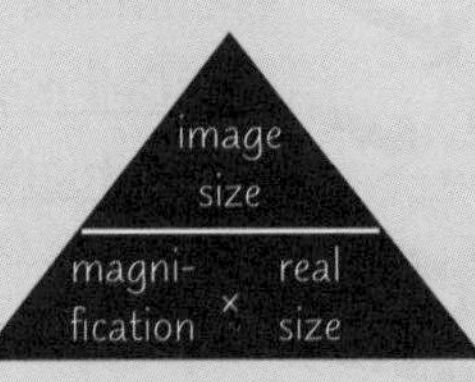

Cover up the thing you're trying to find. The parts you can still see are the formula you need to use.

A specimen is 50 μm wide. Calculate the width of the image of the specimen under a magnification of × 100. Give your answer in mm.

1) Rearrange the formula. — image size = magnification × real size
2) Fill in the values you know. — image size = 100 × 50
3) Remember the units in your answer. — = 5000 μm
4) Convert the units. — = 5 mm

Remember, to convert from micrometres (μm) to millimetres (mm), you need to divide by 1000 (see p.8). E.g. 5000 μm ÷ 1000 = 5 mm

You Need to Know How to Work With Numbers in Standard Form

1) Because microscopes can see such tiny objects, sometimes it's useful to write numbers in standard form.
2) This is where you change very big or small numbers with lots of zeros into something more manageable, e.g. 0.017 can be written 1.7×10^{-2}.
3) To do this you just need to move the decimal point left or right.
4) The number of places the decimal point moves is then represented by a power of 10 — this is positive if the decimal point's moved to the left, and negative if it's moved to the right.

A mitochondrion is approximately 0.0025 mm long. Write this figure in standard form.

1) The first number needs to be between 1 and 10 so the decimal point needs to move after the '2'.

2) Count how many places the decimal point has moved — this is the power of 10. Don't forget the minus sign because the decimal point has moved right.

2.5×10^{-3}

Your resolution to revise should be increasing right now...

Keep an eye on the units for that equation — if they're not the same, it just won't work.

Q1 An onion cell is viewed under a microscope with × 100 magnification. The image of the cell is 7.5 mm wide. What is the real width of the onion cell? Give your answer in μm. [2 marks]

More on Microscopy

PRACTICAL

It's all very well knowing what microscopes do — you also have to know how to actually use one.

You Need to Prepare Your Slide

If you want to look at a specimen (e.g. plant or animal cells) under a light microscope, you need to put it on a microscope slide first. A slide is a strip of clear glass or plastic onto which the specimen is mounted.

Here's how to prepare a slide to view onion cells:

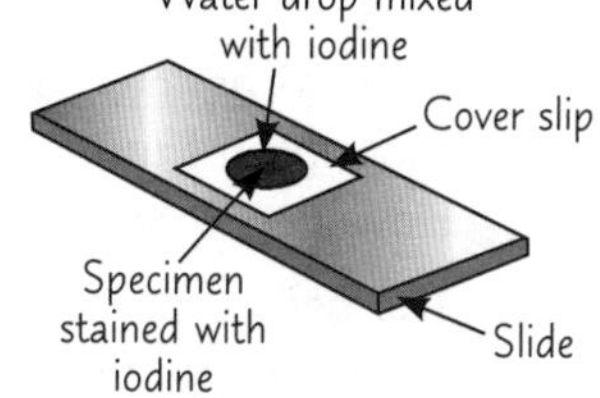

1) Add a drop of water to the middle of a clean slide.
2) Cut up an onion and separate it out into layers. Use tweezers to peel off some epidermal tissue from the bottom of one of the layers.
3) Using the tweezers, place the epidermal tissue into the water on the slide.
4) Add a drop of iodine solution. Iodine solution is a stain. Stains are used to highlight objects in a cell by adding colour to them.
5) Place a cover slip (a square of thin, transparent plastic or glass) on top. To do this, stand the cover slip upright on the slide, next to the water droplet. Then carefully tilt and lower it so it covers the specimen. Try not to get any air bubbles under there — they'll obstruct your view of the specimen.

Use a Light Microscope to Look at Your Slide

To look at your prepared slides, you need to know how to use a light microscope:

1) Clip the slide you've prepared onto the stage.
2) Select the lowest-powered objective lens (i.e. the one that produces the lowest magnification).
3) Use the coarse adjustment knob to move the stage up to just below the objective lens.
4) Look down the eyepiece. Use the coarse adjustment knob to move the stage downwards until the image is roughly in focus.
5) Adjust the focus with the fine adjustment knob, until you get a clear image of what's on the slide.
6) If you need to see the slide with greater magnification, swap to a higher-powered objective lens and refocus.

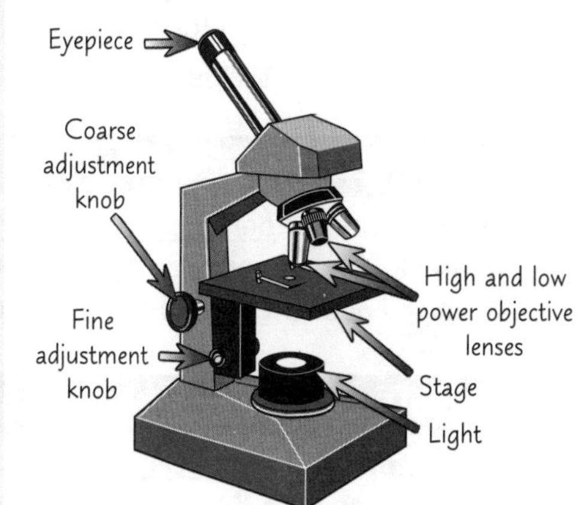

Draw Your Observations Neatly with a Pencil

1) Draw what you see under the microscope using a pencil with a sharp point.
2) Make sure your drawing takes up at least half of the space available and that it is drawn with clear, unbroken lines.
3) Your drawing should not include any colouring or shading.
4) If you are drawing cells, the subcellular structures should be drawn in proportion.
5) Remember to include a title of what you were observing and write down the magnification that it was observed under.
6) Label the important features of your drawing (e.g. nucleus, chloroplasts), using straight, uncrossed lines.

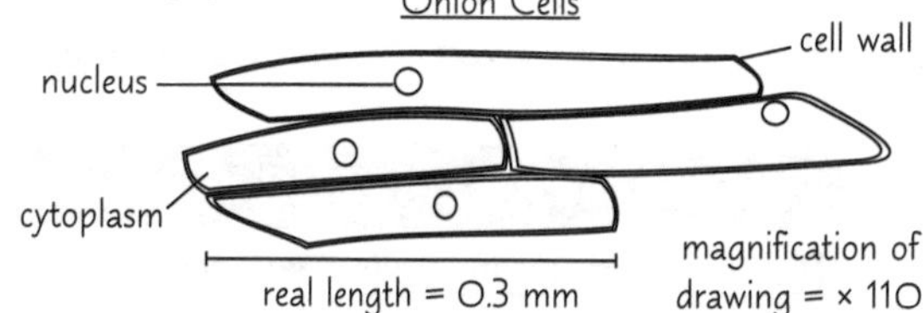

You can work out the real size of a cell by counting the number of cells you can see along 1 mm (see p.234). You can work out the magnification of your drawing using this formula: magnification = length of drawing of cell ÷ real length of cell. So here, magnification = 33 mm ÷ 0.3 mm = × 110.

A light microscope is better than a heavy one...

If you can use a microscope, you're halfway to ruling the world. That's what I like to think, anyway.

Q1 Why might you add stain to the sample on a microscope slide? [1 mark]

Cell Differentiation and Specialisation

Cells don't all look the same. They have different structures to suit their different functions.

Cells Differentiate to Become Specialised

1) Differentiation is the process by which a cell changes to become specialised for its job.
2) As cells change, they develop different subcellular structures and turn into different types of cells. This allows them to carry out specific functions.
3) Most differentiation occurs as an organism develops. In most animal cells, the ability to differentiate is then lost at an early stage, after they become specialised. However, lots of plant cells don't ever lose this ability.

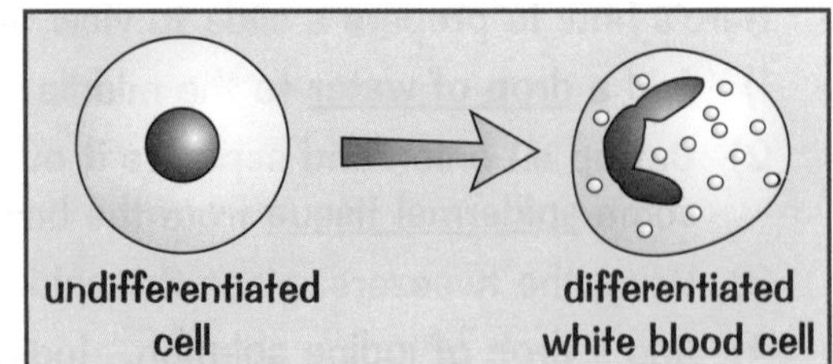

4) The cells that differentiate in mature animals are mainly used for repairing and replacing cells, such as skin or blood cells.

5) Some cells are undifferentiated cells — they're called stem cells. There's more about them on page 16.

You Need To Know These Examples of Specialised Cells

SPERM CELLS are specialised for REPRODUCTION

The function of a sperm is basically to get the male DNA to the female DNA. It has a long tail and a streamlined head to help it swim to the egg. There are a lot of mitochondria in the cell to provide the energy needed. It also carries enzymes in its head to digest through the egg cell membrane.

NERVE CELLS are specialised for RAPID SIGNALLING

The function of nerve cells is to carry electrical signals from one part of the body to another. These cells are long (to cover more distance) and have branched connections at their ends to connect to other nerve cells and form a network throughout the body.

MUSCLE CELLS are specialised for CONTRACTION

The function of a muscle cell is to contract quickly. These cells are long (so that they have space to contract) and contain lots of mitochondria to generate the energy needed for contraction.

ROOT HAIR CELLS are specialised for absorbing WATER and MINERALS

Root hair cells are cells on the surface of plant roots, which grow into long "hairs" that stick out into the soil. This gives the plant a big surface area for absorbing water and mineral ions from the soil.

PHLOEM and XYLEM CELLS are specialised for TRANSPORTING SUBSTANCES

Phloem and xylem cells form phloem and xylem tubes, which transport substances such as food and water around plants. To form the tubes, the cells are long and joined end to end. Xylem cells are hollow in the centre and phloem cells have very few subcellular structures, so that stuff can flow through them.

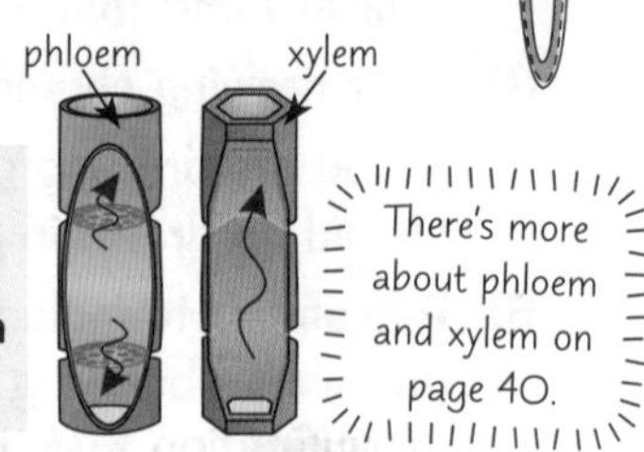

There's more about phloem and xylem on page 40.

Tadpoles and tent pegs — cells are masters of disguise...

You need to know how the structure of each of the cells on this page relates to its function. Lucky you.

Q1 Plants transport food substances from the leaves to growing parts of the plant through phloem tubes. Give one feature of a phloem cell that makes it specialised for its function. [1 mark]

Q2 Describe how a root hair cell is specialised for its function. [2 marks]

Chromosomes and Mitosis

In order to survive and grow, our cells have got to be able to divide. And that means our DNA as well...

Chromosomes Contain Genetic Information

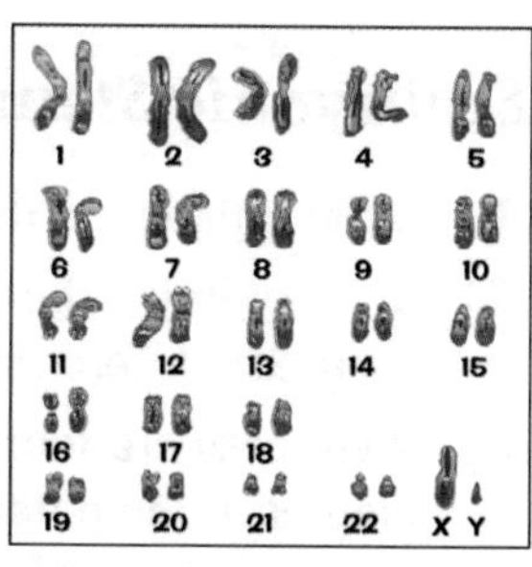

1) Most cells in your body have a nucleus. The nucleus contains your genetic material in the form of chromosomes.
2) Chromosomes are coiled up lengths of DNA molecules.
3) Each chromosome carries a large number of genes. Different genes control the development of different characteristics, e.g. hair colour.
4) Body cells normally have two copies of each chromosome — one from the organism's 'mother', and one from its 'father'. So, humans have two copies of chromosome 1, two copies of chromosome 2, etc.
5) The diagram shows the 23 pairs of chromosomes from a human cell.

The Cell Cycle Makes New Cells for Growth, Development and Repair

1) Body cells in multicellular organisms divide to produce new cells as part of a series of stages called the cell cycle.
2) The stage of the cell cycle when the cell divides is called mitosis.
3) Multicellular organisms use mitosis to grow or replace cells that have been damaged.
4) The end of the cell cycle results in two new cells identical to the original cell, with the same number of chromosomes.
5) You need to know about these two main stages of the cell cycle:

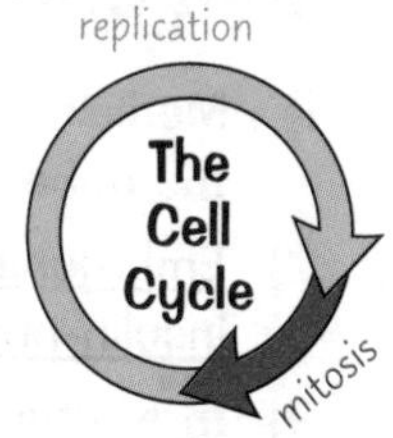

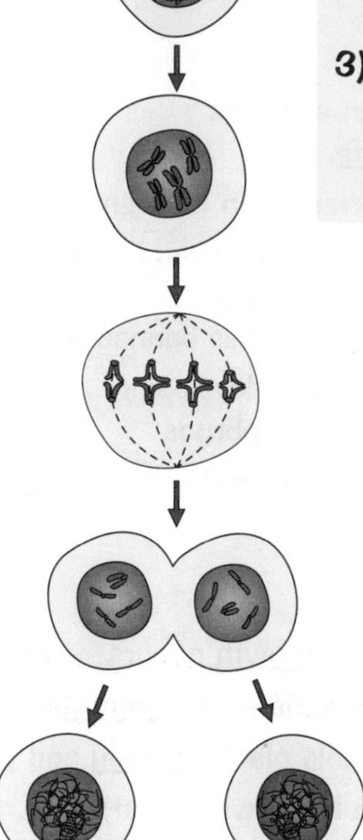

Growth & DNA Replication

1) In a cell that's not dividing, the DNA is all spread out in long strings.
2) Before it divides, the cell has to grow and increase the amount of subcellular structures such as mitochondria and ribosomes.
3) It then duplicates its DNA — so there's one copy for each new cell. The DNA is copied and forms X-shaped chromosomes. Each 'arm' of the chromosome is an exact duplicate of the other.

The left arm has the same DNA as the right arm of the chromosome.

Mitosis

Once its contents and DNA have been copied, the cell is ready for mitosis...

4) The chromosomes line up at the centre of the cell and cell fibres pull them apart. The two arms of each chromosome go to opposite ends of the cell.
5) Membranes form around each of the sets of chromosomes. These become the nuclei of the two new cells — the nucleus has divided.
6) Lastly, the cytoplasm and cell membrane divide.

The cell has now produced two new daughter cells. The daughter cells contain exactly the same DNA — they're identical. Their DNA is also identical to the parent cell.

A cell's favourite computer game — divide and conquer...

Mitosis can seem tricky at first. But don't worry — just go through it slowly, one step at a time. This type of division produces identical cells, but there's another type which doesn't... (see page 70).

Q1 Describe the events of the cell cycle that need to occur before mitosis can begin. [2 marks]

Stem Cells

Stem cell research has exciting possibilities, but it's also pretty controversial.

Embryonic Stem Cells Can Turn into ANY Type of Cell

1) Differentiation is the process by which a cell changes to become specialised for its job — see p.14.
2) Undifferentiated cells, called stem cells, can divide to produce lots more undifferentiated cells. They can differentiate into different types of cell, depending on what instructions they're given.
3) Stem cells are found in early human embryos. They're exciting to doctors and medical researchers because they have the potential to turn into any kind of cell at all. This makes sense if you think about it — all the different types of cell found in a human being have to come from those few cells in the early embryo.
4) Adults also have stem cells, but they're only found in certain places, like bone marrow. Unlike embryonic stem cells, they can't turn into any cell type at all, only certain ones, such as blood cells.
5) Stem cells from embryos and bone marrow can be grown in a lab to produce clones (genetically identical cells) and made to differentiate into specialised cells to use in medicine or research.

Stem Cells May Be Able to Cure Many Diseases

1) Medicine already uses adult stem cells to cure disease. For example, stem cells transferred from the bone marrow of a healthy person can replace faulty blood cells in the patient who receives them.
2) Embryonic stem cells could also be used to replace faulty cells in sick people — you could make insulin-producing cells for people with diabetes, nerve cells for people paralysed by spinal injuries, and so on.
3) In a type of cloning, called therapeutic cloning, an embryo could be made to have the same genetic information as the patient. This means that the stem cells produced from it would also contain the same genes and so wouldn't be rejected by the patient's body if used to replace faulty cells.
4) However, there are risks involved in using stem cells in medicine. For example, stem cells grown in the lab may become contaminated with a virus which could be passed on to the patient and so make them sicker.

Some People Are Against Stem Cell Research

1) Some people are against stem cell research because they feel that human embryos shouldn't be used for experiments since each one is a potential human life.
2) Others think that curing existing patients who are suffering is more important than the rights of embryos.
3) One fairly convincing argument in favour of this point of view is that the embryos used in the research are usually unwanted ones from fertility clinics which, if they weren't used for research, would probably just be destroyed. But of course, campaigners for the rights of embryos usually want this banned too.
4) These campaigners feel that scientists should concentrate more on finding and developing other sources of stem cells, so people could be helped without having to use embryos.
5) In some countries stem cell research is banned. It's allowed in the UK as long as it follows strict guidelines.

Stem Cells Can Produce Identical Plants

1) In plants, stem cells are found in the meristems (parts of the plant where growth occurs — see p.39).
2) Throughout the plant's entire life, cells in the meristem tissues can differentiate into any type of plant cell.
3) These stem cells can be used to produce clones (identical copies) of whole plants quickly and cheaply.
4) They can be used to grow more plants of rare species (to prevent them being wiped out).
5) Stem cells can also be used to grow crops of identical plants that have desired features for farmers, for example, disease resistance.

But florists cell stems, and nobody complains about that...

Whatever your opinion is, make sure know the uses of stem cells and the arguments for and against using them.

Q1 How can stem cells be used to preserve rare plant species? [2 marks]

Diffusion

Particles move about randomly, and after a bit they end up evenly spaced. It's not rocket science, is it...

Don't Be Put Off by the Fancy Word

1) "Diffusion" is simple. It's just the gradual movement of particles from places where there are lots of them to places where there are fewer of them — it's just the natural tendency for stuff to spread out.
2) Unfortunately you also have to learn the fancy way of saying the same thing, which is this:

DIFFUSION is the SPREADING OUT of particles from an area of HIGHER CONCENTRATION to an area of LOWER CONCENTRATION.

4) Diffusion happens in both solutions and gases — that's because the particles in these substances are free to move about randomly.
5) The simplest type is when different gases diffuse through each other. This is what's happening when the smell of perfume diffuses through the air in a room:

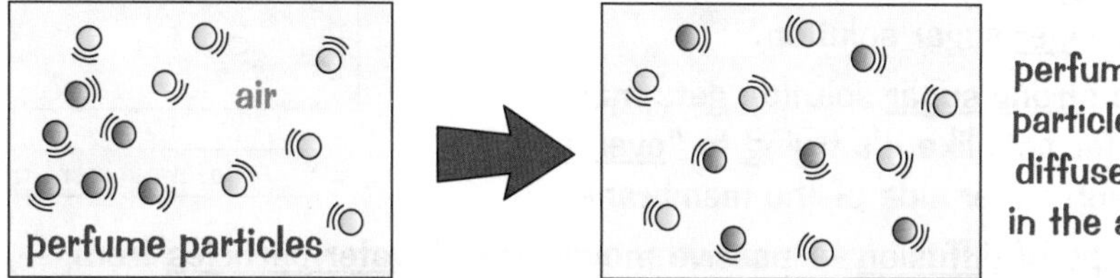

6) The bigger the concentration gradient (the difference in concentration), the faster the diffusion rate.
7) A higher temperature will also give a faster diffusion rate because the particles have more energy, so move around faster.

Cell Membranes Are Kind of Clever...

1) They're clever because they hold the cell together BUT they let stuff in and out as well.
2) Dissolved substances can move in and out of cells by diffusion.
3) Only very small molecules can diffuse through cell membranes though — things like oxygen (needed for respiration — see page 55), glucose, amino acids and water.
4) Big molecules like starch and proteins can't fit through the membrane:

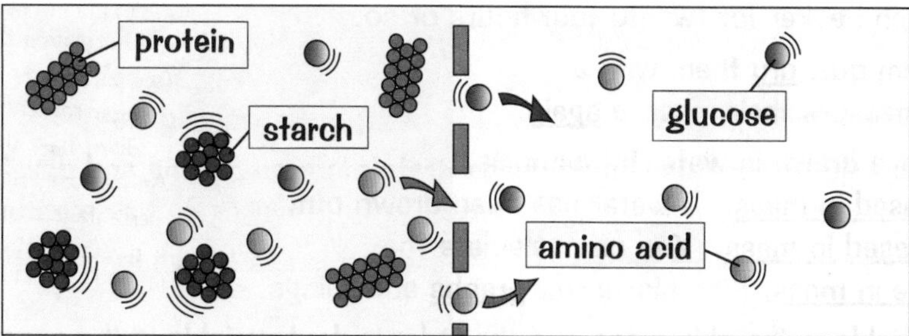

5) Just like with diffusion in air, particles flow through the cell membrane from where there's a higher concentration (a lot of them) to where there's a lower concentration (not such a lot of them).
6) They're only moving about randomly of course, so they go both ways — but if there are a lot more particles on one side of the membrane, there's a net (overall) movement from that side.
7) The larger the surface area of the membrane, the faster the diffusion rate, because more particles can pass through at once — see page 20.

Revision by diffusion — you wish...

Wouldn't it be great if all the ideas in this book would just gradually drift across into your mind...

Q1 A student adds a drop of ink to a glass of cold water.

a) What will the student observe to happen to the drop of ink. Explain your answer. [2 marks]

b) How might the observation differ if the ink was added to a glass of warm water? [1 mark]

Osmosis

If you've got your head round diffusion, osmosis will be a breeze. If not, have another read of the previous page.

Osmosis is a Special Case of Diffusion, That's All

OSMOSIS is the movement of water molecules across a partially permeable membrane from a region of higher water concentration to a region of lower water concentration.

1) A partially permeable membrane is just one with very small holes in it. So small, in fact, only tiny molecules (like water) can pass through them, and bigger molecules (e.g. sucrose) can't.
2) The water molecules actually pass both ways through the membrane during osmosis. This happens because water molecules move about randomly all the time.
3) But because there are more water molecules on one side than on the other, there's a steady net flow of water into the region with fewer water molecules, i.e. into the stronger sugar solution.
4) This means the strong sugar solution gets more dilute. The water acts like it's trying to "even up" the concentration either side of the membrane.

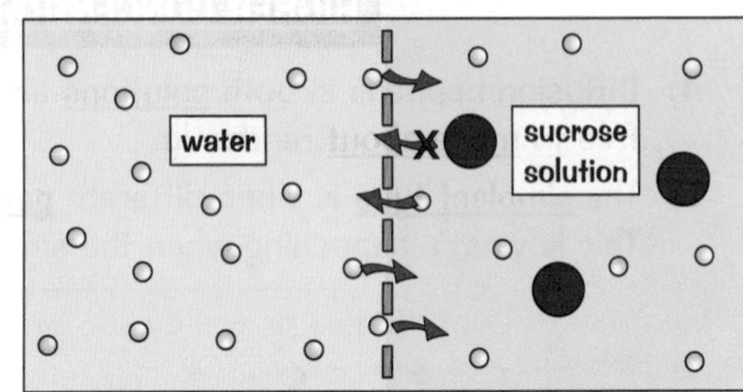

5) Osmosis is a type of diffusion — passive movement of water particles from an area of higher water concentration to an area of lower water concentration.

You can Observe the Effect of Sugar Solutions on Plant Tissue

PRACTICAL

There's a fairly dull experiment you can do to show osmosis at work.

1) You cut up an innocent potato into identical cylinders, and get some beakers with different sugar solutions in them. One should be pure water and another should be a very concentrated sugar solution (e.g. 1 mol/dm^3). Then you can have a few others with concentrations in between (e.g. 0.2 mol/dm^3, 0.4 mol/dm^3, 0.6 mol/dm^3, etc.)

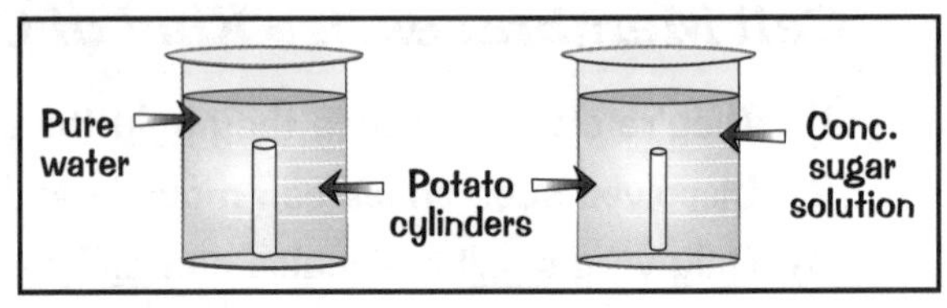

2) You measure the mass of the cylinders, then leave one cylinder in each beaker for twenty four hours or so.
3) Then you take them out, dry them with a paper towel and measure their masses again.
4) If the cylinders have drawn in water by osmosis, they'll have increased in mass. If water has been drawn out, they'll have decreased in mass. You can calculate the percentage change in mass, then plot a few graphs and things.

By calculating the percentage change (see p.241), you can compare the effect of sugar concentration on cylinders that didn't have the same initial mass. An increase in mass will give a positive percentage change and a decrease will give a negative percentage change.

5) The dependent variable is the chip mass and the independent variable is the concentration of the sugar solution. All other variables (volume of solution, temperature, time, type of sugar used, etc. etc.) must be kept the same in each case or the experiment won't be a fair test.
6) Like any experiment, you need to be aware of how errors (see p.5) may arise. Sometimes they may occur when carrying out the method, e.g. if some potato cylinders were not fully dried, the excess water would give a higher mass, or if water evaporated from the beakers, the concentrations of the sugar solutions would change. You can reduce the effect of these errors by repeating the experiment and calculating a mean percentage change at each concentration.

You could also carry out this experiment using different salt solutions and see what effect they have on potato chip mass.

And to all you cold-hearted potato murderers...

Just remember, osmosis is really just a fancy word for the diffusion of water molecules. It's simple really.

Q1 Explain what will happen to the mass of a piece of potato added to a concentrated salt solution. [2 marks]

Active Transport

Sometimes substances need to be absorbed against a concentration gradient, i.e. from a lower to a higher concentration. This process is lovingly referred to as ACTIVE TRANSPORT.

Root Hairs Take In Minerals and Water

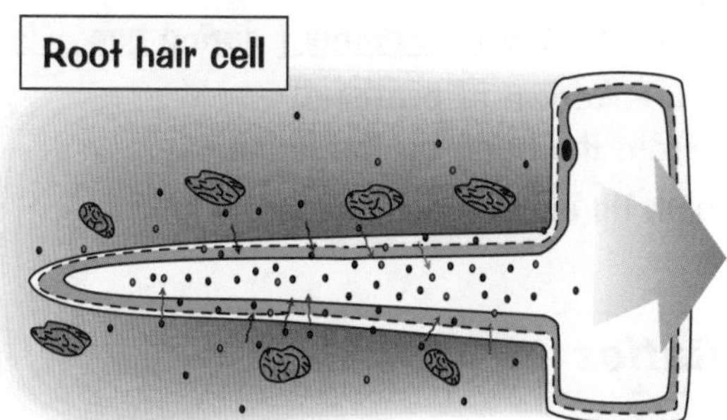

1) As you saw on page 14, the cells on plant roots grow into "hairs" which stick out into the soil.
2) Each branch of a root will be covered in millions of these microscopic hairs.
3) This gives the plant a large surface area for absorbing water and mineral ions from the soil.
4) Plants need these mineral ions for healthy growth.
5) The concentration of minerals is usually higher in the root hair cells than in the soil around them.
6) So the root hair cells can't use diffusion to take up minerals from the soil.

Root Hairs Take in Minerals Using Active Transport

Water is taken into root hair cells by osmosis (see page 18).

1) Minerals should move out of the root hairs if they followed the rules of diffusion. The cells must use another method to draw them in.
2) That method is, in fact, a conveniently mysterious process called "active transport".
3) Active transport allows the plant to absorb minerals from a very dilute solution, against a concentration gradient. This is essential for its growth. But active transport needs ENERGY from respiration to make it work.
4) Active transport also happens in humans, for example in taking glucose from the gut (see below), and from the kidney tubules.

We Need Active Transport to Stop Us Starving

Active transport is used in the gut when there is a lower concentration of nutrients in the gut, but a higher concentration of nutrients in the blood.

1) When there's a higher concentration of glucose and amino acids in the gut they diffuse naturally into the blood.
2) BUT — sometimes there's a lower concentration of nutrients in the gut than there is in the blood.
3) This means that the concentration gradient is the wrong way.
4) The same process used in plant roots is used here...

   ..."Active transport".

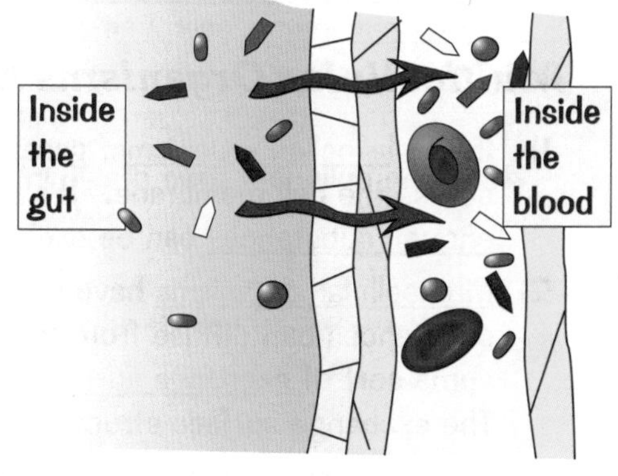

5) Active transport allows nutrients to be taken into the blood, despite the fact that the concentration gradient is the wrong way.
6) This means that glucose can be taken into the bloodstream when its concentration in the blood is already higher than in the gut. It can then be transported to cells, where it's used for respiration (see p.54).

Active transport — get on yer bike...

An important difference between active transport and diffusion is that active transport uses energy. Imagine a pen of sheep in a field. If you open the pen, the sheep will happily diffuse from the area of higher sheep concentration into the field, which has a lower sheep concentration — you won't have to do a thing. To get them back in the pen though, you'll have to put in quite a bit of energy.

Q1 What is the purpose of active transport in the gut? [1 mark]

Exchange Surfaces

How easily stuff moves between an organism and its environment depends on its surface area to volume ratio.

Organisms Exchange Substances with their Environment

1) Cells can use diffusion to take in substances they need and get rid of waste products. For example:
   - Oxygen and carbon dioxide are transferred between cells and the environment during gas exchange.
   - In humans, urea (a waste product produced from the breakdown of proteins) diffuses from cells into the blood plasma for removal from the body by the kidneys.
2) How easy it is for an organism to exchange substances with its environment depends on the organism's surface area to volume ratio (SA : V).

You Can Compare Surface Area to Volume Ratios

A ratio shows how big one value is compared to another. The larger an organism is, the smaller its surface area is compared to its volume. You can show this by calculating surface area to volume ratios:

A hippo can be represented by a 2 cm × 4 cm × 4 cm block.

The area of a surface is found by the equation: LENGTH × WIDTH

So the hippo's total surface area is:

(4 × 4) × 2 (top and bottom surfaces of block)
+ (4 × 2) × 4 (four sides of the block)
= 64 cm^2.

The volume of a block is found by the equation: LENGTH × WIDTH × HEIGHT

So the hippo's volume is 4 × 4 × 2 = 32 cm^3.

The surface area to volume ratio of the hippo can be written as 64 : 32.
To simplify the ratio, divide both sides of the ratio by the volume.
So the surface area to volume ratio of the hippo is 2 : 1.

A mouse can be represented by a 1 cm × 1 cm × 1 cm block.
Its surface area is (1 × 1) × 6 = 6 cm^2.
Its volume is 1 × 1 × 1 = 1 cm^3.
So the surface area to volume ratio of the mouse is 6 : 1.

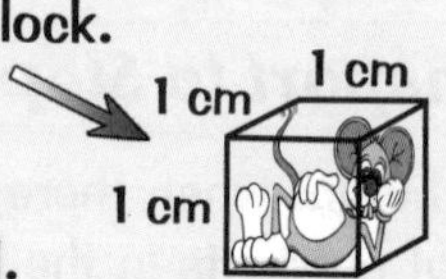

The cube mouse's surface area is six times its volume, but the cube hippo's surface area is only twice its volume. So the mouse has a larger surface area compared to its volume.

Multicellular Organisms Need Exchange Surfaces

1) In single-celled organisms, gases and dissolved substances can diffuse directly into (or out of) the cell across the cell membrane. It's because they have a large surface area compared to their volume, so enough substances can be exchanged across the membrane to supply the volume of the cell.
2) Multicellular organisms have a smaller surface area compared to their volume — not enough substances can diffuse from their outside surface to supply their entire volume. This means they need some sort of exchange surface for efficient diffusion (see pages 21-22 for some examples). The exchange surface structures have to allow enough of the necessary substances to pass through.
3) Exchange surfaces are ADAPTED to maximise effectiveness:
   - They have a thin membrane, so substances only have a short distance to diffuse.
   - They have a large surface area so lots of a substance can diffuse at once.
   - Exchange surfaces in animals have lots of blood vessels, to get stuff into and out of the blood quickly.
   - Gas exchange surfaces in animals (e.g. alveoli) are often ventilated too — air moves in and out.

Not that I'm endorsing putting animals in boxes...

A large surface area is a key way that organisms' exchange surfaces are made more effective.

Q1 A bacterial cell can be represented by a 2 μm × 2 μm × 1 μm block.
Calculate the cell's surface area to volume ratio. [3 marks]

Exchanging Substances

This page is about how two different parts of the human body are adapted so that substances can diffuse through them most effectively. The first bit is about how gases in the lungs get into and out of the blood. The second is about how digested food gets from the gut to the blood.

Gas Exchange Happens in the Lungs

1) The job of the lungs is to transfer oxygen to the blood and to remove waste carbon dioxide from it.
2) To do this the lungs contain millions of little air sacs called alveoli where gas exchange takes place.

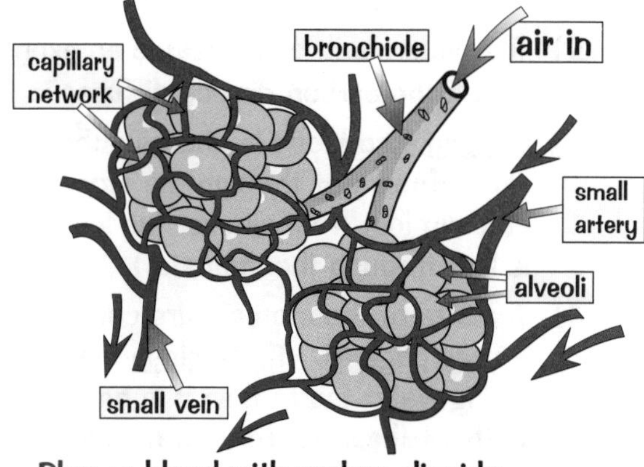

Blue = blood with carbon dioxide.
Red = blood with oxygen.

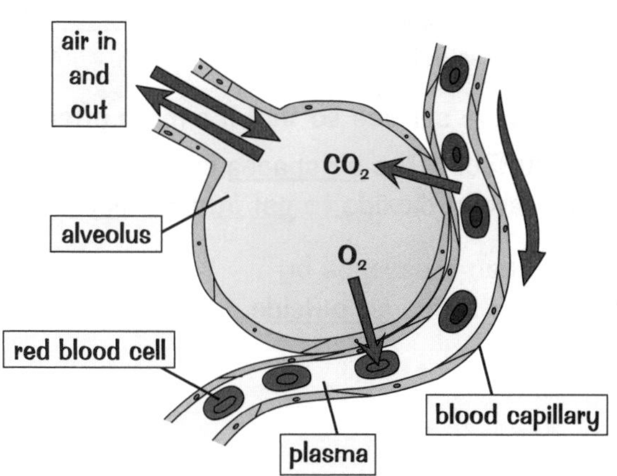

3) The alveoli are specialised to maximise the diffusion of O_2 and CO_2. They have:
   - An enormous surface area (about 75 m^2 in humans).
   - A moist lining for dissolving gases.
   - Very thin walls.
   - A good blood supply.

The Villi Provide a Really Really Big Surface Area

1) The inside of the small intestine is covered in millions and millions of these tiny little projections called villi.
2) They increase the surface area in a big way so that digested food is absorbed much more quickly into the blood.
3) Notice they have:
   - a single layer of surface cells,
   - a very good blood supply to assist quick absorption.

The digested food moves into the blood by diffusion and by active transport (see page 19).

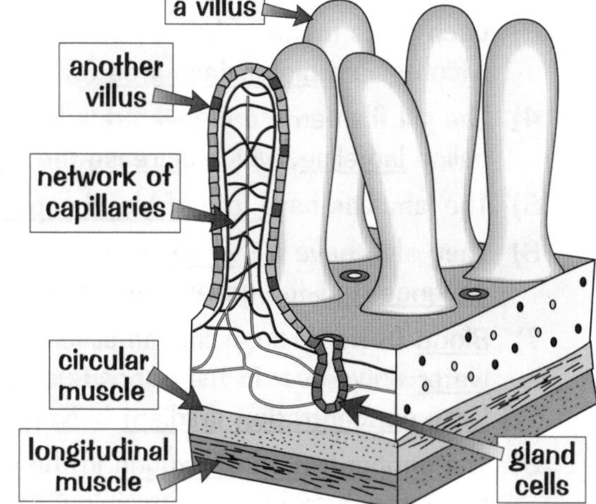

Al Veoli — the Italian gas man...

Thankfully, our bodies are well adapted for efficient diffusion of substances. But the array of life's snazzy exchange surfaces doesn't stop here, oh no — just take a look at what's coming up on the next page...

Q1 Give one way in which alveoli are adapted for gas exchange. [1 mark]

Q2 Describe how the surface area of the small intestine is maximised for absorption. [1 mark]

More on Exchanging Substances

More stuff on adaptations for diffusion now — only this time, it's plants and fish. Whoopee...

The Structure of Leaves Lets Gases Diffuse In and Out of Cells

1) Carbon dioxide diffuses into the air spaces within the leaf, then it diffuses into the cells where photosynthesis happens. The leaf's structure is adapted so that this can happen easily.
2) The underneath of the leaf is an exchange surface. It's covered in biddy little holes called stomata which the carbon dioxide diffuses in through.

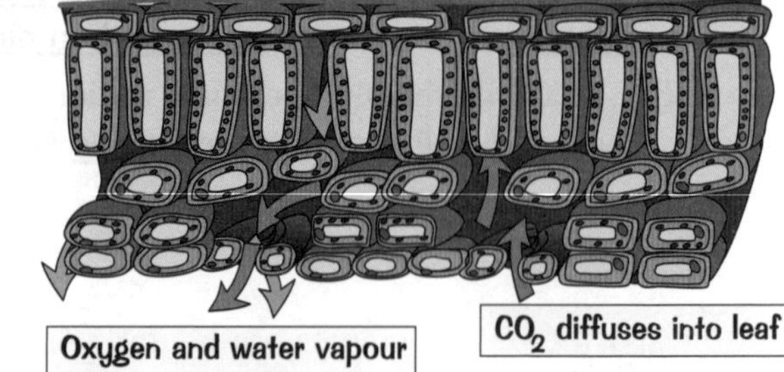

3) Oxygen (produced in photosynthesis) and water vapour also diffuse out through the stomata. (Water vapour is actually lost from all over the leaf surface, but most of it is lost through the stomata.)
4) The size of the stomata are controlled by guard cells — see page 41. These close the stomata if the plant is losing water faster than it is being replaced by the roots. Without these guard cells the plant would soon wilt.
5) The flattened shape of the leaf increases the area of this exchange surface so that it's more effective.
6) The walls of the cells inside the leaf form another exchange surface. The air spaces inside the leaf increase the area of this surface so there's more chance for carbon dioxide to get into the cells.

The water vapour evaporates from the cells inside the leaf. Then it escapes by diffusion because there's a lot of it inside the leaf and less of it in the air outside.

Gills Have a Large Surface Area for Gas Exchange

1) The gills are the gas exchange surface in fish.
2) Water (containing oxygen) enters the fish through its mouth and passes out through the gills. As this happens, oxygen diffuses from the water into the blood in the gills and carbon dioxide diffuses from the blood into the water.
3) Each gill is made of lots of thin plates called gill filaments, which give a big surface area for exchange of gases.

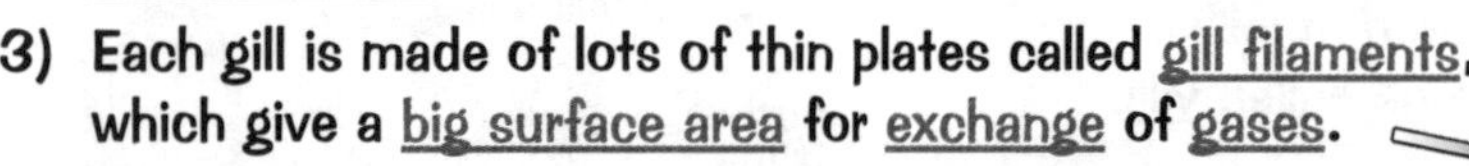

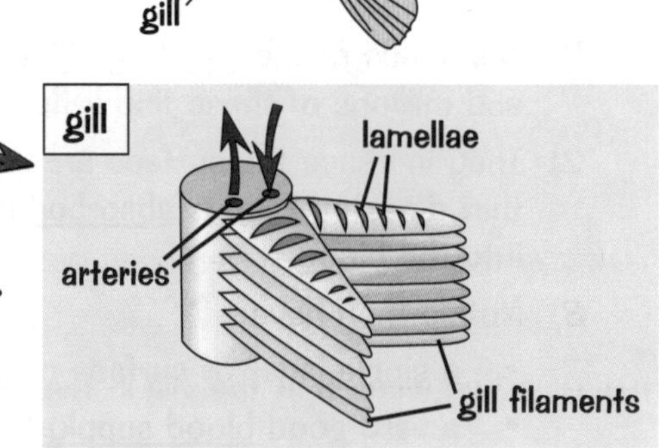

4) The gill filaments are covered in lots of tiny structures called lamellae, which increase the surface area even more.
5) The lamellae have lots of blood capillaries to speed up diffusion.
6) They also have a thin surface layer of cells to minimise the distance that the gases have to diffuse.
7) Blood flows through the lamellae in one direction and water flows over in the opposite direction. This maintains a large concentration gradient between the water and the blood.
8) The concentration of oxygen in the water is always higher than that in the blood, so as much oxygen as possible diffuses from the water into the blood.

In, out, in, out, shake that oxygen about...

There's a theme here — multicellular organisms are really well adapted for getting the substances they need to their cells. It makes sense — if they couldn't do this well, they'd die out. If you're asked in an exam how something's adapted for exchange, think about whether surface area is important — cos it often is.

Q1 Give two ways in which the structure of a gill is adapted for effective gas exchange. [2 marks]

Revision Questions for Topic B

Well, that's Topic B1 done and dusted. Now there's only one way to find out whether you'
from it. And you know what that is, I'll bet. It's obvious... I mean, there's a whole load of
you in the face — chances are, it's got to involve those in some way. And sure enough, it

- Try these questions and tick off each one when you get it right.
- When you've done all the questions under a heading and are completely happy with it, tick it off.

Cells and Microscopy (p.11-13)

1) Name five subcellular structures that both plant and animal cells have.
2) What three things do plant cells have that animal cells don't?
3) Where is the genetic material found in:
   a) animal cells,
   b) bacterial cells?
4) What type of organisms are bacteria — prokaryotes or eukaryotes?
5) Which gives a higher resolution — a light microscope or an electron microscope?

Differentiation and Division (p.14-15)

6) What is cell differentiation?
7) Give three ways that a sperm cell is adapted for swimming to an egg cell.
8) Draw a diagram of a nerve cell. Why is it this shape?
9) What are chromosomes?
10) What is the cell cycle?
11) What is mitosis used for by multicellular organisms?

Stem Cells (p.16)

12) Give two ways that embryonic stem cells could be used to cure diseases.
13) Why might some people be opposed to the use of human embryos in stem cell research?

Exchanging Substances (p.17-22)

14) What is diffusion?
15) Name three substances that can diffuse through cell membranes, and two that can't.
16) What type of molecules move by osmosis?
17) Give the two main differences between active transport and diffusion.
18) Give three adaptations of exchange surfaces that increase the efficiency of diffusion.
19) Give two ways that the villi in the small intestine are adapted for absorbing digested food.
20) Explain how leaves are adapted to maximise the amount of carbon dioxide that gets to their cells.

Cell Organisation

Some organisms contain loads of cells, but how, you might wonder, do all these cells end up making a working human or squirrel... the answer's organisation. Without it, they'd just make a meaty splodge.

Large Multicellular Organisms are Made Up of Organ Systems

1) Cells are the basic building blocks that make up all living organisms.
2) As you know from page 14, specialised cells carry out a particular function.
3) The process by which cells become specialised for a particular job is called differentiation. Differentiation occurs during the development of a multicellular organism.
4) These specialised cells form tissues, which form organs, which form organ systems (see below).
5) Large multicellular organisms (e.g. squirrels) have different systems inside them for exchanging and transporting materials.

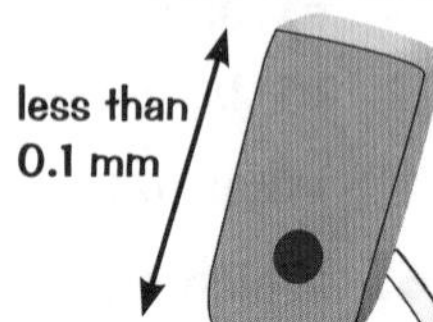

Similar Cells are Organised into Tissues

A tissue is a group of similar cells that work together to carry out a particular function. It can include more than one type of cell.

In mammals (like humans), examples of tissues include:
1) Muscular tissue, which contracts (shortens) to move whatever it's attached to.
2) Glandular tissue, which makes and secretes chemicals like enzymes and hormones.
3) Epithelial tissue, which covers some parts of the body, e.g. the inside of the gut.

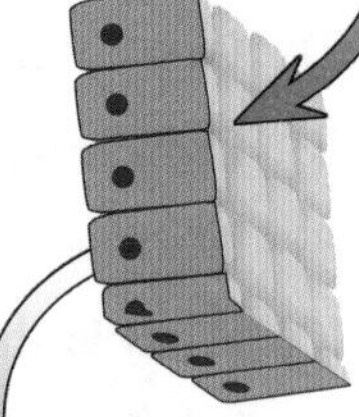

Tissues are Organised into Organs

An organ is a group of different tissues that work together to perform a certain function.

For example, the stomach is an organ made of these tissues:
1) Muscular tissue, which moves the stomach wall to churn up the food.
2) Glandular tissue, which makes digestive juices to digest food.
3) Epithelial tissue, which covers the outside and inside of the stomach.

Stomach

about 10 cm (over 1000 times longer than an epithelial cell)

Organs are Organised into Organ Systems

An organ system is a group of organs working together to perform a particular function.

For example, the digestive system (found in humans and other mammals) breaks down and absorbs food. It's made up of these organs:
1) Glands (e.g. the pancreas and salivary glands), which produce digestive juices.
2) The stomach and small intestine, which digest food.
3) The liver, which produces bile.
4) The small intestine, which absorbs soluble food molecules.
5) The large intestine, which absorbs water from undigested food, leaving faeces.

Organ systems work together to make entire organisms.

Digestive system

Salivary glands
Liver
Stomach
Pancreas
Small intestine
Large intestine

You need to know where these organs are on a diagram — see page 28 too.

Soft and quilted — the best kind of tissues...

So in summary, an organism consists of organ systems, which are groups of organs, which are made of tissues, which are groups of cells working together. Now just for the thrill of it, here's a practice question.

Q1 The bladder is an organ. Explain what this means. [2 marks]

Enzymes

Chemical reactions are what make you work. And enzymes are what make them work.

Enzymes Are Catalysts Produced by Living Things

1) Living things have thousands of different chemical reactions going on inside them all the time. These reactions need to be carefully controlled — to get the right amounts of substances.
2) You can usually make a reaction happen more quickly by raising the temperature. This would speed up the useful reactions but also the unwanted ones too... not good. There's also a limit to how far you can raise the temperature inside a living creature before its cells start getting damaged.
3) So... living things produce enzymes that act as biological catalysts. Enzymes reduce the need for high temperatures and we only have enzymes to speed up the useful chemical reactions in the body.

> A CATALYST is a substance which INCREASES the speed of a reaction, without being CHANGED or USED UP in the reaction.

4) Enzymes are all large proteins and all proteins are made up of chains of amino acids. These chains are folded into unique shapes, which enzymes need to do their jobs (see below).

Enzymes Have Special Shapes So They Can Catalyse Reactions

1) Chemical reactions usually involve things either being split apart or joined together.
2) Every enzyme has an active site with a unique shape that fits onto the substance involved in a reaction.
3) Enzymes are really picky — they usually only catalyse one specific reaction.
4) This is because, for the enzyme to work, the substrate has to fit into its active site. If the substrate doesn't match the enzyme's active site, then the reaction won't be catalysed.

> The substance that an enzyme acts on is called the substrate.

5) This diagram shows the 'lock and key' model of enzyme action. This is simpler than how enzymes actually work. In reality, the active site changes shape a little as the substrate binds to it to get a tighter fit. This is called the 'induced fit' model of enzyme action.

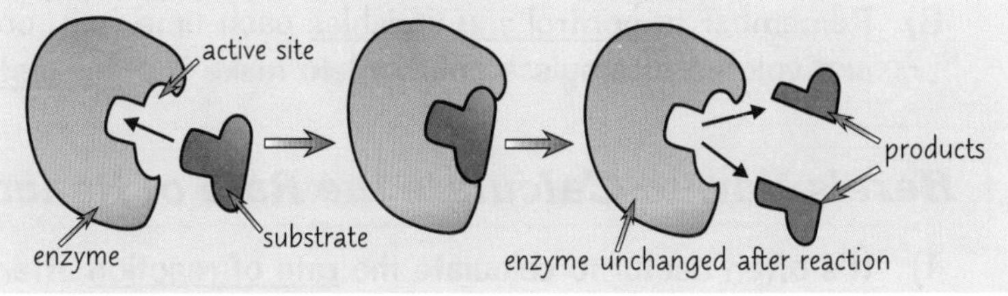

Enzymes Need the Right Temperature and pH

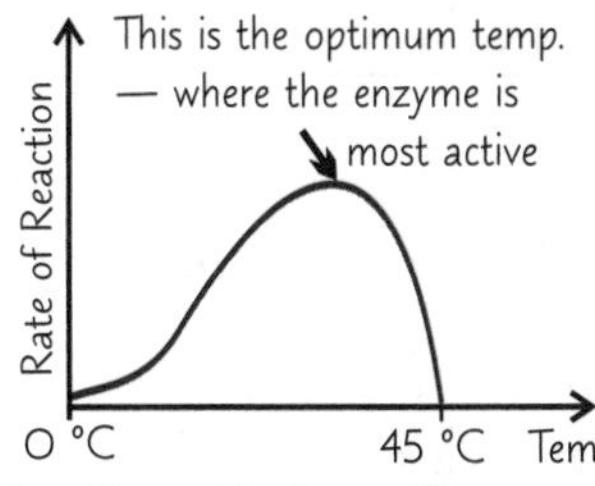

1) Changing the temperature changes the rate of an enzyme-catalysed reaction.
2) Like with any reaction, a higher temperature increases the rate at first. But if it gets too hot, some of the bonds holding the enzyme together break. This changes the shape of the enzyme's active site, so the substrate won't fit any more. The enzyme is said to be denatured.
3) All enzymes have an optimum temperature that they work best at.
4) The pH also affects enzymes. If it's too high or too low, the pH interferes with the bonds holding the enzyme together. This changes the shape of the active site and denatures the enzyme.
5) All enzymes have an optimum pH that they work best at. It's often neutral pH 7, but not always — e.g. pepsin is an enzyme used to break down proteins in the stomach. It works best at pH 2, which means it's well-suited to the acidic conditions there.

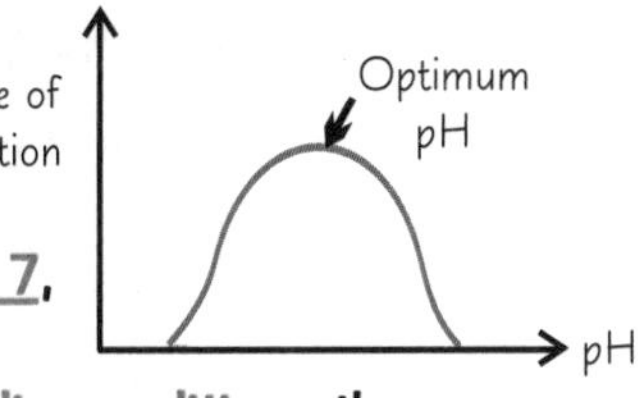

If only enzymes could speed up revision...

Make sure you use the special terms like 'active site' and 'denatured' — the examiners will love it.

Q1 Explain why enzymes have an optimum pH. [2 marks]

Investigating Enzymatic Reactions

You'll soon know how to investigate the effect of pH on the rate of enzyme activity... I bet you're thrilled.

You Can Investigate the Effect of pH on Enzyme Activity

PRACTICAL

The enzyme amylase catalyses the breakdown of starch to maltose. It's easy to detect starch using iodine solution — if starch is present, the iodine solution will change from browny-orange to blue-black. This is how you can investigate how pH affects amylase activity:

You could use an electric water bath, instead of a Bunsen and a beaker of water, to control the temperature.

1) Put a drop of iodine solution into every well of a spotting tile.
2) Place a Bunsen burner on a heat-proof mat, and a tripod and gauze over the Bunsen burner. Put a beaker of water on top of the tripod and heat the water until it is 35 °C (use a thermometer to measure the temperature). Try to keep the temperature of the water constant throughout the experiment.
3) Use a syringe to add 1 cm^3 of amylase solution and 1 cm^3 of a buffer solution with a pH of 5 to a boiling tube. Using test tube holders, put the tube into the beaker of water and wait for five minutes.
4) Next, use a different syringe to add 5 cm^3 of a starch solution to the boiling tube.
5) Immediately mix the contents of the boiling tube and start a stop clock.
6) Use continuous sampling to record how long it takes for the amylase to break down all of the starch. To do this, use a dropping pipette to take a fresh sample from the boiling tube every 30 seconds and put a drop into a well. When the iodine solution remains browny-orange, starch is no longer present.
7) Repeat the whole experiment with buffer solutions of different pH values to see how pH affects the time taken for the starch to be broken down.
8) Remember to control any variables each time (e.g. concentration and volume of amylase solution) to make it a fair test.

mixture sampled every 30 seconds
amylase, starch and buffer solution
dropping pipette
drop of iodine solution
spotting tile

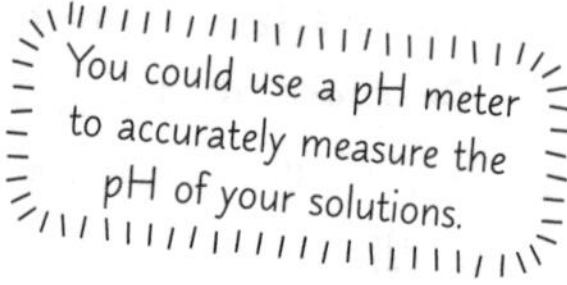

Here's How to Calculate the Rate of Reaction

1) It's often useful to calculate the rate of reaction after an experiment. Rate is a measure of how much something changes over time.
2) For the experiment above, you can calculate the rate of reaction using this formula:

$$\text{Rate} = \frac{1000}{\text{time}}$$

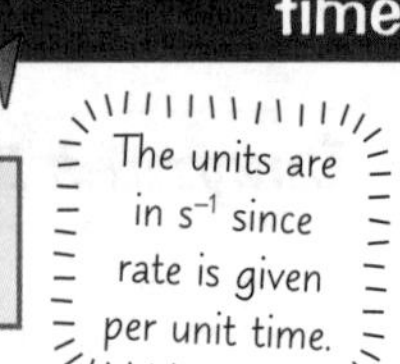

E.g.

At pH 6, the time taken for amylase to break down all of the starch in a solution was 90 seconds. So the rate of the reaction = 1000 ÷ 90 = 11 s^{-1} (2 s.f.)

3) If an experiment measures how much something changes over time, you calculate the rate of reaction by dividing the amount that it has changed by the time taken.

EXAMPLE: The enzyme catalase catalyses the breakdown of hydrogen peroxide into water and oxygen. During an investigation into the activity of catalase, 24 cm^3 of oxygen was released in 50 seconds (s). Calculate the rate of the reaction. Write your answer in $cm^3\ s^{-1}$.

Amount of product formed = change = 24 cm^3

Rate of reaction = change ÷ time = 24 cm^3 ÷ 50 s = 0.48 $cm^3\ s^{-1}$

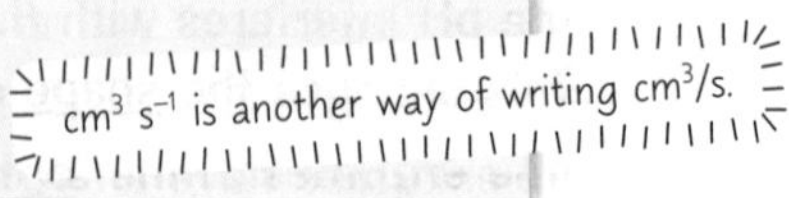

Mad scientists — they're experi-mental...

You could easily adapt this experiment to investigate how factors other than pH affect the rate of amylase activity. For example, you could use a water bath set to different temperatures to investigate the effect of temperature.

Q1 An enzyme-controlled reaction was carried out at pH 4. After 60 seconds, 33 cm^3 of product had been released. Calculate the rate of reaction in $cm^3\ s^{-1}$. [1 mark]

Enzymes and Digestion

The enzymes used in digestion are produced by cells and then released into the gut to mix with food.

Digestive Enzymes Break Down Big Molecules

1) Starch, proteins and fats are BIG molecules. They're too big to pass through the walls of the digestive system, so digestive enzymes break these BIG molecules down into smaller ones like sugars (e.g. glucose and maltose), amino acids, glycerol and fatty acids. These smaller, soluble molecules can pass easily through the walls of the digestive system, allowing them to be absorbed into the bloodstream.

Carbohydrases Convert Carbohydrates into Simple Sugars

Amylase is an example of a carbohydrase. It breaks down starch.

Starch is a carbohydrate.

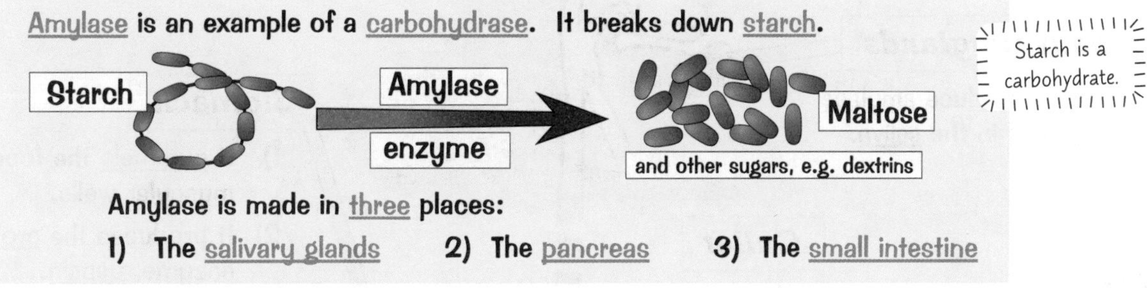

Amylase is made in three places:

1) The salivary glands 2) The pancreas 3) The small intestine

Proteases Convert Proteins into Amino Acids

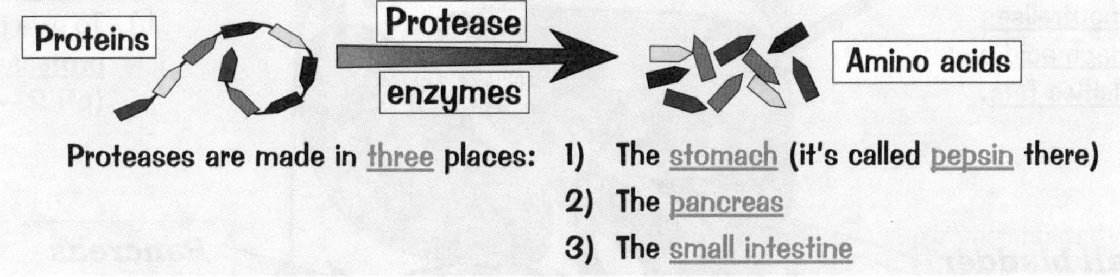

Proteases are made in three places:
1) The stomach (it's called pepsin there)
2) The pancreas
3) The small intestine

Lipases Convert Lipids into Glycerol and Fatty Acids

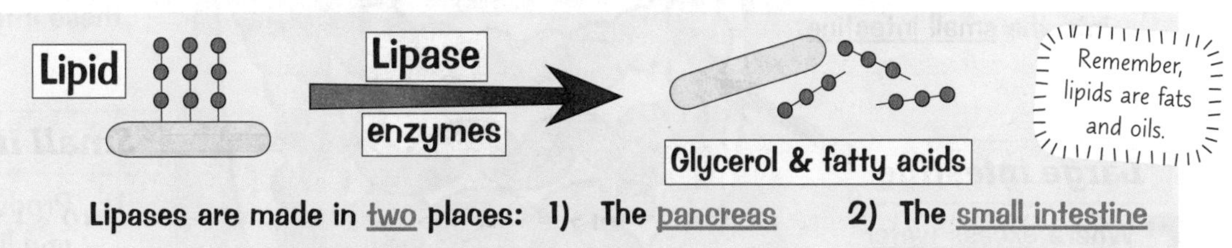

Remember, lipids are fats and oils.

Lipases are made in two places: 1) The pancreas 2) The small intestine

2) The body makes good use of the products of digestion. They can be used to make new carbohydrates, proteins and lipids. Some of the glucose (a sugar) that's made is used in respiration (see p.54).

Bile Neutralises the Stomach Acid and Emulsifies Fats

1) Bile is produced in the liver. It's stored in the gall bladder before it's released into the small intestine.
2) The hydrochloric acid in the stomach makes the pH too acidic for enzymes in the small intestine to work properly. Bile is alkaline — it neutralises the acid and makes conditions alkaline. The enzymes in the small intestine work best in these alkaline conditions.
3) It emulsifies fats. In other words it breaks the fat into tiny droplets. This gives a much bigger surface area of fat for the enzyme lipase to work on — which makes its digestion faster.

What do you call an acid that's eaten all the pies...

Make sure you know the examples of amylase, protease and lipase, and the reactions that they catalyse.

Q1 Bile is a product of the liver. Describe and explain its role in digestion. [4 marks]

More on Enzymes and Digestion

So now you know what the enzymes do, here's a nice big picture of the whole of the digestive system.

The Breakdown of Food is Catalysed by Enzymes

1) Enzymes used in the digestive system are produced by specialised cells in glands and in the gut lining.
2) Different enzymes catalyse the breakdown of different food molecules.

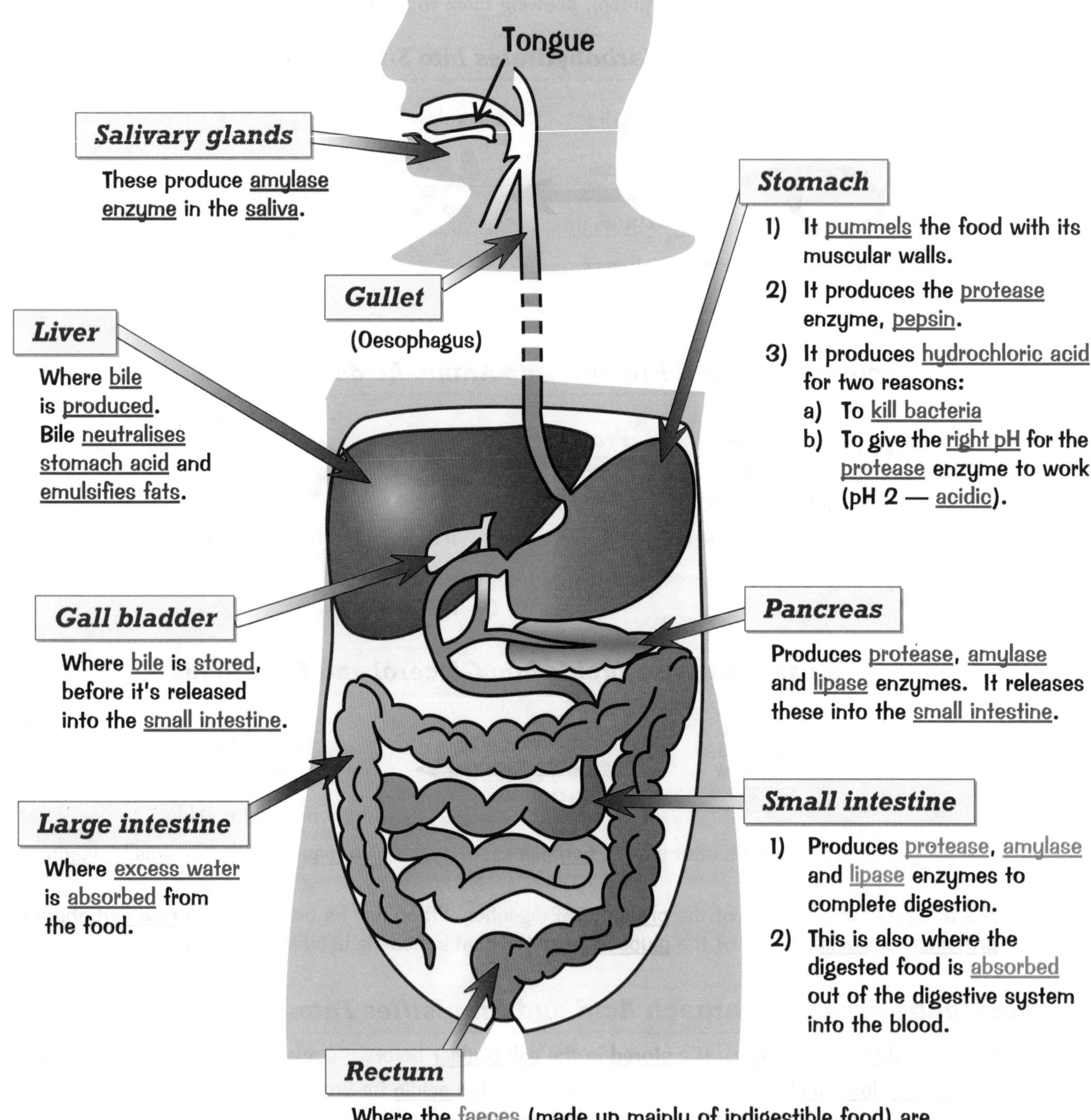

Mmmm — so who's for a chocolate digestive...

Did you know that the whole of your digestive system is actually a hole that goes right through your body. Think about it. It just gets loads of food, digestive juices and enzymes piled into it. Most of it's then absorbed into the body and the rest is politely stored for removal.

Q1 Name the three parts of the digestive system that produce protease enzymes. [3 marks]

Food Tests

PRACTICAL

There are some clever ways to identify what type of food molecule a sample contains. For each of the tests, you need to prepare a food sample. It's the same each time though — here's what you'd do:

1) Get a piece of food and break it up using a pestle and mortar.
2) Transfer the ground up food to a beaker and add some distilled water.
3) Give the mixture a good stir with a glass rod to dissolve some of the food.
4) Filter the solution using a funnel lined with filter paper to get rid of the solid bits of food.

Use the Benedict's Test to Test for Sugars

Sugars are found in all sorts of foods such as biscuits, cereal and bread. There are two types of sugars — non-reducing and reducing. You can test for reducing sugars in foods using the Benedict's test:

1) Prepare a food sample and transfer 5 cm^3 to a test tube.
2) Prepare a water bath so that it's set to 75 °C.
3) Add some Benedict's solution to the test tube (about 10 drops) using a pipette.
4) Place the test tube in the water bath using a test tube holder and leave it in there for 5 minutes. Make sure the tube is pointing away from you.
5) If the food sample contains a reducing sugar, the solution in the test tube will change from the normal blue colour to green, yellow or brick-red — it depends on how much sugar is in the food.

Use Iodine Solution to Test for Starch

You can also check food samples for the presence of starch. Foods like pasta, rice and potatoes contain a lot of starch. Here's how to do the test:

1) Make a food sample and transfer 5 cm^3 of your sample to a test tube.
2) Then add a few drops of iodine solution and gently shake the tube to mix the contents. If the sample contains starch, the colour of the solution will change from browny-orange to black or blue-black.

Use the Biuret Test to Test for Proteins

You can use the biuret test to see if a type of food contains protein.
Meat and cheese are protein rich and good foods to use in this test. Here's how it's done:

1) Prepare a sample of your food and transfer 2 cm^3 of your sample to a test tube.
2) Add 2 cm^3 of biuret solution to the sample and mix the contents of the tube by gently shaking it.
3) If the food sample contains protein, the solution will change from blue to pink or purple. If no protein is present, the solution will stay blue.

Use the Sudan III Test to Test for Lipids

Lipids are found in foods such as olive oil, margarine and milk.
You can test for the presence of lipids in a food using Sudan III stain solution.

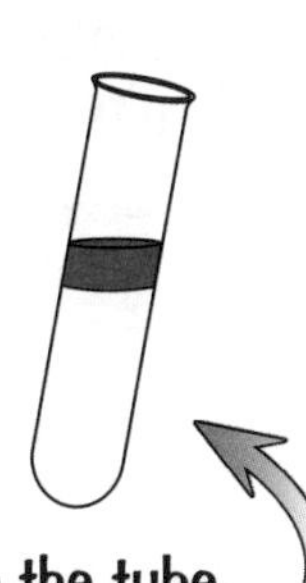

1) Prepare a sample of the food you're testing (but you don't need to filter it). Transfer about 5 cm^3 into a test tube.
2) Use a pipette to add 3 drops of Sudan III stain solution to the test tube and gently shake the tube.
3) Sudan III stain solution stains lipids. If the sample contains lipids, the mixture will separate out into two layers. The top layer will be bright red. If no lipids are present, no separate red layer will form at the top of the liquid.

All this talk of food is making me hungry...

Make sure you do a risk assessment before starting these tests — there are a lot of chemicals to use here.

Q1 Name the chemical that you would use to test a sample for the presence of starch. [1 mark]

The Lungs

You need to get oxygen into your bloodstream to supply your cells for respiration. You also need to get rid of carbon dioxide from your blood. This all happens in your lungs when you breathe air in and out.

The Lungs Are in the Thorax

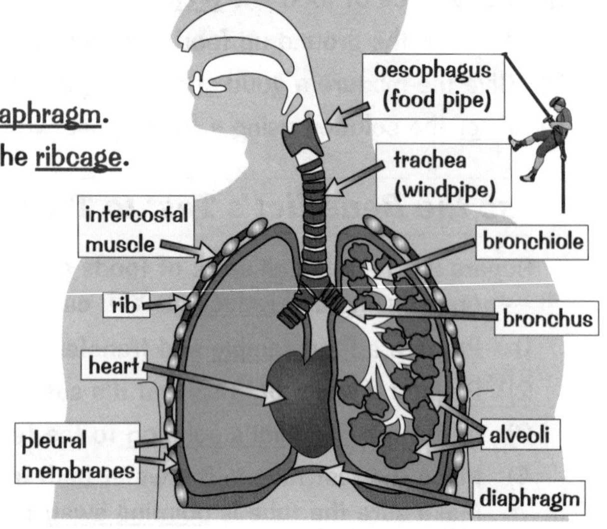

1) The thorax is the top part of your body.
2) It's separated from the lower part of the body by the diaphragm.
3) The lungs are like big pink sponges and are protected by the ribcage. They're surrounded by the pleural membranes.
4) The air that you breathe in goes through the trachea. This splits into two tubes called bronchi (each one is a bronchus), one going to each lung.
5) The bronchi split into progressively smaller tubes called bronchioles.
6) The bronchioles finally end at small bags called alveoli where the gas exchange takes place (see below).

Alveoli Carry Out Gas Exchange in the Body

air in and out
alveolus
CO_2
O_2
blood capillary

1) The lungs contain millions and millions of little air sacs called alveoli, surrounded by a network of blood capillaries. This is where gas exchange happens.
2) The blood passing next to the alveoli has just returned to the lungs from the rest of the body, so it contains lots of carbon dioxide and very little oxygen. Oxygen diffuses out of the alveolus (high concentration) into the blood (low concentration). Carbon dioxide diffuses out of the blood (high concentration) into the alveolus (low concentration) to be breathed out.

body cells
CO_2
O_2
blood capillary

3) When the blood reaches body cells oxygen is released from the red blood cells (where there's a high concentration) and diffuses into the body cells (where the concentration is low).
4) At the same time, carbon dioxide diffuses out of the body cells (where there's a high concentration) into the blood (where there's a low concentration). It's then carried back to the lungs.

You Can Calculate the Breathing Rate in Breaths Per Minute

Rate calculations pop up all the time in biology, and you're expected to know how to do them — thankfully they're pretty easy. Breathing rate is the sort of thing that you could get asked to work out in your exam.

Bob takes 91 breaths in 7 minutes. Calculate his average breathing rate in breaths per minute.

breaths per minute = number of breaths ÷ number of minutes
= 91 ÷ 7
= 13 breaths per minute

Stop huffing and puffing and just learn it...

Alveoli are really well adapted for carrying out gas exchange. It could be a wise move to learn all about exactly how they're adapted. You met them back on page 21, so head back there if you need a reminder.

Q1 During a 12 minute run, Aaqib took 495 breaths.
Calculate his average breathing rate in breaths per minute. [1 mark]

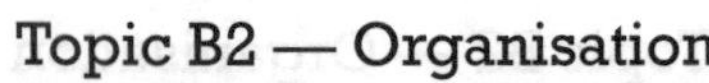

Circulatory System — The Heart

The circulatory system carries food and oxygen to every cell in the body. As well as being a delivery service, it's also a waste collection service — it carries waste products to where they can be removed from the body.

The DOUBLE Circulatory System, Actually

The circulatory system is made up of the heart, blood vessels and blood.
Humans have a double circulatory system — two circuits joined together:

1) In the first one, the right ventricle (see below) pumps deoxygenated blood (blood without oxygen) to the lungs to take in oxygen. The blood then returns to the heart.
2) In the second one, the left ventricle (see below) pumps oxygenated blood around all the other organs of the body. The blood gives up its oxygen at the body cells and the deoxygenated blood returns to the heart to be pumped out to the lungs again.

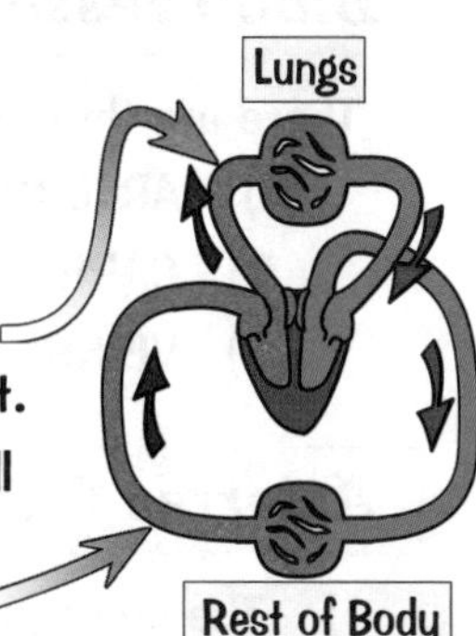

The Heart Contracts to Pump Blood Around The Body

1) The heart is a pumping organ that keeps the blood flowing around the body. The walls of the heart are mostly made of muscle tissue.
2) The heart has valves to make sure that blood flows in the right direction — they prevent it flowing backwards.
3) This is how the heart uses its four chambers (right atrium, right ventricle, left atrium and left ventricle) to pump blood around:

Atrium is when there is just one. Atria is plural.

1) Blood flows into the two atria from the vena cava and the pulmonary vein.
2) The atria contract, pushing the blood into the ventricles.
3) The ventricles contract, forcing the blood into the pulmonary artery and the aorta, and out of the heart.
4) The blood then flows to the organs through arteries, and returns through veins (see next page).
5) The atria fill again and the whole cycle starts over.

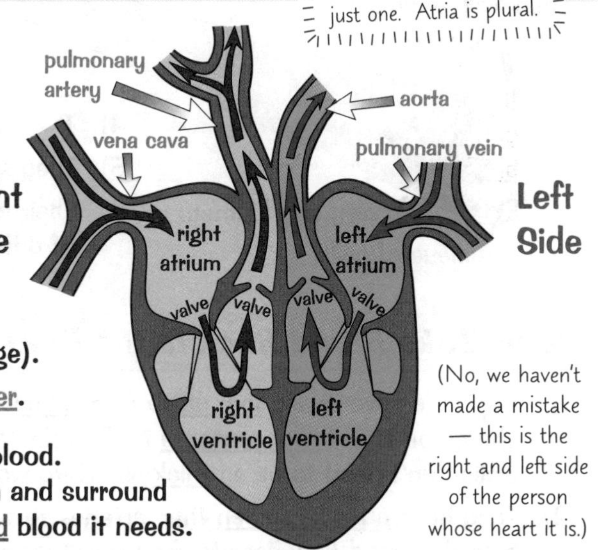

(No, we haven't made a mistake — this is the right and left side of the person whose heart it is.)

The heart also needs its own supply of oxygenated blood. Arteries called coronary arteries branch off the aorta and surround the heart, making sure that it gets all the oxygenated blood it needs.

The Heart Has a Pacemaker

1) Your resting heart rate is controlled by a group of cells in the right atrium wall that act as a pacemaker.
2) These cells produce a small electric impulse which spreads to the surrounding muscle cells, causing them to contract.
3) An artificial pacemaker is often used to control heartbeat if the natural pacemaker cells don't work properly (e.g. if the patient has an irregular heartbeat). It's a little device that's implanted under the skin and has a wire going to the heart. It produces an electric current to keep the heart beating regularly.

Okay — let's get to the heart of the matter...

Interesting fact — when doctors use a stethoscope to listen to your heart, it's the valves closing that they hear.

Q1 Which chamber of the heart pumps deoxygenated blood to the lungs? [1 mark]

Q2 What is the function of the coronary arteries? [1 mark]

Circulatory System — Blood Vessels

Want to know more about the circulatory system... Good. Because here's a whole extra page.

Blood Vessels are Designed for Their Function

There are three different types of blood vessel:

1) ARTERIES — these carry the blood away from the heart.
2) CAPILLARIES — these are involved in the exchange of materials at the tissues.
3) VEINS — these carry the blood to the heart.

Arteries Carry Blood Under Pressure

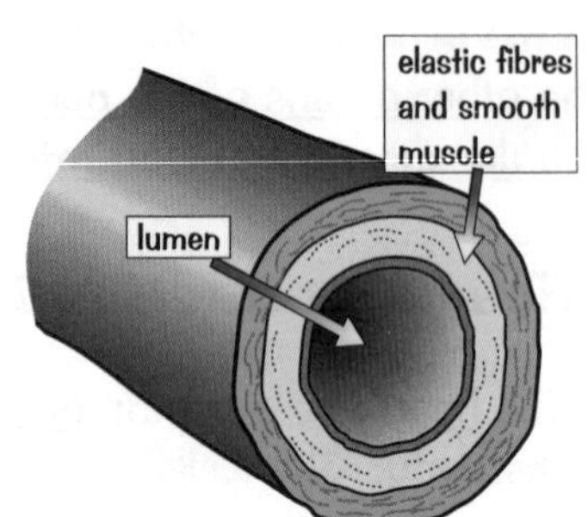

1) The heart pumps the blood out at high pressure so the artery walls are strong and elastic.
2) The walls are thick compared to the size of the hole down the middle (the "lumen" — silly name!).
3) They contain thick layers of muscle to make them strong, and elastic fibres to allow them to stretch and spring back.

Capillaries are Really Small

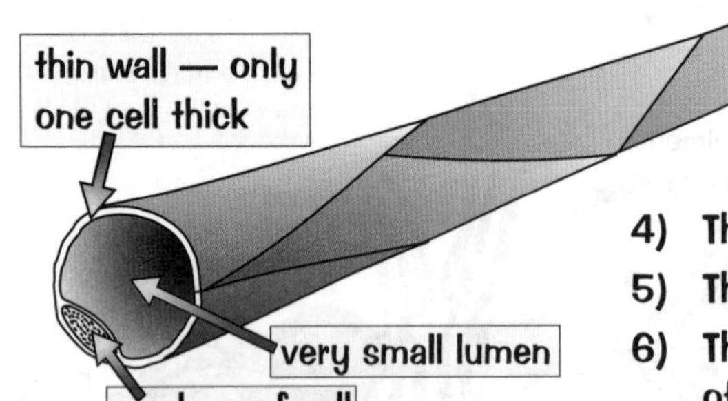

1) Arteries branch into capillaries.
2) Capillaries are really tiny — too small to see.
3) They carry the blood really close to every cell in the body to exchange substances with them.
4) They have permeable walls, so substances can diffuse in and out.
5) They supply food and oxygen, and take away waste like CO_2.
6) Their walls are usually only one cell thick. This increases the rate of diffusion by decreasing the distance over which it occurs.

Veins Take Blood Back to the Heart

1) Capillaries eventually join up to form veins. The blood is at lower pressure in the veins so the walls don't need to be as thick as artery walls.
2) They have a bigger lumen than arteries to help the blood flow despite the lower pressure.
3) They also have valves to help keep the blood flowing in the right direction.

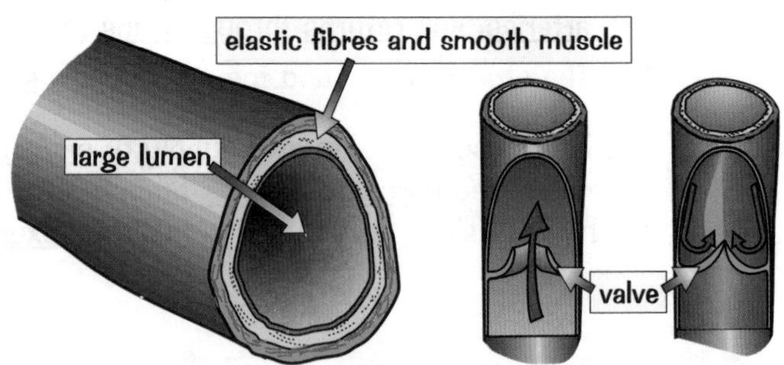

You Can Calculate the Rate of Blood Flow

You might get asked to calculate the rate of blood flow in your exam. Thankfully, it's not too tricky. Take a look at this example:

EXAMPLE: 1464 ml of blood passed through an artery in 4.5 minutes. Calculate the rate of blood flow through the artery in ml/min.

rate of blood flow = volume of blood ÷ number of minutes
= 1464 ÷ 4.5 = 325 ml/min

Learn this page — don't struggle in vein...

Here's an interesting fact for you — your body contains about 60 000 miles of blood vessels.

Q1 Describe how veins are adapted to carry blood back to the heart. [2 marks]

Circulatory System — Blood

Blood is a tissue. One of its jobs is to act as a huge transport system. There are four main things in blood...

Red Blood Cells Carry Oxygen

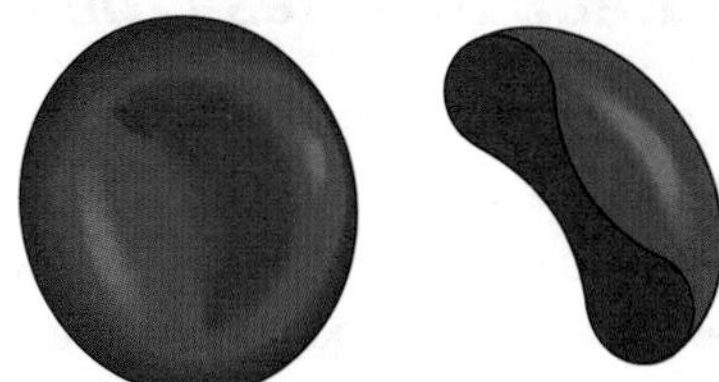

1) The job of red blood cells is to carry oxygen from the lungs to all the cells in the body.
2) Their shape is a biconcave disc (like a doughnut) — this gives a large surface area for absorbing oxygen.
3) They don't have a nucleus — this allows more room to carry oxygen.
4) They contain a red pigment called haemoglobin.
5) In the lungs, haemoglobin binds to oxygen to become oxyhaemoglobin. In body tissues, the reverse happens — oxyhaemoglobin splits up into haemoglobin and oxygen, to release oxygen to the cells.

The more red blood cells you've got, the more oxygen can get to your cells. At high altitudes there's less oxygen in the air — so people who live there produce more red blood cells to compensate.

White Blood Cells Defend Against Infection

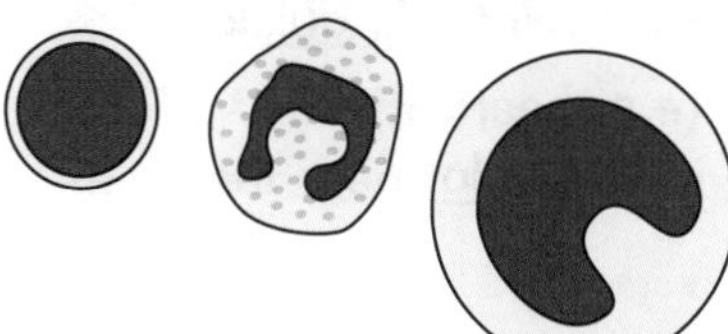

1) Some can change shape to gobble up unwelcome microorganisms, in a process called phagocytosis.
2) Others produce antibodies to fight microorganisms, as well as antitoxins to neutralise any toxins produced by the microorganisms.
3) Unlike red blood cells, they do have a nucleus.

Platelets Help Blood Clot

1) These are small fragments of cells. They have no nucleus.
2) They help the blood to clot at a wound — to stop all your blood pouring out and to stop microorganisms getting in. (So basically platelets just float about waiting for accidents to happen.)
3) Lack of platelets can cause excessive bleeding and bruising.

Plasma is the Liquid That Carries Everything in Blood

This is a pale straw-coloured liquid which carries just about everything:

1) Red and white blood cells and platelets.
2) Nutrients like glucose and amino acids. These are the soluble products of digestion which are absorbed from the gut and taken to the cells of the body.
3) Carbon dioxide from the organs to the lungs.
4) Urea from the liver to the kidneys.
5) Hormones.
6) Proteins.
7) Antibodies and antitoxins produced by the white blood cells.

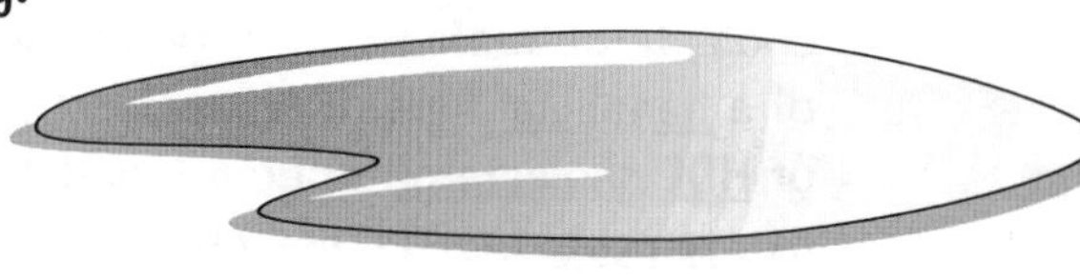

Platelets — ideal for small dinners...

When you're ill the doctor often takes a blood sample for analysis. Blood tests can be used to diagnose loads of things — not just disorders of the blood. This is because the blood transports so many chemicals produced by so many organs... and it's easier to take blood than, say, a piece of muscle.

Q1 Describe the purpose of platelets in blood. [1 mark]

Q2 Outline three ways in which red blood cells are adapted to carry oxygen. [3 marks]

Cardiovascular Disease

Cardiovascular disease is a term used to describe diseases of the heart or blood vessels, for example coronary heart disease. This page tells you all about how stents and statins are used to combat coronary heart disease.

Stents Keep Arteries Open

outside of heart

coronary artery

1) Coronary heart disease is when the coronary arteries that supply the blood to the muscle of the heart get blocked by layers of fatty material building up. This causes the arteries to become narrow, so blood flow is restricted and there's a lack of oxygen to the heart muscle — this can result in a heart attack.
2) Stents are tubes that are inserted inside arteries. They keep them open, making sure blood can pass through to the heart muscles. This keeps the person's heart beating (and the person alive).

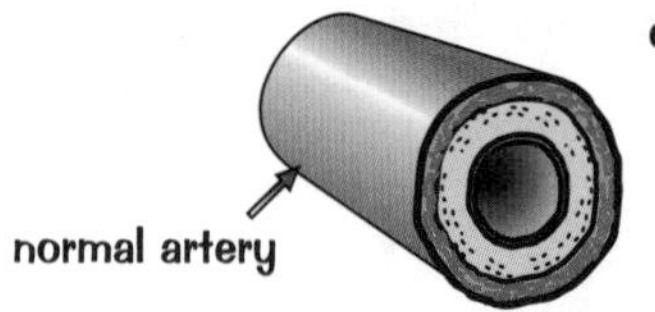

stent pushes artery wall out, squashing fatty deposit

more space in the centre of the artery

3) Stents are a way of lowering the risk of a heart attack in people with coronary heart disease. They are effective for a long time and the recovery time from the surgery is relatively quick.
4) On the down side, there is a risk of complications during the operation (e.g. heart attack) and a risk of infection from surgery. There is also the risk of patients developing a blood clot near the stent — this is called thrombosis.

Statins Reduce Cholesterol in the Blood

1) Cholesterol is an essential lipid that your body produces and needs to function properly. However, too much of a certain type of cholesterol (known as 'bad' or LDL cholesterol) can cause health problems.
2) Having too much of this 'bad' cholesterol in the bloodstream can cause fatty deposits to form inside arteries, which can lead to coronary heart disease.
3) Statins are drugs that can reduce the amount of 'bad' cholesterol present in the bloodstream. This slows down the rate of fatty deposits forming.

Statins Have Advantages and Disadvantages

Advantages

1) By reducing the amount of 'bad' cholesterol in the blood, statins can reduce the risk of strokes, coronary heart disease and heart attacks.
2) As well as reducing the amount of 'bad' cholesterol, statins can increase the amount of a beneficial type of cholesterol (known as 'good' or HDL cholesterol) in your bloodstream. This type can remove 'bad' cholesterol from the blood.
3) Some studies suggest that statins may also help prevent some other diseases.

Disadvantages

1) Statins are a long-term drug that must be taken regularly. There's the risk that someone could forget to take them.
2) Statins can sometimes cause negative side effects, e.g. headaches. Some of these side effects can be serious, e.g. kidney failure, liver damage and memory loss.
3) The effect of statins isn't instant. It takes time for their effect to kick in.

Unlike stents and statins, using CGP books only has advantages...

Stents and statins might be good treatments for coronary heart disease, but they're not perfect. Make sure you're aware of the drawbacks as well as the advantages of each. That way, you'll be covered if they come up in the exam.

Q1 a) How can stents be used to reduce the risk of heart attacks in people with coronary heart disease? [2 marks]

b) Suggest two disadvantages of treating patients using stents. [2 marks]

More on Cardiovascular Disease

With more fakery than a 'Rollecks' watch, this page is about artificial hearts, artificial blood and replacing heart valves. All a bit gruesome, I'll admit — but it's life-saving stuff.

An Artificial Heart Can Pump Blood Around the Body

1) If a patient has heart failure, doctors may perform a heart transplant (or heart and lungs transplant if the lungs are also diseased) using donor organs from people who have recently died. However, if donor organs aren't available right away or they're not the best option, doctors may fit an artificial heart.
2) Artificial hearts are mechanical devices that pump blood for a person whose own heart has failed. They're usually only used as a temporary fix, to keep a person alive until a donor heart can be found or to help a person recover by allowing the heart to rest and heal. In some cases though they're used as a permanent fix, which reduces the need for a donor heart.
3) The main advantage of artificial hearts is that they're less likely to be rejected by the body's immune system than a donor heart. This is because they're made from metals or plastics, so the body doesn't recognise them as 'foreign' and attack in the same way as it does with living tissue.
4) But surgery to fit an artificial heart (as with transplant surgery) can lead to bleeding and infection. Also, artificial hearts don't work as well as healthy natural ones — parts of the heart could wear out or the electrical motor could fail. Blood doesn't flow through artificial hearts as smoothly, which can cause blood clots and lead to strokes. The patient has to take drugs to thin their blood and make sure this doesn't happen, which can cause problems with bleeding if they're hurt in an accident.

Faulty Heart Valves Can Be Replaced With Biological or Mechanical Valves

1) The valves in the heart can be damaged or weakened by heart attacks, infection or old age.
2) The damage may cause the valve tissue to stiffen, so it won't open properly. Or a valve may become leaky, allowing blood to flow in both directions rather than just forward. This means that blood doesn't circulate as effectively as normal.
3) Severe valve damage can be treated by replacing the valve. Replacement valves can be ones taken from humans or other mammals (e.g. cows or pigs) — these are biological valves. Or they can be man-made — these are mechanical valves.
4) Replacing a valve is a much less drastic procedure than a whole heart transplant. But fitting artificial valves is still major surgery and there can still be problems with blood clots.

Artificial Blood Can Keep You Alive In An Emergency

1) When someone loses a lot of blood, e.g. in an accident, their heart can still pump the remaining red blood cells around (to get oxygen to their organs), as long as the volume of their blood can be topped up.
2) Artificial blood is a blood substitute, e.g. a salt solution ("saline"), which is used to replace the lost volume of blood. It's safe (if no air bubbles get into the blood) and can keep people alive even if they lose $2/3$ of their red blood cells. This may give the patient enough time to produce new blood cells. If not, the patient will need a blood transfusion.
3) Ideally, an artificial blood product would replace the function of the lost red blood cells, so that there's no need for a blood transfusion. Scientists are currently working on products that can do this.

Pity they can't fit me an artificial brain before the exam...

Make sure you know about the consequences of faulty heart valves or heart failure, as well as the advantages and disadvantages of the treatments on this page. Obviously if someone is really ill, it's unlikely that they'd turn down an artificial heart, artificial blood or a valve replacement — but these treatments aren't perfect.

Q1 a) Describe how faulty heart valves can lead to poor blood circulation. [2 marks]
b) Suggest how severe damage to a heart valve can be treated. [1 mark]

Q2 Suggest one disadvantage of treating coronary heart disease with an artificial heart. [1 mark]

Health and Disease

There's not a great deal about diseases and health problems that you can laugh about, so excuse me if this page is a bit dull. It's important stuff to know about though, so you'd best get cracking.

Diseases are a Major Cause of Ill Health

Health is the state of physical and mental wellbeing. Diseases are often responsible for causing ill health.

Diseases Can be Communicable or Non-Communicable

1) Communicable diseases are those that can spread from person to person or between animals and people. They can be caused by things like bacteria, viruses, parasites and fungi. They're sometimes described as contagious or infectious diseases. Measles and malaria are examples of communicable diseases. There's more about them on pages 43-45.
2) Non-communicable diseases are those that cannot spread between people or between animals and people. They generally last for a long time and get worse slowly. Asthma, cancer and coronary heart disease (see page 34) are examples of non-communicable diseases.

Different Types of Disease Sometimes Interact

Sometimes diseases can interact and cause other physical and mental health issues that don't immediately seem related. Here are a few examples:

Pathogen is just the fancy term for a microorganism that can cause a disease when it infects its host.

1) People who have problems with their immune system (the system that your body uses to help fight off infection — see p.46) have an increased chance of suffering from communicable diseases such as influenza (flu), because their body is less likely to be able to defend itself against the pathogen that causes the disease.
2) Some types of cancer can be triggered by infection by certain viruses. For example, infection with some types of hepatitis virus can cause long-term infections in the liver, where the virus lives in the cells. This can lead to an increased chance of developing liver cancer. Another example is infection with HPV (human papilloma virus), which can cause cervical cancer in women.
3) Immune system reactions in the body caused by infection by a pathogen can sometimes trigger allergic reactions such as skin rashes or worsen the symptoms of asthma for asthma sufferers.
4) Mental health issues such as depression can be triggered when someone is suffering from severe physical health problems, particularly if they have an impact on the person's ability to carry out everyday activities or if they affect the person's life expectancy.

Other Factors Can Also Affect Your Health

There are plenty of factors other than diseases that can also affect your health. For example:

1) Whether or not you have a good, balanced diet that provides your body with everything it needs, and in the right amounts. A poor diet can affect your physical and mental health.
2) The stress you are under — being constantly under lots of stress can lead to health issues.
3) Your life situation — for example, whether you have easy access to medicines to treat illness, or whether you have access to things that can prevent you from getting ill in the first place, e.g. being able to buy healthy food or access condoms to prevent the transmission of some sexually transmitted diseases.

If stress can affect your health, why do we have exams...

You really need to get the terms communicable and non-communicable disease into your head. They could come up in the exam and you'd be really sad if you didn't understand the question.

Q1 What is meant by 'health'? [1 mark]

Q2 Why is influenza classed as a communicable disease? [1 mark]

Risk Factors for Non-Communicable Diseases

You've probably heard the term 'risk factor' before. This page has all the info you need to know about them.

Risk Factors Increase Your Chance of Getting a Disease

1) Risk factors are things that are linked to an increase in the likelihood that a person will develop a certain disease during their lifetime. They don't guarantee that someone will get the disease.
2) Risk factors are often aspects of a person's lifestyle (e.g. how much exercise they do). They can also be the presence of certain substances in the environment (e.g. air pollution) or substances in your body (e.g. asbestos fibres — asbestos was a material used in buildings until it was realised that the fibres could build up in your airways and cause diseases such as cancer later in life).
3) Many non-communicable diseases are caused by several different risk factors interacting with each other rather than one factor alone.
4) Lifestyle factors can have different impacts locally, nationally and globally. E.g. in developed countries, non-communicable diseases are more common as people generally have a higher income and can buy high-fat food. Nationally, people from deprived areas are more likely to smoke, have a poor diet and not exercise. This means the incidence of cardiovascular disease, obesity and Type 2 diabetes is higher in those areas. Your individual choices affect the local incidence of disease.

Some Risk Factors Can Cause a Disease Directly

1) Some risk factors are able to directly cause a disease. For example:

   1) Smoking has been proven to directly cause cardiovascular disease, lung disease and lung cancer. It damages the walls of arteries and the cells in the lining of the lungs.
   2) It's thought that obesity can directly cause Type 2 diabetes by making the body less sensitive or resistant to insulin, meaning that it struggles to control the concentration of glucose in the blood.
   3) Drinking too much alcohol has been shown to cause liver disease. Too much alcohol can affect brain function too. It can damage the nerve cells in the brain, causing the brain to lose volume.
   4) Smoking when pregnant can cause lots of health problems for the unborn baby. Drinking alcohol has similar effects.
   5) Cancer can be directly caused by exposure to certain substances or radiation. Things that cause cancer are known as carcinogens. Ionising radiation (e.g. from X-rays) is an example of a carcinogen.

2) However, risk factors are identified by scientists looking for correlations in data, and correlation doesn't always equal cause (see p.9). Some risk factors aren't capable of directly causing a disease. For example, a lack of exercise and a high fat diet are heavily linked to an increased chance of cardiovascular disease, but they can't cause the disease directly. It's the resulting high blood pressure and high 'bad' cholesterol levels (see p.34) that can actually cause it.

Non-Communicable Diseases Can Be Costly

1) The HUMAN cost of non-communicable diseases is obvious. Tens of millions of people around the world die from non-communicable diseases per year. People with these diseases may have a lower quality of life or a shorter lifespan. This not only affects the sufferers themselves, but their loved ones too.
2) It's also important to think about the FINANCIAL cost. The cost to the NHS of researching and treating these diseases is huge — and it's the same for other health services and organisations around the world. Families may have to move or adapt their home to help a family member with a disease, which can be costly. Also, if the family member with the disease has to give up work or dies, the family's income will be reduced. A reduction in the number of people able to work can also affect a country's economy.

Best put down that cake and go for a run...

You might be asked to interpret data about risk factors. See p.9 for a few tips on what you can and can't say.

Q1 Give an example of a type of risk factor other than an aspect of a person's lifestyle. [1 mark]

Cancer

Cancer's not a pleasant topic, but the more we understand about it, the better our chances of avoiding and beating it (and getting good marks in the exam). You're a good way through the topic, so keep going.

Cancer is Caused by Uncontrolled Cell Growth and Division

This uncontrolled growth and division is a result of changes that occur to the cells and results in the formation of a tumour (a mass of cells). Not all tumours are cancerous. They can be benign or malignant:

1) Benign — This is where the tumour grows until there's no more room. The tumour stays in one place (usually within a membrane) rather than invading other tissues in the body. This type isn't normally dangerous, and the tumour isn't cancerous.
2) Malignant — This is where the tumour grows and spreads to neighbouring healthy tissues. Cells can break off and spread to other parts of the body by travelling in the bloodstream. The malignant cells then invade healthy tissues elsewhere in the body and form secondary tumours. Malignant tumours are dangerous and can be fatal — they are cancers.

Risk Factors Can Increase the Chance of Some Cancers

Anyone can develop cancer. Having risk factors doesn't mean that you'll definitely get cancer. It just means that you're at an increased risk of developing the disease. Cancer survival rates have increased due to medical advances such as improved treatment, being able to diagnose cancer earlier and increased screening for the disease.

Risk Factors Can Be Associated With Lifestyle

Scientists have identified lots of lifestyle risk factors for various types of cancer. For example:

1) Smoking — It's a well known fact that smoking is linked to lung cancer, but research has also linked it to other types of cancer too, including mouth, bowel, stomach and cervical cancer.
2) Obesity — Obesity has been linked to many different cancers, including bowel, liver and kidney cancer. It's the second biggest preventable cause of cancer after smoking.
3) UV exposure — People who are often exposed to UV radiation from the Sun have an increased chance of developing skin cancer. People who live in sunny climates and people who spend a lot of time outside are at higher risk of the disease. People who frequently use sun beds are also putting themselves at higher risk of developing skin cancer.
4) Viral infection — Infection with some viruses has been shown to increase the chances of developing certain types of cancer. For example, infection with hepatitis B and hepatitis C viruses can increase the risk of developing liver cancer. The likelihood of becoming infected with these viruses sometimes depends on lifestyle — e.g. they can be spread between people through unprotected sex or sharing needles.

Risk Factors Can Also Be Associated With Genetics

1) Sometimes you can inherit faulty genes that make you more susceptible to cancer.
2) For example, mutations (changes) in the BRCA genes have been linked to an increased likelihood of developing breast and ovarian cancer.

At least our rubbish summers reduce our UV exposure...

Joking aside, UV radiation can still reach us through the clouds, and like many other lifestyle risk factors, we can take steps to reduce the risk, e.g. by keeping covered up outside and wearing sun block.

Q1 What are tumours the result of? [1 mark]

Q2 List three lifestyle factors that can increase the risk of developing cancer. [3 marks]

Plant Cell Organisation

You saw on page 24 how animals keep their specialised cells neat and tidy — plants are in on the act too.

Plant Cells Are Organised Into Tissues And Organs

Plants are made of organs like stems, roots and leaves. Plant organs work together to make organ systems. These can perform the various tasks that a plant needs to carry out to survive and grow — for example, transporting substances around the plant. Plant organs are made of tissues. Examples of plant tissues are:

1) Epidermal tissue — this covers the whole plant.
2) Palisade mesophyll tissue — this is the part of the leaf where most photosynthesis happens.
3) Spongy mesophyll tissue — this is also in the leaf, and contains big air spaces to allow gases to diffuse in and out of cells.
4) Xylem and phloem — they transport things like water, mineral ions and food around the plant (through the roots, stems and leaves — see next page for more).
5) Meristem tissue — this is found at the growing tips of shoots and roots and is able to differentiate (change) into lots of different types of plant cell, allowing the plant to grow.

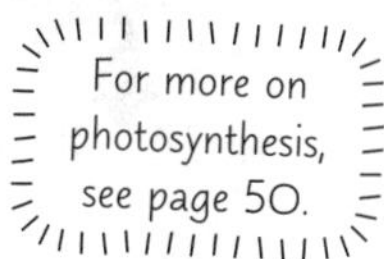

A merry stem.

The Leaf is an Organ Made Up of Several Types of Tissue

Leaves contain epidermal, mesophyll, xylem and phloem tissues.

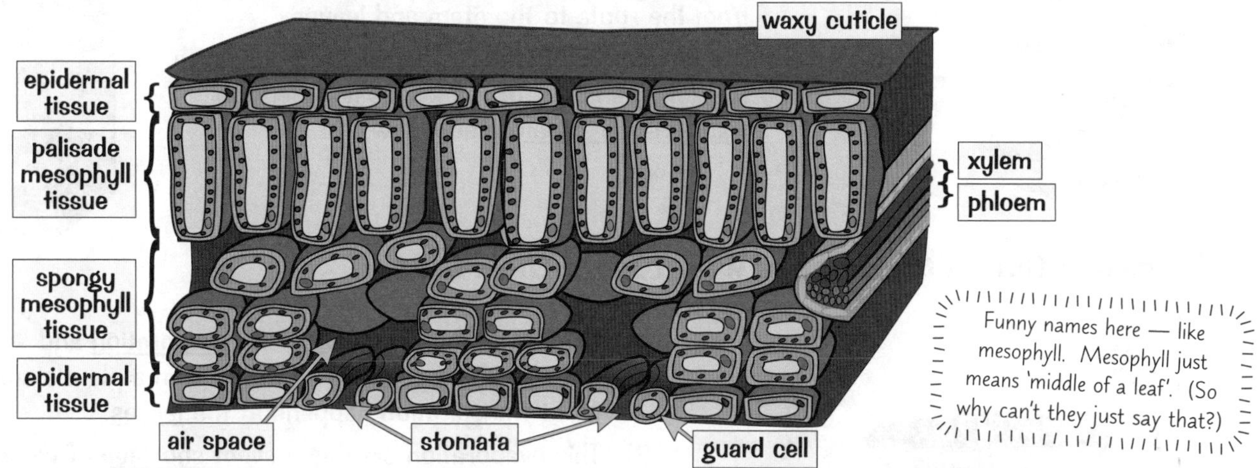

You need to know how the structures of the tissues that make up the leaf are related to their function:

1) The epidermal tissues are covered with a waxy cuticle, which helps to reduce water loss by evaporation.
2) The upper epidermis is transparent so that light can pass through it to the palisade layer.
3) The palisade layer has lots of chloroplasts (the little structures where photosynthesis takes place). This means that they're near the top of the leaf where they can get the most light.
4) The xylem and phloem form a network of vascular bundles, which deliver water and other nutrients to the entire leaf and take away the glucose produced by photosynthesis. They also help support the structure.
5) The tissues of leaves are also adapted for efficient gas exchange (see page 22). E.g. the lower epidermis is full of little holes called stomata, which let CO_2 diffuse directly into the leaf. The opening and closing of stomata is controlled by guard cells in response to environmental conditions. The air spaces in the spongy mesophyll tissue increase the rate of diffusion of gases.

Plant cell organisation — millions of members worldwide...

There are a lot of weird names here, so make sure you spend plenty of time on this page. Maybe you could draw your own leaf diagram and label it with descriptions of the different tissue types. It would make an excellent Christmas present for someone, or an art collector might even want it.

Q1 Describe the characteristics of meristem tissue. [2 marks]

Transpiration and Translocation

You might be surprised to learn that there aren't tiny trucks that transport substances around plants. Then again, you might not be — either way, you need to learn the stuff on this page...

Phloem Tubes Transport Food:

1) Made of columns of elongated living cells with small pores in the end walls to allow cell sap to flow through.
2) They transport food substances (mainly dissolved sugars) made in the leaves to the rest of the plant for immediate use (e.g. in growing regions) or for storage.
3) The transport goes in both directions.
4) This process is called translocation.

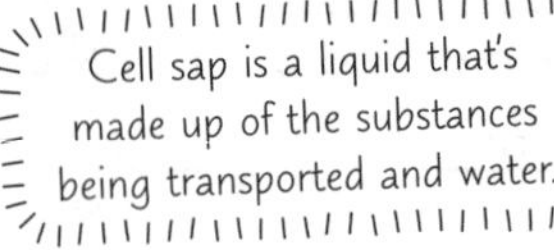

Xylem Tubes Take Water Up:

1) Made of dead cells joined end to end with no end walls between them and a hole down the middle. They're strengthened with a material called lignin.
2) They carry water and mineral ions from the roots to the stem and leaves.
3) The movement of water from the roots, through the xylem and out of the leaves is called the transpiration stream (see below).

Transpiration is the Loss of Water from the Plant

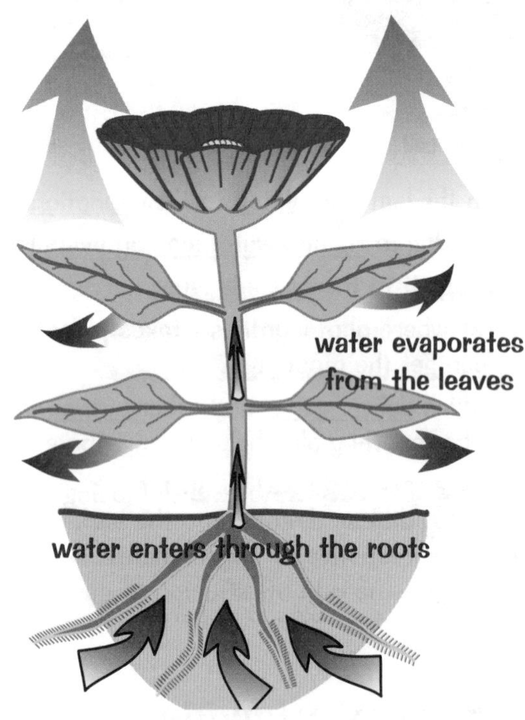

1) Transpiration is caused by the evaporation and diffusion (see page 17) of water from a plant's surface. Most transpiration happens at the leaves.
2) This evaporation creates a slight shortage of water in the leaf, and so more water is drawn up from the rest of the plant through the xylem vessels to replace it.
3) This in turn means more water is drawn up from the roots, and so there's a constant transpiration stream of water through the plant.

Head back to page 19 to see how root hair cells are adapted for taking up water.

Transpiration is just a side-effect of the way leaves are adapted for photosynthesis. They have to have stomata in them so that gases can be exchanged easily (see page 22). Because there's more water inside the plant than in the air outside, the water escapes from the leaves through the stomata by diffusion.

Don't let revision stress you out — just go with the phloem...

Phloem transports substances in both directions, but xylem only transports things upwards — xy to the sky.

Q1 Describe the structure of xylem. [3 marks]

Transpiration and Stomata

Sorry, more on transpiration. But then it's a quick dash through stomata and out of the other end of the topic.

Transpiration Rate is Affected by Four Main Things

1) LIGHT INTENSITY — the brighter the light, the greater the transpiration rate.
   Stomata begin to close as it gets darker. Photosynthesis can't happen in the dark, so they don't need to be open to let CO_2 in. When the stomata are closed, very little water can escape.
2) TEMPERATURE — the warmer it is, the faster transpiration happens.
   When it's warm the water particles have more energy to evaporate and diffuse out of the stomata.
3) AIR FLOW — the better the air flow around a leaf (e.g. stronger wind), the greater the transpiration rate.
   If air flow around a leaf is poor, the water vapour just surrounds the leaf and doesn't move away. This means there's a high concentration of water particles outside the leaf as well as inside it, so diffusion doesn't happen as quickly. If there's good air flow, the water vapour is swept away, maintaining a low concentration of water in the air outside the leaf. Diffusion then happens quickly, from an area of higher concentration to an area of lower concentration.
4) HUMIDITY — the drier the air around a leaf, the faster transpiration happens.
   This is like what happens with air flow. If the air is humid there's a lot of water in it already, so there's not much of a difference between the inside and the outside of the leaf. Diffusion happens fastest if there's a really high concentration in one place, and a really low concentration in the other.

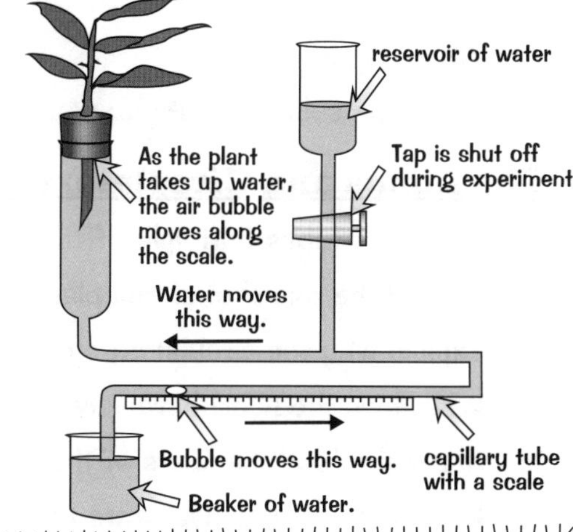

This piece of apparatus is called a potometer. Setting it up is quite tough — there are some tips on page 236.

You can estimate the rate of transpiration by measuring the uptake of water by a plant. This is because you can assume that water uptake by the plant is directly related to water loss by the leaves (transpiration).

Set up the apparatus as in the diagram, and then record the starting position of the air bubble. Start a stopwatch and record the distance moved by the bubble per unit time, e.g. per hour. Keep the conditions constant throughout the experiment, e.g. the temperature and air humidity.

Guard Cells Are Adapted to Open and Close Stomata

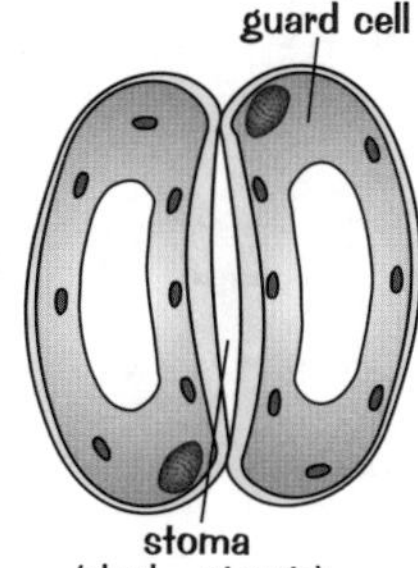

1) They have a kidney shape which opens and closes the stomata (page 22) in a leaf.
2) When the plant has lots of water the guard cells fill with it and go plump and turgid. This makes the stomata open so gases can be exchanged for photosynthesis.
3) When the plant is short of water, the guard cells lose water and become flaccid, making the stomata close. This helps stop too much water vapour escaping.
4) Thin outer walls and thickened inner walls make the opening and closing work.
5) They're also sensitive to light and close at night to save water without losing out on photosynthesis.
6) You usually find more stomata on the undersides of leaves than on the top. The lower surface is shaded and cooler — so less water is lost through the stomata than if they were on the upper surface.
7) Guard cells are therefore adapted for gas exchange and controlling water loss within a leaf.

I say stomaaarta, you say stomaaayta...

Different leaves will have different distributions of stomata. You can peel the epidermal tissue off some leaves and mount them on microscope slides (see page 13) to compare them. It's thrilling stuff.

Q1 Explain how low light intensity affects the rate of transpiration. [3 marks]

Revision Questions for Topic B2

Topic B2 finished. Now it's time for *the* greatest quiz on Earth. Please hold your excitement in.

- Try these questions and tick off each one when you get it right.
- When you've done all the questions under a heading and are completely happy with it, tick it off.

Cell Organisation (p.24)

1) What is a tissue?
2) Explain what is meant by the term 'organ system'.

The Role of Enzymes and Food Tests (p.25-29)

3) Why can enzymes be described as biological catalysts?
4) Why do enzymes only usually catalyse one reaction?
5) What does it mean when an enzyme has been 'denatured'?
6) Describe how you could investigate the effect of pH on the rate of amylase activity.
7) List the three places where amylase is made in the human body.
8) What is the role of lipases?
9) Where is bile stored?
10) Name the solution that you would use to test for the presence of lipids in a food sample.

The Lungs and Circulatory System (p.30-33)

11) Name the tubes that split off the trachea.
12) Explain the role that alveoli play in gas exchange.
13) Explain why the circulatory system in humans is described as a 'double circulatory system'.
14) Why does the heart have valves?
15) Name the four chambers of the heart.
16) How is the resting heart rate controlled in a healthy heart?
17) How are arteries adapted to carry blood away from the heart?
18) Why do red blood cells not have a nucleus?

Diseases and Risk Factors (p.34-38)

19) Give two advantages and two disadvantages of statins.
20) What is the difference between biological and mechanical replacement heart valves?
21) What is meant by a non-communicable disease?
22) Give an example of where different types of disease might interact in the body.
23) What is meant by a risk factor of a disease?
24) Which type of tumour is cancerous?

Plant Cell Organisation and Transport (p.39-41)

25) List the tissues that make up a leaf.
26) Explain how the structure of the upper epidermal tissue in a leaf is related to its function.
27) What is the function of phloem?
28) What is transpiration?
29) List the four main things that affect transpiration.
30) How could you measure the rate of transpiration?
31) Name the type of cell that helps open and close stomata.

Communicable Disease

If you're hoping I'll ease you gently into this new topic... no such luck. Straight on to the baddies of biology.

There Are Several Types of Pathogen

1) Pathogens are microorganisms that enter the body and cause disease.
2) They cause communicable (infectious) diseases — diseases that can easily spread (see p.36).
3) Both plants and animals can be infected by pathogens.

1. Bacteria Are Very Small Living Cells

1) Bacteria are very small cells (about 1/100th the size of your body cells), which can reproduce rapidly inside your body.
2) They can make you feel ill by producing toxins (poisons) that damage your cells and tissues.

2. Viruses Are Not Cells — They're Much Smaller

1) Viruses are not cells. They're tiny, about 1/100th the size of a bacterium.
2) Like bacteria, they can reproduce rapidly inside your body.
3) They live inside your cells and replicate themselves using the cells' machinery to produce many copies of themselves. The cell will usually then burst, releasing all the new viruses.
4) This cell damage is what makes you feel ill.

A virus

A body cell

eek!

3. Protists are Single-Celled Eukaryotes

1) There are lots of different types of protists. But they're all eukaryotes (see page 11) and most of them are single-celled.
2) Some protists are parasites. Parasites live on or inside other organisms and can cause them damage. They are often transferred to the organism by a vector, which doesn't get the disease itself — e.g. an insect that carries the protist.

4. Fungi Come in Different Shapes

1) Some fungi are single-celled. Others have a body which is made up of hyphae (thread-like structures).
2) These hyphae can grow and penetrate human skin and the surface of plants, causing diseases.
3) The hyphae can produce spores, which can be spread to other plants and animals.

Pathogens Can Be Spread in Different Ways

Pathogens can be spread in many ways. Here are a few that you need to know about.

1) WATER — Some pathogens can be picked up by drinking or bathing in dirty water. E.g. cholera is a bacterial infection that's spread by drinking water contaminated with the diarrhoea of other sufferers.
2) AIR — Pathogens can be carried in the air and can then be breathed in. Some airborne pathogens are carried in the air in droplets produced when you cough or sneeze — e.g. the influenza virus that causes flu is spread this way.
3) DIRECT CONTACT — Some pathogens can be picked up by touching contaminated surfaces, including the skin. E.g. athlete's foot is a fungus which makes skin itch and flake off. It's most commonly spread by touching the same things as an infected person, e.g. shower floors and towels.

Hooray, I've avoided the classic 'he was a fungi to be with' joke...

Yuck, lots of nasties out there that can cause disease. Plants need to be worried too, as you'll find out.

Q1 Describe how viruses cause cell damage. [2 marks]

Viral, Fungal and Protist Diseases

There are heaps of diseases caused by viruses, fungi and protists, but you just need to know about these ones.

You Need to Know About Three Viral Diseases...

1) Measles is a viral disease. It is spread by droplets from an infected person's sneeze or cough.
2) People with measles develop a red skin rash, and they'll show signs of a fever (a high temperature).
3) Measles can be very serious, or even fatal, if there are complications. For example, measles can sometimes lead to pneumonia (a lung infection) or a brain infection called encephalitis.
4) Most people are vaccinated against measles when they're young.

1) HIV is a virus spread by sexual contact, or by exchanging bodily fluids such as blood. This can happen when people share needles when taking drugs.
2) HIV initially causes flu-like symptoms for a few weeks. Usually, the person doesn't then experience any symptoms for several years. During this time, HIV can be controlled with antiretroviral drugs. These stop the virus replicating in the body.
3) The virus attacks the immune cells (see page 46).
4) If the body's immune system is badly damaged, it can't cope with other infections or cancers. At this stage, the virus is known as late stage HIV infection, or AIDS.

1) Tobacco mosaic virus (TMV) is a virus that affects many species of plants, e.g. tomatoes.
2) It causes a mosaic pattern on the leaves of the plants — parts of the leaves become discoloured.
3) The discolouration means the plant can't carry out photosynthesis as well, so the virus affects growth.

Photosynthesis is important for plant growth because it produces glucose — see page 50.

...a Fungal Disease...

1) Rose black spot is a fungus that causes purple or black spots to develop on the leaves of rose plants. Who'd have guessed. The leaves can then turn yellow and drop off.
2) This means that less photosynthesis can happen, so the plant doesn't grow very well.
3) It spreads through the environment in water or by the wind.
4) Gardeners can treat the disease using fungicides and by stripping the plant of its affected leaves. These leaves then need to be destroyed so that the fungus can't spread to other rose plants.

...and a Disease Caused by a Protist

1) Malaria is caused by a protist (see the previous page).
2) Part of the malarial protist's life cycle takes place inside the mosquito. The mosquitoes are vectors (see the previous page) — they pick up the malarial protist when they feed on an infected animal.
3) Every time the mosquito feeds on another animal, it infects it by inserting the protist into the animal's blood vessels.
4) Malaria causes repeating episodes of fever. It can be fatal.
5) The spread of malaria can be reduced by stopping the mosquitoes from breeding.
6) People can be protected from mosquitoes using insecticides and mosquito nets.

I've heard this page has gone viral...

The examiner could grill you on any one of these diseases, so make sure you know them all inside out.

Q1 What symptom of measles is shown on the skin? [1 mark]

Q2 How can rose black spot be treated so that it doesn't spread to other plants? [2 marks]

Bacterial Diseases and Preventing Disease

Sorry — I'm afraid there are some more diseases to learn about here. This time, they're diseases caused by bacteria. I don't know about you, but I'm starting to feel a bit itchy all over...

You Need to Know About Two Bacterial Diseases

1) Salmonella is a type of bacteria that causes food poisoning.
2) Infected people can suffer from fever, stomach cramps, vomiting and diarrhoea. Pleasant.
3) These symptoms are caused by the toxins that the bacteria produce (see page 43).
4) You can get Salmonella food poisoning by eating food that's been contaminated with Salmonella bacteria, e.g. eating chicken that caught the disease whilst it was alive, or eating food that has been contaminated by being prepared in unhygienic conditions.
5) In the UK, most poultry (e.g. chickens and turkeys) is given a vaccination against Salmonella. This is to control the spread of the disease.

1) Gonorrhoea is a sexually transmitted disease (STD).
2) STDs are passed on by sexual contact, e.g. having unprotected sex.
3) Gonorrhoea is caused by bacteria.
4) A person with gonorrhoea will get pain when they urinate. Another symptom is a thick yellow or green discharge from the vagina or the penis.
5) Gonorrhoea was originally treated with an antibiotic called penicillin, but this has become trickier now because strains of the bacteria have become resistant to it (see page 48).
6) To prevent the spread of gonorrhoea, people can be treated with antibiotics and should use barrier methods of contraception (see page 65), such as condoms.

The Spread of Disease Can Be Reduced or Prevented

There are things that we can do to reduce, and even prevent, the spread of disease. For example:

1) Being hygienic — Using simple hygiene measures can prevent the spread of disease. For example, doing things like washing your hands thoroughly before preparing food or after you've sneezed can stop you infecting another person.

2) Destroying vectors — By getting rid of the organisms that spread disease, you can prevent the disease from being passed on. Vectors that are insects can be killed using insecticides or by destroying their habitat so that they can no longer breed.

3) Isolating infected individuals — If you isolate someone who has a communicable disease, it prevents them from passing it on to anyone else.

4) Vaccination — Vaccinating people and animals against communicable diseases means that they can't develop the infection and then pass it on to someone else. There's more about how vaccination works on page 47.

The spread of disease — mouldy margarine...

OK, I promise, that's it. No more diseases to learn about in this Topic. You may be sick of them already (geddit?) but don't turn this page until you've got all the facts firmly attached to your cranial material.

Q1 What has made it harder to treat gonorrhoea? [1 mark]

Q2 It is important for chefs to wash their hands thoroughly before cooking. Suggest why. [1 mark]

Fighting Disease

The human body has some pretty neat features when it comes to fighting disease.

Your Body Has a Pretty Sophisticated Defence System

1) The human body has got features that stop a lot of nasties getting inside in the first place.
2) The skin acts as a barrier to pathogens. It also secretes antimicrobial substances which kill pathogens.
3) Hairs and mucus in your nose trap particles that could contain pathogens.
4) The trachea and bronchi (breathing pipework — see page 30) secrete mucus to trap pathogens.
5) The trachea and bronchi are lined with cilia. These are hair-like structures, which waft the mucus up to the back of the throat where it can be swallowed.
6) The stomach produces hydrochloric acid. This kills pathogens that make it that far from the mouth.

Your Immune System Can Attack Pathogens

1) If pathogens do make it into your body, your immune system kicks in to destroy them.
2) The most important part of your immune system is the white blood cells. They travel around in your blood and crawl into every part of you, constantly patrolling for microbes. When they come across an invading microbe they have three lines of attack.

1. Consuming Them

White blood cells can engulf foreign cells and digest them. This is called phagocytosis.

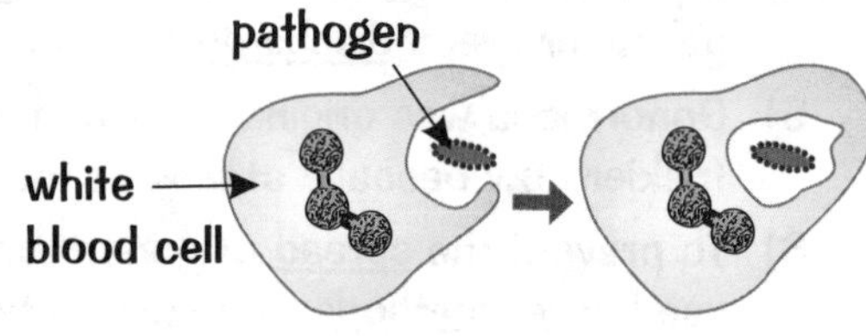

2. Producing Antibodies

1) Every invading pathogen has unique molecules (called antigens) on its surface.
2) When some types of white blood cell come across a foreign antigen (i.e. one they don't recognise), they will start to produce proteins called antibodies to lock onto the invading cells so that they can be found and destroyed by other white blood cells. The antibodies produced are specific to that type of antigen — they won't lock on to any others.
3) Antibodies are then produced rapidly and carried around the body to find all similar bacteria or viruses.
4) If the person is infected with the same pathogen again the white blood cells will rapidly produce the antibodies to kill it — the person is naturally immune to that pathogen and won't get ill.

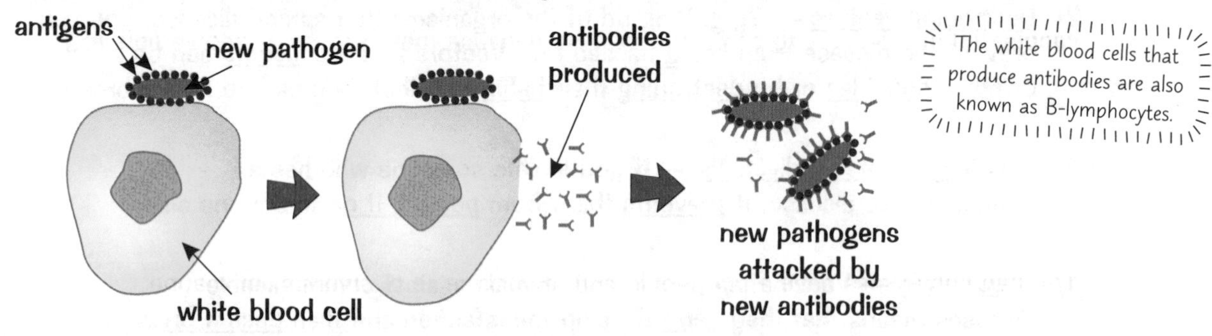

The white blood cells that produce antibodies are also known as B-lymphocytes.

3. Producing Antitoxins

These counteract toxins produced by the invading bacteria.

Fight disease — blow your nose with boxing gloves...

If you have a low level of white blood cells, you'll be more susceptible to infections. HIV attacks white blood cells and weakens the immune system, making it easier for other pathogens to invade.

Q1 What is phagocytosis? [1 mark]

Q2 How are the trachea and the bronchi adapted to defend against the entry of pathogens? [3 marks]

Fighting Disease — Vaccination

Vaccinations have changed the way we fight disease. We don't always have to deal with the problem once it's happened — we can prevent it happening in the first place.

Vaccination — Protects from Future Infections

1) When you're infected with a new pathogen, it takes your white blood cells a few days to learn how to deal with it. But by that time, you can be pretty ill.
2) Vaccinations involve injecting small amounts of dead or inactive pathogens. These carry antigens, which cause your body to produce antibodies to attack them — even though the pathogen is harmless (since it's dead or inactive). For example, the MMR vaccine contains weakened versions of the viruses that cause measles, mumps and rubella (German measles) all in one vaccine.
3) But if live pathogens of the same type appear after that, the white blood cells can rapidly mass-produce antibodies to kill off the pathogen. Cool.

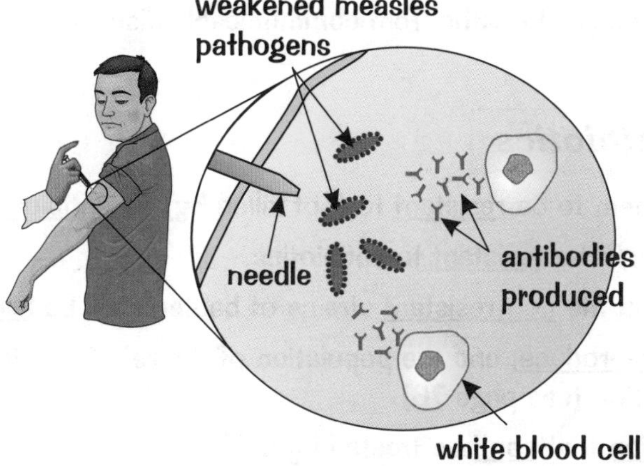

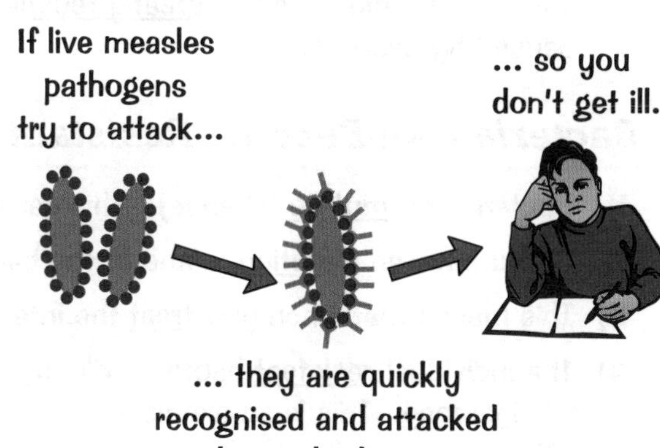

There are Pros and Cons of Vaccination

PROS

1) Vaccines have helped control lots of communicable diseases that were once common in the UK (e.g. polio, measles, whooping cough, rubella, mumps, tetanus...). Smallpox no longer occurs at all, and polio infections have fallen by 99%.
2) Big outbreaks of disease — called epidemics — can be prevented if a large percentage of the population is vaccinated. That way, even the people who aren't vaccinated are unlikely to catch the disease because there are fewer people able to pass it on. But if a significant number of people aren't vaccinated, the disease can spread quickly through them and lots of people will be ill at the same time.

CONS

1) Vaccines don't always work — sometimes they don't give you immunity.
2) You can sometimes have a bad reaction to a vaccine (e.g. swelling, or maybe something more serious like a fever or seizures). But bad reactions are very rare.

Prevention is better than cure...

Deciding whether to have a vaccination means balancing risks — the risk of catching the disease if you don't have a vaccine, against the risk of having a bad reaction if you do. As always, you need to look at the evidence. For example, if you get measles (the disease), there's about a 1 in 15 chance that you'll get complications (e.g. pneumonia) — and about 1 in 500 people who get measles actually die. However, the number of people who have a problem with the vaccine is more like 1 in 1 000 000.

Q1 What do vaccinations stimulate white blood cells to produce? [1 mark]

Fighting Disease — Drugs

...a biscuit, nurse? Thanks very much. Sorry, couldn't face that last page — I'm squeamish about needles.*

Some Drugs Relieve Symptoms — Others Cure the Problem

1) Painkillers (e.g. aspirin) are drugs that relieve pain (no, really). However, they don't actually tackle the cause of the disease or kill pathogens, they just help to reduce the symptoms.
2) Other drugs do a similar kind of thing — reduce the symptoms without tackling the underlying cause. For example, lots of "cold remedies" don't actually cure colds.
3) Antibiotics (e.g. penicillin) work differently — they actually kill (or prevent the growth of) the bacteria causing the problem without killing your own body cells. Different antibiotics kill different types of bacteria, so it's important to be treated with the right one.
4) But antibiotics don't destroy viruses (e.g. flu or cold viruses). Viruses reproduce using your body cells, which makes it very difficult to develop drugs that destroy just the virus without killing the body's cells.
5) The use of antibiotics has greatly reduced the number of deaths from communicable diseases caused by bacteria.

Bacteria Can Become Resistant to Antibiotics

1) Bacteria can mutate (change). This can cause them to be resistant to (not killed by) an antibiotic.
2) If you have an infection, some of the bacteria might be resistant to antibiotics.
3) This means that when you treat the infection, only the non-resistant strains of bacteria will be killed.
4) The individual resistant bacteria will survive and reproduce, and the population of the resistant strain will increase. This is an example of natural selection (see page 76).
5) This resistant strain could cause a serious infection that can't be treated by antibiotics. E.g. MRSA (meticillin-resistant *Staphylococcus aureus*) causes serious wound infections and is resistant to the powerful antibiotic meticillin.
6) To slow down the rate of development of resistant strains, it's important for doctors to avoid over-prescribing antibiotics. So you won't get them for a sore throat, only for something more serious.
7) It's also important that you finish the whole course of antibiotics and don't just stop once you feel better.

Many Drugs Originally Came From Plants

1) Plants produce a variety of chemicals to defend themselves against pests and pathogens.
2) Some of these chemicals can be used as drugs to treat human diseases or relieve symptoms. A lot of our current medicines were discovered by studying plants used in traditional cures. For example:
   - Aspirin is used as a painkiller and to lower fever. It was developed from a chemical found in willow.
   - Digitalis is used to treat heart conditions. It was developed from a chemical found in foxgloves.
3) Some drugs were extracted from microorganisms. For example:
   - Alexander Fleming was clearing out some Petri dishes containing bacteria. He noticed that one of the dishes of bacteria also had mould on it and the area around the mould was free of the bacteria.
   - He found that the mould (called *Penicillium notatum*) on the Petri dish was producing a substance that killed the bacteria — this substance was penicillin.
4) These days, drugs are made on a large scale in the pharmaceutical industry — they're synthesised by chemists in labs. However, the process still might start with a chemical extracted from a plant.

Ahh...Ahh... Ahhhhh Choooooooo — urghh, this page is catching...

Drug development is a big industry. And guess what — you're about to find out some more about it.

Q1 Which type of pathogen can antibiotics be used to kill? [1 mark]

*That's my excuse, you'll have to think of your own.

Developing Drugs

New drugs are constantly being developed. But before they can be given to the general public, they have to go through a thorough testing procedure. This is what usually happens...

There are Three Main Stages in Drug Testing

1) In preclinical testing, drugs are tested on human cells and tissues in the lab.
2) However, you can't use human cells and tissues to test drugs that affect whole or multiple body systems, e.g. testing a drug for blood pressure must be done on a whole animal because it has an intact circulatory system.

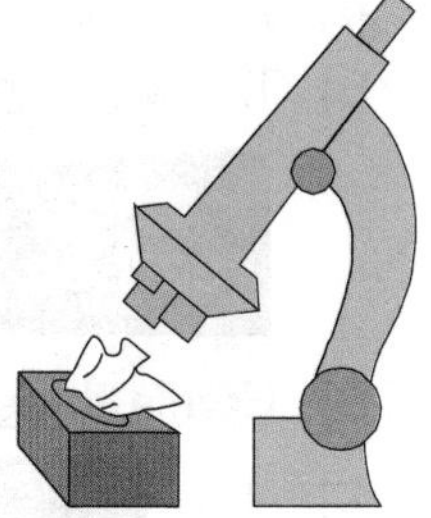

1) The next step in preclinical testing is to test the drug on live animals. This is to test efficacy (whether the drug works and produces the effect you're looking for), to find out about its toxicity (how harmful it is) and to find the best dosage (the concentration that should be given, and how often it should be given).
2) The law in Britain states that any new drug must be tested on two different live mammals. Some people think it's cruel to test on animals, but others believe this is the safest way to make sure a drug isn't dangerous before it's given to humans.

But some people think that animals are so different from humans that testing on animals is pointless.

1) If the drug passes the tests on animals then it's tested on human volunteers in a clinical trial.
2) First, the drug is tested on healthy volunteers. This is to make sure that it doesn't have any harmful side effects when the body is working normally. At the start of the trial, a very low dose of the drug is given and this is gradually increased.
3) If the results of the tests on healthy volunteers are good, the drugs can be tested on people suffering from the illness. The optimum dose is found — this is the dose of drug that is the most effective and has few side effects.
4) To test how well the drug works, patients are randomly put into two groups. One is given the new drug, the other is given a placebo (a substance that's like the drug being tested but doesn't do anything). This is so the doctor can see the actual difference the drug makes — it allows for the placebo effect (when the patient expects the treatment to work and so feels better, even though the treatment isn't doing anything).
5) Clinical trials are blind — the patient in the study doesn't know whether they're getting the drug or the placebo. In fact, they're often double-blind — neither the patient nor the doctor knows until all the results have been gathered. This is so the doctors monitoring the patients and analysing the results aren't subconsciously influenced by their knowledge.
6) The results of drug testing and drug trials aren't published until they've been through peer review. This helps to prevent false claims.

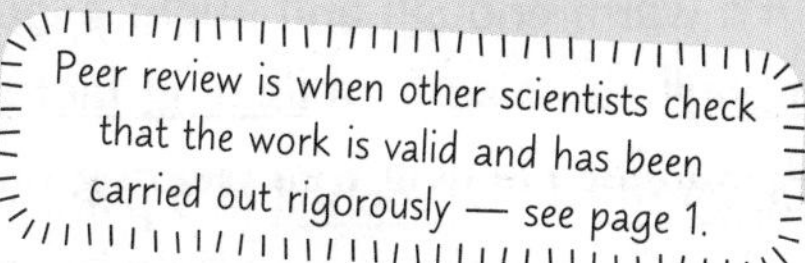

The placebo effect doesn't work with revision...

... you can't just expect to get a good mark and then magically get it. I know, I know, there's a lot of information to take in on this page, but just read it through slowly. There's nothing too tricky here — it's just a case of going over it again and again until you've got it all firmly lodged in your memory.

Q1 What is meant by the efficacy of a drug? [1 mark]

Q2 Why do clinical trials of a new drug begin with healthy volunteers? [1 mark]

Q3 Why must the results from drug testing be assessed by peer review? [1 mark]

Photosynthesis and Limiting Factors

First, photosynthesis equations. Then there are some more bits 'n' bobs you should know...

Photosynthesis Produces Glucose Using Light

1) Photosynthesis uses energy to change carbon dioxide and water into glucose and oxygen.
2) It takes place in chloroplasts in green plant cells — they contain pigments like chlorophyll that absorb light.
3) Energy is transferred to the chloroplasts from the environment by light.
4) Photosynthesis is endothermic — this means energy is transferred from the environment in the process.
5) The word equation for photosynthesis is:

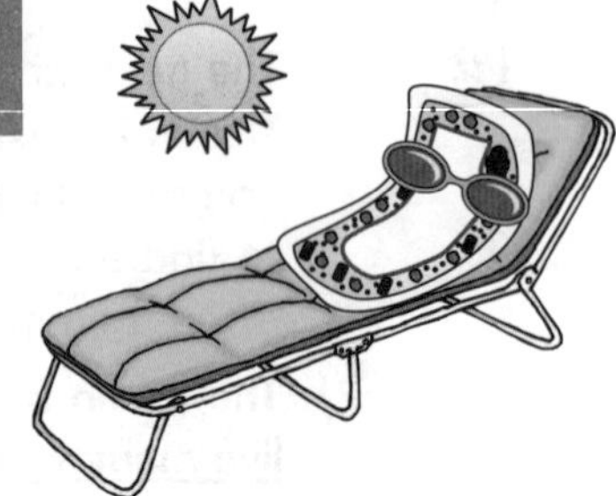

6) Here's the symbol equation too:

Plants Use Glucose in Five Main Ways...

1) For respiration — This transfers energy from glucose (see p.54) which enables the plants to convert the rest of the glucose into various other useful substances.
2) Making cellulose — Glucose is converted into cellulose for making strong plant cell walls (see p.11).
3) Making amino acids — Glucose is combined with nitrate ions (absorbed from the soil) to make amino acids, which are then made into proteins.
4) Stored as oils or fats — Glucose is turned into lipids (fats and oils) for storing in seeds.
5) Stored as starch — Glucose is turned into starch and stored in roots, stems and leaves, ready for use when photosynthesis isn't happening, like in the winter. Starch is insoluble, which makes it much better for storing than glucose — a cell with lots of glucose in would draw in loads of water and swell up.

Limiting Factors Affect the Rate of Photosynthesis

1) The rate of photosynthesis is affected by intensity of light, concentration of CO_2 and temperature.
2) Any of these three factors can become the limiting factor — this just means that it's stopping photosynthesis from happening any faster.
3) These factors have a combined effect on the rate of photosynthesis, but which factor is limiting at a particular time depends on the environmental conditions:
   - at night it's pretty obvious that light is the limiting factor,
   - in winter it's often the temperature,
   - if it's warm enough and bright enough, the amount of CO_2 is usually limiting.
4) Chlorophyll can also be a limiting factor of photosynthesis.

The amount of chlorophyll in a plant can be affected by disease (e.g. infection with the tobacco mosaic virus) or environmental stress, such as a lack of nutrients. These factors can cause chloroplasts to become damaged or to not make enough chlorophyll. This means the rate of photosynthesis is reduced because they can't absorb as much light.

Now you'll have something to bore the great-grandkids with...

You'll be able to tell them how, in your day, all you needed was a bit of carbon dioxide and some water and you could make your own entertainment. But at the moment you need to learn this page...

Q1 Name the products of photosynthesis. [2 marks]

Q2 Apart from temperature, name three other limiting factors of photosynthesis. [3 marks]

The Rate of Photosynthesis

Now that you know light, CO_2 and temperature all affect the rate of photosynthesis, you also need to know how they affect the rate, so you can take a gander at a load of lovely pictures... well, graphs. I've also thrown an experiment and an equation in for good measure. I can tell these pages are going to be your favourites...

Three Important Graphs for Rate of Photosynthesis

1) Not Enough Light Slows Down the Rate of Photosynthesis

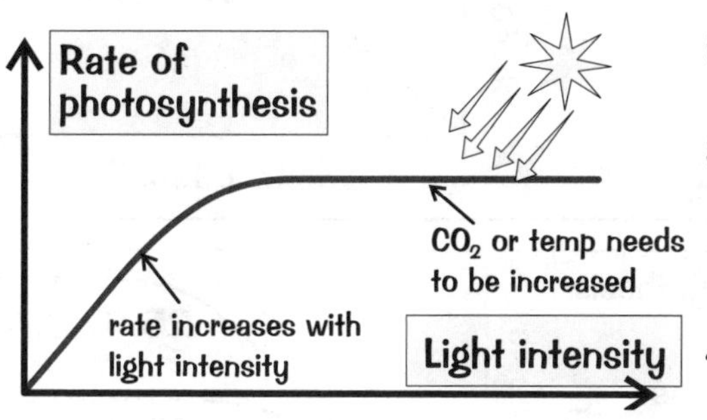

1) Light provides the energy needed for photosynthesis.
2) As the light level is raised, the rate of photosynthesis increases steadily — but only up to a certain point.
3) Beyond that, it won't make any difference — as light intensity increases, the rate will no longer increase. This is because it'll be either the temperature or the CO_2 level which is now the limiting factor, not light.
4) In the lab you can change the light intensity by moving a lamp closer to or further away from your plant (see the next page for this experiment).
5) But if you just plot the rate of photosynthesis against "distance of lamp from the plant", you get a weird-shaped graph. To get a graph like the one above you either need to measure the light intensity at the plant using a light meter or do a bit of nifty maths with your results.

2) Too Little Carbon Dioxide Also Slows it Down

1) CO_2 is one of the raw materials needed for photosynthesis.
2) As with light intensity, the amount of CO_2 will only increase the rate of photosynthesis up to a point. After this the graph flattens out — as the amount of CO_2 increases, the rate no longer increases. This shows that CO_2 is no longer the limiting factor.
3) As long as light and CO_2 are in plentiful supply then the factor limiting photosynthesis must be temperature.

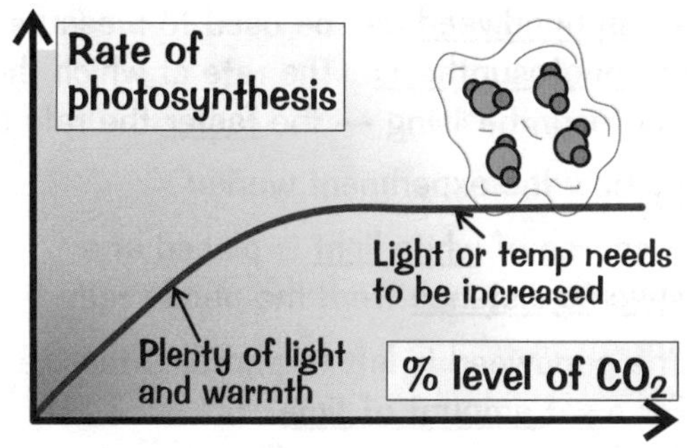

3) The Temperature has to be Just Right

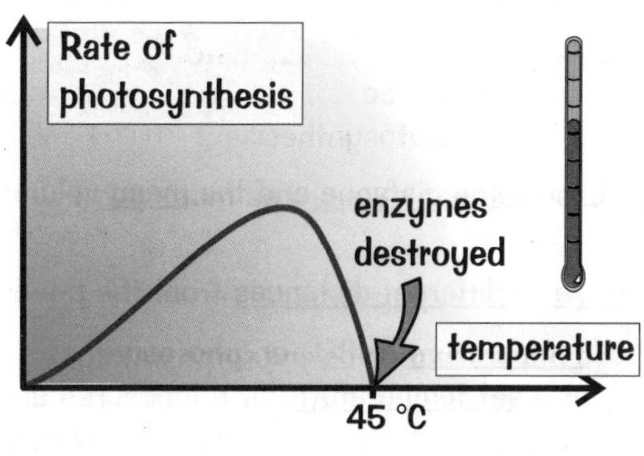

1) Usually, if the temperature is the limiting factor it's because it's too low — the enzymes needed for photosynthesis work more slowly at low temperatures.
2) But if the plant gets too hot, the enzymes it needs for photosynthesis and its other reactions will be damaged.
3) This happens at about 45 °C (which is pretty hot for outdoors, although greenhouses can get that hot if you're not careful).

The Rate of Photosynthesis

One Graph May Show the Effect of Many Limiting Factors

You could get a graph that shows more than one limiting factor on the rate of photosynthesis, for example:

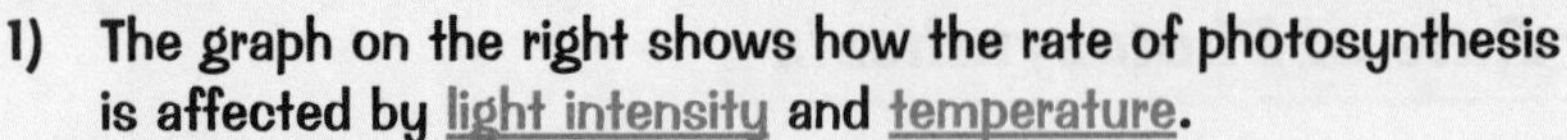

1) The graph on the right shows how the rate of photosynthesis is affected by light intensity and temperature.
2) At the start, both of the lines show that as the light intensity increases, the rate of photosynthesis increases steadily.
3) But the lines level off when light is no longer the limiting factor. The line at 25 °C levels off at a higher point than the one at 15 °C, showing that temperature must have been a limiting factor at 15 °C.

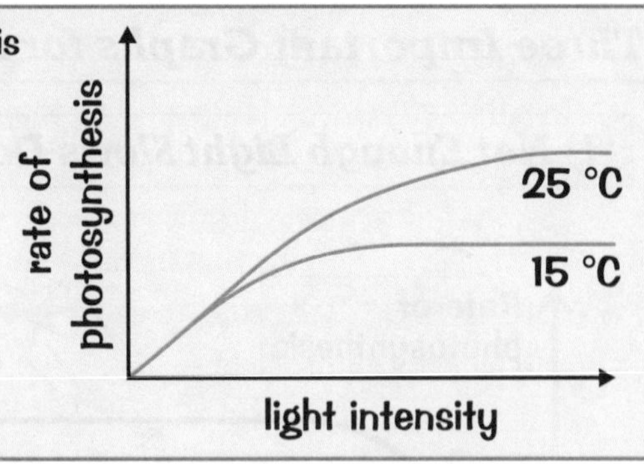

1) The graph on the right shows how the rate of photosynthesis is affected by light intensity and CO_2 concentration.
2) Again, both the lines level off when light is no longer the limiting factor.
3) The line at the higher CO_2 concentration of 0.4% levels off at a higher point than the one at 0.04%. This means CO_2 concentration must have been a limiting factor at 0.04% CO_2. The limiting factor here isn't temperature because it's the same for both lines (25 °C).

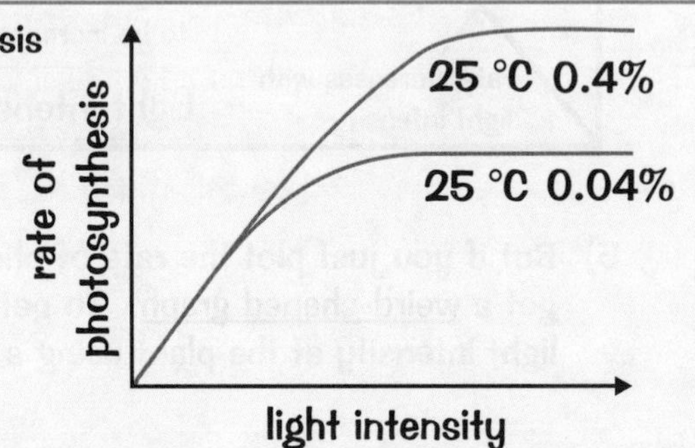

Oxygen Production Shows the Rate of Photosynthesis

PRACTICAL

Canadian pondweed can be used to measure the effect of light intensity on the rate of photosynthesis. The rate at which the pondweed produces oxygen corresponds to the rate at which it's photosynthesising — the faster the rate of oxygen production, the faster the rate of photosynthesis.

Here's how the experiment works:

1) A source of white light is placed at a specific distance from the pondweed.
2) The pondweed is left to photosynthesise for a set amount of time. As it photosynthesises, the oxygen released will collect in the capillary tube.
3) At the end of the experiment, the syringe is used to draw the gas bubble in the tube up alongside a ruler and the length of the gas bubble is measured. This is proportional to the volume of O_2 produced.

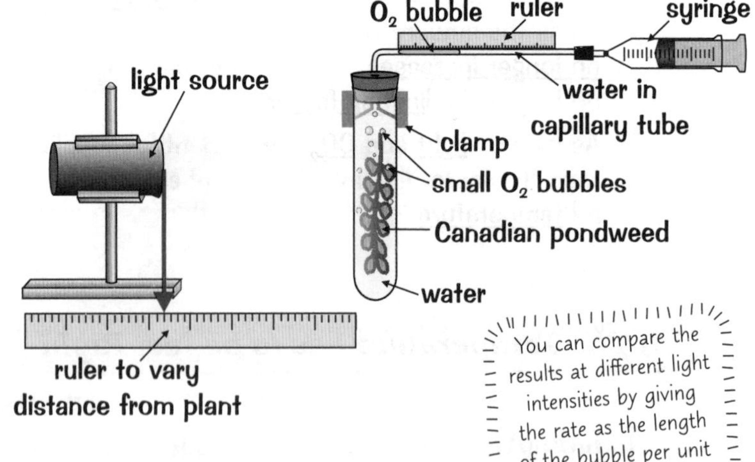

4) For this experiment, any variables that could affect the results should be controlled, e.g. the temperature and time the pondweed is left to photosynthesise.
5) The experiment is repeated twice with the light source at the same distance and the mean volume of O_2 produced is calculated.
6) Then the whole experiment is repeated with the light source at different distances from the pondweed.

You can compare the results at different light intensities by giving the rate as the length of the bubble per unit time, e.g. cm/min.

The apparatus above can be altered to measure the effect of temperature or CO_2 on photosynthesis. E.g. the test tube of pondweed can be put into a water bath at a set temperature, or a measured amount of sodium hydrogencarbonate can be dissolved in the water (which gives off CO_2). The experiment can then be repeated with different temperatures of water / concentrations of sodium hydrogencarbonate.

The Rate of Photosynthesis

The Inverse Square Law Links Light Intensity and Distance

1) In the experiment on the previous page, when the lamp is moved away from the pondweed, the amount of light that reaches the pondweed decreases.
2) You can say that as the distance increases, the light intensity decreases. In other words, distance and light intensity are inversely proportional to each other.
3) However, it's not quite as simple as that. It turns out that light intensity decreases in proportion to the square of the distance. This is called the inverse square law and is written out like this:

$$\text{light intensity} \propto \frac{1}{\text{distance (d)}^2}$$

This is the 'proportional to' symbol. Putting one over the distance shows the inverse. The distance is squared.

4) The inverse square law means that if you halve the distance, the light intensity will be four times greater and if you third the distance, the light intensity will be nine times greater. Likewise, if you double the distance, the light intensity will be four times smaller and if you treble the distance, the light intensity will be nine times smaller.
5) You can use $1/d^2$ as a measure of light intensity.

EXAMPLE: Use the inverse square law to calculate the light intensity when the lamp is 10 cm from the pondweed.

1) Use the formula $\frac{1}{d^2}$. — light intensity $= \frac{1}{d^2}$
2) Fill in the values you know — you're given the distance, so put that in. — light intensity $= \frac{1}{10^2}$
3) Calculate the answer. — $= 0.01$ a.u.

'a.u.' stands for 'arbitrary units'.

You can Artificially Create the Ideal Conditions for Farming

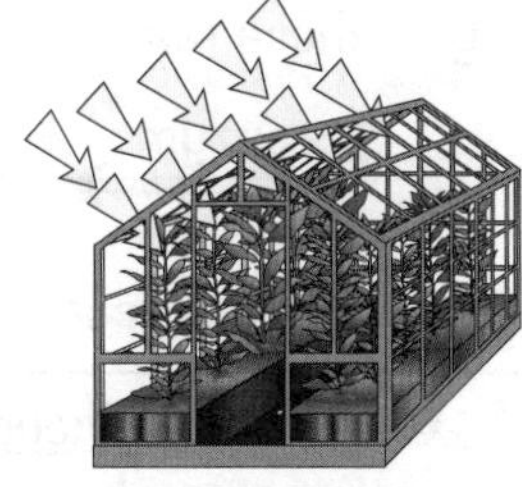

1) The most common way to artificially create the ideal environment for plants is to grow them in a greenhouse.
2) Greenhouses help to trap the Sun's heat, and make sure that the temperature doesn't become limiting. In winter a farmer or gardener might use a heater as well to keep the temperature at the ideal level. In summer it could get too hot, so they might use shades and ventilation to cool things down.
3) Light is always needed for photosynthesis, so commercial farmers often supply artificial light after the Sun goes down to give their plants more quality photosynthesis time.
4) Farmers and gardeners can also increase the level of carbon dioxide in the greenhouse. E.g. by using a paraffin heater to heat the greenhouse. As the paraffin burns, it makes carbon dioxide as a by-product.
5) Keeping plants enclosed in a greenhouse also makes it easier to keep them free from pests and diseases. The farmer can add fertilisers to the soil as well, to provide all the minerals needed for healthy growth.
6) Sorting all this out costs money — but if the farmer can keep the conditions just right for photosynthesis, the plants will grow much faster and a decent crop can be harvested much more often, which can then be sold. It's important that a farmer supplies just the right amount of heat, light, etc. — enough to make the plants grow well, but not more than the plants need, as this would just be wasting money.

Don't blame it on the sunshine, don't blame it on the CO_2...

Now don't let the inverse square law put you off learning everything on these past three pages.

Q1 An experiment was carried out to find out the effect of temperature on the rate of photosynthesis. Name two variables that should have been controlled in this experiment. [2 marks]

Q2 Write down the inverse square law. [1 mark]

Respiration and Metabolism

You need energy to keep your body going. Energy comes from food, and it's transferred by respiration.

Respiration is NOT "Breathing In and Out"

Respiration involves many reactions. These are really important reactions, as respiration transfers the energy that the cell needs to do just about everything — this energy is used for all living processes.

1) Respiration is not breathing in and breathing out, as you might think.
2) Respiration is the process of transferring energy from the breakdown of glucose (sugar) — and it goes on in every cell in your body continuously.
3) It happens in plants too. All living things respire. It's how they transfer energy from their food to their cells.

RESPIRATION is the process of TRANSFERRING ENERGY FROM GLUCOSE, which goes on IN EVERY CELL.

4) Respiration is exothermic — it transfers energy to the environment.

Respiration Transfers Energy for All Kinds of Things

Here are three examples of how organisms use the energy transferred by respiration:

1) To build up larger molecules from smaller ones (like proteins from amino acids — see below).
2) In animals it's used to allow the muscles to contract (so they can move about).
3) In mammals and birds the energy is used to keep their body temperature steady in colder surroundings. (Unlike other animals, mammals and birds keep their bodies constantly warm.)

Metabolism is ALL the Chemical Reactions in an Organism

1) In a cell there are lots of chemical reactions happening all the time, which are controlled by enzymes.
2) Many of these reactions are linked together to form bigger reactions:

reactant —enzyme→ product —enzyme→ product —enzyme→ product

Enzymes are biological catalysts — see p.25.

3) In some of these reactions, larger molecules are made from smaller ones. For example:
   - Lots of small glucose molecules are joined together in reactions to form starch (a storage molecule in plant cells), glycogen (a storage molecule in animal cells) and cellulose (a component of plant cell walls).
   - Lipid molecules are each made from one molecule of glycerol and three fatty acids.
   - Glucose is combined with nitrate ions to make amino acids, which are then made into proteins.
4) In other reactions, larger molecules are broken down into smaller ones. For example:
   - Glucose is broken down in respiration. Respiration transfers energy to power all the reactions in the body that make molecules.
   - Excess protein is broken down in a reaction to produce urea. Urea is then excreted in urine.
5) The sum (total) of all of the reactions that happen in a cell or the body is called its metabolism.

Don't stop respirin' — hold onto that feelin'...

Isn't it strange to think that each individual living cell in your body is respiring every second of every day, transferring energy from the food you eat. This energy is used to make molecules that our cells need.

Q1 Give two examples of how animals use the energy transferred by respiration. [2 marks]

Q2 What is metabolism? [1 mark]

Aerobic and Anaerobic Respiration

There are two types of respiration, don't cha know...

Aerobic Respiration Needs Plenty of Oxygen

1) Aerobic respiration is respiration using oxygen.
   It's the most efficient way to transfer energy from glucose.
2) Aerobic respiration goes on all the time in plants and animals.
3) Most of the reactions in aerobic respiration happen inside mitochondria (see page 11).
4) Here are the word and symbol equations for aerobic respiration:

glucose + oxygen ⟶ carbon dioxide + water

$$C_6H_{12}O_6 + 6O_2 \longrightarrow 6CO_2 + 6H_2O$$

Anaerobic Respiration is Used if There's Not Enough Oxygen

When you do vigorous exercise and your body can't supply enough oxygen to your muscles, they start doing anaerobic respiration as well as aerobic respiration.

1) "Anaerobic" just means "without oxygen". It's the incomplete breakdown of glucose, making lactic acid.
2) Here's the word equation for anaerobic respiration in muscle cells:

glucose ⟶ lactic acid

3) Anaerobic respiration does not transfer nearly as much energy as aerobic respiration.
   This is because glucose isn't fully oxidised (because it doesn't combine with oxygen).
4) So, anaerobic respiration is only useful in emergencies, e.g. during exercise when it allows you to keep on using your muscles for a while longer.

Anaerobic Respiration in Plants and Yeast is Slightly Different

1) Plants and yeast cells can respire without oxygen too, but they produce ethanol (alcohol) and carbon dioxide instead of lactic acid.
2) Here is the word equation for anaerobic respiration in plants and yeast cells:

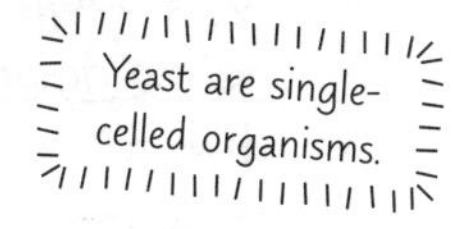

glucose ⟶ ethanol + carbon dioxide

3) Anaerobic respiration in yeast cells is called fermentation.
4) In the food and drinks industry, fermentation by yeast is of great value because it's used to make bread and alcoholic drinks, e.g. beer and wine.
5) In bread-making, it's the carbon dioxide from fermentation that makes bread rise.
6) In beer and wine-making, it's the fermentation process that produces alcohol.

I'd like a ham and fermentation sandwich please... yum

Fermentation is a really important process because of its use in making alcoholic drinks and bread. We drink and eat so much of these that making them is big bucks. And it's all down to tiny yeast cells.

Q1 What are the reactants of aerobic respiration? [2 marks]

Q2 What is the process of anaerobic respiration in yeast called? [1 mark]

Exercise

When you exercise, your body responds in different ways to get enough energy to your cells.

When You Exercise You Respire More

1) Muscles need energy from respiration to contract. When you exercise, some of your muscles contract more frequently than normal so you need more energy. This energy comes from increased respiration.
2) The increase in respiration in your cells means you need to get more oxygen into them.
3) Your breathing rate and breath volume increase to get more oxygen into the blood, and your heart rate increases to get this oxygenated blood around the body faster. This removes CO_2 more quickly at the same time.
4) When you do really vigorous exercise (like sprinting) your body can't supply oxygen to your muscles quickly enough, so they start respiring anaerobically (see the previous page).
5) This is NOT the best way to transfer energy from glucose because lactic acid builds up in the muscles, which gets painful.
6) Long periods of exercise also cause muscle fatigue — the muscles get tired and then stop contracting efficiently.

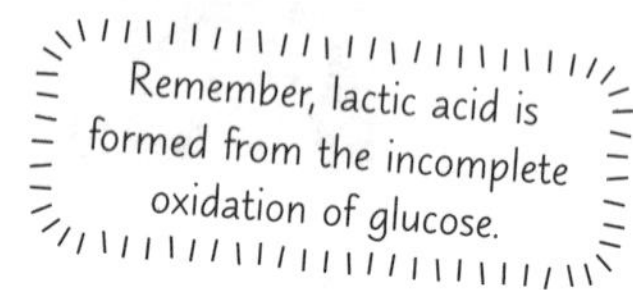

Anaerobic Respiration Leads to an Oxygen Debt

1) After resorting to anaerobic respiration, when you stop exercising you'll have an "oxygen debt".
2) An oxygen debt is the amount of extra oxygen your body needs to react with the build up of lactic acid and remove it from the cells. Oxygen reacts with the lactic acid to form harmless CO_2 and water.
3) In other words you have to "repay" the oxygen that you didn't get to your muscles in time, because your lungs, heart and blood couldn't keep up with the demand earlier on.
4) This means you have to keep breathing hard for a while after you stop, to get more oxygen into your blood, which is transported to the muscle cells.
5) The pulse and breathing rate stay high whilst there are high levels of lactic acid and CO_2.
6) Your body also has another way of coping with the high level of lactic acid — the blood that enters your muscles transports the lactic acid to the liver. In the liver, the lactic acid is converted back to glucose.

You Can Investigate The Effect of Exercise on The Body

1) You can measure breathing rate by counting breaths, and heart rate by taking the pulse.
2) E.g. you could take your pulse after:
   - sitting down for 5 minutes,
   - then after 5 minutes of gentle walking,
   - then again after 5 minutes of slow jogging,
   - then again after running for 5 minutes,

   and plot your results in a bar chart.

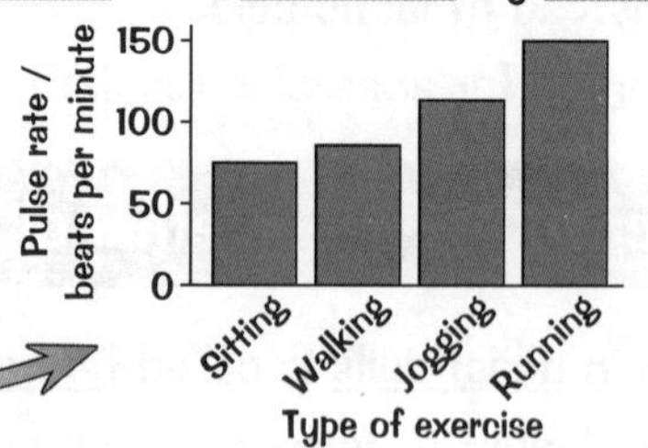

You put two fingers on the inside of your wrist or your neck and count the number of pulses in 1 minute.

3) Your pulse rate will increase the more intense the exercise is, as your body needs to get more oxygen to the muscles and take more carbon dioxide away from the muscles.
4) To reduce the effect of any random errors on your results, do it as a group and plot the average pulse rate for each exercise.

There's more about random error on page 5.

Oxygen debt — cheap to pay back...

At the end of a sprinting race you often see athletes breathing hard — now you know this is to get rid of the lactic acid that's built up in the muscles. But remember, the liver plays a role in breaking it down too.

Q1 What causes muscle fatigue? [1 mark]

Q2 Explain what an "oxygen debt" is. [1 mark]

Revision Questions for Topics B3 &

It's all over for Topics B3 and B4 folks. I know how much you'll miss them, so here are s

- Try these questions and tick off each one when you get it right.
- When you've done all the questions under a heading and are completely happy with it, tick it off.

Types of Disease (p.43-45)

1) How can bacteria make us feel ill?
2) How does tobacco mosaic virus affect a plant's growth?
3) How are mosquitoes involved in the spread of malaria?
4) What are the symptoms of gonorrhoea?
5) How can destroying vectors help to prevent the spread of disease?

Fighting Disease (p.46-49)

6) What does the stomach produce that can kill pathogens?
7) Give three ways that the white blood cells can defend against pathogens.
8) Give one pro and one con of vaccination.
9) Why is it difficult to develop drugs that kill viruses without also damaging body tissues?
10) Which plant does the painkiller aspirin originate from?
11) What two things are drugs tested on in preclinical testing?
12) What is a placebo?

Photosynthesis (p.50-53)

13) Where in a plant cell does photosynthesis take place?
14) What is an endothermic reaction?
15) What is the word equation for photosynthesis?
16) Why do plants store glucose as starch?
17) What is meant by a 'limiting factor' of photosynthesis?
18) What effect would a low carbon dioxide concentration have on the rate of photosynthesis?
19) Describe how you could measure the effect of light intensity on the rate of photosynthesis.
20) In the inverse square law, how are light intensity and distance linked?

Respiration and Metabolism (p.54-56)

21) What is respiration?
22) What is an exothermic reaction?
23) Name the products of aerobic respiration.
24) What is produced by anaerobic respiration in muscle cells?
25) What is the word equation for anaerobic respiration in yeast cells?
26) Name two products of the food and drink industry that fermentation is needed for.
27) Give three things that increase to supply the muscles with more oxygenated blood during exercise.
28) In what organ is lactic acid converted back to glucose?

Homeostasis

Homeostasis — a word that strikes fear into the heart of many a GCSE student. But it's really not that bad at all. This page is a brief introduction to the topic, so you need to nail all of this before you can move on.

Homeostasis — Maintaining a Stable Internal Environment

I'm not really a doctor — this clipboard isn't holding anything. But take it from me, homeostasis is one important topic.

1) The conditions inside your body need to be kept steady, even when the external environment changes. This is really important because your cells need the right conditions in order to function properly, including the right conditions for enzyme action (see p.25).
2) Homeostasis is all about the regulation of the conditions inside your body (and cells) to maintain a stable internal environment, in response to changes in both internal and external conditions.
3) You have loads of automatic control systems in your body that regulate your internal environment — these include both nervous and hormonal communication systems. For example, there are control systems that maintain your body temperature, blood glucose level (see page 63) and your water content.

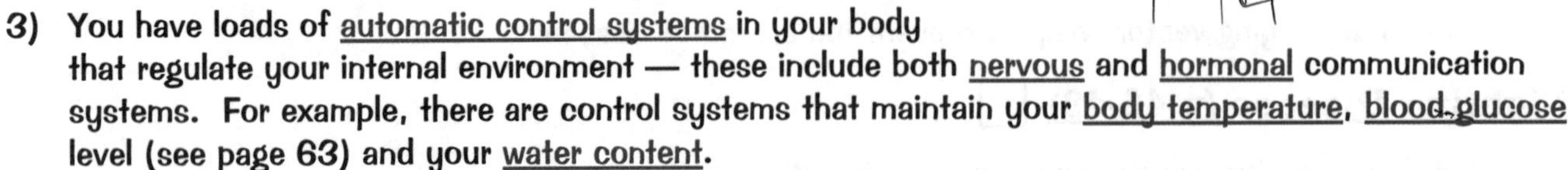

4) All your automatic control systems are made up of three main components which work together to maintain a steady condition — cells called receptors, coordination centres (including the brain, spinal cord and pancreas) and effectors.

Negative Feedback Counteracts Changes

Your automatic control systems keep your internal environment stable using a mechanism called negative feedback. When the level of something (e.g. water or glucose) gets too high or too low, your body uses negative feedback to bring it back to normal.

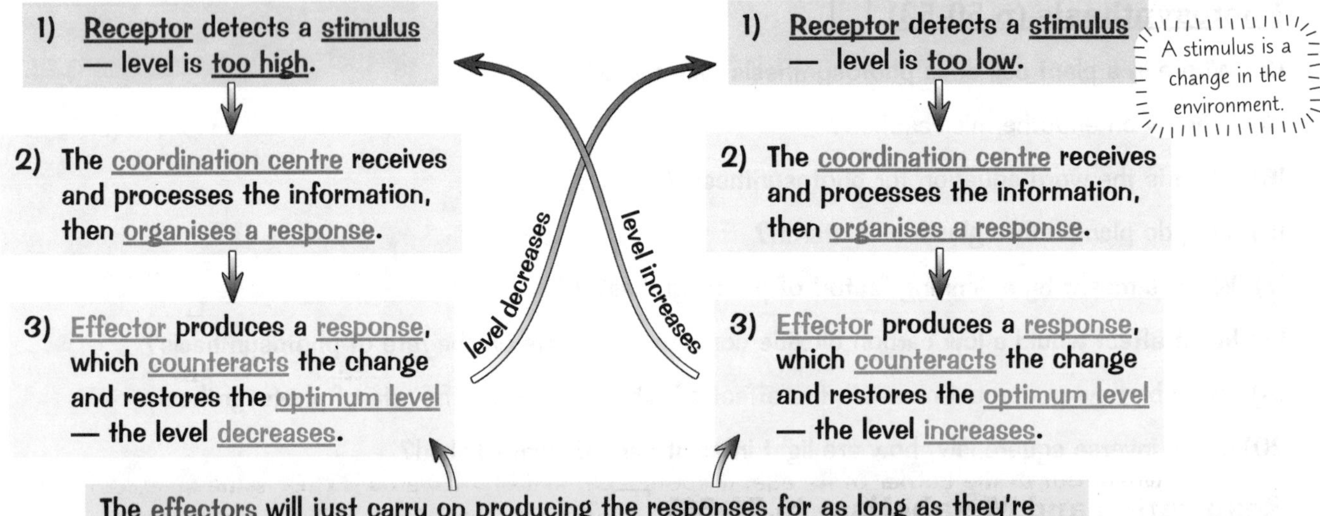

The effectors will just carry on producing the responses for as long as they're stimulated by the coordination centre. This might cause the opposite problem — making the level change too much (away from the ideal). Luckily the receptor detects if the level becomes too different and negative feedback starts again.

This process happens without you thinking about it — it's all automatic.

If you do enough revision, you can avoid negative feedback...

Negative feedback is a fancy-sounding name for a not-very-complicated idea. It's common sense really. For example, if you looked sad, I'd try and cheer you up. And if you looked really happy, I'd probably start to annoy you by flicking the backs of your ears. It stops things getting out of balance, I think.

Q1 Why do the internal conditions of your body need to be regulated? [1 mark]

Q2 Name the component of a control system that detects stimuli. [1 mark]

The Nervous System

Organisms need to respond to stimuli (changes in the environment) in order to survive. A single-celled organism can just respond to its environment, but the cells of multicellular organisms need to communicate with each other first. So as multicellular organisms evolved, they developed nervous and hormonal communication systems.

The Nervous System Detects and Reacts to Stimuli

The nervous system means that humans can react to their surroundings and coordinate their behaviour.

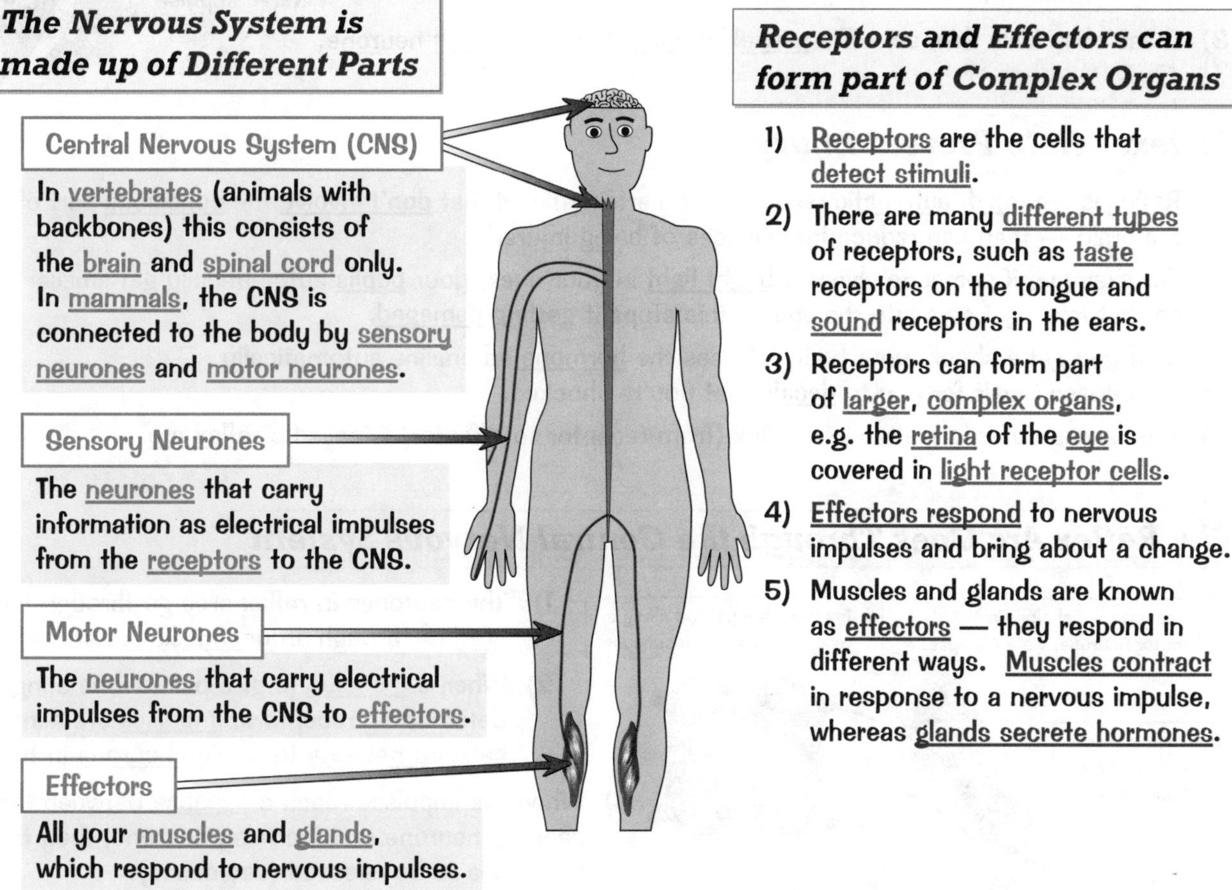

The Nervous System is made up of Different Parts

Central Nervous System (CNS)

In vertebrates (animals with backbones) this consists of the brain and spinal cord only. In mammals, the CNS is connected to the body by sensory neurones and motor neurones.

Sensory Neurones

The neurones that carry information as electrical impulses from the receptors to the CNS.

Motor Neurones

The neurones that carry electrical impulses from the CNS to effectors.

Effectors

All your muscles and glands, which respond to nervous impulses.

Receptors and Effectors can form part of Complex Organs

1) Receptors are the cells that detect stimuli.
2) There are many different types of receptors, such as taste receptors on the tongue and sound receptors in the ears.
3) Receptors can form part of larger, complex organs, e.g. the retina of the eye is covered in light receptor cells.
4) Effectors respond to nervous impulses and bring about a change.
5) Muscles and glands are known as effectors — they respond in different ways. Muscles contract in response to a nervous impulse, whereas glands secrete hormones.

The Central Nervous System (CNS) Coordinates the Response

The CNS is a coordination centre — it receives information from the receptors and then coordinates a response (decides what to do about it). The response is carried out by effectors.

For example, a small bird is eating some seed...

1) ...when, out of the corner of its eye, it spots a cat skulking towards it (this is the stimulus).
2) The receptors in the bird's eye are stimulated. Sensory neurones carry the information from the receptors to the CNS.
3) The CNS decides what to do about it.
4) The CNS sends information to the muscles in the bird's wings (the effectors) along motor neurones. The muscles contract and the bird flies away to safety.

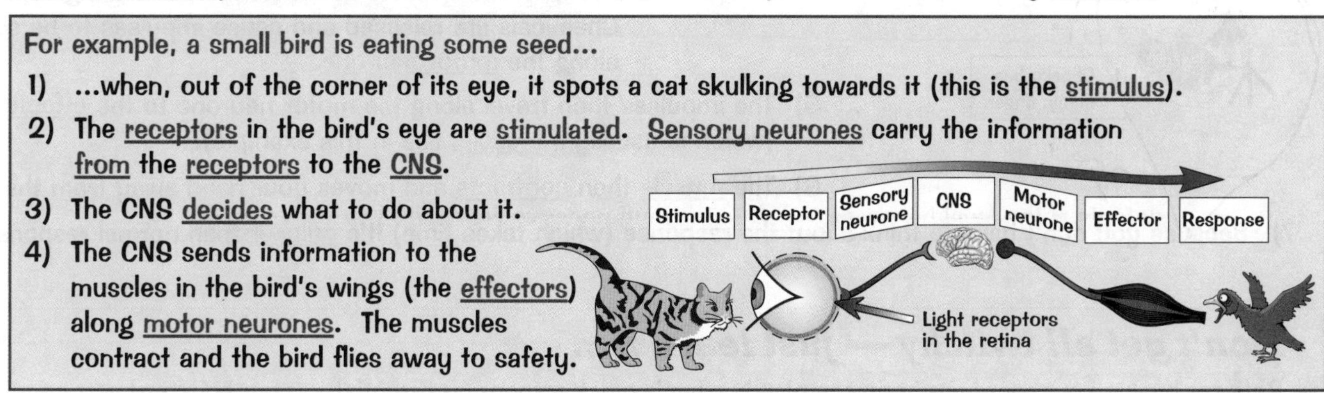

Don't let the thought of exams play on your nerves...

Don't forget that it's only large animals like mammals and birds that have complex nervous systems. Simple animals like jellyfish don't — everything they do is a reflex response (see next page).

Q1 Name two types of effector. [2 marks]

Synapses and Reflexes

Neurones transmit information very quickly to and from the brain, and your brain quickly decides how to respond to a stimulus. But reflexes are even quicker...

Synapses Connect Neurones

1) The connection between two neurones is called a synapse.
2) The nerve signal is transferred by chemicals which diffuse (move) across the gap.
3) These chemicals then set off a new electrical signal in the next neurone.

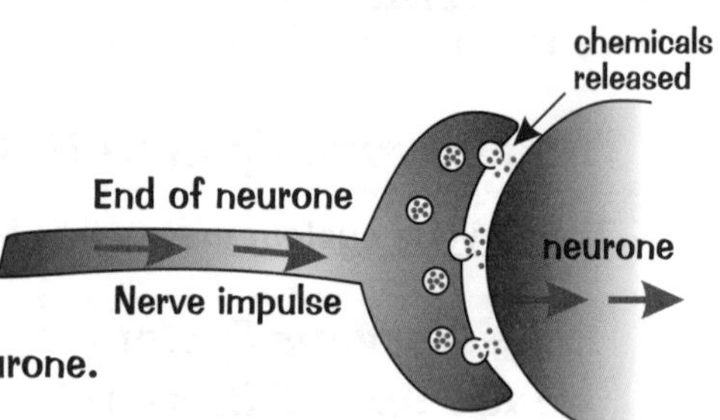

Reflexes Help Prevent Injury

1) Reflexes are rapid, automatic responses to certain stimuli that don't involve the conscious part of the brain — they can reduce the chances of being injured.
2) For example, if someone shines a bright light in your eyes, your pupils automatically get smaller so that less light gets into the eye — this stops it getting damaged.
3) Or if you get a shock, your body releases the hormone adrenaline automatically — it doesn't wait for you to decide that you're shocked.
4) The passage of information in a reflex (from receptor to effector) is called a reflex arc.

The Reflex Arc Goes Through the Central Nervous System

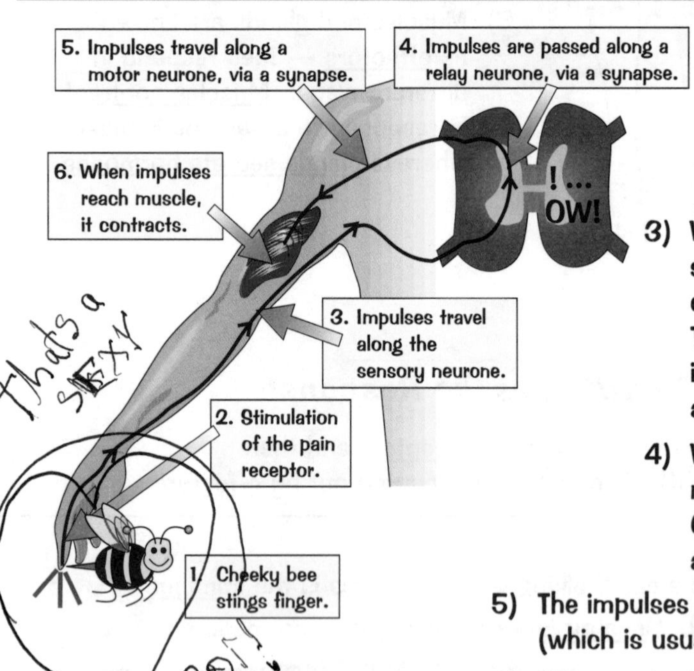

1) The neurones in reflex arcs go through the spinal cord or through an unconscious part of the brain.
2) When a stimulus (e.g. a painful bee sting) is detected by receptors, impulses are sent along a sensory neurone to a relay neurone in the CNS.
3) When the impulses reach a synapse between the sensory neurone and the relay neurone, they trigger chemicals to be released (see above). These chemicals cause impulses to be sent along the relay neurone.

Relay neurones connect sensory neurones to motor neurones.

4) When the impulses reach a synapse between the relay neurone and a motor neurone, the same thing happens. Chemicals are released and cause impulses to be sent along the motor neurone.
5) The impulses then travel along the motor neurone to the effector (which is usually a muscle, like in this example).
6) The muscle then contracts and moves your hand away from the bee.
7) Because you don't have to think about the response (which takes time) it's quicker than normal responses.

Don't get all twitchy — just learn it...

Reflexes bypass your conscious brain completely when a quick response is essential — your body just gets on with things. If you had to stop and think first, you'd end up a lot more sore (or worse).

Q1 What is a reflex action? [1 mark]

Q2 A chef touches a hot tray. A reflex reaction causes him to immediately move his hand away.
a) State the effector in this reflex reaction. [1 mark]
b) Describe the pathway of the reflex from stimulus to effector. [4 marks]

Investigating Reaction Time

PRACTICAL

On your marks... get set... read this page.

Reaction Time is How Quickly You Respond

Reaction time is the time it takes to respond to a stimulus — it's often less than a second. It can be affected by factors such as age, gender or drugs.

You Can Measure Reaction Time

Caffeine is a drug that can speed up a person's reaction time. The effect of caffeine on reaction time can be measured like this...

1) The person being tested should sit with their arm resting on the edge of a table (this should stop them moving their arm up or down during the test).
2) Hold a ruler vertically between their thumb and forefinger. Make sure that the zero end of the ruler is level with their thumb and finger. Then let go without giving any warning.
3) The person being tested should try to catch the ruler as quickly as they can — as soon as they see it fall.
4) Reaction time is measured by the number on the ruler where it's caught. The number should be read from the top of the thumb. The further down the ruler it's caught (i.e. the higher the number), the slower their reaction time.

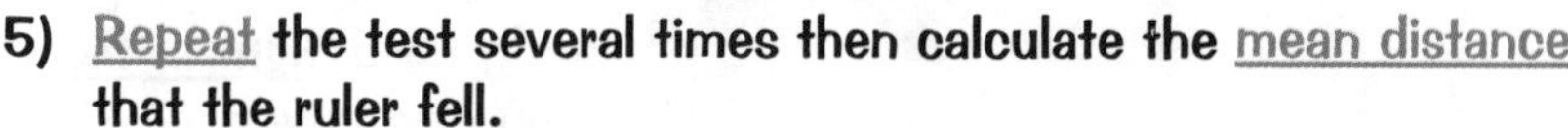

5) Repeat the test several times then calculate the mean distance that the ruler fell.

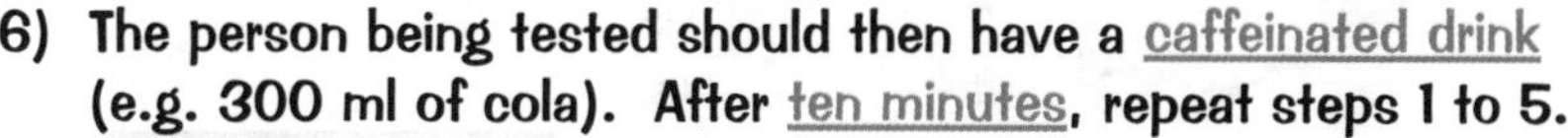

6) The person being tested should then have a caffeinated drink (e.g. 300 ml of cola). After ten minutes, repeat steps 1 to 5.

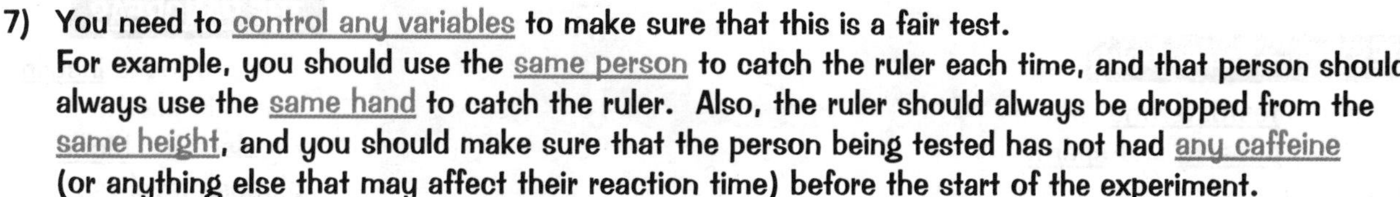

7) You need to control any variables to make sure that this is a fair test. For example, you should use the same person to catch the ruler each time, and that person should always use the same hand to catch the ruler. Also, the ruler should always be dropped from the same height, and you should make sure that the person being tested has not had any caffeine (or anything else that may affect their reaction time) before the start of the experiment.
8) Too much caffeine can cause unpleasant side-effects, so the person being tested should avoid drinking any more caffeine for the rest of the day after the experiment is completed.

With a little bit of maths, it's possible to work out the reaction time in seconds using the mean distance.

Reaction Time Can Be Measured Using a Computer

1) Simple computer tests can also be used to measure reaction time. For example, the person being tested has to click the mouse (or press a key) as soon as they see a stimulus on the screen, e.g. a box change colour.
2) Computers can give a more precise reaction time because they remove the possibility of human error from the measurement.
3) As the computer can record the reaction time in milliseconds, it can also give a more accurate measurement.
4) Using a computer can also remove the possibility that the person can predict when to respond — using the ruler test, the catcher may learn to anticipate the drop by reading the tester's body language.

Ready... Steady...

... Ah, too slow.

Q1 A student was measuring her reaction time using a computer test. She had to click the mouse when the screen changed from red to green. She repeated the test five times. Her results were as follows: 242 ms, 256 ms, 253 ms, 249 ms, 235 ms.
Calculate the mean reaction time of the student. [2 marks]

The Endocrine System

The other way to send information around the body (apart from along nerves) is by using hormones.

Hormones Are Chemical Messengers Sent in the Blood

1) Hormones are chemical molecules released directly into the blood. They are carried in the blood to other parts of the body, but only affect particular cells in particular organs (called target organs). Hormones control things in organs and cells that need constant adjustment.
2) Hormones are produced in (and secreted by) various glands, called endocrine glands. These glands make up your endocrine system.
3) Hormones tend to have relatively long-lasting effects.
4) Here are some examples of glands:

THE PITUITARY GLAND

The pituitary gland produces many hormones that regulate body conditions. It is sometimes called the 'master gland' because these hormones act on other glands, directing them to release hormones that bring about change.

THYROID

This produces thyroxine, which is involved in regulating things like the rate of metabolism, heart rate and temperature.

ADRENAL GLAND

This produces adrenaline, which is used to prepare the body for a 'fight or flight' response (see page 67).

OVARIES — females only

Produce oestrogen, which is involved in the menstrual cycle (see page 64).

THE PANCREAS

This produces insulin, which is used to regulate the blood glucose level (see next page).

TESTES — males only

Produce testosterone, which controls puberty and sperm production in males (see page 64).

Hormones and Nerves Have Differences

NERVES:
- Very FAST action.
- Act for a very SHORT TIME.
- Act on a very PRECISE AREA.

HORMONES:
- SLOWER action.
- Act for a LONG TIME.
- Act in a more GENERAL way.

So if you're not sure whether a response is nervous or hormonal, have a think...

1) If the response is really quick, it's probably nervous. Some information needs to be passed to effectors really quickly (e.g. pain signals, or information from your eyes telling you about the lion heading your way), so it's no good using hormones to carry the message — they're too slow.
2) But if a response lasts for a long time, it's probably hormonal. For example, when you get a shock, a hormone called adrenaline is released into the body (causing the fight or flight response, where your body is hyped up ready for action). You can tell it's a hormonal response (even though it kicks in pretty quickly) because you feel a bit wobbly for a while afterwards.

Nerves, hormones — no wonder revision makes me tense...

Hormones control various organs and cells in the body, though they tend to control things that aren't immediately life-threatening (so things like sexual development, blood sugar level, water content, etc.).

Q1 Why is the pituitary gland referred to as the 'master gland'? [1 mark]

Controlling Blood Glucose

Blood glucose is also controlled as part of homeostasis. Insulin and glucagon are the two hormones involved.

Insulin and Glucagon Control Blood Glucose Level

1) Eating foods containing carbohydrate puts glucose (a type of sugar) into the blood from the gut.
2) The normal metabolism of cells removes glucose from the blood.
3) Vigorous exercise removes much more glucose from the blood.
4) Excess glucose can be stored as glycogen in the liver and in the muscles.
5) The level of glucose in the blood must be kept steady. Changes are monitored and controlled by the pancreas, using the hormones insulin and glucagon, in a negative feedback cycle:

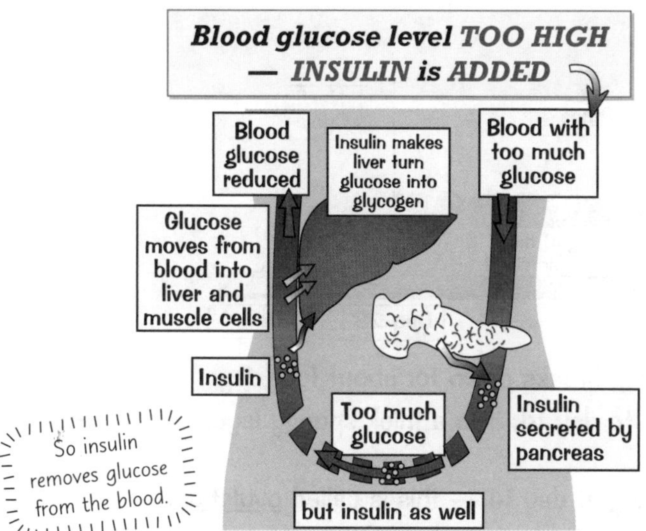

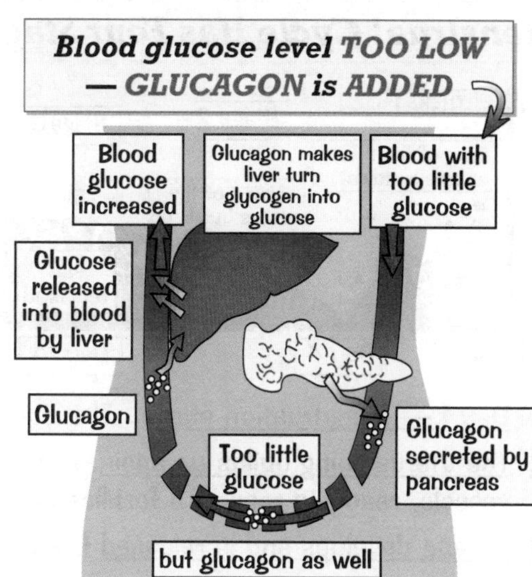

With Diabetes, You Can't Control Your Blood Sugar Level

Diabetes is a condition that affects your ability to control your blood sugar level. There are two types:

1) Type 1 diabetes is where the pancreas produces little or no insulin. This means a person's blood glucose level can rise to a level that can kill them. People with Type 1 diabetes need insulin therapy — this usually involves several injections of insulin throughout the day, most likely at mealtimes. This makes sure that glucose is removed from the blood quickly once the food has been digested, stopping the level getting too high. It's a very effective treatment. The amount of insulin that needs to be injected depends on the person's diet and how active they are. As well as insulin therapy, people with Type 1 diabetes need to think about limiting the intake of food rich in simple carbohydrates, e.g. sugars (which cause the blood glucose to rise rapidly) and taking regular exercise (which helps to remove excess glucose from the blood).
2) Type 2 diabetes is where a person becomes resistant to their own insulin (they still produce insulin, but their body's cells don't respond properly to the hormone). This can also cause a person's blood sugar level to rise to a dangerous level. Being overweight can increase your chance of developing Type 2 diabetes, as obesity is a major risk factor in the development of the disease. Type 2 diabetes can be controlled by eating a carbohydrate-controlled diet and getting regular exercise.

And people used to think the pancreas was just a cushion... (true)

This stuff can seem a bit confusing at first, but if you learn those two diagrams, it should get a bit easier. In the exam, you might be given a graph showing the effect of insulin on blood glucose level and be asked to interpret the data — if you do, just use what you know about reading graphs. Easy really.

Q1 Describe how the blood glucose level is returned to normal when it is too high. [3 marks]

Puberty and the Menstrual Cycle

The monthly release of an egg from a woman's ovaries is part of the menstrual cycle.

Hormones Promote Sexual Characteristics at Puberty

At puberty, your body starts releasing sex hormones that trigger off secondary sexual characteristics (such as the development of facial hair in men and breasts in women) and cause eggs to mature in women.

- In men, the main reproductive hormone is testosterone. It's produced by the testes and stimulates sperm production.
- In women, the main reproductive hormone is oestrogen. It's produced by the ovaries. As well as bringing about physical changes, oestrogen is also involved in the menstrual cycle.

The Menstrual Cycle Has Four Stages

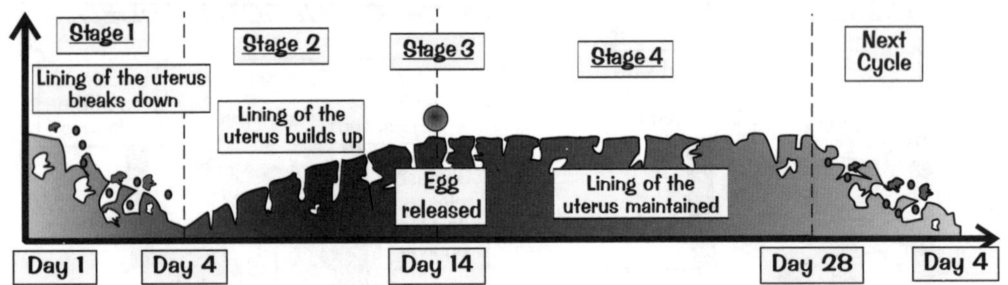

Stage 1 Day 1 — menstruation starts. The uterus lining breaks down for about four days.

Stage 2 The uterus lining builds up again, from day 4 to day 14, into a thick spongy layer full of blood vessels, ready to receive a fertilised egg.

Stage 3 An egg develops and is released from the ovary at day 14 — this is called ovulation.

Stage 4 The wall is then maintained for about 14 days until day 28. If no fertilised egg has landed on the uterus wall by day 28, the spongy lining starts to break down and the whole cycle starts again.

It's Controlled by Four Hormones

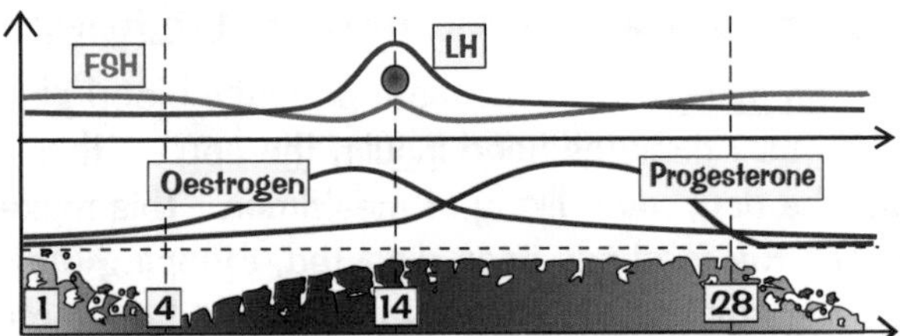

1 FSH (Follicle-Stimulating Hormone)

1) Produced in the pituitary gland.
2) Causes an egg to mature in one of the ovaries, in a structure called a follicle.
3) Stimulates the ovaries to produce oestrogen.

2 Oestrogen

1) Produced in the ovaries.
2) Causes the lining of the uterus to grow.
3) Stimulates the release of LH (which causes the release of an egg) and inhibits release of FSH.

3 LH (Luteinising Hormone)

1) Produced by the pituitary gland.
2) Stimulates the release of an egg at day 14 (ovulation).

4 Progesterone

1) Produced in the ovaries by the remains of the follicle after ovulation.
2) Maintains the lining of the uterus during the second half of the cycle. When the level of progesterone falls, the lining breaks down.
3) Inhibits the release of LH and FSH.

Which came first — the chicken or the luteinising hormone...

Female or not, learn this page... till you know what hormone does what and understand that there graph.

Q1 Name the hormone that stimulates an egg to mature in the ovary. [1 mark]

Q2 Where is testosterone produced in the male body? [1 mark]

Controlling Fertility

Pregnancy can happen if sperm reaches the ovulated egg. Contraception tries to stop this happening.

Hormones Can Be Used to Reduce Fertility

1) Oestrogen can be used to prevent the release of an egg — so it can be used as a method of contraception.
2) This may seem kind of strange (since naturally oestrogen helps stimulate the release of eggs). But if oestrogen is taken every day to keep the level of it permanently high, it inhibits the production of FSH, and after a while egg development and production stop and stay stopped.
3) Progesterone also reduces fertility, e.g. by stimulating the production of thick mucus which prevents any sperm getting through and reaching an egg.
4) The pill is an oral contraceptive containing oestrogen and progesterone (known as the combined oral contraceptive pill).
5) It's over 99% effective at preventing pregnancy, but it can cause side effects like headaches and nausea and it doesn't protect against sexually transmitted diseases.
6) There's also a progesterone-only pill — it has fewer side effects than the pill, and is just as effective.
7) There are other methods of contraception that use hormones:

- The contraceptive patch contains oestrogen and progesterone (the same as the combined pill). It's a small (5 cm × 5 cm) patch that's stuck to the skin. Each patch lasts one week.
- The contraceptive implant is inserted under the skin of the arm. It releases a continuous amount of progesterone, which stops the ovaries releasing eggs, makes it hard for sperm to swim to the egg, and stops any fertilised egg implanting in the uterus. An implant can last for three years.
- The contraceptive injection also contains progesterone. Each dose lasts 2 to 3 months.
- An intrauterine device (IUD) is a T-shaped device that is inserted into the uterus to kill sperm and prevent implantation of a fertilised egg. There are two main types — plastic IUDs that release progesterone and copper IUDs that prevent the sperm surviving in the uterus.

Barriers Stop Egg and Sperm Meeting

1) Non-hormonal forms of contraception are designed to stop the sperm from getting to the egg.
2) Condoms are worn over the penis during intercourse to prevent the sperm entering the vagina. There are also female condoms that are worn inside the vagina. Condoms are the only form of contraception that will protect against sexually transmitted diseases.
3) A diaphragm is a shallow plastic cup that fits over the cervix (the entrance to the uterus) to form a barrier. It has to be used with spermicide (a substance that disables or kills the sperm).
4) Spermicide can be used alone as a form of contraception, but it is not as effective (only about 70-80%).

There are More Drastic Ways to Avoid Pregnancy

STERILISATION — Sterilisation involves cutting or tying the fallopian tubes (which connect the ovaries to the uterus) in a female, or the sperm duct (the tube between the testes and penis) in a male. This is a permanent procedure. However, there is a very small chance that the tubes can rejoin.

'NATURAL' METHODS — Pregnancy may be avoided by finding out when in the menstrual cycle the woman is most fertile and avoiding sexual intercourse on those days. It's popular with people who think that hormonal and barrier methods are unnatural, but it's not very effective.

ABSTINENCE — The only way to be completely sure that sperm and egg don't meet is to not have intercourse.

The winner of best contraceptive ever — just not doing it...

You might be asked to evaluate the different hormonal and non-hormonal methods of contraception in your exam. If you do, make sure you weigh up and write about both the pros and the cons of each method. Exciting stuff.

Q1 Name two forms of contraception that reduce fertility by releasing oestrogen. [2 marks]

More on Controlling Fertility

Scientific advances in understanding fertility have led to many infertile women being helped to have babies.

Hormones Can Be Used to Increase Fertility

1) Some women have levels of FSH (follicle-stimulating hormone) that are too low to cause their eggs to mature. This means that no eggs are released and the women can't get pregnant.
2) The hormones FSH and LH can be given to women in a fertility drug to stimulate ovulation.

PROS It helps a lot of women to get pregnant when previously they couldn't... pretty obvious.

CONS It doesn't always work — some women may have to do it many times, which can be expensive.
Too many eggs could be stimulated, resulting in unexpected multiple pregnancies (twins, triplets, etc.).

IVF Can Also Help Couples to Have Children

If a woman cannot get pregnant using medication, she may chose to try IVF ("*in vitro* fertilisation").

1) IVF involves collecting eggs from the woman's ovaries and fertilising them in a lab using the man's sperm.
2) IVF treatment can also involve a technique called Intra-Cytoplasmic Sperm Injection (ICSI), where the sperm is injected directly into an egg. It's useful if the man has a very low sperm count.
3) The fertilised eggs are then grown into embryos in a laboratory incubator.
4) Once the embryos are tiny balls of cells, one or two of them are transferred to the woman's uterus to improve the chance of pregnancy.
5) FSH and LH are given before egg collection to stimulate several eggs to mature (so more than one egg can be collected).

PRO Fertility treatment can give an infertile couple a child — a pretty obvious benefit.

CONS

Multiple births can happen if more than one embryo grows into a baby — these are risky for the mother and babies (there's a higher risk of miscarriage, stillbirth...).

The success rate of IVF is low — the average success rate in the UK is about 26%. This makes the process incredibly stressful and often upsetting, especially if it ends in multiple failures.

As well as being emotionally stressful, the process is also physically stressful for the woman. Some women have a strong reaction to the hormones — e.g. abdominal pain, vomiting, dehydration.

Advances in microscope techniques have helped to improve the techniques (and therefore the success rate) of IVF. Specialised micro-tools have been developed to use on the eggs and sperm under the microscope. They're also used to remove single cells from the embryo for genetic testing (to check that it is healthy — see page 74). More recently, the development of time-lapse imaging (using a microscope and camera built into the incubator) means that the growth of the embryos can be continuously monitored to help identify those that are more likely to result in a successful pregnancy.

Some People Are Against IVF

1) The process of IVF often results in unused embryos that are eventually destroyed. Because of this, some people think it is unethical because each embryo is a potential human life.
2) The genetic testing of embryos before implantation also raises ethical issues as some people think it could lead to the selection of preferred characteristics, such as gender or eye colour.

Nothing funny here, sorry...

Fertility treatment can help to increase the chance of pregnancy, but it can be hard on those involved.

Q1 What is the role of FSH and LH during IVF? [1 mark]

Q2 Give one drawback to using hormones to increase fertility. [1 mark]

Adrenaline and Thyroxine

You've met a lot of human hormones so far, but two more won't hurt. Then that's it, I promise...

Adrenaline Prepares You for "Fight or Flight"

1) Adrenaline is a hormone released by the adrenal glands, which are just above the kidneys (see p.62).
2) Adrenaline is released in response to stressful or scary situations — your brain detects fear or stress and sends nervous impulses to the adrenal glands, which respond by secreting adrenaline.
3) It gets the body ready for 'fight or flight' by triggering mechanisms that increase the supply of oxygen and glucose to cells in the brain and muscles. For example, adrenaline increases heart rate.

Hormone Release can be Affected by Negative Feedback

Your body can control the levels of hormones (and other substances) in the blood using negative feedback systems. When the body detects that the level of a substance has gone above or below the normal level, it triggers a response to bring the level back to normal again. Here's an example of just that:

Thyroxine Regulates Metabolism

Thyroxine is made in the thyroid gland from iodine and amino acids.

1) Thyroxine is a hormone released by the thyroid gland, which is in the neck (see p.62).
2) It plays an important role in regulating the basal metabolic rate — the speed at which chemical reactions in the body occur while the body is at rest. Thyroxine is also important for loads of processes in the body, such as stimulating protein synthesis for growth and development.
3) Thyroxine is released in response to thyroid stimulating hormone (TSH), which is released from the pituitary gland.
4) A negative feedback system keeps the amount of thyroxine in the blood at the right level — when the level of thyroxine in the blood is higher than normal, the secretion of TSH from the pituitary gland is inhibited (stopped). This reduces the amount of thyroxine released from the thyroid gland, so the level in the blood falls back towards normal.

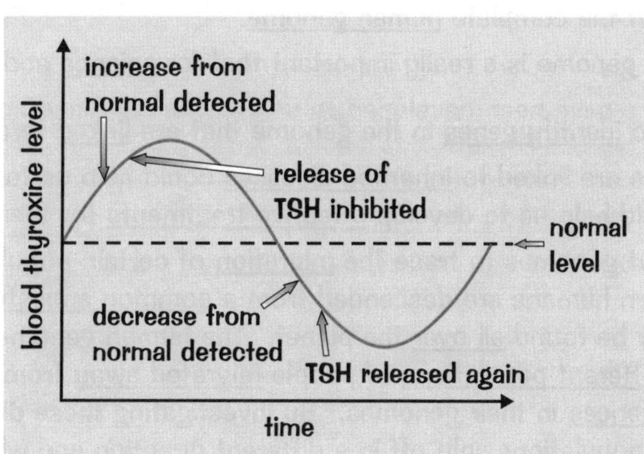

Negative feedback sucks, especially from your science teacher...

You can think about negative feedback working like a thermostat — if the temperature gets too low, the thermostat will turn the heating on, then if the temperature gets too high, it'll turn the heating off again.

Q1 Name the gland that releases thyroxine. [1 mark]

Q2 Describe the response if the level of thyroxine in the blood gets too high. [3 marks]

DNA

The first step in understanding genetics is getting to grips with DNA and genes.

Chromosomes Are Really Long Molecules of DNA

1) DNA stands for deoxyribonucleic acid. It's the chemical that all of the genetic material in a cell is made up from.
2) It contains coded information — basically all the instructions to put an organism together and make it work.
3) So it's what's in your DNA that determines what inherited characteristics you have.
4) DNA is found in the nucleus of animal and plant cells, in really long structures called chromosomes.
5) Chromosomes normally come in pairs.
6) DNA is a polymer. It's made up of two strands coiled together in the shape of a double helix.

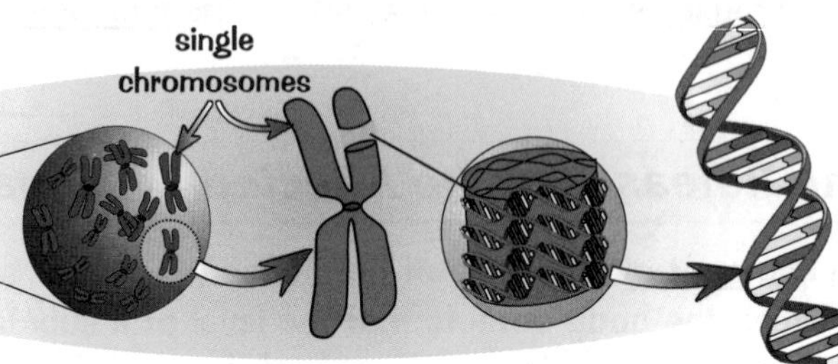

A Gene Codes for a Specific Protein

1) A gene is a small section of DNA found on a chromosome.
2) Each gene codes for (tells the cells to make) a particular sequence of amino acids which are put together to make a specific protein.
3) Only 20 amino acids are used, but they make up thousands of different proteins.
4) Genes simply tell cells in what order to put the amino acids together.
5) DNA also determines what proteins the cell produces, e.g. haemoglobin, keratin.
6) That in turn determines what type of cell it is, e.g. red blood cell, skin cell.

Every Organism Has a Genome

1) Genome is just the fancy term for the entire set of genetic material in an organism.
2) Scientists have worked out the complete human genome.
3) Understanding the human genome is a really important tool for science and medicine for many reasons.
   1) It allows scientists to identify genes in the genome that are linked to different types of disease.
   2) Knowing which genes are linked to inherited diseases could help us to understand them better and could help us to develop effective treatments for them.
   3) Scientists can look at genomes to trace the migration of certain populations of people around the world. All modern humans are descended from a common ancestor who lived in Africa, but humans can now be found all over the planet. The human genome is mostly identical in all individuals, but as different populations of people migrated away from Africa, they gradually developed tiny differences in their genomes. By investigating these differences, scientists can work out when new populations split off in a different direction and what route they took.

Insert joke about genes and jeans here...

There are so many, I thought you could come up with your own as a bit of light relief.
Make sure that you're clued up on this stuff about DNA, genes and proteins before you move on.

Q1 What is a gene? [3 marks]

Q2 What is an organism's genome? [1 mark]

Reproduction

Ooo err, reproduction... Surely you knew it'd come up at some point. It can happen in two different ways...

Sexual Reproduction Produces Genetically Different Cells

1) Sexual reproduction is where genetic information from two organisms (a father and a mother) is combined to produce offspring which are genetically different to either parent.
2) In sexual reproduction, the mother and father produce gametes by meiosis (see next page) — e.g. egg and sperm cells in animals.
3) In humans, each gamete contains 23 chromosomes — half the number of chromosomes in a normal cell. (Instead of having two of each chromosome, a gamete has just one of each.)
4) The egg (from the mother) and the sperm cell (from the father) then fuse together (fertilisation) to form a cell with the full number of chromosomes (half from the father, half from the mother).

SEXUAL REPRODUCTION involves the fusion of male and female gametes.
Because there are TWO parents, the offspring contain a mixture of their parents' genes.

Fertilisation:

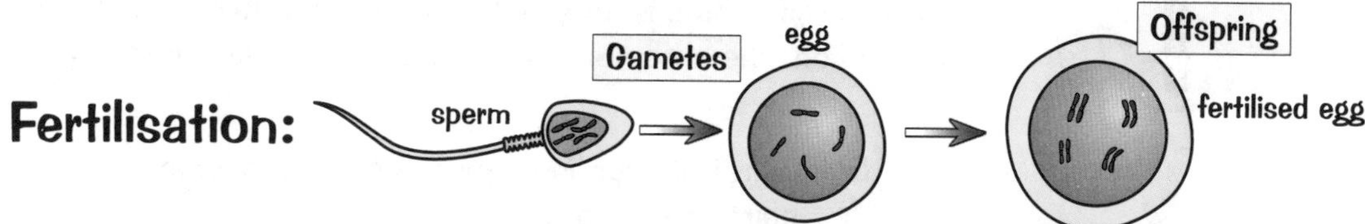

5) This is why the offspring inherits features from both parents — it's received a mixture of chromosomes from its mum and its dad (and it's the chromosomes that decide how you turn out).
6) This mixture of genetic information produces variation in the offspring. Pretty cool, eh.
7) Flowering plants can reproduce in this way too. They also have egg cells, but their version of sperm is known as pollen. Hmm... I'm having second thoughts about frolicking in that meadow now.

Asexual Reproduction Produces Genetically Identical Cells

1) In asexual reproduction there's only one parent so the offspring are genetically identical to that parent.
2) Asexual reproduction happens by mitosis — an ordinary cell makes a new cell by dividing in two (see page 15).
3) The new cell has exactly the same genetic information (i.e. genes) as the parent cell — it's called a clone.

In ASEXUAL REPRODUCTION there's only ONE parent. There's no fusion of gametes, no mixing of chromosomes and no genetic variation between parent and offspring. The offspring are genetically identical to the parent — they're clones.

4) Bacteria, some plants and some animals reproduce asexually.

You need to reproduce these facts in the exam...

The main messages on this page are that: 1) sexual reproduction needs two parents and forms cells that are genetically different to the parents, so there's lots of genetic variation. And 2) asexual reproduction needs just one parent to make genetically identical cells, so there's no genetic variation in the offspring.

Q1 What type of cell division is involved in asexual reproduction? [1 mark]

Q2 Suggest why there is variation in the offspring of sexual reproduction. [2 marks]

Meiosis

Now I bet you're wondering how gametes end up with half the number of chromosomes of a normal cell... or maybe you're not. Well, I'm going to tell you anyway. Step forward the marvellous process of meiosis.

Gametes Are Produced by Meiosis

1) As you know from the previous page, gametes only have one copy of each chromosome, so that when gamete fusion takes place, you get the right amount of chromosomes again (two copies of each).
2) To make gametes which only have half the original number of chromosomes, cells divide by meiosis. This process involves two cell divisions. In humans, it only happens in the reproductive organs (the ovaries in females and testes in males).

Meiosis Produces Cells Which Have Half the Normal Number of Chromosomes

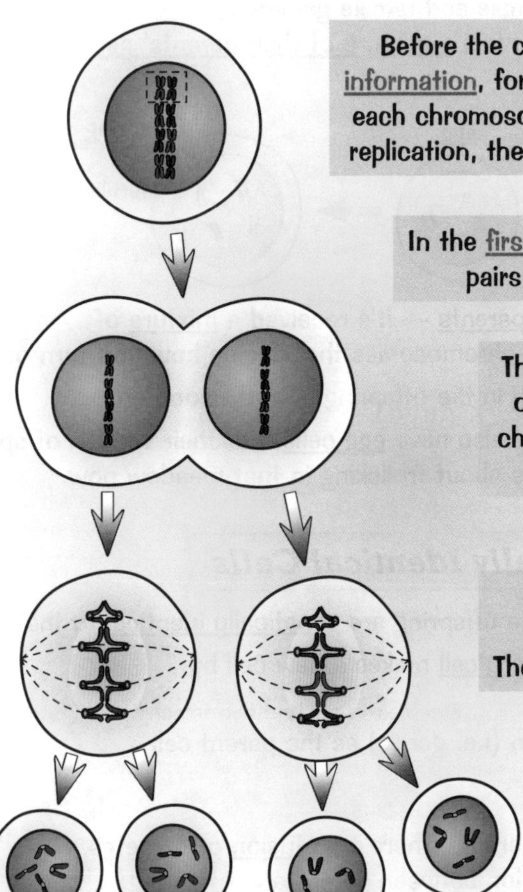

Before the cell starts to divide, it duplicates its genetic information, forming two armed chromosomes — one arm of each chromosome is an exact copy of the other arm. After replication, the chromosomes arrange themselves into pairs.

The genetic information is stored in DNA — see p.68.

In the first division in meiosis the chromosome pairs line up in the centre of the cell.

The pairs are then pulled apart so each new cell only has one copy of each chromosome. Some of the father's chromosomes (shown in blue) and some of the mother's chromosomes (shown in red) go into each new cell.

In the second division, the chromosomes line up again in the centre of the cell. The arms of the chromosomes are pulled apart.

You get four gametes, each with only a single set of chromosomes in it. Each of the gametes is genetically different from the others because the chromosomes all get shuffled up during meiosis and each gamete only gets half of them, at random.

The Cell Produced by Gamete Fusion Replicates Itself

1) After two gametes have fused during fertilisation, the resulting new cell divides by mitosis to make a copy of itself.
2) Mitosis repeats many times to produce lots of new cells in an embryo.
3) As the embryo develops, these cells then start to differentiate (see page 14) into the different types of specialised cell that make up a whole organism.

There's loads on mitosis on page 15.

Now that I have your undivided attention...

Remember, in humans, meiosis only occurs in reproductive organs where gametes are being made.

Q1 How many cell divisions take place in meiosis? [1 mark]

X and Y Chromosomes

Now for a couple of very important little chromosomes...

Your Chromosomes Control Whether You're Male or Female

There are 23 pairs of chromosomes in every human body cell (page 15). Of these, 22 are matched pairs of chromosomes that just control characteristics. The 23rd pair are labelled XY or XX. They're the two chromosomes that decide your sex — whether you turn out male or female.

> Males have an X and a Y chromosome: XY
> The Y chromosome causes male characteristics.
>
> Females have two X chromosomes: XX
> The XX combination allows female characteristics to develop.

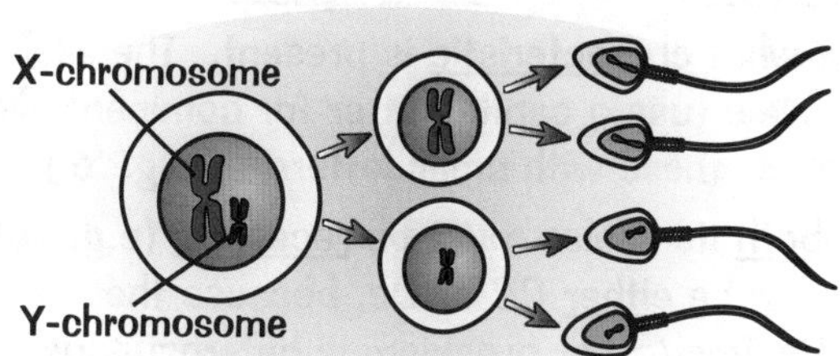

When making sperm, the X and Y chromosomes are drawn apart in the first division in meiosis (see the previous page). There's a 50% chance each sperm cell gets an X-chromosome and a 50% chance it gets a Y-chromosome. A similar thing happens when making eggs. But the original cell has two X-chromosomes, so all the eggs have one X-chromosome.

Genetic Diagrams Show the Possible Gamete Combinations

1) To find the probability of getting a boy or a girl, you can draw a genetic diagram.
2) Genetic diagrams are just models that are used to show all the possible genetic outcomes when you cross together different genes or chromosomes.
3) Put the possible gametes (eggs or sperm) from one parent down the side, and those from the other parent along the top.
4) Then in each middle square you fill in the letters from the top and side that line up with that square. The pairs of letters in the middle show the possible combinations of the gametes.

This type of genetic diagram is called a Punnett square.

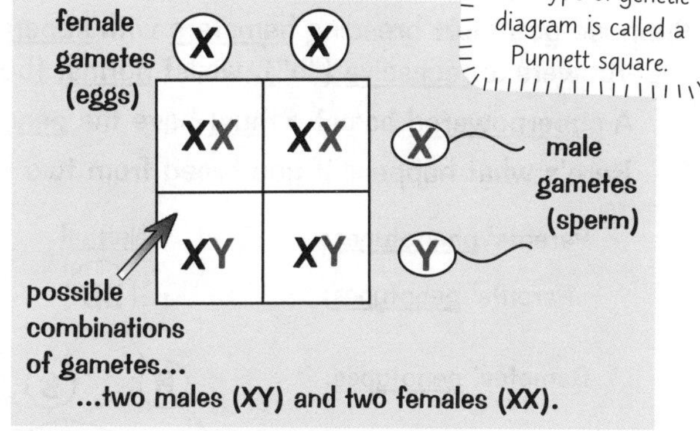

5) There are two XX results and two XY results, so there's the same probability of getting a boy or a girl.
6) Don't forget that this 50:50 ratio is only a probability at each pregnancy.

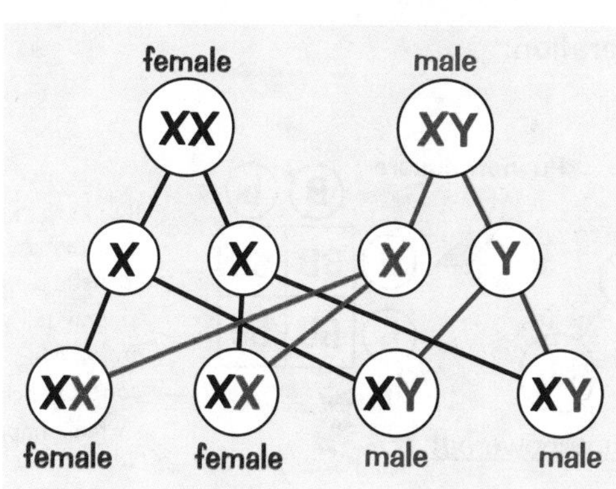

The other type of genetic diagram looks a bit more complicated, but it shows exactly the same thing.

1) At the top are the parents.
2) The middle circles show the possible gametes that are formed. One gamete from the female combines with one gamete from the male (during fertilisation).
3) The criss-cross lines show all the possible ways the X and Y chromosomes could combine. The possible combinations of the offspring are shown in the bottom circles.
4) Remember, only one of these possibilities would actually happen for any one offspring.

Have you got the Y-factor...

Most genetic diagrams you'll see in exams concentrate on a gene instead of a chromosome.
But the principle's the same. Don't worry — there are loads of other examples on the following pages.

Q1 What combination of sex chromosomes do human females have? [1 mark]

Genetic Diagrams

Genetic diagrams, eh. They're not as scary as they look — you just need to practise them...

Some Characteristics are Controlled by Single Genes

1) What genes you inherit control what characteristics you develop.
2) Different genes control different characteristics. Some characteristics are controlled by a single gene, e.g. mouse fur colour and red-green colour blindness in humans.
3) However, most characteristics are controlled by several genes interacting.
4) All genes exist in different versions called alleles (which are represented by letters in genetic diagrams).
5) You have two versions (alleles) of every gene in your body — one on each chromosome in a pair.
6) If an organism has two alleles for a particular gene that are the same, then it's homozygous for that trait. If its two alleles for a particular gene are different, then it's heterozygous.
7) If the two alleles are different, only one can determine what characteristic is present. The allele for the characteristic that's shown is called the dominant allele (use a capital letter for dominant alleles — e.g. 'C'). The other one is called recessive (and you show these with small letters — e.g. 'c').
8) For an organism to display a recessive characteristic, both its alleles must be recessive (e.g. cc). But to display a dominant characteristic the organism can be either CC or Cc, because the dominant allele overrules the recessive one if the plant/animal/other organism is heterozygous.
9) Your genotype is the combination of alleles you have. Your alleles work at a molecular level to determine what characteristics you have — your phenotype.

Genetic Diagrams Show the Possible Alleles of Offspring

Suppose you start breeding hamsters with superpowers. The allele which causes hamsters to have superpowers is recessive ("b"), whilst normal (boring) behaviour is due to a dominant allele ("B").

1) A superpowered hamster must have the genotype bb. But a normal hamster could be BB or Bb.
2) Here's what happens if you breed from two homozygous hamsters:

genotype = BB or Bb, phenotype = normal

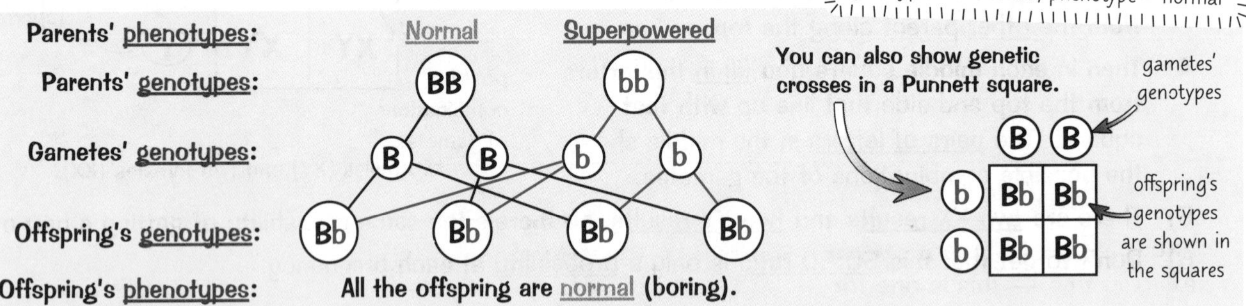

	B	B
b	Bb	Bb
b	Bb	Bb

3) If two of these offspring now breed, you'll get the next generation:

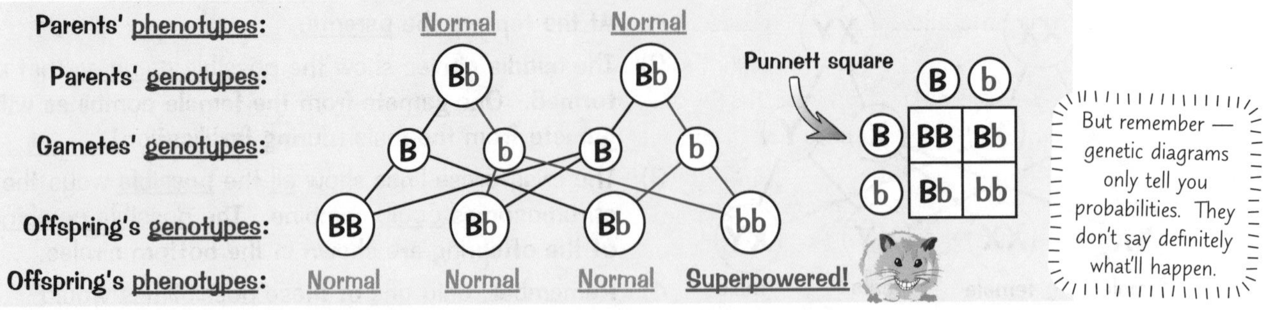

	B	b
B	BB	Bb
b	Bb	bb

But remember — genetic diagrams only tell you probabilities. They don't say definitely what'll happen.

4) That's a 3:1 ratio of normal to superpowered offspring in this generation (a 1 in 4 or 25% probability of superpowers).

Your meanotype determines how nice you are to your sibling...

You need to be able to produce and interpret both of these types of genetic diagram for the exam.

Q1 Define genotype and phenotype. [2 marks]

More Genetic Diagrams

You've got to be able to predict and explain the outcomes of crosses between individuals for each possible combination of dominant and recessive alleles of a gene. You should be able to draw a genetic diagram and work it out — but it'll be easier if you've seen them all before. So here are a couple more examples for you. You also need to know how to interpret another type of genetic diagram called a family tree...

All the Offspring are Normal

For a reminder on the terms homozygous and heterozygous, head to page 72.

Let's take another look at the superpowered hamster example from page 72:

In this cross, a homozygous dominant hamster (BB) is crossed with a homozygous recessive hamster (bb). All the offspring are normal (boring).

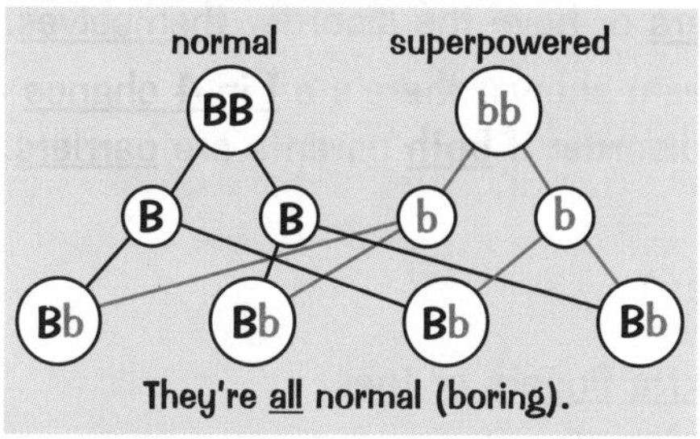

But, if you crossed a homozygous dominant hamster (BB) with a heterozygous hamster (Bb), you would also get all normal (boring) offspring.

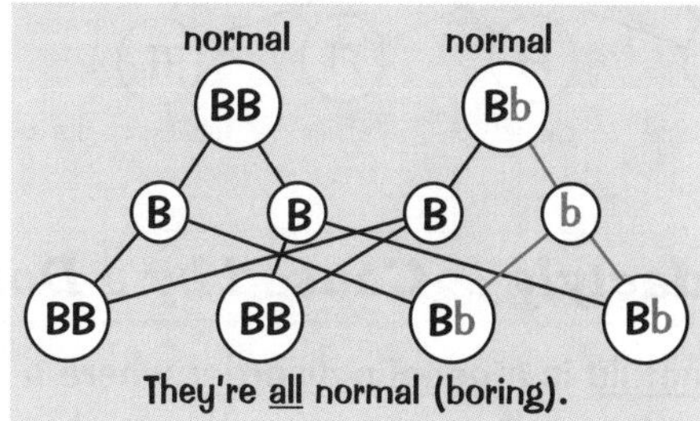

To find out which it was you'd have to breed the offspring together and see what kind of ratio you got that time — then you'd have a good idea. If it was 3:1, it's likely that you originally had BB and bb.

There's a 1:1 Ratio in the Offspring

A cat with long hair was bred with another cat with short hair. The long hair is caused by a dominant allele 'H', and the short hair by a recessive allele 'h'.

They had 8 kittens — 4 with long hair and 4 with short hair.

This is a 1:1 ratio — it's what you'd expect when a parent with only one dominant allele (heterozygous — Hh) is crossed with a parent with two recessive alleles (homozygous recessive — hh).

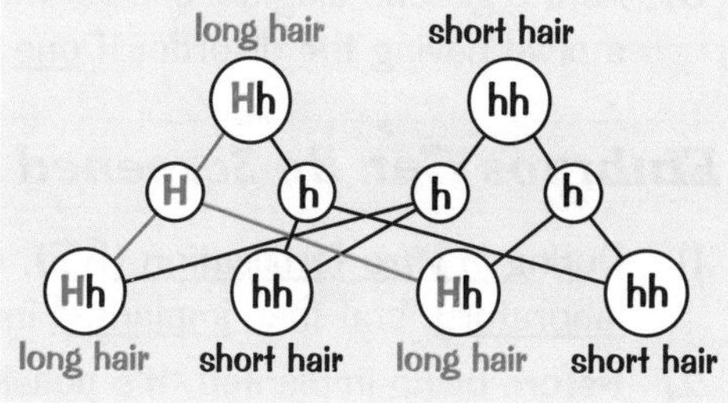

You Need to be Able to Interpret Family Trees

Knowing how inheritance works can help you to interpret a family tree — this is one for cystic fibrosis (p.74).

1) From the family tree, you can tell that the allele for cystic fibrosis isn't dominant because plenty of the family carry the allele but don't have the disorder.
2) There is a 25% chance that the new baby will have the disorder and a 50% chance that it will be a carrier, as both of its parents are carriers but are unaffected. The case of the new baby is just the same as in the genetic diagram on page 74 — so the baby could be unaffected (FF), a carrier (Ff) or have cystic fibrosis (ff).

John
Susan
Mark
Caroline
Eve
Phil
Will
new baby

Key
Male
Female
Have cystic fibrosis
Cystic fibrosis carriers
unaffected and not carriers

It's enough to make you go cross-eyed...

In the exam, you might get a family tree showing the inheritance of a dominant allele — in this case, there won't be any carriers shown. Now, here's a practice question from the realm of mythical creatures.

Q1 In merpeople, the dominant allele, T, causes a long tail and the recessive allele, t, causes a short tail. Using a Punnett square, predict the ratio of long to short tailed merbabies for a cross between a heterozygous merman and a mermaid who is homozygous recessive for tail length. [3 marks]

Inherited Disorders

Some disorders can be inherited from your parents. Many of these can be screened for in embryos.

Cystic Fibrosis is Caused by a Recessive Allele

Cystic fibrosis is a genetic disorder of the cell membranes. It results in the body producing a lot of thick sticky mucus in the air passages and in the pancreas.

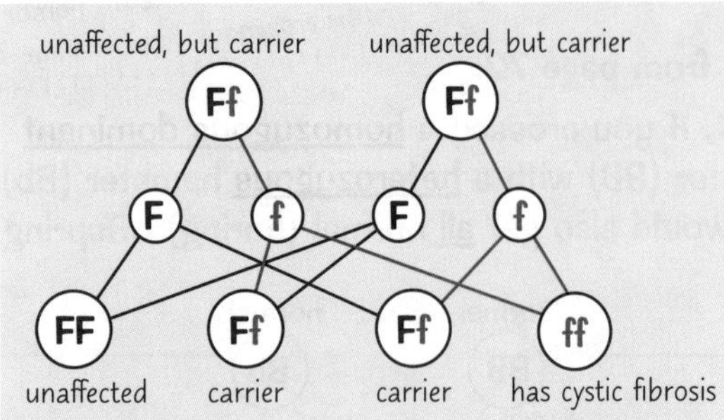

1) The allele which causes cystic fibrosis is a recessive allele, 'f', carried by about 1 person in 25.
2) Because it's recessive, people with only one copy of the allele won't have the disorder — they're known as carriers.
3) For a child to have the disorder, both parents must be either carriers or have the disorder themselves.
4) As the diagram shows, there's a 1 in 4 chance of a child having the disorder if both parents are carriers.

Polydactyly is Caused by a Dominant Allele

Polydactyly is a genetic disorder where a baby's born with extra fingers or toes. It doesn't usually cause any other problems so isn't life-threatening.

1) The disorder is caused by a dominant allele, 'D', and so can be inherited if just one parent carries the defective allele.
2) The parent that has the defective allele will have the condition too since the allele is dominant.
3) As the genetic diagram shows, there's a 50% chance of a child having the disorder if one parent has one D allele.

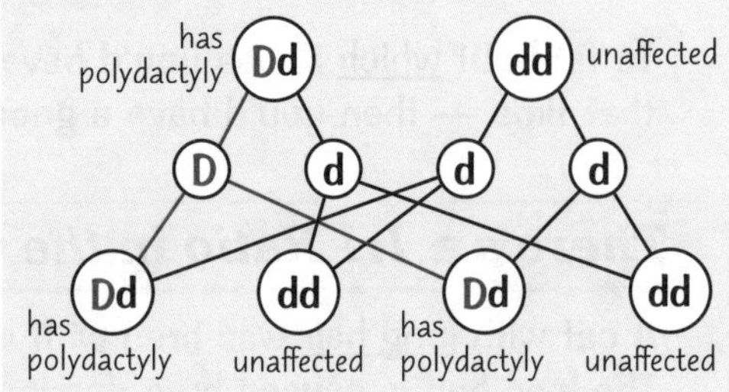

Embryos Can Be Screened for Genetic Disorders

1) During *in vitro* fertilisation (IVF), embryos are fertilised in a laboratory, and then implanted into the mother's womb.
2) Before being implanted, it's possible to remove a cell from each embryo and analyse its genes.
3) Many genetic disorders can be detected in this way, such as cystic fibrosis.
4) It's also possible to get DNA from an embryo in the womb and test that for disorders.
5) There are lots of ethical, social and economic concerns surrounding embryo screening.
6) Embryonic screening is quite controversial because of the decisions it can lead to.
7) For embryos produced by IVF — after screening, embryos with 'bad' alleles would be destroyed.
8) For embryos in the womb — screening could lead to the decision to terminate the pregnancy.
9) Here are some more arguments for and against screening:

Against Embryonic Screening	For Embryonic Screening
1) It implies that people with genetic problems are 'undesirable' — this could increase prejudice. 2) There may come a point where everyone wants to screen their embryos so they can pick the most 'desirable' one, e.g. they want a blue-eyed, blond-haired, intelligent boy. 3) Screening is expensive.	1) It will help to stop people suffering. 2) Treating disorders costs the Government (and the taxpayers) a lot of money. 3) There are laws to stop it going too far. At the moment parents cannot even select the sex of their baby (unless it's for health reasons).

Embryo screening — it's a tricky one...

Try writing a balanced argument for and against embryo screening — it's good practice.

Q1 Why won't someone heterozygous for the cystic fibrosis allele have the disorder? [3 marks]

Variation

You'll probably have noticed that not all people are identical. There are reasons for this.

Organisms of the Same Species Have Differences

1) Different species look... well... different — my dog definitely doesn't look like a daisy.
2) But even organisms of the same species will usually look at least slightly different — e.g. in a room full of people you'll see different colour hair, individually shaped noses, a variety of heights, etc.
3) These differences are called the variation within a species. Variation can be huge within a population.
4) Variation can be genetic — this means it's caused by differences in genotype. Genotype is all of the genes and alleles that an organism has. An organism's genotype affects its phenotype — the characteristics that it displays.
5) An organism's genes are inherited (passed down) from its parents (see page 69).
6) It's not only genotype that can affect an organism's phenotype though — interactions with its environment (conditions in which it lives) can also influence phenotype. For example, a plant grown on a nice sunny windowsill could grow luscious and green. The same plant grown in darkness would grow tall and spindly and its leaves would turn yellow — these are environmental variations.
7) Most variation in phenotype is determined by a mixture of genetic and environmental factors. For example, the maximum height that an animal or plant could grow to is determined by its genes. But whether it actually grows that tall depends on its environment (e.g. how much food it gets).

Mutations are Changes to the Genome

1) Occasionally, a gene may mutate. A mutation is a rare, random change in an organism's DNA that can be inherited. Mutations occur continuously.
2) Mutations mean that the gene is altered, which produces a genetic variant (a different form of the gene).

Alleles (see page 72) are genetic variants.

3) As the gene codes for the sequence of amino acids that make up a protein, gene mutations sometimes lead to changes in the protein that it codes for.
4) Most genetic variants have very little or no effect on the protein the gene codes for. Some will change it to such a small extent that its function is unaffected. This means that most mutations have no effect on an organism's phenotype.
5) Some variants have a small influence on the organism's phenotype — they alter the individual's characteristics but only slightly. For example:

> Some characteristics, e.g. eye colour, are controlled by more than one gene. A mutation in one of the genes may change the eye colour a bit, but the difference might not be huge.

6) Very occasionally, variants can have such a dramatic effect that they determine phenotype. For example:

> The genetic disorder, cystic fibrosis, is caused by a mutation that has a huge effect on phenotype. The gene codes for a protein that controls the movement of salt and water into and out of cells. However, the protein produced by the mutated gene doesn't work properly. This leads to excess mucus production in the lungs and digestive system, which can make it difficult to breathe and to digest food.

7) If the environment changes, and the new phenotype makes an individual more suited to the new environment, it can become common throughout the species relatively quickly by natural selection — see the next page.

My mum's got no trousers — cos I've got her jeans...

So you can't blame all of your faults on your parents — the environment usually plays a role too.

Q1 Explain what is meant by environmental variation. [2 marks]

Evolution

THEORY OF EVOLUTION: All of today's species have evolved from simple life forms that first started to develop over three billion years ago.

Only the Fittest Survive

Charles Darwin came up with a really important theory about evolution, called evolution by natural selection.

1) Darwin knew that organisms in a species show wide variation in their characteristics (phenotypic variation). He also knew that organisms have to compete for limited resources in an ecosystem.
2) Darwin concluded that the organisms with the most suitable characteristics for the environment would be more successful competitors and would be more likely to survive. This idea is called the 'survival of the fittest'.

Charles Darwin

3) The successful organisms that survive are more likely to reproduce and pass on the genes for the characteristics that made them successful to their offspring.

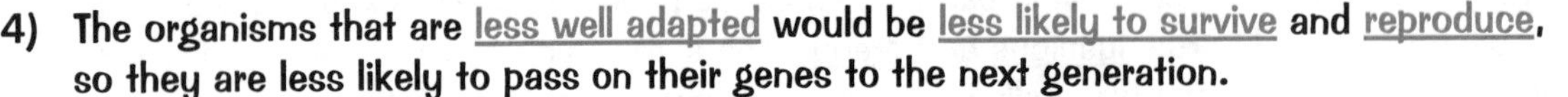

4) The organisms that are less well adapted would be less likely to survive and reproduce, so they are less likely to pass on their genes to the next generation.
5) Over time, beneficial characteristics become more common in the population and the species changes — it evolves.

New Discoveries Have Helped to Develop the Theory

1) Darwin's theory wasn't perfect. Because the relevant scientific knowledge wasn't available at the time, he couldn't give a good explanation for why new characteristics appeared or exactly how individual organisms passed on beneficial adaptations to their offspring.
2) However, the discovery of genetics supported Darwin's idea — it provided an explanation of how organisms born with beneficial characteristics can pass them on (i.e. via their genes) and showed that it is genetic variants (see page 75) that give rise to phenotypes that are suited to the environment. Other evidence was also found by looking at fossils of different ages (the fossil record) — this allows you to see how changes in organisms developed slowly over time. The relatively recent discovery of how bacteria are able to evolve to become resistant to antibiotics also further supports evolution by natural selection. The theory of evolution by natural selection is now widely accepted.

The Development of a New Species is Called Speciation

1) Over a long period of time, the phenotype of organisms can change so much because of natural selection that a completely new species is formed. This is called speciation.
2) Speciation happens when populations of the same species change enough to become reproductively isolated — this means that they can't interbreed to produce fertile offspring.

Extinction is When No Individuals of a Species Remain

The fossil record contains many species that don't exist any more — these species are said to be extinct.

Species become extinct for these reasons:

1) The environment changes too quickly (e.g. destruction of habitat).
2) A new predator kills them all (e.g. humans hunting them).
3) A new disease kills them all.
4) They can't compete with another (new) species for food.
5) A catastrophic event happens that kills them all (e.g. a volcanic eruption or a collision with an asteroid).

Dodos are now extinct. Humans not only hunted them, but introduced other animals which ate all their eggs, and we destroyed the forest where they lived — they really didn't stand a chance...

"Natural selection" — sounds like vegan chocolates...

Natural selection's all about the organisms with the best characteristics surviving to pass on their genes.

Q1 Give three factors that can lead to a species becoming extinct. [3 marks]

Selective Breeding

'Selective breeding' sounds like it has the potential to be a tricky topic, but it's actually dead simple. You take the best plants or animals and breed them together to get the best possible offspring. That's it.

Selective Breeding is Very Simple

Selective breeding is when humans artificially select the plants or animals that are going to breed so that the genes for particular characteristics remain in the population. Organisms are selectively bred to develop features that are useful or attractive, for example:

- Animals that produce more meat or milk.
- Crops with disease resistance.
- Dogs with a good, gentle temperament.
- Decorative plants with big or unusual flowers.

This is the basic process involved in selective breeding:

1) From your existing stock, select the ones which have the characteristics you're after.
2) Breed them with each other.
3) Select the best of the offspring, and breed them together.
4) Continue this process over several generations, and the desirable trait gets stronger and stronger. Eventually, all the offspring will have the characteristic.

Selective breeding is also known as 'artificial selection'.

In agriculture (farming), selective breeding can be used to improve yields. E.g. to improve meat yields, a farmer could breed together the cows and bulls with the best characteristics for producing meat, e.g. large size. After doing this for several generations the farmer would get cows with a very high meat yield.

5) Selective breeding is nothing new — people have been doing it for thousands of years. It's how we ended up with edible crops from wild plants and how we got domesticated animals like cows and dogs.

The Main Drawback is a Reduction in the Gene Pool

1) The main problem with selective breeding is that it reduces the gene pool — the number of different alleles (forms of a gene) in a population. This is because the farmer keeps breeding from the "best" animals or plants — which are all closely related. This is known as inbreeding.
2) Inbreeding can cause health problems because there's more chance of the organisms inheriting harmful genetic defects when the gene pool is limited. Some dog breeds are particularly susceptible to certain defects because of inbreeding — e.g. pugs often have breathing problems.
3) There can also be serious problems if a new disease appears, because there's not much variation in the population. All the stock are closely related to each other, so if one of them is going to be killed by a new disease, the others are also likely to succumb to it.

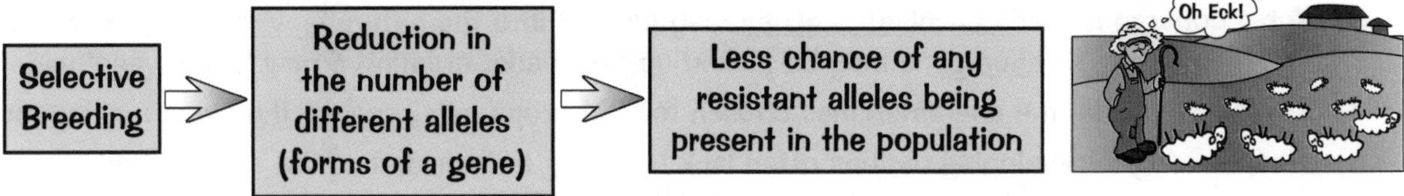

I use the same genes all the time too — they flatter my hips...

Different breeds of dog came from selective breeding. For example, somebody thought 'I really like this small, yappy wolf — I'll breed it with this other one'. After thousands of generations, we got poodles.

Q1 Why might a plant nursery use selective breeding? [1 mark]

Q2 What potential issues can selective breeding cause? [3 marks]

Genetic Engineering

Genetic engineering is an interesting area of science with exciting possibilities, but there might be dangers too...

Genetic Engineering Transfers Genes Between Organisms

The basic idea of genetic engineering is to transfer a gene responsible for a desirable characteristic from one organism's genome into another organism, so that it also has the desired characteristic.

1) A useful gene is isolated (cut) from one organism's genome using enzymes and is inserted into a vector.
2) The vector is usually a virus or a bacterial plasmid (a fancy piece of circular DNA found in bacterial cells), depending on the type of organism that the gene is being transferred to.
3) When the vector is introduced to the target organism, the useful gene is inserted into its cell(s).
4) Scientists use this method to do all sorts of things. For example:

    1) Bacteria have been genetically modified to produce human insulin that can be used to treat diabetes.
    2) Genetically modified (GM) crops have had their genes modified, e.g. to improve the size and quality of their fruit, or make them resistant to disease, insects and herbicides (chemicals used to kill weeds).
    3) Sheep have been genetically engineered to produce substances, like drugs, in their milk that can be used to treat human diseases.

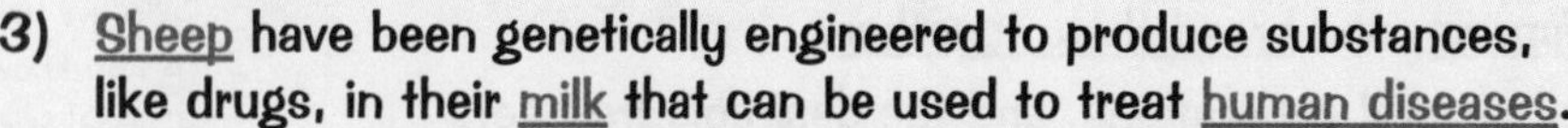

    4) Scientists are researching genetic modification treatments for inherited diseases caused by faulty genes, e.g. by inserting working genes into people with the disease. This is called gene therapy.

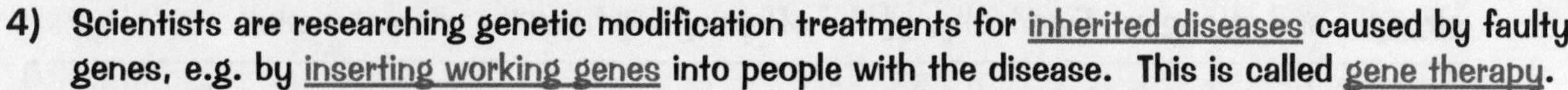

5) In some cases, the transfer of the gene is carried out when the organism receiving the gene is at an early stage of development (e.g. egg or embryo). This means that the organism develops with the characteristic coded for by the gene.

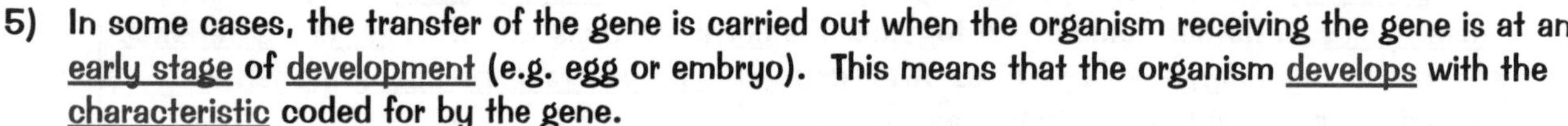

Genetic Engineering is a Controversial Topic

1) Genetic engineering is an exciting area of science, which has the potential for solving many of our problems (e.g. treating diseases, more efficient food production etc.), but not everyone thinks it's a great idea.
2) There are worries about the long-term effects of genetic engineering — that changing an organism's genes might accidentally create unplanned problems, which could get passed on to future generations.

There Are Pros and Cons of GM Crops

1) Some people say that growing GM crops will affect the number of wild flowers (and so the population of insects) that live in and around the crops — reducing farmland biodiversity.
2) Not everyone is convinced that GM crops are safe and some people are concerned that we might not fully understand the effects of eating them on human health. E.g. people are worried they may develop allergies to the food — although there's probably no more risk for this than for eating usual foods.
3) A big concern is that transplanted genes may get out into the natural environment. For example, the herbicide resistance gene may be picked up by weeds, creating a new 'superweed' variety.
4) On the plus side, the characteristics chosen for GM crops can increase the yield, making more food.
5) People living in developing nations often lack nutrients in their diets. GM crops could be engineered to contain the nutrient that's missing. For example, 'golden rice' is a GM rice crop that contains beta-carotene — lack of this substance causes blindness.

6) GM crops are already being grown in some places, often without any problems.

If only there was a gene to make revision easier...

Make sure you've got everything on this page firmly in your noggin. You need to understand the lot.

Q1 Outline one benefit and one concern about GM crops. [2 marks]

Fossils

Fossils are great. If they're well-preserved, you can see what oldy-worldy creatures looked like. They also show how living things have evolved. Although we're not sure how life started in the first place...

Fossils are the Remains of Plants and Animals

Fossils are the remains of organisms from many thousands of years ago, which are found in rocks. They provide the evidence that organisms lived ages ago. Fossils can tell us a lot about how much or how little organisms have changed (evolved) over time. Fossils form in rocks in one of three ways:

1) FROM GRADUAL REPLACEMENT BY MINERALS (Most fossils happen this way.)

1) Things like teeth, shells, bones etc., which don't decay easily, can last a long time when buried.
2) They're eventually replaced by minerals as they decay, forming a rock-like substance shaped like the original hard part.
3) The surrounding sediments also turn to rock, but the fossil stays distinct inside the rock and eventually someone digs it up.

2) FROM CASTS AND IMPRESSIONS

1) Sometimes, fossils are formed when an organism is buried in a soft material like clay. The clay later hardens around it and the organism decays, leaving a cast of itself. An animal's burrow or a plant's roots (rootlet traces) can be preserved as casts.
2) Things like footprints can also be pressed into these materials when soft, leaving an impression when it hardens.

3) FROM PRESERVATION IN PLACES WHERE NO DECAY HAPPENS

1) In amber (a clear yellow 'stone' made from fossilised resin) and tar pits there's no oxygen or moisture so decay microbes can't survive.
2) In glaciers it's too cold for the decay microbes to work.
3) Peat bogs are too acidic for decay microbes.
(A fully preserved man they named 'Pete Marsh' was found in a bog.)

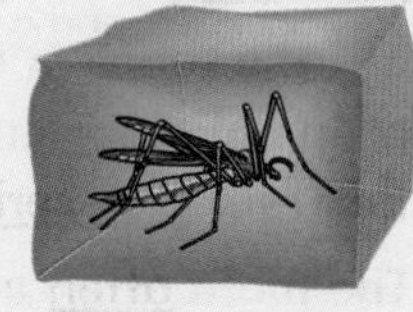

But No One Knows How Life Began

Fossils show how much or how little different organisms have changed (evolved) as life has developed on Earth over millions of years. But where did the first living thing come from...

1) There are various hypotheses suggesting how life first came into being, but no one really knows.
2) Maybe the first life forms came into existence in a primordial swamp (or under the sea) here on Earth. Maybe simple organic molecules were brought to Earth on comets — these could have then become more complex organic molecules, and eventually very simple life forms.
3) These hypotheses can't be supported or disproved because there's a lack of good, valid evidence:
   - Many early forms of life were soft-bodied, and soft tissue tends to decay away completely — so the fossil record is incomplete.
   - Fossils that did form millions of years ago may have been destroyed by geological activity, e.g. the movement of tectonic plates may have crushed fossils already formed in the rock.

Don't get bogged down by all this information...

It's a bit mind-boggling really how fossils can still exist even millions of years after the organism died. They really are fascinating things, and scientists have learned a whole lot from studying them in detail.

Q1 Suggest what makes low-oxygen environments suitable for the formation of fossils. [2 marks]

Antibiotic-Resistant Bacteria

The discovery of antibiotics, like penicillin, was a huge benefit to medicine — suddenly bacterial infections that had often been fatal could be cured. But unfortunately they might not be a permanent solution.

Bacteria can Evolve and Become Antibiotic-Resistant

1) Like all organisms, bacteria sometimes develop random mutations (changes) in their DNA. These can lead to changes in the bacteria's characteristics, e.g. being less affected by a particular antibiotic. This can lead to antibiotic-resistant strains forming as the gene for antibiotic resistance becomes more common in the population.
2) To make matters worse, because bacteria are so rapid at reproducing, they can evolve quite quickly.
3) For the bacterium, the ability to resist antibiotics is a big advantage. It's better able to survive, even in a host who's being treated to get rid of the infection, and so it lives for longer and reproduces many more times. This increases the population size of the antibiotic-resistant strain.
4) Antibiotic-resistant strains are a problem for people who become infected with these bacteria because they aren't immune to the new strain and there is no effective treatment. This means that the infection easily spreads between people. Sometimes drug companies can come up with a new antibiotic that's effective, but 'superbugs' that are resistant to most known antibiotics are becoming more common.
5) MRSA is a relatively common 'superbug' that's really hard to get rid of. It often affects people in hospitals and can be fatal if it enters their bloodstream.

The gene for antibiotic resistance becomes more common in the population because of natural selection — see page 76 for more.

Antibiotic Resistance is Becoming More Common

1) For the last few decades, we've been able to deal with bacterial infections pretty easily using antibiotics. The death rate from infectious bacterial diseases (e.g. pneumonia) has fallen dramatically.
2) But the problem of antibiotic resistance is getting worse — partly because of the overuse and inappropriate use of antibiotics, e.g. doctors prescribing them for non-serious conditions or infections caused by viruses.
3) The more often antibiotics are used, the bigger the problem of antibiotic resistance becomes, so it's important that doctors only prescribe antibiotics when they really need to:

   It's not that antibiotics actually cause resistance — they create a situation where naturally resistant bacteria have an advantage and so increase in numbers.

4) It's also important that you take all the antibiotics a doctor prescribes for you:

   Taking the full course makes sure that all the bacteria are destroyed, which means that there are none left to mutate and develop into antibiotic-resistant strains.

5) In farming, antibiotics can be given to animals to prevent them becoming ill and to make them grow faster. This can lead to the development of antibiotic-resistant bacteria in the animals which can then spread to humans, e.g. during meat preparation and consumption. Increasing concern about the overuse of antibiotics in agriculture has led to some countries restricting their use.
6) The increase in antibiotic resistance has encouraged drug companies to work on developing new antibiotics that are effective against the resistant strains. Unfortunately, the rate of development is slow, which means we're unlikely to be able to keep up with the demand for new drugs as more antibiotic-resistant strains develop and spread. It's also a very costly process.

Antibiotics don't kill viruses — see p.48.

Aaargh, a giant earwig! Run from the attack of the superbug...

The reality of 'superbugs' is even scarier than giant earwigs. Microorganisms that are resistant to all our drugs are a worrying thought. It'll be like going back in time to before antibiotics were invented.

Q1 Suggest a situation where antibiotics could be prescribed inappropriately. [1 mark]

Q2 Explain why it's important that people take the full course of antibiotics they are prescribed. [2 marks]

Classification

It seems to be a basic human urge to want to classify things — that's the case in biology anyway...

Classification is Organising Living Organisms into Groups

1) Traditionally, organisms have been classified according to a system first proposed in the 1700s by Carl Linnaeus, which groups living things according to their characteristics and the structures that make them up.
2) In this system (known as the Linnaean system), living things are first divided into kingdoms (e.g. the plant kingdom).
3) The kingdoms are then subdivided into smaller and smaller groups — phylum, class, order, family, genus, species.

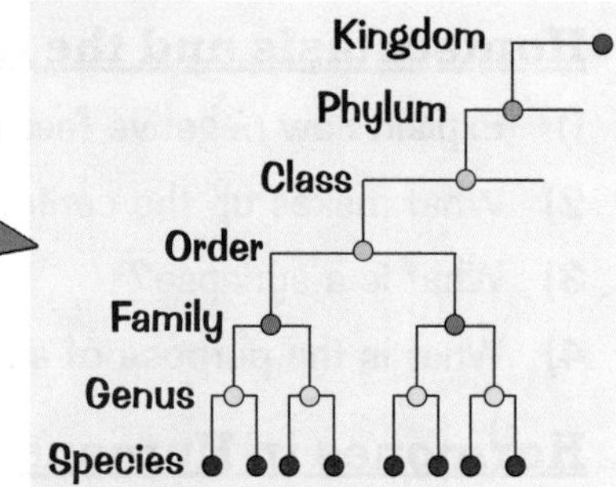

Classification Systems Change Over Time

1) As knowledge of the biochemical processes taking place inside organisms developed and microscopes improved (which allowed us to find out more about the internal structures of organisms), scientists put forward new models of classification.
2) In 1990, Carl Woese proposed the three-domain system. Using evidence gathered from new chemical analysis techniques such as RNA sequence analysis, he found that in some cases, species thought to be closely related in traditional classification systems are in fact not as closely related as first thought.
3) In the three-domain system, organisms are first of all split into three large groups called domains:
   1) ARCHAEA — Organisms in this domain are primitive bacteria. They're often found in extreme places such as hot springs and salt lakes.
   2) BACTERIA — This domain contains true bacteria like *E. coli* and *Staphylococcus*. Although they often look similar to Archaea, there are lots of biochemical differences between them.
   3) EUKARYOTA — This domain includes a broad range of organisms including fungi (page 43), plants, animals and protists (page 43).
4) These are then subdivided into smaller groups — kingdom, phylum, class, order, family, genus, species.

Organisms Are Named According to the Binomial System

1) In the binomial system, every organism is given its own two-part Latin name.
2) The first part refers to the genus that the organism belongs to. This gives you information on the organism's ancestry. The second part refers to the species. E.g. humans are known as *Homo sapiens*. '*Homo*' is the genus and '*sapiens*' is the species.
3) The binomial system is used worldwide and means that scientists in different countries or who speak different languages all refer to a particular species by the same name — avoiding potential confusion.

Evolutionary Trees Show Evolutionary Relationships

1) Evolutionary trees show how scientists think different species are related to each other.
2) They show common ancestors and relationships between species. The more recent the common ancestor, the more closely related the two species — and the more characteristics they're likely to share.
3) Scientists analyse lots of different types of data to work out evolutionary relationships. For living organisms, they use the current classification data (e.g. DNA analysis and structural similarities). For extinct species, they use information from the fossil record (see page 76).

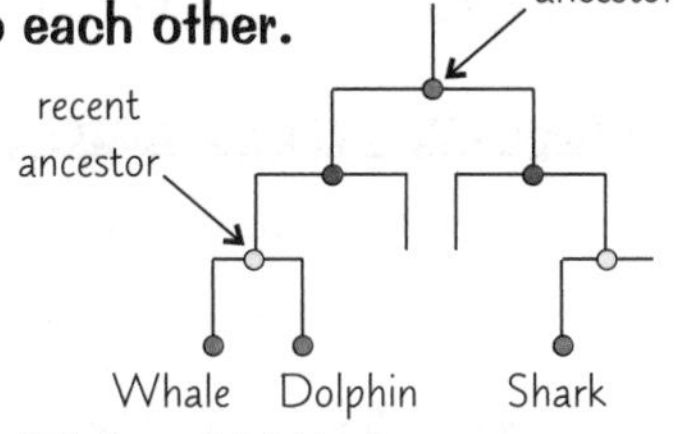

Whales and dolphins have a recent common ancestor so are closely related. They're both more distantly related to sharks.

Binomial system — uh oh, sounds like maths...

Sometimes, the genus in a binomial name is abbreviated to a capital letter with a full stop after it.

Q1 What genus does the Eurasian beaver, *Castor fiber*, belong to? [1 mark]

Revision Questions for Topics B5 & B6

So you've finished Topics B5 and B6 — Hoorah. Now here's a page full of questions to test your knowledge.

- Try these questions and tick off each one when you get it right.
- When you've done all the questions under a heading and are completely happy with it, tick it off.

Homeostasis and the Nervous System (p.58-61)

1) Explain how negative feedback helps to maintain a stable internal environment.
2) What makes up the central nervous system and what does it do?
3) What is a synapse?
4) What is the purpose of a reflex action?

Hormones in Humans (p.62-67)

5) Give two differences between nervous and hormonal responses.
6) What effect does the hormone glucagon have on blood glucose level?
7) Describe two effects of FSH on the body.
8) Which of the following is a hormonal contraceptive — condom, plastic IUD or diaphragm?
9) Briefly describe how IVF is carried out.
10) How does adrenaline prepare the body for 'fight or flight'?

DNA, Genes, Reproduction and Meiosis (p.68-70)

11) What is meant by 'double helix'?
12) What do genes code for?
13) What is the name for the entire set of genetic material in an organism?
14) Name the male and female gametes of animals.
15) State the type of cell division used to make gametes in humans.

Sex Chromosomes, Genetic Diagrams and Inherited Disorders (p.71-74)

16) What is the probability that offspring will have the XX combination of sex chromosomes?
17) What are alleles?
18) What does it mean if someone is heterozygous for a gene?
19) What is the chance of a child being born with polydactyly if one parent has a single dominant allele for the gene that controls it?
20) Give two arguments for and two arguments against screening embryos for genetic disorders.

Variation and Evolution (p.75-76)

21) What is variation?
22) Explain how beneficial characteristics can become more common in a population over time.

Selective Breeding and Genetic Engineering (p.77-78)

23) How might farmers use selective breeding?
24) What is genetic engineering?

Fossils, Antibiotic-Resistant Bacteria and Classification (p.79-81)

25) Give two ways that fossils can be formed.
26) What leads to the formation of antibiotic-resistant strains of bacteria?
27) Name the groups that organisms are classified into in the Linnaean system.
28) Who proposed the 'three-domain system' of classification in 1990?

Competition

Ecology is all about organisms and the environment they live in, and how the two interact. Simples.

First Learn Some Words to Help You Understand Ecology...

This topic will make a lot more sense if you become familiar with these terms first:

1) Habitat — the place where an organism lives.
2) Population — all the organisms of one species living in a habitat.
3) Community — the populations of different species living in a habitat.
4) Abiotic factors — non-living factors of the environment, e.g. temperature.
5) Biotic factors — living factors of the environment, e.g. food.
6) Ecosystem — the interaction of a community of living organisms (biotic) with the non-living (abiotic) parts of their environment.

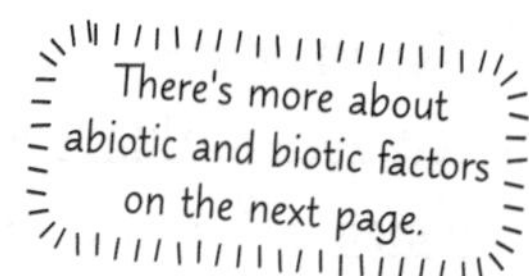

Organisms Compete for Resources to Survive

Organisms need things from their environment and from other organisms in order to survive and reproduce:

1) Plants need light and space, as well as water and mineral ions (nutrients) from the soil.
2) Animals need space (territory), food, water and mates.

Organisms compete with other species (and members of their own species) for the same resources.

Any Change in Any Environment can Have Knock-on Effects

In a community, each species depends on other species for things such as food, shelter, pollination and seed dispersal — this is called interdependence.

The interdependence of all the living things in an ecosystem means that any major change in the ecosystem (such as one species being removed) can have far-reaching effects.

The diagram on the right shows part of a food web (a diagram of what eats what) from a stream.

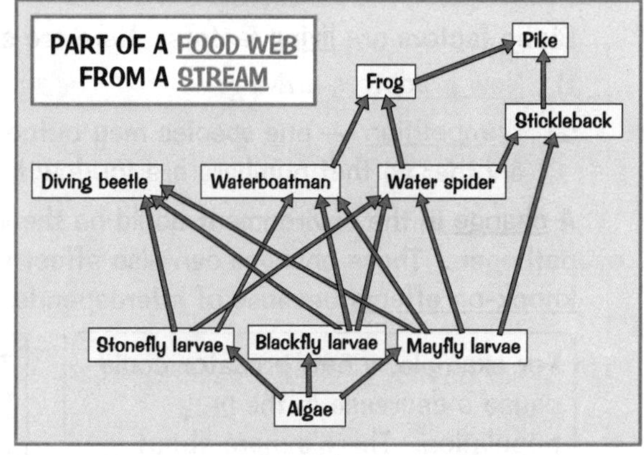

Stonefly larvae are particularly sensitive to pollution. Suppose pollution killed them in this stream. The table below shows some of the effects this might have on some of the other organisms in the food web.

Organism	Effect of loss of stonefly larvae	Effect on population
Blackfly larvae	Less competition for algae	Increase
	More likely to be eaten by predators	Decrease
Water spider	Less food	Decrease
Stickleback	Less food (if water spider or mayfly larvae numbers decrease)	Decrease

Remember that food webs are very complex and that these effects are difficult to predict accurately.

In some communities, all the species and environmental factors are in balance so that the population sizes are roughly constant (they may go up and down in cycles — see p.86). These are called stable communities. Stable communities include tropical rainforests and ancient oak woodlands.

I'm dependent on the cocoa tree...

If my source of chocolate was removed, it would have far-reaching effects on my revision and exam grades. Seriously though, make sure you know what organisms need and compete for in an ecosystem. Then try these...

Q1 What is an ecosystem? [1 mark]

Q2 Give three things plants compete for in an ecosystem. [3 marks]

Q3 What is meant by a 'stable community'? [1 mark]

Abiotic and Biotic Factors

The environment in which organisms live changes all the time. The things that change are either abiotic (non-living) or biotic (living) factors. These can have a big effect on a community...

Abiotic Factors Can Vary in an Ecosystem...

Abiotic factors are non-living factors. For example:

1) Moisture level
2) Light intensity
3) Temperature
4) Carbon dioxide level (for plants)
5) Wind intensity and direction
6) Oxygen level (for aquatic animals)
7) Soil pH and mineral content

A change in the environment could be an increase or decrease in an abiotic factor, e.g. an increase in temperature. These changes can affect the size of populations in a community. This means they can also affect the population sizes of other organisms that depend on them (see previous page).

For example, a decrease in light intensity, temperature or level of carbon dioxide could decrease the rate of photosynthesis in a plant species (see p.50). This could affect plant growth and cause a decrease in the population size.

For example, a decrease in the mineral content of the soil (e.g. a lack of nitrates) could cause nutrient deficiencies. This could also affect plant growth and cause a decrease in the population size.

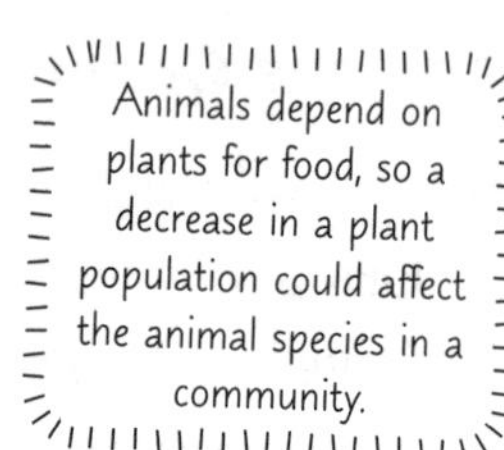

...and So Can Biotic Factors

Biotic factors are living factors. Here are some examples:

1) New predators arriving
2) Competition — one species may outcompete another so that numbers are too low to breed
3) New pathogens
4) Availability of food

A change in the environment could be the introduction of a new biotic factor, e.g. a new predator or pathogen. These changes can also affect the size of populations in a community, which can have knock-on effects because of interdependence (see previous page).

For example, a new predator could cause a decrease in the prey population. There's more about predator-prey populations on p.86.

For example, red and grey squirrels live in the same habitat and eat the same food. Grey squirrels outcompete the red squirrels — so the population of red squirrels is decreasing.

The following graph shows the effect of a new pathogen on Species A. The population size of species A was increasing up until 1985, when it decreased rapidly until 1990 — suggesting that 1985 was the year that the new pathogen arrived. The population started to rise again after 1990.

Population size of Species A

1960 1970 1980 1990 2000 2010

Exams — a type of abiotic factor affecting my environment...

So, two lists of factors that would be a good idea to learn. I reckon this is a prime time for shutting the book, scribbling them all down and then checking how you did. It's the only way they'll get firmly wedged in your brain.

Q1 Give four examples of abiotic factors that could affect a plant species. [4 marks]

Q2 Cutthroat trout are present in lakes in Yellowstone National Park. In the last few decades, lake trout have been introduced to the lakes. However, lake trout have emerged as predators of the cutthroat trout. Give two other biotic factors that could affect the size of the cutthroat trout population. [2 marks]

Adaptations

Life exists in so many different environments because the organisms that live in them have adapted to them.

Adaptations Allow Organisms to Survive

Organisms, including microorganisms, are adapted to live in different environmental conditions. The features or characteristics that allow them to do this are called adaptations. Adaptations can be:

1) Structural

These are features of an organism's body structure — such as shape or colour. For example:

Arctic animals like the Arctic fox have white fur so they're camouflaged against the snow. This helps them avoid predators and sneak up on prey.

Animals that live in cold places (like whales) have a thick layer of blubber (fat) and a low surface area to volume ratio to help them retain heat.

Animals that live in hot places (like camels) have a thin layer of fat and a large surface area to volume ratio to help them lose heat.

2) Behavioural

These are ways that organisms behave. Many species (e.g. swallows) migrate to warmer climates during the winter to avoid the problems of living in cold conditions.

3) Functional

These are things that go on inside an organism's body that can be related to processes like reproduction and metabolism (all the chemical reactions happening in the body). For example:

Desert animals conserve water by producing very little sweat and small amounts of concentrated urine.

Brown bears hibernate over winter. They lower their metabolism which conserves energy, so they don't have to hunt when there's not much food about.

Microorganisms Have a Huge Variety of Adaptations...

...so that they can live in a wide range of environments:

Some microorganisms (e.g. bacteria) are known as extremophiles — they're adapted to live in very extreme conditions. For example, some can live at high temperatures (e.g. in super hot volcanic vents), and others can live in places with a high salt concentration (e.g. very salty lakes) or at high pressure (e.g. deep sea vents).

In a nutshell, it's horses for courses...

In the exam, you might have to say how an organism is adapted to its environment. Look at its characteristics (e.g. colour/shape) as well as the conditions it has to cope with (e.g. predation/temperature) and you'll be sorted.

Q1 The diagram on the right shows a penguin. Penguins live in the cold, icy environment of the Antarctic. They swim in the sea to hunt for fish to eat. Some penguins also huddle together in large groups to keep warm.

a) What type of adaptation is being described when penguins 'huddle together'? [1 mark]

b) Explain one structural adaptation a penguin has to its environment. [2 marks]

Food Chains

If you like food, and you like chains, then food chains might just blow your mind. Strap yourself in and prepare for some 'edge of your seat' learning, because the show is about to begin...

Food Chains Show What's Eaten by What in an Ecosystem

1) Food chains always start with a producer.
   Producers make (produce) their own food using energy from the Sun.
2) Producers are usually green plants or algae — they make glucose by photosynthesis (see page 50).
3) When a green plant produces glucose, some of it is used to make other biological molecules in the plant.
4) These biological molecules are the plant's biomass — the mass of living material.
5) Biomass can be thought of as energy stored in a plant.
6) Energy is transferred through living organisms in an ecosystem when organisms eat other organisms.
7) Producers are eaten by primary consumers. Primary consumers are then eaten by secondary consumers and secondary consumers are eaten by tertiary consumers. Here's an example of a food chain:

Consumers are organisms that eat other organisms. 'Primary' means 'first', so primary consumers are the first consumers in a food chain. Secondary consumers are second and tertiary consumers are third.

Populations of Prey and Predators Go in Cycles

Consumers that hunt and kill other animals are called predators, and their prey are what they eat.
In a stable community containing prey and predators (as most of them do of course):

1) The population of any species is usually limited by the amount of food available.
2) If the population of the prey increases, then so will the population of the predators.
3) However as the population of predators increases, the number of prey will decrease.

For more about a stable community see page 83.

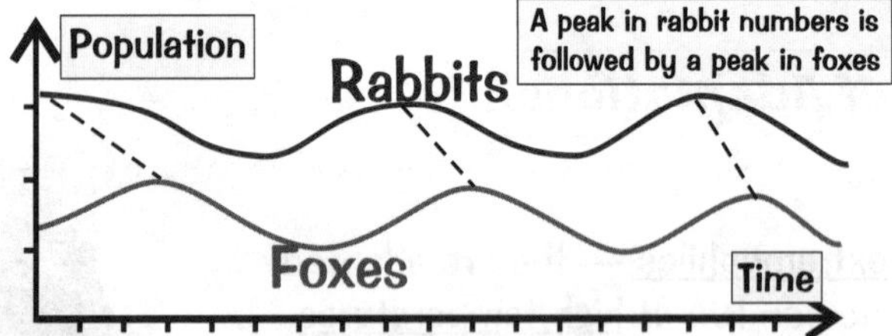

E.g. More grass means more rabbits.
More rabbits means more foxes.
But more foxes means fewer rabbits.
Eventually fewer rabbits will mean fewer foxes again.
This up and down pattern continues...

4) Predator-prey cycles are always out of phase with each other. This is because it takes a while for one population to respond to changes in the other population. E.g. when the number of rabbits goes up, the number of foxes doesn't increase immediately because it takes time for them to reproduce.

When the TV volume goes up... my revision goes down...

You might think that the start of a food chain always has to be a plant. In most cases it is, but sometimes organisms like algae can be too because they photosynthesise. No wonder those algae I saw were looking smug...

Q1 Look at the following food chain for a particular area: grass → grasshopper → rat → snake

a) Name the producer in the food chain. [1 mark]
b) How many consumers are there in the food chain? [1 mark]
c) Name the primary consumer in the food chain. [1 mark]
d) All the rats in the area are killed. Explain two effects that this could have on the food chain. [4 marks]

Using Quadrats

PRACTICAL

This is where the fun starts. Studying ecology gives you the chance to rummage around in bushes, get your hands dirty and look at some real organisms, living in the wild. Hold on to your hats folks...

Organisms Live in Different Places Because The Environment Varies

1) As you know from page 83, a habitat is the place where an organism lives, e.g. a playing field.
2) The distribution of an organism is where an organism is found, e.g. in a part of the playing field.
3) Where an organism is found is affected by environmental factors (see page 84). An organism might be more common in one area than another due to differences in environmental factors between the two areas. For example, in the playing field, you might find that daisies are more common in the open than under trees, because there's more light available in the open.
4) There are a couple of ways to study the distribution of an organism. You can:
   - measure how common an organism is in two sample areas (e.g. using quadrats) and compare them.
   - study how the distribution changes across an area, e.g. by placing quadrats along a transect (p.88).

   Both of these methods give quantitative data (numbers) about the distribution.

Use Quadrats to Study The Distribution of Small Organisms

A quadrat is a square frame enclosing a known area, e.g. 1 m^2. To compare how common an organism is in two sample areas (e.g. shady and sunny spots in that playing field) just follow these simple steps:

1) Place a 1 m^2 quadrat on the ground at a random point within the first sample area. E.g. divide the area into a grid and use a random number generator to pick coordinates.
2) Count all the organisms within the quadrat.
3) Repeat steps 1 and 2 as many times as you can.
4) Work out the mean number of organisms per quadrat within the first sample area.

A quadrat

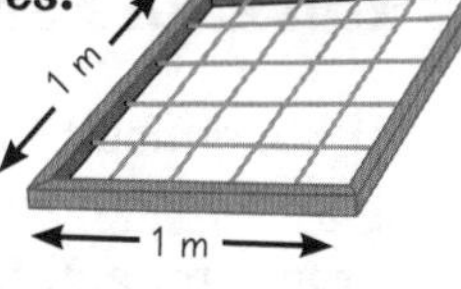

Anna counted the number of daisies in 7 quadrats within her first sample area and recorded the following results: 18, 20, 22, 23, 23, 23, 25

Here the MEAN is: $\frac{\text{TOTAL number of organisms}}{\text{NUMBER of quadrats}} = \frac{154}{7} = 22$ daisies per quadrat

5) Repeat steps 1 to 4 in the second sample area.
6) Finally compare the two means. E.g. you might find 2 daisies per m^2 in the shade, and 22 daisies per m^2 (lots more) in the open field.

You Can Also Work Out the Population Size of an Organism in One Area

Students used 0.5 m^2 quadrats to randomly sample daisies on an open field. The students found a mean of 10.5 daisies per quadrat. The field had an area of 800 m^2. Estimate the population of daisies on the field.

1) Work out the mean number of organisms per m^2. $1 \div 0.5 = 2$
   $2 \times 10.5 = 21$ daisies per m^2
2) Then multiply the mean by the total area (in m^2) of the habitat. $800 \times 21 = 16\ 800$ daisies on the open field

The population size of an organism is sometimes called its abundance.

If your quadrat has an area of 1 m^2, the mean number of organisms per m^2 is just the same as the mean number per quadrat.

Drat, drat, and double drat — my favourite use of quadrats...

It's key that you make sure you put your quadrat down in a random place before you start counting.

Q1 A field was randomly sampled for buttercups using 0.25 m^2 quadrats. The field had an area of 1200 m^2. A mean of 0.75 buttercups were found per quadrat. Estimate the total population of buttercups. [2 marks]

Using Transects

So, now you think you've learnt all about distribution. Well hold on — there's more ecology fun to be had.

Use Transects to Study The Distribution of Organisms Along a Line

You can use lines called transects to help find out how organisms (like plants) are distributed across an area — e.g. if an organism becomes more or less common as you move from a hedge towards the middle of a field. Here's what to do:

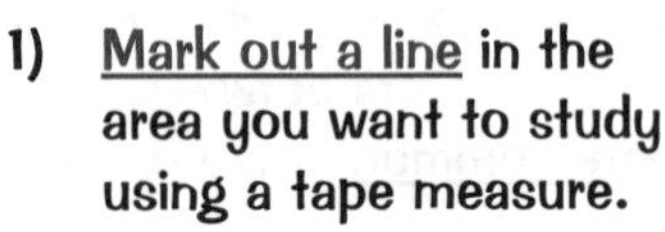

1) Mark out a line in the area you want to study using a tape measure.
2) Then collect data along the line.
3) You can do this by just counting all the organisms you're interested in that touch the line.
4) Or, you can collect data by using quadrats (see previous page). These can be placed next to each other along the line or at intervals, for example, every 2 m.

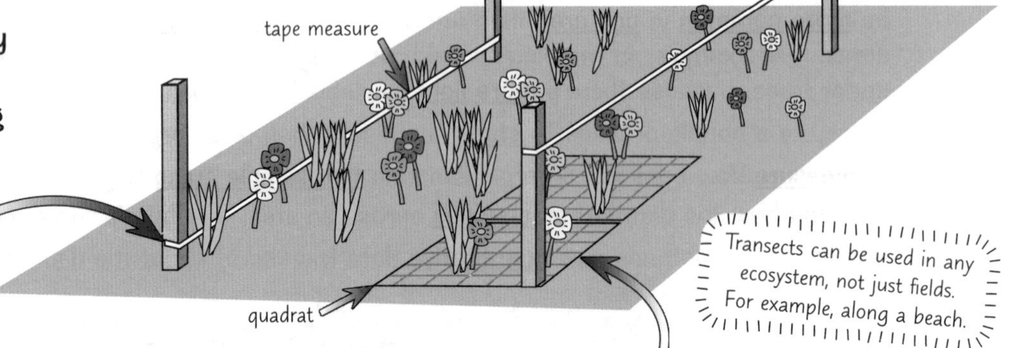

You Can Estimate the Percentage Cover of a Quadrat

If it's difficult to count all the individual organisms in the quadrat (e.g. if they're grass) you can calculate the percentage cover. This means estimating the percentage area of the quadrat covered by a particular type of organism, e.g. by counting the number of little squares covered by the organisms.

Some students were measuring the distribution of organisms from one corner of a school playing field to another, using quadrats placed at regular intervals along a transect. Below is a picture of one of the quadrats. Calculate the percentage cover of each organism, A and B.

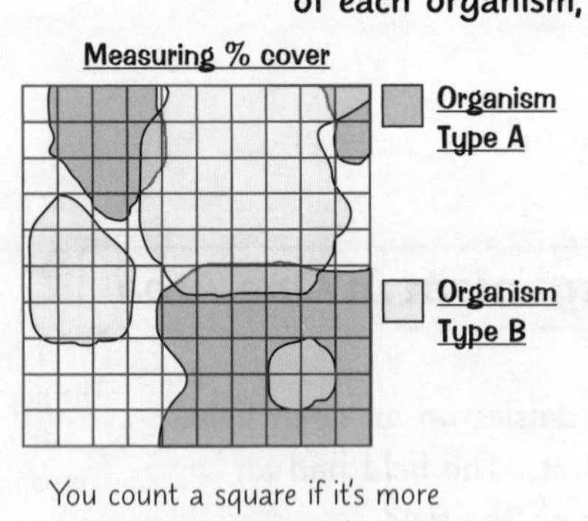

You count a square if it's more than half covered.

1) Count the number of squares covered by organism A. — Type A = 42 squares
2) Make this into a percentage — divide the number of squares covered by the organism by the total number of squares in the quadrat (100), then multiply the result by 100. — (42/100) × 100 = 0.42 × 100 = 42%
3) Do the same for organism B. — Type B = 47 squares; (47/100) × 100 = 0.47 × 100 = 47%

A slug that's been run over — definitely a widely-spread organism

So if you want to measure the distribution of a organism across an area, you could use a transect. You can either use them alone or along with quadrats. Now who's for a game of tennis... I've got my transect up.

Q1 What is a transect? [1 mark]

Q2 Some students want to measure how the distribution of dandelions changes across a field, from one corner to another. Describe a method they could use to do this. [2 marks]

Q3 How could you estimate the number of organisms in a quadrat, if they are difficult to count? [1 mark]

The Water Cycle

Water on planet Earth is constantly recycled. This is lucky for us because without water, we wouldn't survive. And I don't just mean there'd be no paddling pools, ice lollies or bubble baths...

The Water Cycle Means Water is Endlessly Recycled

The water here on planet Earth is constantly recycled. Strange but true...

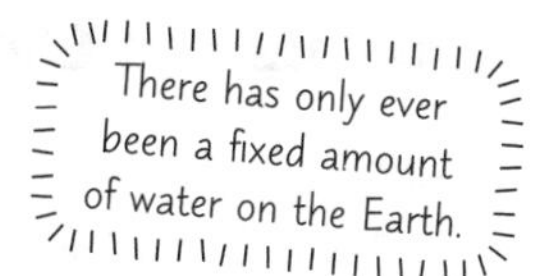

1) Energy from the Sun makes water evaporate from the land and sea, turning it into water vapour.
2) Water also evaporates from plants — this is known as transpiration (see p.40).
3) The warm water vapour is carried upwards (as warm air rises). When it gets higher up it cools and condenses to form clouds.
4) Water falls from the clouds as precipitation (usually rain, but sometimes snow or hail) onto land, where it provides fresh water for plants and animals.
5) Some of this water is absorbed by the soil and is taken up by plant roots. This provides plants with fresh water for things like photosynthesis. Some of the water taken up by plants becomes part of the plants' tissues and is passed along to animals in food chains.
6) Like plants, animals need water for the chemical reactions that happen in their bodies. Animals return water to the soil and atmosphere through excretion (processes that get rid of the waste products of chemical reactions, e.g. sweating, urination and breathing out).
7) Water that doesn't get absorbed by the soil will runoff into streams and rivers.
8) From here, the water then drains back into the sea, before it evaporates all over again.

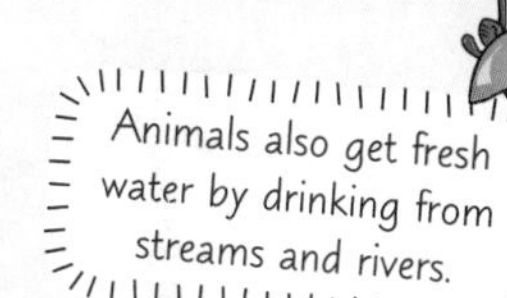

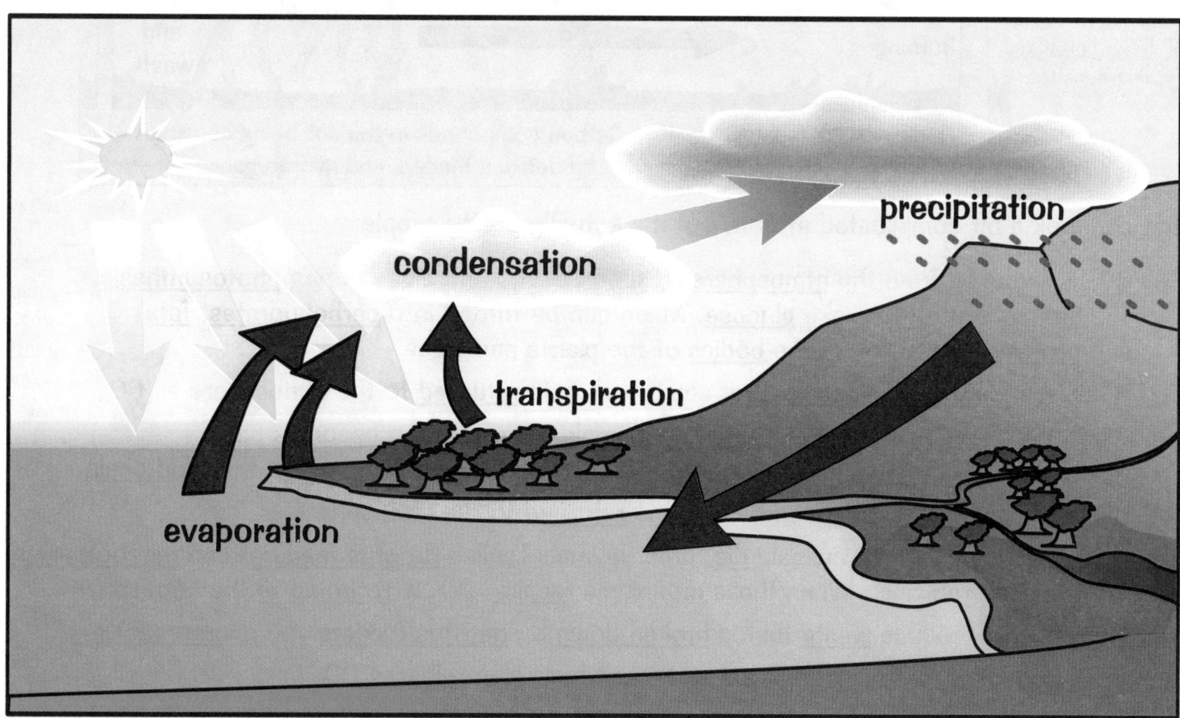

Come on out, it's only a little water cycle, it won't hurt you...

The most important thing to remember is that it's a cycle — a continuous process with no beginning or end. Water that falls to the ground as rain (or any other kind of precipitation) will eventually end up back in the clouds again.

Q1 a) In the water cycle, how does water move from the land into the air? [1 mark]

b) How does the water cycle benefit plants and animals? [1 mark]

The Carbon Cycle

Recycling may be a buzz word for us but it's old school for nature. All the nutrients in our environment are constantly being recycled — there's a nice balance between what goes in and what goes out again.

Elements are Cycled Back to the Start of the Food Chain by Decay

1) Living things are made of materials they take from the world around them. E.g. plants turn elements like carbon, oxygen, hydrogen and nitrogen from the soil and the air into the complex compounds (carbohydrates, proteins and fats) that make up living organisms. These get passed up the food chain.
2) These materials are returned to the environment in waste products, or when the organisms die and decay.
3) Materials decay because they're broken down (digested) by microorganisms. This happens faster in warm, moist, aerobic (oxygen rich) conditions because microorganisms are more active in these conditions.
4) Decay puts the stuff that plants need to grow (e.g. mineral ions — see point 1) back into the soil.
5) In a stable community, the materials that are taken out of the soil and used by plants etc. are balanced by those that are put back in. There's a constant cycle happening.

The Constant Cycling of Carbon is called the Carbon Cycle

Fossil fuels are made of decayed plant and animal matter.

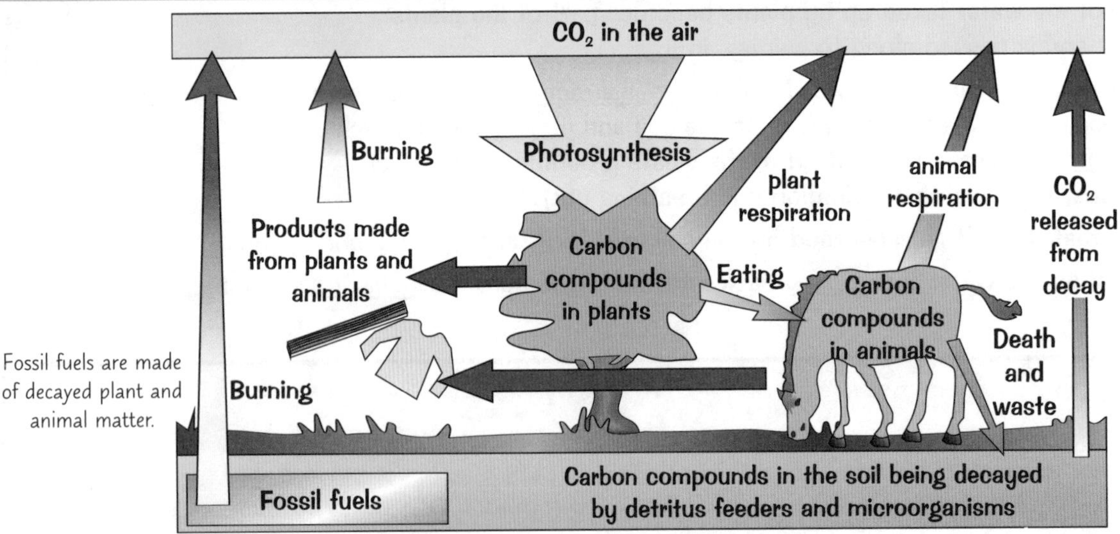

That can look a bit complicated at first, but it's actually pretty simple:

1) CO_2 is removed from the atmosphere by green plants and algae during photosynthesis. The carbon is used to make glucose, which can be turned into carbohydrates, fats and proteins that make up the bodies of the plants and algae.
2) When the plants and algae respire, some carbon is returned to the atmosphere as CO_2.
3) When the plants and algae are eaten by animals, some carbon becomes part of the fats and proteins in their bodies. The carbon then moves through the food chain.
4) When the animals respire, some carbon is returned to the atmosphere as CO_2.
5) When plants, algae and animals die, other animals (called detritus feeders) and microorganisms feed on their remains. When these organisms respire, CO_2 is returned to the atmosphere.
6) Animals also produce waste that is broken down by detritus feeders and microorganisms.
7) The combustion (burning) of wood and fossil fuels also releases CO_2 back into the air.
8) So the carbon (and energy) is constantly being cycled — from the air, through food chains (via plants, algae and animals, and detritus feeders and microorganisms) and eventually back out into the air again.

The energy that green plants and algae get from photosynthesis is transferred up the food chain.

What goes around comes around...

Carbon is very important for living things — it's the basis for all the organic molecules in our bodies.

Q1 What causes materials to decay? [1 mark]

Q2 Describe how carbon is removed from the atmosphere in the carbon cycle. [1 mark]

Biodiversity and Waste Management

Unfortunately, human activity can negatively affect the planet and its variety of life. Read on for bad news...

Earth's Biodiversity is Important

Biodiversity is the variety of different species of organisms on Earth, or within an ecosystem.

1) High biodiversity is important. It makes sure that ecosystems (see p.83) are stable because different species depend on each other for things like shelter and food. Different species can also help to maintain the right physical environment for each other (e.g. the acidity of the soil).
2) For the human species to survive, it's important that a good level of biodiversity is maintained.
3) Lots of human actions, including waste production (see below) and deforestation (see p.93), as well as global warming (see next page) are reducing biodiversity. However, it's only recently that we've started taking measures to stop this from continuing.

There are Over Seven Billion People in the World...

1) The population of the world is currently rising very quickly, and it's not slowing down — look at the graph...
2) This is mostly due to modern medicine and farming methods, which have reduced the number of people dying from disease and hunger.
3) This is great for all of us humans, but it means we're having a bigger effect on the environment we live in.

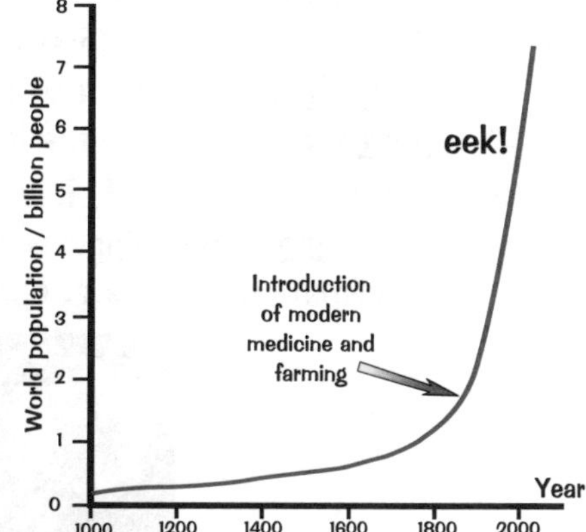

...With Increasing Demands on the Environment

When the Earth's population was much smaller, the effects of human activity were usually small and local. Nowadays though, our actions can have a far more widespread effect.

1) Our increasing population puts pressure on the environment, as we take the resources we need to survive.
2) But people around the world are also demanding a higher standard of living (and so demand luxuries to make life more comfortable — cars, computers, etc.). So we use more raw materials (e.g. oil to make plastics), but we also use more energy for the manufacturing processes. This all means we're taking more and more resources from the environment more and more quickly.
3) Unfortunately, many raw materials are being used up quicker than they're being replaced. So if we carry on like we are, one day we're going to run out.

We're Also Producing More Waste

As we make more and more things we produce more and more waste, including waste chemicals. And unless this waste is properly handled, more harmful pollution will be caused. Pollution affects water, land and air and kills plants and animals, reducing biodiversity.

Water — Sewage and toxic chemicals from industry can pollute lakes, rivers and oceans, affecting the plants and animals that rely on them for survival (including humans). And the chemicals used on land (e.g. fertilisers, pesticides and herbicides) can be washed into water.

Land — We use toxic chemicals for farming (e.g. pesticides and herbicides). We also bury nuclear waste underground, and we dump a lot of household waste in landfill sites.

Air — Smoke and acidic gases released into the atmosphere can pollute the air, e.g. sulfur dioxide can cause acid rain.

More people, more mess, less space, fewer resources...

Biodiversity's a useful thing, but the increasing rate of species extinction means that it's being reduced every day.

Q1 What is meant by the term 'biodiversity'? [1 mark]

Global Warming

The Earth is getting warmer. Climate scientists are now trying to work out what the effects of global warming might be — sadly, it's not as simple as everyone having nicer summers.

Carbon Dioxide and Methane Trap Energy from the Sun

1) The temperature of the Earth is a balance between the energy it gets from the Sun and the energy it radiates back out into space.
2) Gases in the atmosphere naturally act like an insulating layer. They absorb most of the energy that would normally be radiated out into space, and re-radiate it in all directions (including back towards the Earth). This increases the temperature of the planet.
3) If this didn't happen, then at night there'd be nothing to keep any energy in, and we'd quickly get very cold indeed. But recently we've started to worry that this effect is getting a bit out of hand...
4) There are several different gases in the atmosphere which help keep the energy in. They're called "greenhouse gases", and the main ones whose levels we worry about are carbon dioxide (CO_2) and methane — because the levels of these two gases are rising quite sharply.
5) The Earth is gradually heating up because of the increasing levels of greenhouse gases — this is global warming. Global warming is a type of climate change and causes other types of climate change, e.g. changing rainfall patterns.

This is what happens in a greenhouse. The Sun shines in, and the glass helps keeps some of the energy in.

The Consequences of Global Warming Could be Pretty Serious

There are several reasons to be worried about global warming. Here are a few:

1) Higher temperatures cause seawater to expand and ice to melt, causing the sea level to rise. It has risen a little bit over the last 100 years. If it keeps rising it'll be bad news for people and animals living in low-lying places. It will lead to flooding, resulting in the loss of habitats (where organisms live).
2) The distribution of many wild animal and plant species may change as temperatures increase and the amount of rainfall changes in different areas. Some species may become more widely distributed, e.g. species that need warmer temperatures may spread further as the conditions they thrive in exist over a wider area. Other species may become less widely distributed, e.g. species that need cooler temperatures may have smaller ranges as the conditions they thrive in exist over a smaller area.
3) There could be changes in migration patterns, e.g. some birds may migrate further north, as more northern areas are getting warmer.
4) Biodiversity (see p.91) could be reduced if some species are unable to survive a change in the climate, so become extinct.

The greenhouse effect — when you start growing into a tomato...

Global warming is rarely out of the news. Most scientists accept that it's happening and that human activity has caused most of the recent warming. However, they don't know exactly what the effects will be.

Q1 Explain how global warming could lead to the loss of low-lying habitats. [3 marks]

Deforestation and Land Use

Trees and peat bogs trap carbon dioxide and lock it up. The problems start when it escapes...

Humans Use Lots of Land for Lots of Purposes

1) We use land for things like building, quarrying, farming and dumping waste.
2) This means that there's less land available for other organisms.
3) Sometimes, the way we use land has a bad effect on the environment — for example, if it requires deforestation or the destruction of habitats like peat bogs and other areas of peat.

Deforestation Means Chopping Down Trees

Deforestation is the cutting down of forests. This causes big problems when it's done on a large-scale, such as cutting down rainforests in tropical areas. It's done for various reasons, including:

- To clear land for farming (e.g. cattle or rice crops) to provide more food.
- To grow crops from which biofuels based on ethanol can be produced.

Deforestation Can Cause Many Problems

More CO_2 in the atmosphere causes global warming (see previous page), which leads to climate change.

LESS CARBON DIOXIDE TAKEN IN

1) Cutting down loads of trees means that the amount of carbon dioxide removed from the atmosphere during photosynthesis is reduced.
2) Trees 'lock up' some of the carbon that they absorb during photosynthesis in their wood, which can remove it from the atmosphere for hundreds of years. Removing trees means that less is locked up.

MORE CARBON DIOXIDE IN THE ATMOSPHERE

1) Carbon dioxide is released when trees are burnt to clear land. (Carbon in wood doesn't contribute to atmospheric pollution until it's released by burning.)
2) Microorganisms feeding on bits of dead wood release carbon dioxide as a waste product of respiration.

LESS BIODIVERSITY

1) Biodiversity (p.91) is the variety of different species — the more species, the greater the biodiversity.
2) Habitats like forests can contain a huge number of different species of plants and animals, so when they are destroyed there is a danger of many species becoming extinct — biodiversity is reduced.

Destroying Peat Bogs Adds More CO_2 to the Atmosphere

1) Bogs are areas of land that are acidic and waterlogged. Plants that live in bogs don't fully decay when they die, because there's not enough oxygen. The partly-rotted plants gradually build up to form peat.
2) So the carbon in the plants is stored in the peat instead of being released into the atmosphere.
3) However, peat bogs are often drained so that the area can be used as farmland, or the peat is cut up and dried to use as fuel. It's also sold to gardeners as compost. Peat is being used faster than it forms.
4) When peat is drained, it comes into more contact with air and some microorganisms start to decompose it. When these microorganisms respire, they use oxygen and release carbon dioxide, contributing to global warming (see the previous page).
5) Carbon dioxide is also released when peat is burned as a fuel.
6) Destroying the bogs also destroys (or reduces the area of) the habitats of some of the animals, plants and microorganisms that live there, so reduces biodiversity.

Pete Boggs Demolition Ltd — the name in habitat destruction...

So removing trees and peat results in more atmospheric CO_2, which contributes to global warming. Bad times.

Q1 Suggest why deforestation can result in a higher CO_2 concentration in the atmosphere. [3 marks]

Maintaining Ecosystems and Biodiversity

It's really important that biodiversity is maintained, but other factors also have to be taken into account.

Programmes Can be Set Up to Protect Ecosystems and Biodiversity

It's important that biodiversity is maintained at a high enough level to make sure that ecosystems are stable (see page 83). In some areas, programmes have been set up by concerned citizens and scientists to minimise damage by human activities (see p.91) to ecosystems and biodiversity. Here are a few examples:

1) Breeding programmes have been set up to help prevent endangered species from becoming extinct. These are where animals are bred in captivity to make sure the species survives if it dies out in the wild. Individuals can sometimes be released into the wild to boost or re-establish a population.
2) Programmes to protect and regenerate rare habitats like mangroves, heathland and coral reefs have been started. Protecting these habitats helps to protect the species that live there — preserving the ecosystem and biodiversity in the area.
3) There are programmes to reintroduce hedgerows and field margins around fields on farms where only a single type of crop is grown. Field margins are areas of land around the edges of fields where wild flowers and grasses are left to grow. Hedgerows and field margins provide a habitat for a wider variety of organisms than could survive in a single crop habitat.
4) Some governments have introduced regulations and programmes to reduce the level of deforestation taking place and the amount of carbon dioxide being released into the atmosphere by businesses. This could reduce the increase of global warming (see page 92).
5) People are encouraged to recycle to reduce the amount of waste that gets dumped in landfill sites. This could reduce the amount of land taken over for landfill, leaving ecosystems in place.

Conflicting Pressures Can Affect How Biodiversity is Maintained

Sadly for noble biodiversity warriors, maintaining biodiversity isn't as simple as you would hope. There are lots of conflicting pressures that have to be taken into account. For example:

1) Protecting biodiversity costs money. For example, governments sometimes pay farmers a subsidy to reintroduce hedgerows and field margins to their land. It can also cost money to keep a watch on whether the programmes and regulations designed to maintain biodiversity are being followed. There can be conflict between protecting biodiversity and saving money — money may be prioritised for other things.
2) Protecting biodiversity may come at a cost to local people's livelihood. For example, reducing the amount of deforestation is great for biodiversity, but the people who were previously employed in the tree-felling industry could be left unemployed. This could affect the local economy if people move away with their family to find work.
3) There can be conflict between protecting biodiversity and protecting our food security. Sometimes certain organisms are seen as pests by farmers (e.g. locusts and foxes) and are killed to protect crops and livestock so that more food can be produced. As a result, however, the food chain and biodiversity can be affected.
4) Development is important, but it can affect the environment. Many people want to protect biodiversity in the face of development, but sometimes land is in such high demand that previously untouched land with high biodiversity has to be used for development, e.g. for housing developments on the edge of towns, or for new agricultural land in developing countries.

Revision or sleep — now that's a conflicting pressure...

Like many situations in ecology, maintaining biodiversity isn't black and white. There are lots of factors to take into account before decisions on the best way to go forward can be made.

Q1 Give an example of how biodiversity can be increased in areas that farm single crops. [2 marks]

Q2 How could wild populations of endangered species be preserved by breeding programmes? [2 marks]

Revision Questions for Topic B7

That's Topic B7 done with. I bet you're right in the mood for a long list of revision question now. You're in luck.

- Try these questions and tick off each one when you get it right.
- When you've done all the questions under a heading and are completely happy with it, tick it off.

Competition, Abiotic and Biotic Factors, and Adaptations (p.83-85) ☐

1) Define 'habitat'. ☐
2) What things do animals compete for in an ecosystem? ☐
3) What are biotic and abiotic factors? ☐
4) What are functional adaptations? ☐

Food Chains (p.86) ☐

5) What do food chains always start with? ☐
6) Explain what happens to the population size of a predator if its prey becomes more common in an ecosystem. ☐

Quadrats and Transects (p.87-88) ☐

7) Explain how a quadrat can be used to investigate the distribution of clover plants in two areas. ☐
8) Suggest why you might use a transect when investigating the distribution of organisms. ☐

The Water and Carbon Cycles (p.89-90) ☐

9) When water vapour cools and condenses in the atmosphere, what does it change into? ☐
10) Explain how microorganisms return carbon to the atmosphere. ☐

Human Impacts on the Planet (p.91-94) ☐

11) Suggest why it's important to have high biodiversity in an ecosystem. ☐
12) Name two gases linked to global warming. ☐
13) Give an example of how global warming could reduce biodiversity. ☐
14) Why might humans carry out deforestation? ☐
15) Explain why the destruction of peat bogs adds more carbon dioxide to the atmosphere. ☐
16) How can recycling programmes help to protect ecosystems? ☐

Atoms

All substances are made of atoms. They're really tiny — too small to see, even with your microscope. Atoms are so tiny that a 50p piece contains about 77 400 000 000 000 000 000 000 of them. Quite a lot then...

Atoms Contain Protons, Neutrons and Electrons

Atoms have a radius of about 0.1 nanometers (that's 1×10^{-10} m). There are a few different (and equally useful) modern models of the atom — but chemists tend to like the model below best.

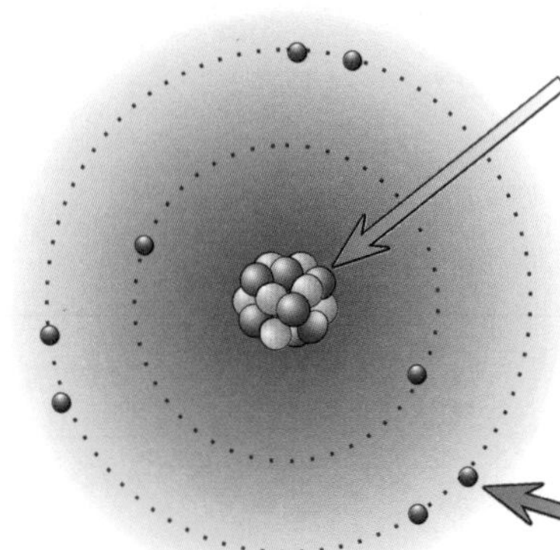

The Nucleus

1) It's in the middle of the atom.
2) It contains protons and neutrons.
3) The nucleus has a radius of around 1×10^{-14} m (that's around 1/10 000 of the radius of an atom)
4) It has a positive charge because of the protons.
5) Almost the whole mass of the atom is concentrated in the nucleus.

A nanometer (nm) is one billionth of a meter. Shown in standard form, that's 1×10^{-9} m. Standard form is used for showing really large or really small numbers.

Protons are heavy and positively charged.
Neutrons are heavy and neutral.
Electrons are tiny and negatively charged.

Particle	Relative Mass	Charge
Proton	1	+1
Neutron	1	0
Electron	Very small	–1

(Electron mass is often taken as zero.)

The Electrons

1) Move around the nucleus in electron shells.
2) They're negatively charged and tiny, but they cover a lot of space.
3) The volume of their orbits determines the size of the atom.
4) Electrons have virtually no mass.

Number of Protons Equals Number of Electrons

1) Atoms are neutral — they have no charge overall (unlike ions).
2) This is because they have the same number of protons as electrons.
3) The charge on the electrons is the same size as the charge on the protons, but opposite — so the charges cancel out.
4) In an ion, the number of protons doesn't equal the number of electrons. This means it has an overall charge. For example, an ion with a 2– charge, has two more electrons than protons.

An ion is an atom or group of atoms that has lost or gained electrons.

Atomic Number and Mass Number Describe an Atom

1) The nuclear symbol of an atom tells you its atomic (proton) number and mass number.
2) The atomic number tells you how many protons there are.
3) The mass number tells you the total number of protons and neutrons in the atom.
4) To get the number of neutrons, just subtract the atomic number from the mass number.

Let's be positive about this — unless you're an electron of course...

Atoms may be tiny, and the things inside them even smaller, but this stuff is still super important. If you can get to grips with the basic facts then you'll have a better chance understanding the rest of chemistry. Crack on.

Q1 An atom of nitrogen has an atomic number of 7 and a mass number of 14.
Give the number of electrons, protons and neutrons in the atom. [3 marks]

Elements

An element is a substance made up of atoms that all have the same number of protons in their nucleus.

Elements Consist of Atoms With the Same Atomic Number

1) Atoms can have different numbers of protons, neutrons and electrons. It's the number of protons in the nucleus that decides what type of atom it is.
2) For example, an atom with one proton in its nucleus is hydrogen and an atom with two protons is helium.
3) If a substance only contains atoms with the same number of protons it's called an element. There are about 100 different elements
4) So all the atoms of a particular element (e.g. nitrogen) have the same number of protons and different elements have atoms with different numbers of protons.

Atoms Can be Represented by Symbols

Atoms of each element can be represented by a one or two letter symbol — it's a type of shorthand that saves you the bother of having to write the full name of the element.

Some make perfect sense, e.g. C = carbon O = oxygen Mg = magnesium

Others less so, e.g. Na = sodium Fe = iron Pb = lead

You'll see these symbols on the periodic table (see page 106).

Most of these odd symbols actually come from the Latin names of the elements.

Isotopes are the Same Except for Extra Neutrons

1) Isotopes are different forms of the same element, which have the same number of protons but a different number of neutrons.
2) So isotopes have the same atomic number but different mass numbers.
3) A very popular example of a pair of isotopes are carbon-12 and carbon-13.

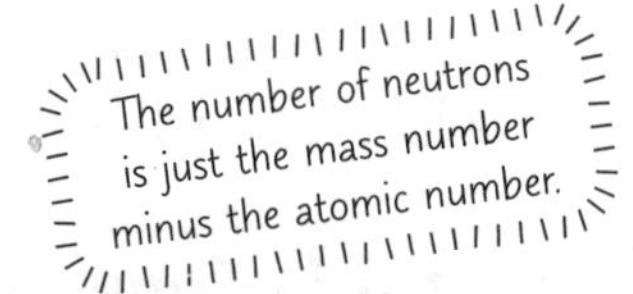

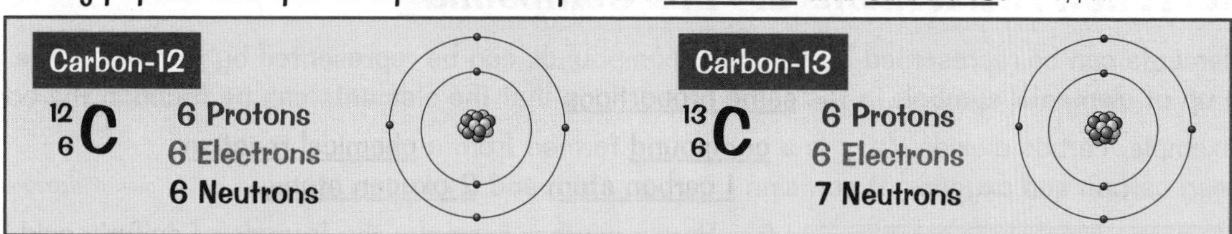

4) Because many elements can exist as a number of different isotopes, relative atomic mass (A_r) is used instead of mass number when referring to the element as a whole. This is an average mass taking into account the different masses and abundances (amounts) of all the isotopes that make up the element.
5) You can use this formula to work out the relative atomic mass of an element:

$$\text{relative atomic mass } (A_r) = \frac{\text{sum of (isotope abundance} \times \text{isotope mass number)}}{\text{sum of abundances of all the isotopes}}$$

EXAMPLE: Copper has two stable isotopes. Cu-63 has an abundance of 69.2% and Cu-65 has an abundance of 30.8%. Calculate the relative atomic mass of copper to 1 decimal place.

$$\text{Relative atomic mass} = \frac{(69.2 \times 63) + (30.8 \times 65)}{69.2 + 30.8} = \frac{4359.6 + 2002}{100} = \frac{6361.6}{100} = 63.616 = \mathbf{63.6}$$

It's elemental my dear Watson...

Atoms, elements and isotopes — make sure you know what they are and the differences between them.

Q1 A substance consists of atoms which all have the same number of protons and electrons but different numbers of neutrons. Explain why this substance is an element. [1 mark]

Q2 An isotope of iron, Fe, has a mass number of 56 and atomic number 26. Give the number of protons and neutrons in an atom of this isotope. [2 marks]

Compounds

It would be great if we only had to deal with elements. But unluckily for you, elements can mix and match to make lots of new substances called compounds. And this makes things a little bit more complicated...

Atoms Join Together to Make Compounds

1) When elements react, atoms combine with other atoms to form compounds.
2) Compounds are substances formed from two or more elements, the atoms of each are in fixed proportions throughout the compound and they're held together by chemical bonds.
3) Making bonds involves atoms giving away, taking or sharing electrons. Only the electrons are involved — the nuclei of the atoms aren't affected at all when a bond is made.
4) It's usually difficult to separate the original elements of a compound out again — a chemical reaction is needed to do this.
5) A compound which is formed from a metal and a non-metal consists of ions. The metal atoms lose electrons to form positive ions and the non-metal atoms gain electrons to form negative ions. The opposite charges (positive and negative) of the ions mean that they're strongly attracted to each other. This is called ionic bonding. Examples of compounds which are bonded ionically include sodium chloride, magnesium oxide and calcium oxide.

During a chemical reaction, at least one new substance is made. You can usually measure a change in energy, such as a temperature change, as well.

6) A compound formed from non-metals consists of molecules. Each atom shares an electron with another atom — this is called covalent bonding. Examples of compounds that are bonded covalently include hydrogen chloride gas, carbon monoxide, and water.
7) The properties of a compound are usually totally different from the properties of the original elements. For example, if iron (a lustrous magnetic metal) and sulfur (a nice yellow powder) react, the compound formed (iron sulfide) is a dull grey solid lump, and doesn't behave anything like either iron or sulfur.

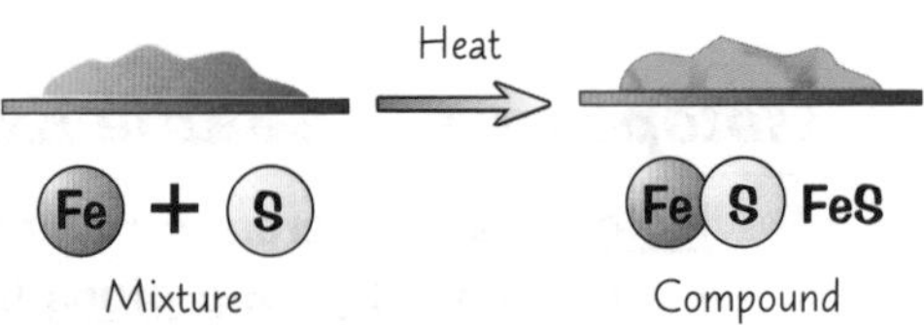

A Formula Shows What Atoms are in a Compound

Just as elements can be represented by symbols, compounds can be represented by formulas. The formulas are made up of elemental symbols in the same proportions that the elements can be found in the compound.

1) For example, carbon dioxide, CO_2, is a compound formed from a chemical reaction between carbon and oxygen. It contains 1 carbon atom and 2 oxygen atoms.

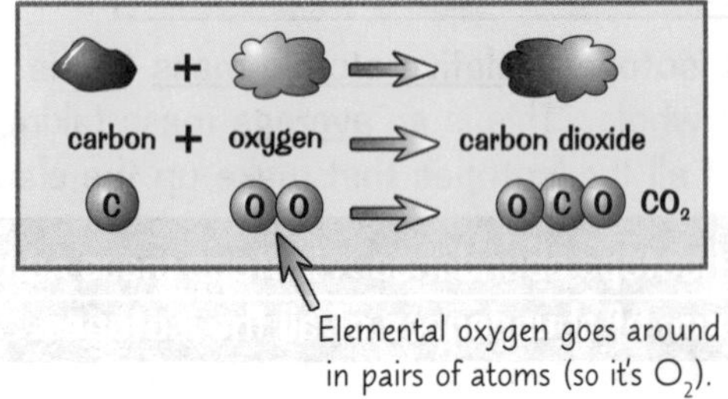

Elemental oxygen goes around in pairs of atoms (so it's O_2).

2) Here's another example: the formula of sulfuric acid is H_2SO_4. So, each molecule contains 2 hydrogen atoms, 1 sulfur atom and 4 oxygen atoms.
3) There might be brackets in a formula, e.g. calcium hydroxide is $Ca(OH)_2$. The little number outside the bracket applies to everything inside the brackets. So in $Ca(OH)_2$ there's 1 calcium atom, 2 oxygen atoms and 2 hydrogen atoms.

Here are some examples of formulas which might come in handy:

1) Carbon dioxide — CO_2	4) Sodium chloride — NaCl	7) Calcium chloride — $CaCl_2$
2) Ammonia — NH_3	5) Carbon monoxide — CO	8) Sodium carbonate — Na_2CO_3
3) Water — H_2O	6) Hydrochloric acid — HCl	9) Sulfuric acid — H_2SO_4

If you don't learn this stuff it will only compound your problems...

You know when you were little and taught to share things? Turns out atoms have been doing this since the start of the universe. Maybe we could all learn a thing or two from those little guys.

Q1 How many atoms are in one particle of Na_2CO_3? [1 mark]

Q2 A compound has the formula $CaCl_2$. Name the compound and the elements it contains. [2 marks]

Chemical Equations

Chemical equations are fundamental to chemistry. Pretty much like tomato ketchup is to a bacon butty. Mmm... bacon butties... Sorry, I got distracted. Let's do this.

Chemical Changes are Shown Using Chemical Equations

One way to show a chemical reaction is to write a word equation. It's not as quick as using chemical symbols and you can't tell straight away what's happened to each of the atoms, but it's dead easy.

Here's an example — you're told that methane burns in oxygen giving carbon dioxide and water:

The molecules on the left-hand side of the equation are called the reactants (because they react with each other).

methane + oxygen → carbon dioxide + water

The molecules on the right-hand side are called the products (because they've been produced from the reactants).

Symbol Equations Show the Atoms on Both Sides

Chemical changes can be shown in a kind of shorthand using symbol equations. Symbol equations just show the symbols or formulas of the reactants and products...

magnesium + oxygen	→	magnesium oxide
$2Mg + O_2$	→	$2MgO$

You'll have spotted that there's a '2' in front of the Mg and the MgO. The reason for this is explained below...

Symbol Equations Need to be Balanced

1) There must always be the same number of atoms on both sides — they can't just disappear.
2) You balance the equation by putting numbers in front of the formulas where needed. Take this equation for reacting sulfuric acid with sodium hydroxide:

$$H_2SO_4 + NaOH \rightarrow Na_2SO_4 + H_2O$$

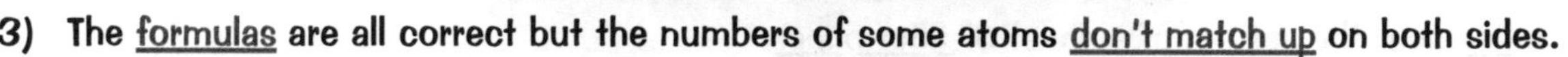

3) The formulas are all correct but the numbers of some atoms don't match up on both sides.
4) You can't change formulas like H_2SO_4 to H_2SO_5. You can only put numbers in front of them.

$E=mc^2$

The more you practise, the quicker you get, but all you do is this:

1) Find an element that doesn't balance and pencil in a number to try and sort it out.
2) See where it gets you. It may create another imbalance, but if so, pencil in another number and see where that gets you.
3) Carry on chasing unbalanced elements and it'll sort itself out pretty quickly.

EXAMPLE: In the equation above you'll notice we're short of H atoms on the RHS (Right-Hand Side).

1) The only thing you can do about that is make it $2H_2O$ instead of just H_2O:

$$H_2SO_4 + NaOH \rightarrow Na_2SO_4 + 2H_2O$$

2) But that now gives too many H atoms and O atoms on the RHS, so to balance that up you could try putting 2NaOH on the LHS (Left-Hand Side):

$$H_2SO_4 + 2NaOH \rightarrow Na_2SO_4 + 2H_2O$$

3) And suddenly there it is! Everything balances. And you'll notice the Na just sorted itself out.

Revision is all about getting the balance right...

Balancing equations is all about practice. Once you have a few goes you'll see it's much less scary than it seemed before you took on, challenged and defeated this page. Go grab some chemistry glory.

Q1 Balance the equation: $Fe + Cl_2 \rightarrow FeCl_3$ [1 mark]

Q2 Hydrogen and oxygen molecules are formed in a reaction where water splits apart. For this reaction: a) State the word equation. b) Give a balanced symbol equation. [3 marks]

Mixtures and Chromatography

Mixtures in chemistry are just like mixtures in baking, lots of separate things all mixed together. But most of the time they're considerably less delicious. And you probably shouldn't eat them. Or put them in an oven.

Mixtures are Easily Separated — Not Like Compounds

1) Unlike in a compound, there's no chemical bond between the different parts of a mixture.
2) The parts of a mixture can be either elements or compounds, and they can be separated out by physical methods such as filtration (p. 101), crystallisation (p.101), simple distillation (p.102), fractional distillation (p.102) and chromatography (see below).

A physical method is one that doesn't involve a chemical reaction, so doesn't form any new substances.

3) Air is a mixture of gases, mainly nitrogen, oxygen, carbon dioxide and argon. The gases can all be separated out fairly easily.
4) Crude oil is a mixture of different length hydrocarbon molecules.
5) The properties of a mixture are just a mixture of the properties of the separate parts — the chemical properties of a substance aren't affected by it being part of a mixture.

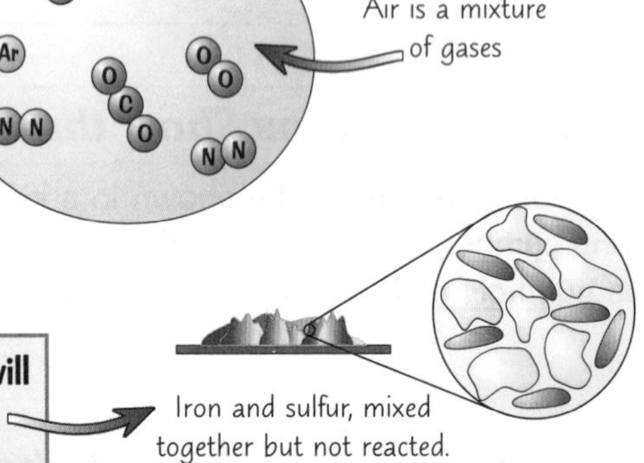

For example, a mixture of iron powder and sulfur powder will show the properties of both iron and sulfur. It will contain grey magnetic bits of iron and bright yellow bits of sulfur.

Iron and sulfur, mixed together but not reacted.

You Need to Know How to Do Paper Chromatography

PRACTICAL

One method of separating substances in a mixture is through chromatography.
This technique can be used to separate different dyes in an ink. Here's how you can do it:

1) Draw a line near the bottom of a sheet of filter paper. (Use a pencil to do this — pencil marks are insoluble and won't dissolve in the solvent.)
2) Add a spot of the ink to the line and place the sheet in a beaker of solvent, e.g water.
3) The solvent used depends on what's being tested. Some compounds dissolve well in water, but sometimes other solvents, like ethanol, are needed.

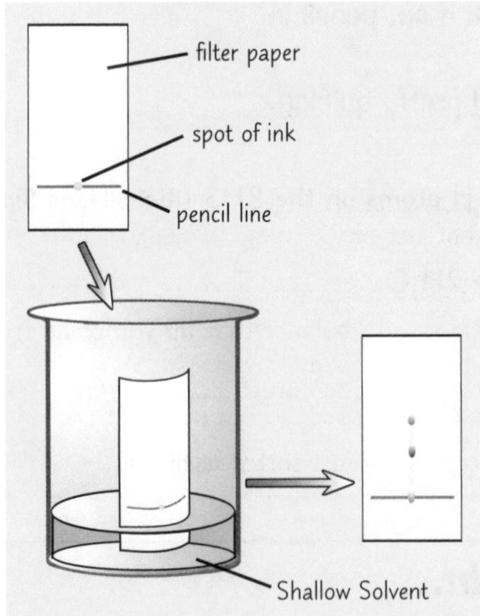

4) Make sure the ink isn't touching the solvent — you don't want it to dissolve into it.
5) Place a lid on top of the container to stop the solvent evaporating.
6) The solvent seeps up the paper, carrying the ink with it.
7) Each different dye in the ink will move up the paper at a different rate so the dyes will separate out. Each dye will form a spot in a different place — 1 spot per dye in the ink.
8) If any of the dyes in the ink are insoluble (won't dissolve) in the solvent you've used, they'll stay on the baseline.
9) When the solvent has nearly reached the top of the paper, take the paper out of the beaker and leave it to dry.
10) The end result is a pattern of spots called a chromatogram.

The point the solvent has reached as it moves up the paper is the solvent front.

Chemistry and fun are a mixture — easily separated...

Chromatography is actually mighty useful in real life. It's used to test athletes' urine samples for performance enhancing drugs, and also to test unknown substances at crime scenes. Eeek...

Q1 Explain why you shouldn't use a pen to draw a line on the filter paper for paper chromatography. [1 mark]

More Separation Techniques

PRACTICAL

Filtration and crystallisation are methods of separating mixtures. Chemists use these techniques all the time to separate solids from liquids, so it's worth making sure you know how to do them.

Filtration Separates Insoluble Solids from Liquids

1) Filtration can be used if your product is an insoluble solid that needs to be separated from a liquid reaction mixture.
2) It can be used in purification as well. For example, solid impurities in the reaction mixture can be separated out using filtration.

Insoluble means the solid can't be dissolved in the liquid.

Filter paper folded into a cone shape — the solid is left in the filter paper.

Two Ways to Separate Soluble Solids from Solutions

If a solid can be dissolved it's described as being soluble. There are two methods you can use to separate a soluble salt from a solution — evaporation and crystallisation.

Evaporation

1) Pour the solution into an evaporating dish.
2) Slowly heat the solution. The solvent will evaporate and the solution will get more concentrated. Eventually, crystals will start to form.
3) Keep heating the evaporating dish until all you have left are dry crystals.

evaporating dish

You don't have to use a Bunsen burner, you could use a water bath, or an electric heater.

Evaporation is a really quick way of separating a soluble salt from a solution, but you can only use it if the salt doesn't decompose (break down) when its heated. Otherwise, you'll have to use crystallisation.

Crystallisation

1) Pour the solution into an evaporating dish and gently heat the solution. Some of the solvent will evaporate and the solution will get more concentrated.
2) Once some of the solvent has evaporated, or when you see crystals start to form (the point of crystallisation), remove the dish from the heat and leave the solution to cool.
3) The salt should start to form crystals as it becomes insoluble in the cold, highly concentrated solution.
4) Filter the crystals out of the solution, and leave them in a warm place to dry. You could also use a drying oven or a desiccator.

You should also use crystallisation if you want to make nice big crystals of your salt.

Salt crystallising out of solution.

Filtration and Crystallisation can be Used to Separate Rock Salt

1) Rock salt is simply a mixture of salt and sand (they spread it on the roads in winter).
2) Salt and sand are both compounds — but salt dissolves in water and sand doesn't. This vital difference in their physical properties gives a great way to separate them. Here's what to do...

1) Grind the mixture to make sure the salt crystals are small, so will dissolve easily.
2) Put the mixture in water and stir. The salt will dissolve, but the sand won't.
3) Filter the mixture. The grains of sand won't fit through the tiny holes in the filter paper, so they collect on the paper instead. The salt passes through the filter paper as it's part of the solution.
4) Evaporate the water from the salt so that it forms dry crystals.

You can heat the mixture to help dissolve the salt.

You could also use crystallisation here if you wanted to make nice, big crystals.

Revise mixtures — just filter out the important bits...

Two out of three pages on separating mixtures done, phew... But before you dash on to the next page (I know, it's just so exciting), make sure you know this page to a T. Talking about Tea, I need a cuppa...

Q1 A student needs to produce pure crystals of copper sulfate from an aqueous solution of copper sulfate. Describe how the student could use crystallisation for this process. [4 marks]

Distillation

Distillation is used to separate mixtures which contain liquids. There are two types that you should know about — simple and fractional. Hopefully, this page will 'distil' everything you need to know... ho ho.

Simple Distillation is Used to Separate Out Solutions

PRACTICAL

1) Simple distillation is used for separating out a liquid from a solution.
2) The solution is heated. The part of the solution that has the lowest boiling point evaporates first.
3) The vapour is then cooled, condenses (turns back into a liquid) and is collected.
4) The rest of the solution is left behind in the flask.
5) You can use simple distillation to get pure water from seawater. The water evaporates and is condensed and collected. Eventually you'll end up with just the salt left in the flask.
6) The problem with simple distillation is that you can only use it to separate things with very different boiling points — if the temperature goes higher than the boiling point of the substance with the higher boiling point, they will mix again.
7) If you have a mixture of liquids with similar boiling points you need another method to separate them — like fractional distillation...

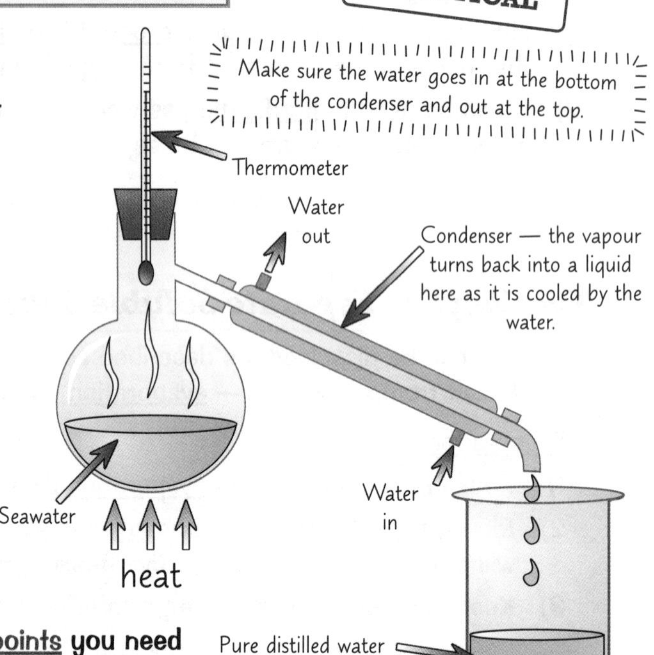

Fractional Distillation is Used to Separate a Mixture of Liquids

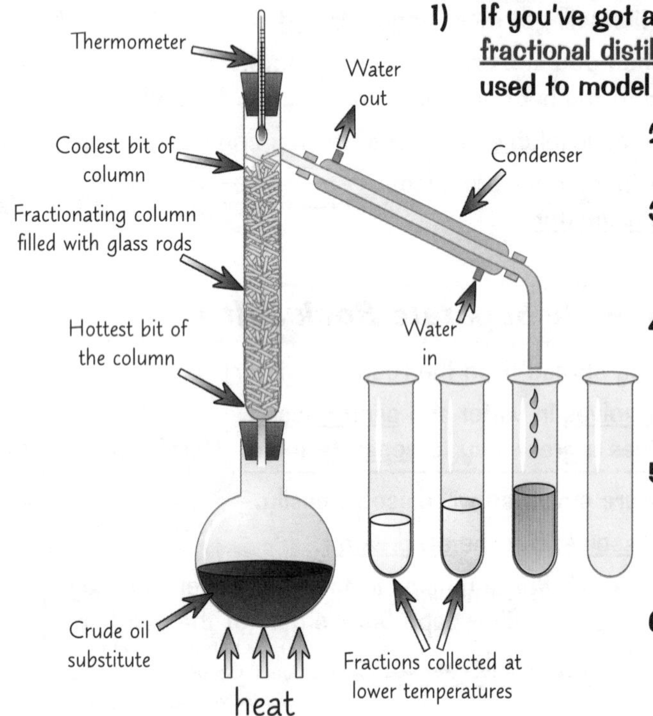

1) If you've got a mixture of liquids you can separate it using fractional distillation. Here is a lab demonstration that can be used to model fractional distillation of crude oil at a refinery.
2) You put your mixture in a flask and stick a fractionating column on top. Then you heat it.
3) The different liquids will all have different boiling points — so they will evaporate at different temperatures.
4) The liquid with the lowest boiling point evaporates first. When the temperature on the thermometer matches the boiling point of this liquid, it will reach the top of the column.
5) Liquids with higher boiling points might also start to evaporate. But the column is cooler towards the top. So they will only get part of the way up before condensing and running back down towards the flask.
6) When the first liquid has been collected, you raise the temperature until the next one reaches the top.

Fractionating — sounds a bit too much like maths to me...

You made it to the end of separation techniques. Congratulations. Now all you need to do is learn these techniques. Shouldn't be too tricky. Make sure you scribble all this stuff down — you'd be crazy not to.

Q1 Propan-1-ol, methanol and ethanol have boiling points of 97 °C, 65 °C and 78 °C respectively. A student uses fractional distillation to separate a mixture of these compounds. State which liquid will be collected in the second fraction and explain why. [2 marks]

The History of the Atom

You might have thought you were done with the atom after page 96. Unfortunately amigo, you don't get away that easily — there's more you need to learn. Hold on to your hat, you're going on a journey through time...

The Theory of Atomic Structure Has Changed Over Time

1) At the start of the 19th century John Dalton described atoms as solid spheres, and said that different spheres made up the different elements.
2) In 1897 J J Thomson concluded from his experiments that atoms weren't solid spheres. His measurements of charge and mass showed that an atom must contain even smaller, negatively charged particles — electrons. The 'solid sphere' idea of atomic structure had to be changed. The new theory was known as the 'plum pudding model'.
3) The plum pudding model showed the atom as a ball of positive charge with electrons stuck in it.

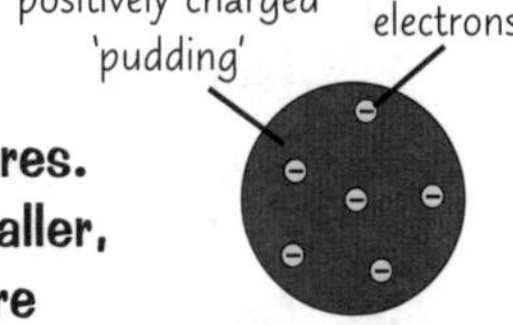

delicious pudding

Rutherford Showed that the Plum Pudding Model Was Wrong

1) In 1909 Ernest Rutherford and his student Ernest Marsden conducted the famous alpha particle scattering experiments. They fired positively charged alpha particles at an extremely thin sheet of gold.
2) From the plum pudding model, they were expecting the particles to pass straight through the sheet or be slightly deflected at most. This was because the positive charge of each atom was thought to be very spread out through the 'pudding' of the atom. But, whilst most of the particles did go straight through the gold sheet, some were deflected more than expected, and a small number were deflected backwards. So the plum pudding model couldn't be right.
3) Rutherford came up with an idea to explain this new evidence — the nuclear model of the atom. In this, there's a tiny, positively charged nucleus at the centre, where most of the mass is concentrated. A 'cloud' of negative electrons surrounds this nucleus — so most of the atom is empty space. When alpha particles came near the concentrated, positive charge of the nucleus, they were deflected. If they were fired directly at the nucleus, they were deflected backwards. Otherwise, they passed through the empty space.

A few particles are deflected backwards by the nucleus.

Most of the particles pass through empty space, but a few are deflected.

Bohr's Nuclear Model Explains a Lot

1) Scientists realised that electrons in a 'cloud' around the nucleus of an atom, as Rutherford described, would be attracted to the nucleus, causing the atom to collapse. Niels Bohr's nuclear model of the atom suggested that all the electrons were contained in shells.
2) Bohr proposed that electrons orbit the nucleus in fixed shells and aren't anywhere in between. Each shell is a fixed distance from the nucleus.
3) Bohr's theory of atomic structure was supported by many experiments and it helped to explain lots of other scientists' observations at the time.

nucleus
shells
electrons

Further Experiments Showed the Existence of Protons

1) Further experiments by Rutherford and others showed that the nucleus can be divided into smaller particles, which each have the same charge as a hydrogen nucleus. These particles were named protons.
2) About 20 years after scientists had accepted that atoms have nuclei, James Chadwick carried out an experiment which provided evidence for neutral particles in the nucleus which are now called neutrons. The discovery of neutrons resulted in a model of the atom which was pretty close to the modern day accepted version, known as the nuclear model (see page 96).

I wanted to be a model — but I ate too much plum pudding...

In science, other people's work is constantly being built upon — increasing our understanding of a topic.

Q1 Describe the 'plum pudding' model of the atom. [1 mark]

Q2 Rutherford devised an experiment where alpha particles were fired through gold foil. Most of the particles passed through the foil, but some were deflected by different angles, and some were even deflected backwards. Explain why this disproves the plum pudding model. [2 marks]

Electronic Structure

The fact that electrons occupy 'shells' around the nucleus is what causes the whole of chemistry. Remember that, and watch how it applies to each bit of it. It's ace.

Electron Shell Rules:

1) Electrons always occupy shells (sometimes called energy levels).
2) The lowest energy levels are always filled first — these are the ones closest to the nucleus.
3) Only a certain number of electrons are allowed in each shell:
   1st shell: 2   2nd shell: 8   3rd shell: 8
4) Atoms are much happier when they have full electron shells — like the noble gases in Group 0.
5) In most atoms, the outer shell is not full and this makes the atom want to react to fill it.

Electron configurations can be shown as diagrams like this...

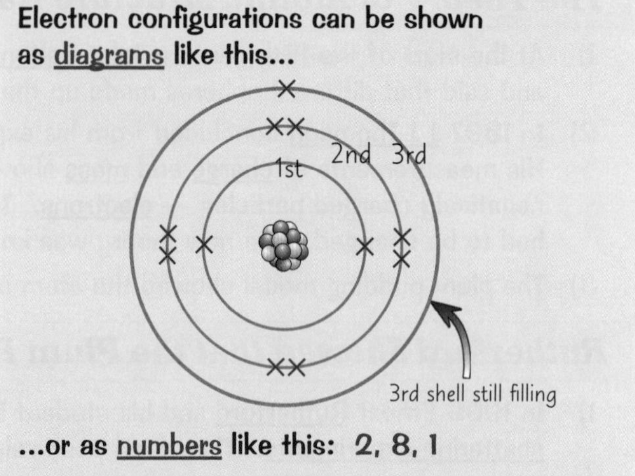

...or as numbers like this: 2, 8, 1

Both of the configurations above are for sodium.

Follow the Rules to Work Out Electronic Structures

You can easily work out the electronic structures for the first 20 elements of the periodic table (things get a bit more complicated after that).

What is the electronic structure of nitrogen?

1) Nitrogen's atomic number is 7. This means it has 7 protons... so it must have 7 electrons.
2) Follow the 'Electron Shell Rules' above. The first shell can only take 2 electrons and the second shell can take a maximum of 8 electrons.

So the electronic structure for nitrogen must be 2, 5.

What is the electronic structure of magnesium?

1) Magnesium's atomic number is 12. This means it has 12 protons... so it must have 12 electrons.
2) Follow the 'Electron Shell Rules' above. The first shell can only take 2 electrons and the second shell can take a maximum of 8 electrons, so the third shell must also be partially filled.

So the electronic structure for magnesium must be 2, 8, 2

Here are some more examples of electronic structures:

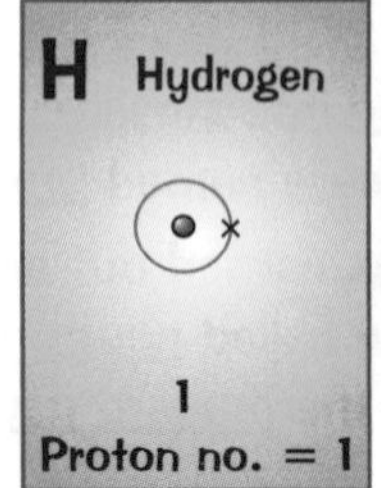

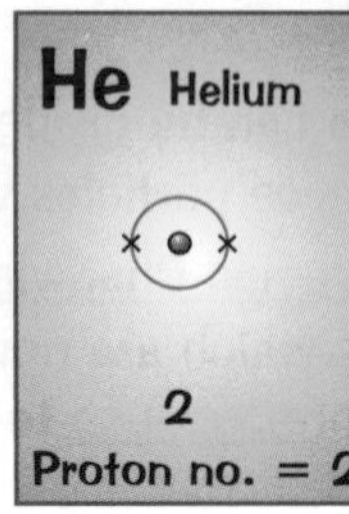

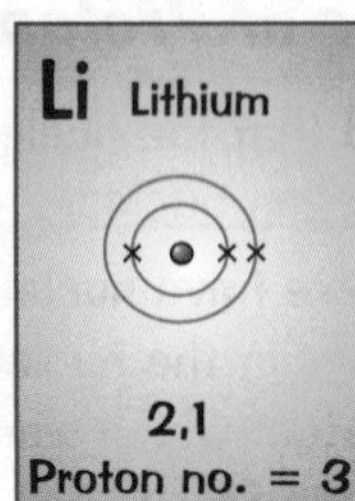

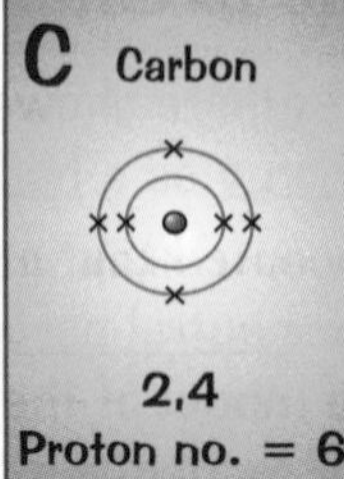

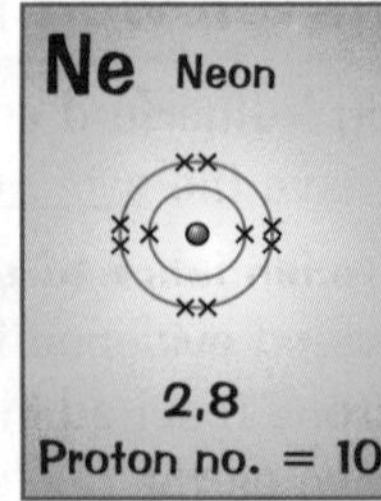

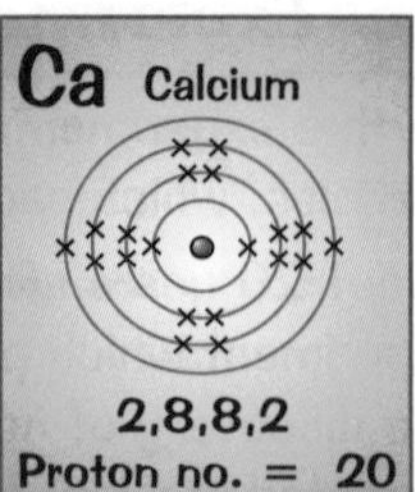

The electronic structure of the fifth element — it's a bit boron...

Electronic structures may seem a bit complicated at first but once you learn the rules, it's a piece of cake. And just like cake, you'll never regret going back for some more. Better get practising.

Q1 Give the electronic structure of aluminium (atomic number = 13). [1 mark]

Q2 Give the electronic structure of argon (atomic number = 18). [1 mark]

Development of the Periodic Table

We haven't always known as much about chemistry as we do now. No sirree. Early chemists looked to try and understand patterns in the elements' properties to get a bit of understanding.

In the Early 1800s Elements Were Arranged By Atomic Mass

Until quite recently, there were two obvious ways to categorise elements:

1) Their physical and chemical properties. 2) Their relative atomic mass.

Remember — the relative atomic mass is the average mass of one atom of an element.

1) Remember, scientists had no idea of atomic structure or of protons, neutrons or electrons, so there was no such thing as atomic number to them. (It was only in the 20th century after protons and electrons were discovered that it was realised the elements were best arranged in order of atomic number.)
2) Back then, the only thing they could measure was relative atomic mass, and so the known elements were arranged in order of atomic mass. When this was done, a periodic pattern was noticed in the properties of the elements. This is where the name 'periodic table' comes from — ta da...
3) Early periodic tables were not complete and some elements were placed in the wrong group. This is because elements were placed in the order of relative atomic mass and did not take into account their properties.

Dmitri Mendeleev Left Gaps and Predicted New Elements

1) In 1869, Dmitri Mendeleev overcame some of the problems of early periodic tables by taking 50 known elements and arranging them into his Table of Elements — with various gaps as shown.

Mendeleev's Table of the Elements

H																
Li	Be											B	C	N	O	F
Na	Mg											Al	Si	P	S	Cl
K	Ca	*	Ti	V	Cr	Mn	Fe	Co	Ni	Cu	Zn	*	*	As	Se	Br
Rb	Sr	Y	Zr	Nb	Mo	*	Ru	Rh	Pd	Ag	Cd	In	Sn	Sb	Te	I
Cs	Ba	*	*	Ta	W	*	Os	Ir	Pt	Au	Hg	Tl	Pb	Bi		

2) Mendeleev put the elements mainly in order of atomic mass but did switch that order if the properties meant it should be changed. An example of this can been seen with Te and I — iodine actually has a smaller relative atomic mass but is placed after tellurium as it has similar properties to the elements in that group.
3) Gaps were left in the table to make sure that elements with similar properties stayed in the same groups. Some of these gaps indicated the existence of undiscovered elements and allowed Mendeleev to predict what their properties might be. When they were found and they fitted the pattern it helped confirm Mendeleev's ideas. For example, Mendeleev made really good predictions about the chemical and physical properties of an element he called ekasilicon, which we know today as germanium.

The discovery of isotopes (see page 97) in the early 20th century confirmed that Mendeleev was correct to not place elements in a strict order of atomic mass but to also take account of their properties. Isotopes of the same element have different atomic masses but have the same chemical properties so occupy the same position on the periodic table.

You should come back to this page periodically...

Ahh more history... This is science at its best, discoveries building upon discoveries — all leading to the point where you have to learn it. Mendeleev would be proud... of himself and you of course.

Q1 How were elements classified in the early 1800s? [1 mark]

Q2 Describe two changes that Mendeleev made to early periodic tables. [2 marks]

The Modern Periodic Table

So, as you've seen it took a while to get to the periodic table that you will (soon) know and love. I present to you a chemist's best friend...

The Periodic Table Helps you to See Patterns in Properties

1) There are 100ish elements, which all materials are made of.
2) In the periodic table the elements are laid out in order of increasing atomic (proton) number. Arranging the elements like this means there are repeating patterns in the properties of the elements. (The properties are said to occur periodically, hence the name periodic table.)
3) If it wasn't for the periodic table organising everything, you'd have a heck of a job remembering all those properties. It's ace.
4) It's a handy tool for working out which elements are metals and which are non-metals. Metals are found to the left and non-metals to the right.

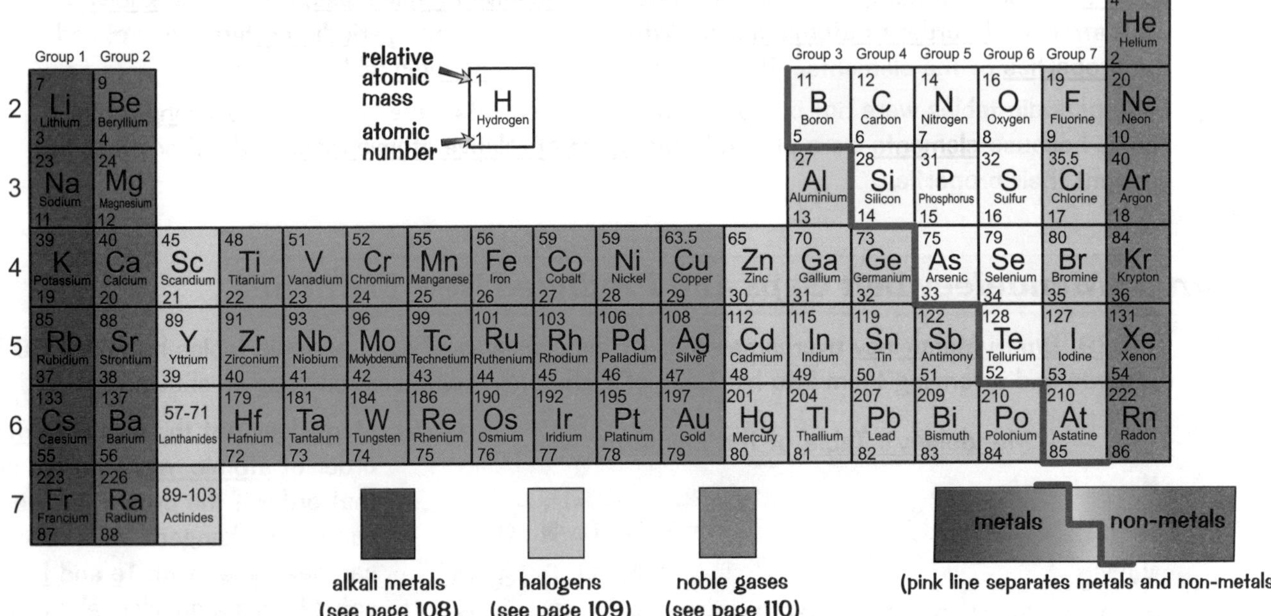

5) Elements with similar properties form columns.
6) These vertical columns are called groups.
7) The group number tells you how many electrons there are in the outer shell. For example, Group 1 elements all have one electron in their outer shell and Group 7 all have seven electrons in their outer shell. The exception to the rule is group 0, for example Helium has two electrons in its outer shell. This is useful as the way atoms react depends upon the number of electrons in their outer shell. So all elements in the same group are likely to react in a similar way.
8) If you know the properties of one element, you can predict properties of other elements in that group — and in the exam, you might be asked to do this. For example the Group 1 elements are Li, Na, K, Rb, Cs and Fr. They're all metals and they react in a similar way (see page 108).
9) You can also make predictions about trends in reactivity. E.g. in Group 1, the elements react more vigorously as you go down the group. And in Group 7, reactivity decreases as you go down the group.
10) The rows are called periods. Each new period represents another full shell of electrons.

I'm in a chemistry band — I play the symbols...

Because the periodic table is organised into groups and periods, it allows us to see trends in both reactivity and properties. And this means we can make predictions on how reactions will occur. How neat is that?

Q1 Using a periodic table, state how many electrons beryllium has in its outer shell. [1 mark]

Q2 Chlorine reacts in a similar way to bromine. Suggest a reason why. [1 mark]

Q3 Sodium readily forms 1+ ions. Suggest what ions potassium forms and explain why. [1 mark]

Metals and Non-Metals

I can almost guarantee you'll touch something metallic today, that's how important metals are to modern life.

Most Elements are Metals

1) Metals are elements which can form positive ions when they react.
2) They're towards the bottom and to the left of the periodic table.
3) Most elements in the periodic table are metals.
4) Non-metals are at the far right and top of the periodic table.
5) Non-metals don't generally form positive ions when they react.

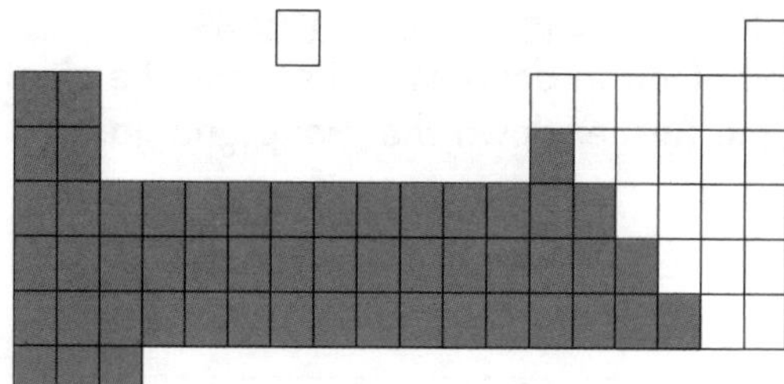

The orange elements are metals
The white elements are non-metals

The Electronic Structure of Atoms Affects How They Will React

1) Atoms generally react to form a full outer shell. They do this via losing, gaining or sharing electrons.
2) Metals to the left of the periodic table don't have many electrons to remove and metals towards the bottom of the periodic table have outer electrons which are a long way from the nucleus so feel a weaker attraction. Both these effects means that not much energy is needed to remove the electrons so it's feasible for the elements to react to form positive ions with a full outer shell.
3) For non-metals, forming positive ions is much more difficult. This is as they are either to the right of the periodic table — where they have lots of electrons to remove to get a full outer shell, or towards the top — where the outer electrons are close to the nucleus so feel a strong attraction. It's far more feasible for them to either share or gain electrons to get a full outer shell.

Metals and Non-Metals Have Different Physical Properties

1) All metals have metallic bonding which causes them to have similar basic physical properties.
   - They're strong (hard to break), but can be bent or hammered into different shapes (malleable).
   - They're great at conducting heat and electricity.
   - They have high boiling and melting points.

Don't try this at home, you'll die.

2) As non-metals don't have metallic bonding, they don't tend to exhibit the same properties as metals. They tend to be dull looking, more brittle, aren't always solids at room temperature, don't generally conduct electricity and often have a lower density.

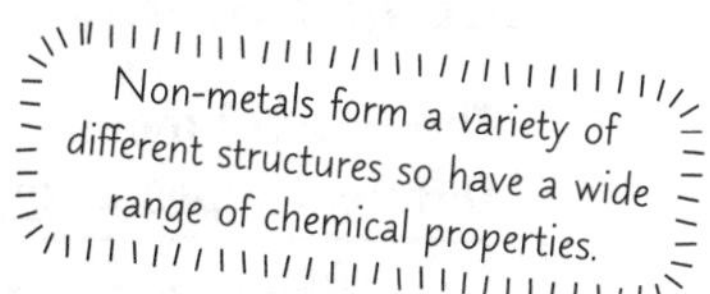

You can 'rock out' to metal, you can sway gently to non-metal...

Metals and non-metals are like chalk and cheese... Though I hope there's no metal in your cheese.

Q1 Iodine generally reacts by forming negative ions. Is iodine a metal or a non-metal? [1 mark]

Q2 State three properties of metals. [3 marks]

Q3 State whether metals generally form positive or negative ions. Explain why they form these ions with reference to their position in the periodic table. [4 marks]

Group 1 Elements

Group 1 elements are known as the alkali metals. As metals go, they're pretty reactive.

The Group 1 Elements are Reactive, Soft Metals

1) The alkali metals are lithium, sodium, potassium, rubidium, caesium and francium.
2) They all have one electron in their outer shell which makes them very reactive and gives them similar properties.
3) The alkali metals are all soft and have low density.
4) The trends for the alkali metals as you go down Group 1 include:
   - Increasing reactivity — the outer electron is more easily lost as the attraction between the nucleus and electron decreases, because the electron is further away from the nucleus the further down the group you go.
   - Lower melting and boiling points.
   - Higher relative atomic mass.

Alkali Metals Form Ionic Compounds with Non-Metals

Don't worry, there's more on ionic compounds on page 114.

1) The Group 1 elements don't need much energy to lose their one outer electron to form a full outer shell, so they readily form 1+ ions.
2) It's so easy for them to lose their outer electron that they only ever react to form ionic compounds. These compounds are generally white solids that dissolve in water to form colourless solutions.

Reaction with Water Produces Hydrogen Gas

1) When Group 1 metals are put in water, they react very vigorously.
2) The more reactive (lower down in the group) an alkali metal is, the more violent the reaction.
3) Lithium, sodium and potassium float and move around the surface, fizzing furiously.
4) They produce hydrogen. The amount of energy given out when they react increases down the group. For potassium and below in the group, there's enough energy to ignite hydrogen.
5) They also form hydroxides that dissolve in water to give alkaline solutions.

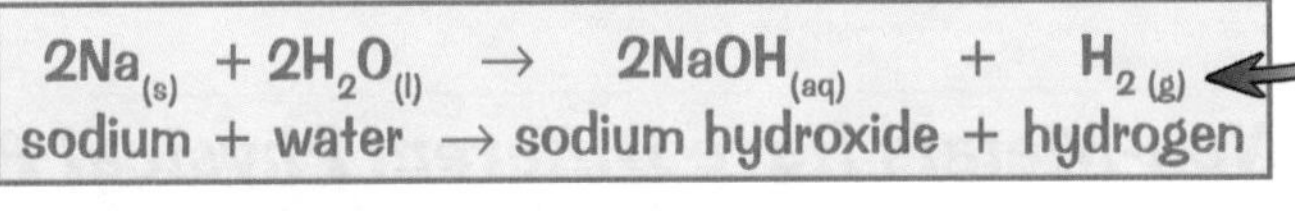

$$2Na_{(s)} + 2H_2O_{(l)} \rightarrow 2NaOH_{(aq)} + H_{2\,(g)}$$

sodium + water → sodium hydroxide + hydrogen

The other Group 1 metals react with water in a similar way.

Reaction with Chlorine Produces a Salt

1) Group 1 metals react vigorously when heated in chlorine gas to form white salts called metal chlorides.
2) As you go down the group, reactivity increases so the reaction with chlorine gets more vigorous.

$$2Na_{(s)} + Cl_{2(g)} \rightarrow 2NaCl_{(s)}$$

sodium + chlorine → sodium chloride

Group 1 Metals React with Oxygen

- The Group 1 metals can react with oxygen to form a metal oxide. Different types of oxide will form depending on the Group 1 metal.

The reactions with oxygen are why Group 1 metals tarnish in the air — the metal reacts with oxygen in the air to form a dull metal oxide layer.

- Lithium reacts to form lithium oxide (Li_2O).
- Sodium reacts to form a mixture of sodium oxide (Na_2O) and sodium peroxide (Na_2O_2).
- Potassium reacts to form a mixture of potassium peroxide (K_2O_2) and potassium superoxide (KO_2).

Back to the drawing board with my lithium swim shorts design...

Reactions of alkali metals need safety precautions, but they fizz in water and might explode. Cool.

Q1 Explain the trend in reactivity as you go down Group 1. [2 marks]

Q2 Write a balanced equation for the reaction between potassium and water. [2 marks]

Group 7 Elements

The Group 7 elements are known as the halogens. The whole 'trend thing' happens with the halogens as well — that shouldn't come as a surprise.

The Halogens are All Non-Metals with Coloured Vapours

Fluorine is a very reactive, poisonous yellow gas.
Chlorine is a fairly reactive, poisonous dense green gas.
Bromine is a dense, poisonous, red-brown volatile liquid.
Iodine is a dark grey crystalline solid or a purple vapour.
They all exist as molecules which are pairs of atoms.

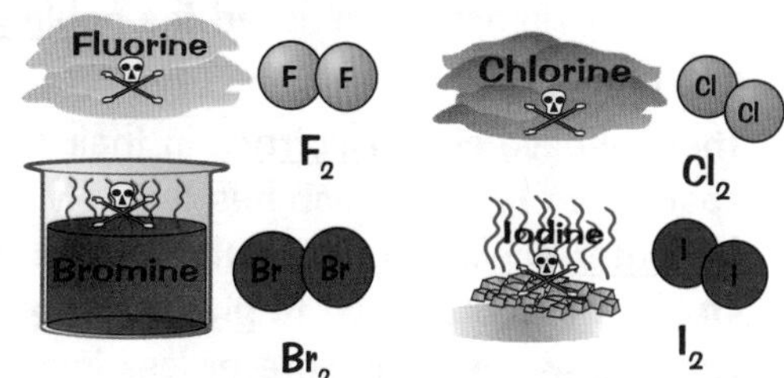

Learn These Trends:

As you go DOWN Group 7, the halogens:

1) become LESS REACTIVE — it's harder to gain an extra electron, because the outer shell's further from the nucleus.
2) have HIGHER MELTING AND BOILING POINTS.
3) have HIGHER RELATIVE ATOMIC MASSES.

All the Group 7 elements react in similar ways. This is because they all have seven electrons in their outer shell.

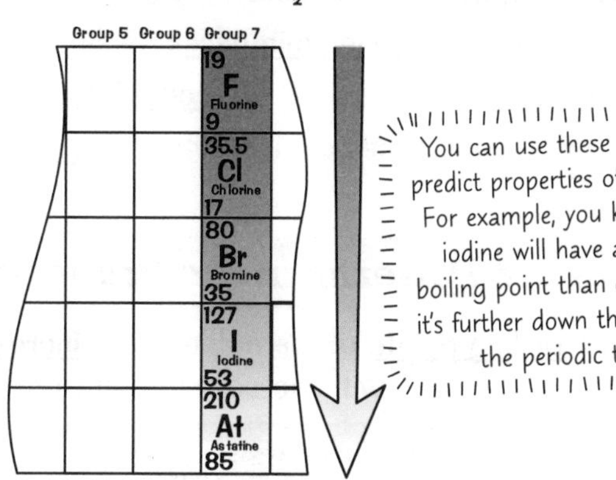

You can use these trends to predict properties of halogens. For example, you know that iodine will have a higher boiling point than chlorine as it's further down the group in the periodic table.

Halogens can Form Molecular Compounds

Halogen atoms can share electrons via covalent bonding (see page 115) with other non-metals so as to achieve a full outer shell. For example HCl, PCl_5, HF and CCl_4 contain covalent bonds. The compounds that form when halogens react with non-metals all have simple molecular structures (see p.116).

Halogens Form Ionic Bonds with Metals

1) The halogens form 1– ions called halides (F^-, Cl^-, Br^- and I^-) when they bond with metals, for example Na^+Cl^- or $Fe^{3+}Br^-_3$.
2) The compounds that form have ionic structures.
3) The diagram shows the bonding in sodium chloride, NaCl.

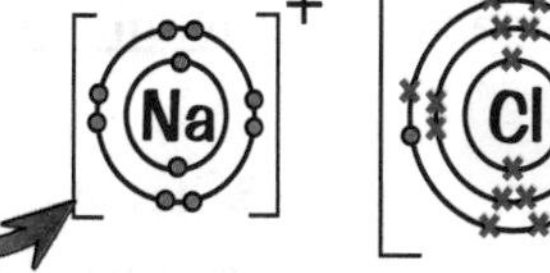

More Reactive Halogens Will Displace Less Reactive Ones

A displacement reaction can occur between a more reactive halogen and the salt of a less reactive one. E.g. chlorine can displace bromine and iodine from an aqueous solution of its salt (a bromide or iodide). Bromine will also displace iodine because of the trend in reactivity.

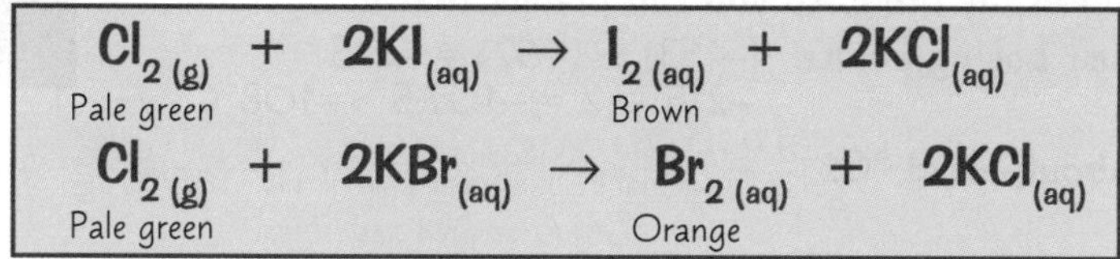

$$Cl_{2\,(g)} + 2KI_{(aq)} \rightarrow I_{2\,(aq)} + 2KCl_{(aq)}$$

Pale green — Brown

$$Cl_{2\,(g)} + 2KBr_{(aq)} \rightarrow Br_{2\,(aq)} + 2KCl_{(aq)}$$

Pale green — Orange

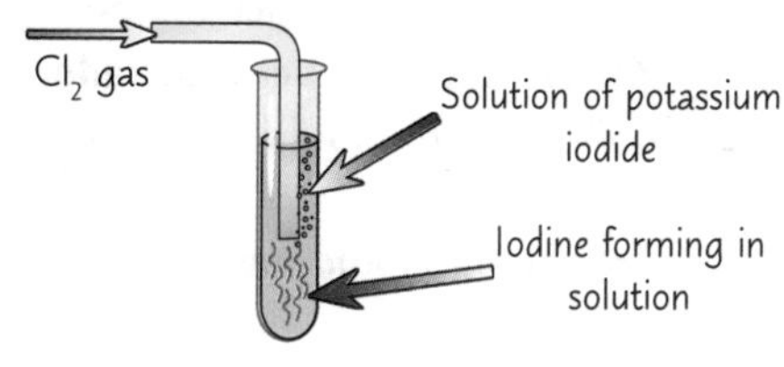

I can see your halo(gen), halo(gen) halo(gen)...

You say 'halo-gen' I say 'ha-logen', let's call the whole thing off... Apart from revision, let's call that whole thing 'on'. Displacement reactions are pretty important in chemistry — better learn the facts.

Q1 Predict whether bromine would displace iodine from sodium iodide and explain why. [2 marks]

Q2 Why do Group 7 elements get less reactive as you go down the group from fluorine to iodine? [3 marks]

Group 0 Elements

The Group 0 elements are known as noble gases — stuffed full of every honourable virtue. They don't react with very much and you can't even see them — making them, well, a bit dull really.

Group 0 Elements are All Inert, Colourless Gases

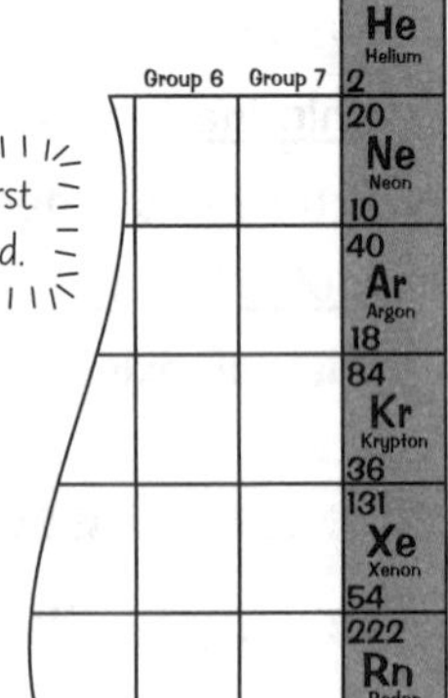

1) Group 0 elements are called the noble gases and include the elements helium, neon and argon (plus a few others).
2) They all have eight electrons in their outer energy level, apart from helium which has two, giving them a full outer-shell. As their outer shell is energetically stable they don't need to give up or gain electrons to become more stable. This means they are more or less inert — they don't react with much at all.

   Helium only has electrons in the first shell, which only needs 2 to be filled.

3) They exist as monatomic gases — single atoms not bonded to each other.
4) All elements in Group 0 are colourless gases at room temperature.
5) As the noble gases are inert they're non-flammable — they won't set on fire.

There are Patterns in the Properties of the Noble Gases

1) The boiling points of the noble gases increase as you move down the group along with increasing relative atomic mass.

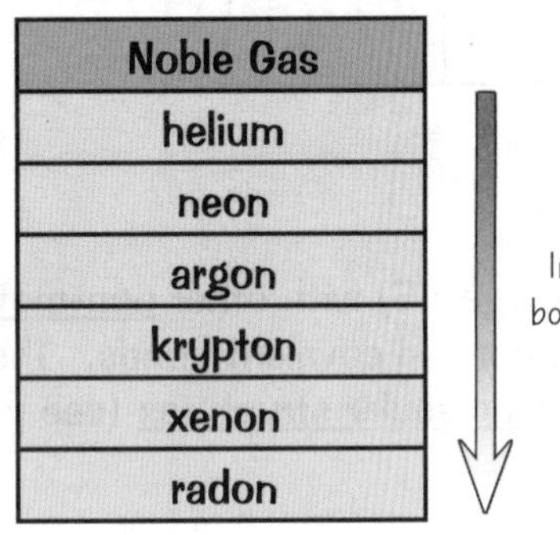

Noble Gas
helium
neon
argon
krypton
xenon
radon

2) The increase in boiling point is due to an increase in the number of electrons in each atom leading to greater intermolecular forces between them which need to be overcome. There's more on intermolecular forces for small molecules on page 116.

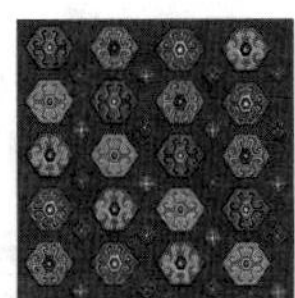
Here's another pattern. You don't have to learn this one...

3) In the exam you may be given the boiling point of one noble gas and asked to estimate the value for another one. So make sure you know the pattern.

EXAMPLE: Neon is a gas at 25 °C. Predict what state helium is at this temperature.

Helium has a lower boiling point than neon as it is further up the group.

So, helium must also be a gas at 25 °C.

EXAMPLE: Radon and krypton have boiling points of –62 °C and –153 °C respectively. Predict the boiling point of xenon.

Xenon comes in between radon and krypton in the group so you can predict that its boiling point would be halfway between their boiling points: (–153) + (–62) = –215
–215 ÷ 2 = –107.5 ≈ –108°C

So, xenon should have a boiling point of about –108 °C.

The actual boiling point of xenon is –108 °C — just as predicted. Neat!

...or this one.

Arrrgon — the pirate element...

As noble gases don't really react there isn't too much to learn about them. If you understand why they are unreactive and the trend in boiling points as you go down the group you're sorted.

Q1 Does xenon or neon have the higher boiling point? [1 mark]

Q2 Argon is very unreactive. Using your knowledge of its electronic structure, explain why. [2 marks]

Revision Questions for Topic C1

Topic C1 — finished. But hold on there my friend, don't rush on to Topic C2 just yet.
There's one more thing for you to do...

- Try these questions and tick off each one when you get it right.
- When you've done all the questions under a heading and are completely happy with it, tick it off.

Atoms, Elements and Compounds (p.96-99)

1) Sketch an atom. Label the nucleus and the electrons.
2) What is the charge of a proton?
3) True or False? Elements contain more than one type of atom.
4) Give the formula for:
   a) Carbon dioxide   b) Sodium carbonate
5) Balance these equations:
   a) $Mg + O_2 \rightarrow MgO$ b) $H_2SO_4 + NaOH \rightarrow Na_2SO_4 + H_2O$

Mixtures and Separation (p.100-102)

6) What is the difference between a compound and a mixture?
7) What is the name of the pattern formed from carrying out paper chromatography?
8) Which method of separation is useful to separate an insoluble solid from a liquid?
9) Give the name of a method to separate a soluble solid from a liquid.
10) Which method of distillation would you use to separate liquids with similar boiling points?

Electronic Structure and the History of the Periodic Table (p.103-106)

11) Who discovered that the plum pudding model was wrong?
12) Who first devised an experiment that proved the existence of the neutron?
13) What is the electronic structure of sodium?
14) Why did Mendeleev leave gaps in his Table of Elements?

Groups of the Periodic Table (p.107-110)

15) How are the group number and the number of electrons in the outer shell of an element related?
16) What kind of ions do metals form?
17) Where are non-metals on the periodic table?
18) State three trends as you go down Group 1.
19) State the products of the reaction of sodium and water.
20) How do the boiling points of halogens change as you go down the group from fluorine to astatine?
21) What is the charge of the ions that halogens form when they react with metals?
22) Predict whether iodine is displaced by chlorine in a solution of potassium iodide.
23) What is the trend in boiling point as you go down Group 0?

Formation of Ions

Ions crop up all over the place in chemistry. You're gonna have to be able to explain how they form and predict the charges of simple ions formed by elements in Groups 1, 2, 6 and 7. You'd better get on...

Ions are Made When Electrons are Transferred

1) Ions are charged particles — they can be single atoms (e.g. Cl^-) or groups of atoms (e.g. NO_3^-).
2) When atoms lose or gain electrons to form ions, all they're trying to do is get a full outer shell like a noble gas (also called a "stable electronic structure"). Atoms with full outer shells are very stable.
3) When metals form ions, they lose electrons from their outer shell to form positive ions.
4) When non-metals form ions, they gain electrons into their outer shell to form negative ions.
5) The number of electrons lost or gained is the same as the charge on the ion. E.g. If 2 electrons are lost the charge is 2+. If 3 electrons are gained the charge is 3–.

Remember that the noble gases are in Group 0 of the periodic table.

Groups 1 & 2 and 6 & 7 are the Most Likely to Form Ions

1) The elements that most readily form ions are those in Groups 1, 2, 6 and 7.
2) Group 1 and 2 elements are metals and they lose electrons to form positive ions (cations).
3) Group 6 and 7 elements are non-metals. They gain electrons to form negative ions (anions).
4) You don't have to remember what ions most elements form — nope, you just look at the periodic table.
5) Elements in the same group all have the same number of outer electrons. So they have to lose or gain the same number to get a full outer shell. And this means that they form ions with the same charges.

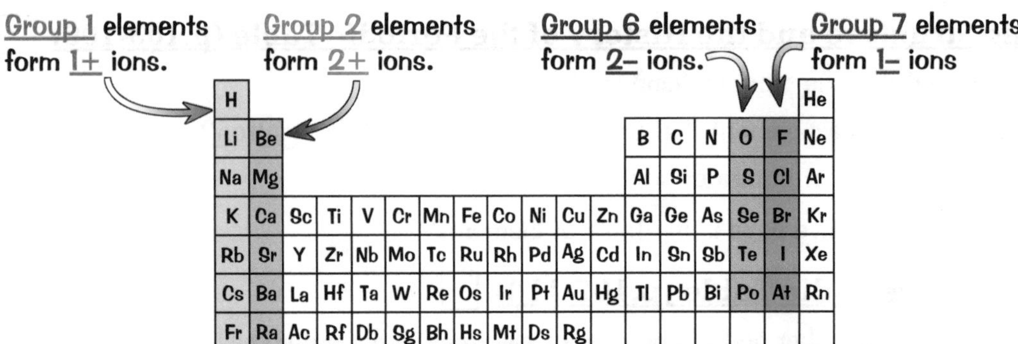

- A sodium atom (Na) is in Group 1 so it loses 1 electron to form a sodium ion (Na^+) with the same electronic structure as neon: $Na \rightarrow Na^+ + e^-$.
- A magnesium atom (Mg) is in Group 2 so it loses 2 electrons to form a magnesium ion (Mg^{2+}) with the same electronic structure as neon: $Mg \rightarrow Mg^{2+} + 2e^-$.
- A chlorine atom (Cl) is in Group 7 so it gains 1 electron to form a chloride ion (Cl^-) with the same electronic structure as argon: $Cl + e^- \rightarrow Cl^-$.
- An oxygen atom (O) is in Group 6 so it gains 2 electrons to form an oxide ion (O^{2-}) with the same electronic structure as neon: $O + 2e^- \rightarrow O^{2-}$.

Dougal was a few electrons short of a full shell.

Have a look back at page 104 for how to work out electronic structures.

I've got my ion you...

Some elements like to gain electrons, some elements like to lose electrons, but they all want to have a full outer shell. Poor little electron shells, all they want in life is to be full...

Q1 Explain why simple ions often have noble gas electronic structures. [2 marks]

Q2 Predict the charges of the ions formed by the following elements:
a) Bromine (Br) b) Calcium (Ca) c) Potassium (K) [3 marks]

Ionic Bonding

Time to find out how particles bond together to form compounds (bet you can't wait). There are three types of bonding you need to know about — ionic, covalent and metallic. First up, it's ionic bonds.

Ionic Bonding — Transfer of Electrons

When a metal and a non-metal react together, the metal atom loses electrons to form a positively charged ion and the non-metal gains these electrons to form a negatively charged ion. These oppositely charged ions are strongly attracted to one another by electrostatic forces. This attraction is called an ionic bond.

Dot and Cross Diagrams Show How Ionic Compounds are Formed

Dot and cross diagrams show the arrangement of electrons in an atom or ion. Each electron is represented by a dot or a cross. So these diagrams can show which atom the electrons in an ion originally came from.

Sodium Chloride (NaCl)

The sodium atom gives up its outer electron, becoming an Na^+ ion. The chlorine atom picks up the electron, becoming a Cl^- (chloride) ion.

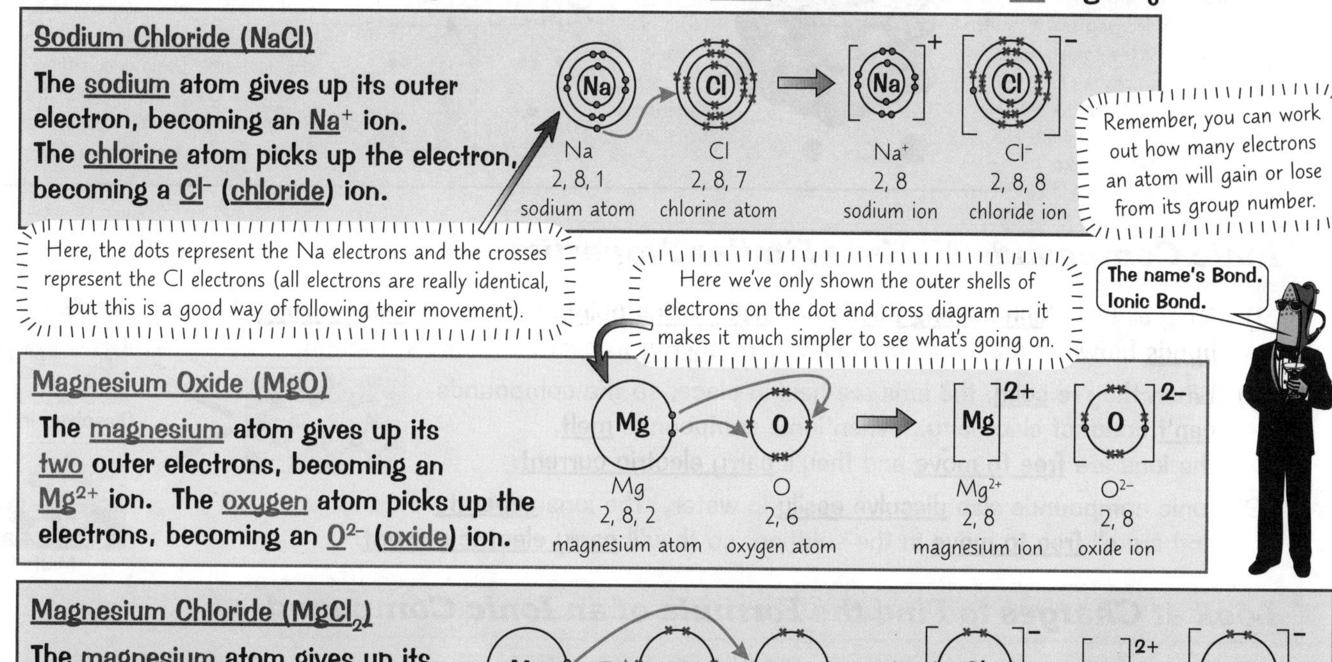

Magnesium Oxide (MgO)

The magnesium atom gives up its two outer electrons, becoming an Mg^{2+} ion. The oxygen atom picks up the electrons, becoming an O^{2-} (oxide) ion.

Magnesium Chloride ($MgCl_2$)

The magnesium atom gives up its two outer electrons, becoming an Mg^{2+} ion. The two chlorine atoms pick up one electron each, becoming two Cl^- (chloride) ions.

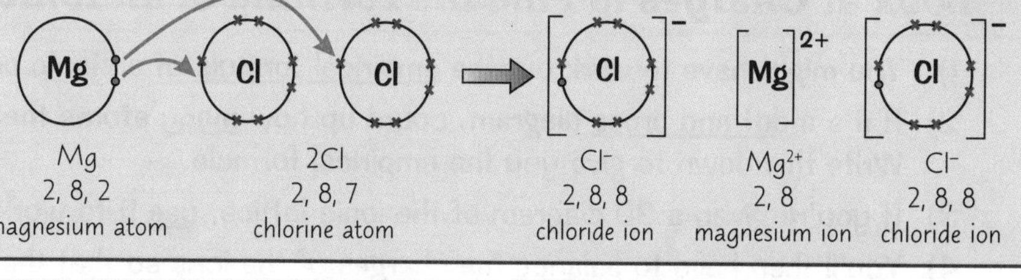

Sodium Oxide (Na_2O)

Two sodium atoms each give up their single outer electron, becoming two Na^+ ions. The oxygen atom picks up the two electrons, becoming an O^{2-} ion.

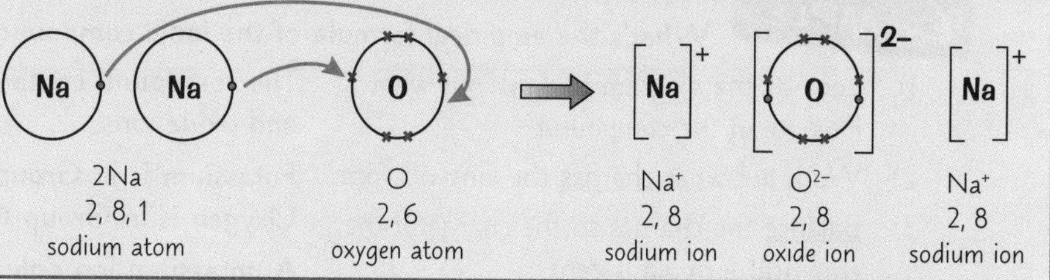

Dot and cross diagrams are useful for showing how ionic compounds are formed, but they don't show the structure of the compound, the size of the ions or how they're arranged. But hey-ho — nothing's perfect.

Any old ion, any old ion — any, any, any old ion...

You need to be able to describe how ionic compounds are formed using both words and dot and cross diagrams. It gets easier with practice, so here are some questions to get you started.

Q1 Describe, in terms of electron transfer, how sodium (Na) and chlorine (Cl) react to form sodium chloride (NaCl). [3 marks]

Q2 Draw a dot and cross diagram to show how potassium (a Group 1 metal) and bromine (a Group 7 non metal) form potassium bromide (KBr). [3 marks]

Ionic Compounds

I'd take everything on this page with a pinch of salt if I were you... Ho ho ho — I jest, it's important really.

Ionic Compounds Have A Regular Lattice Structure

The electrostatic attraction between the oppositely charged ions is ionic bonding.

1) Ionic compounds have a structure called a giant ionic lattice.
2) The ions form a closely packed regular lattice arrangement and there are very strong electrostatic forces of attraction between oppositely charged ions, in all directions in the lattice.

A single crystal of sodium chloride (table salt) is one giant ionic lattice. The Na^+ and Cl^- ions are held together in a regular lattice. The lattice can be represented in different ways...

This model shows the relative sizes of the ions, as well as the regular pattern of an ionic crystal, but it only lets you see the outer layer of the compound.

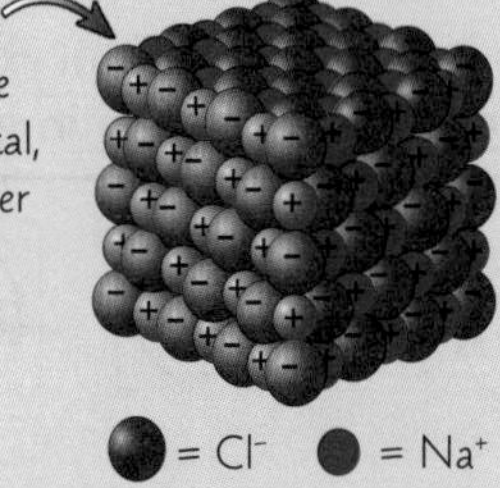

Make sure you learn what the structure of sodium chloride looks like.

The Na^+ and Cl^- ions alternate.

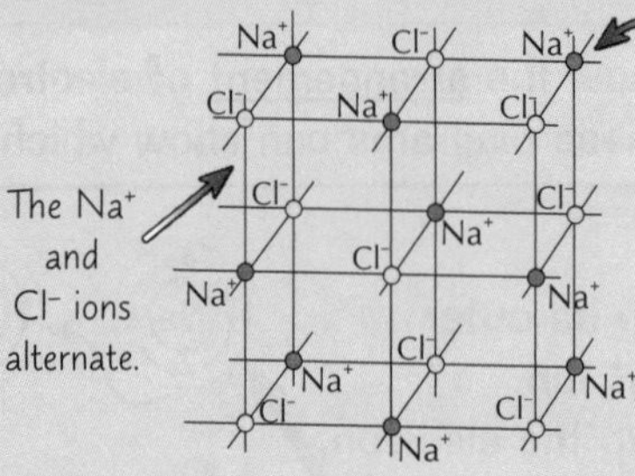

This is a ball and stick model. It shows the regular pattern of an ionic crystal and shows how all the ions are arranged. It also suggests that the crystal extends beyond what's shown in the diagram. The model isn't to scale though, so the relative sizes of the ions may not be shown. Also, in reality, there aren't gaps between the ions.

Ionic Compounds All Have Similar Properties

1) They all have high melting points and high boiling points due to the many strong bonds between the ions. It takes lots of energy to overcome this attraction.
2) When they're solid, the ions are held in place, so the compounds can't conduct electricity. When ionic compounds melt, the ions are free to move and they'll carry electric current.
3) Ionic compounds also dissolve easily in water. The ions separate and are all free to move in the solution, so they'll carry electric current.

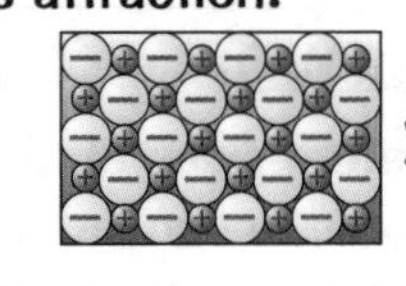

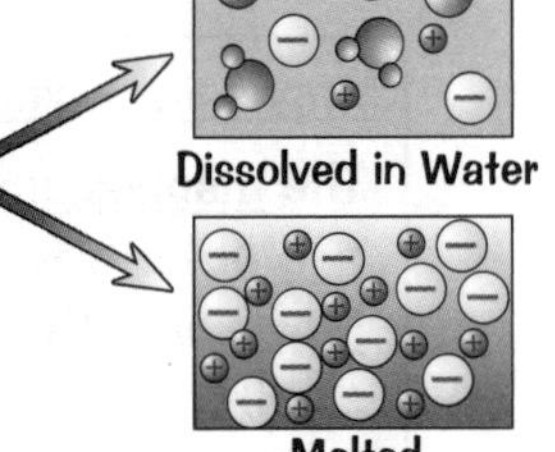

Dissolved in Water

Melted

Look at Charges to Find the Formula of an Ionic Compound

1) You might have to work out the empirical formula of an ionic compound from a diagram of the compound.
2) If it's a dot and cross diagram, count up how many atoms there are of each element. Write this down to give you the empirical formula.
3) If you're given a 3D diagram of the ionic lattice, use it to work out what ions are in the ionic compound.
4) You'll then have to balance the charges of the ions so that the overall charge on the compound is zero.

EXAMPLE: What's the empirical formula of the ionic compound shown on the right?

1) Look at the diagram to work out what ions are in the compound.
   The compound contains potassium and oxide ions.
2) Work out what charges the ions will form.
   Potassium is in Group 1 so forms 1+ ions. Oxygen is in Group 6 so forms 2– ions.
3) Balance the charges so the charge of the empirical formula is zero.
   A potassium ion only has a 1+ charge, so you'll need two of them to balance out the 2– charge of an oxide ion. The empirical formula is K_2O.

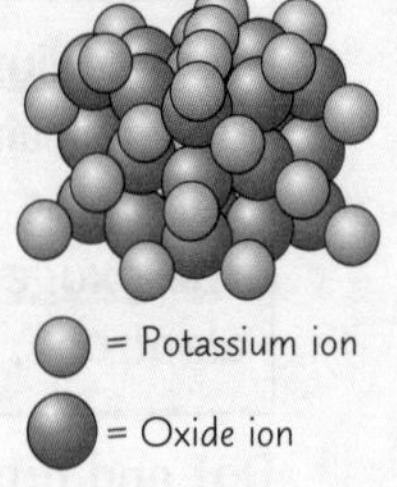

Giant ionic lattices — all over your chips...

Here's where you can get a little practice working out formulas for ionic compounds.

Q1 The structure of an ionic compound is shown on the right.

a) Predict, with reasoning, whether the compound has a high or a low melting point. [2 marks]

b) Explain why the compound can conduct electricity when molten. [1 mark]

c) Use the diagram to find the empirical formula of the compound. [3 marks]

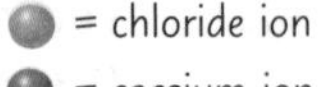

Covalent Bonding

Some elements bond ionically (see page 113) but others form strong covalent bonds.
This is where atoms share electrons with each other so that they've got full outer shells.

Covalent Bonds — Sharing Electrons

1) When non-metal atoms bond together, they share pairs of electrons to make covalent bonds.
2) The positively charged nuclei of the bonded atoms are attracted to the shared pair of electrons by electrostatic forces, making covalent bonds very strong.
3) Atoms only share electrons in their outer shells (highest energy levels).
4) Each single covalent bond provides one extra shared electron for each atom.
5) Each atom involved generally makes enough covalent bonds to fill up its outer shell. Having a full outer shell gives them the electronic structure of a noble gas, which is very stable.
6) Covalent bonding happens in compounds of non-metals (e.g. H_2O) and in non-metal elements (e.g. Cl_2).

There are Different Ways of Drawing Covalent Bonds

1) You can use dot and cross diagrams to show the bonding in covalent compounds.
2) Electrons drawn in the overlap between the outer orbitals of two atoms are shared between those atoms.
3) Dot and cross diagrams are useful for showing which atoms the electrons in a covalent bond come from, but they don't show the relative sizes of the atoms, or how the atoms are arranged in space.

Nitrogen has five outer electrons...

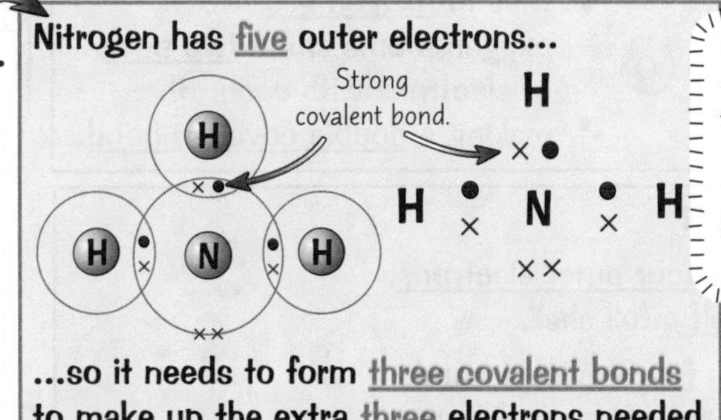

...so it needs to form three covalent bonds to make up the extra three electrons needed.

You don't have to draw the orbitals in these diagrams. The important thing is that you get all the dots and crosses in the right places.

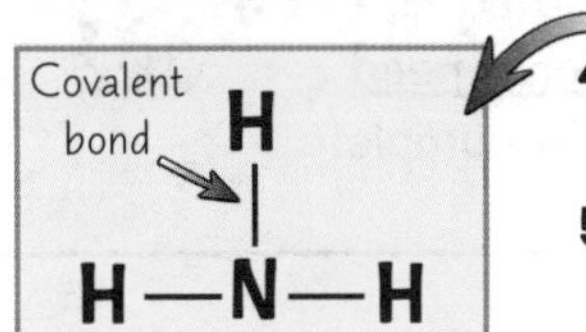

4) The displayed formula of ammonia (NH_3) shows the covalent bonds as single lines between atoms.
5) This is a great way of showing how atoms are connected in large molecules. However, they don't show the 3D structure of the molecule, or which atoms the electrons in the covalent bond have come from.
6) The 3D model of ammonia shows the atoms, the covalent bonds and their arrangement in space next to each other. But 3D models can quickly get confusing for large molecules where there are lots of atoms to include. They don't show where the electrons in the bonds have come from, either.

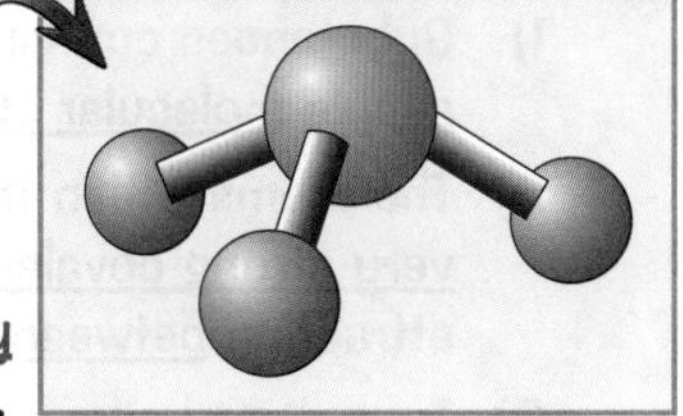

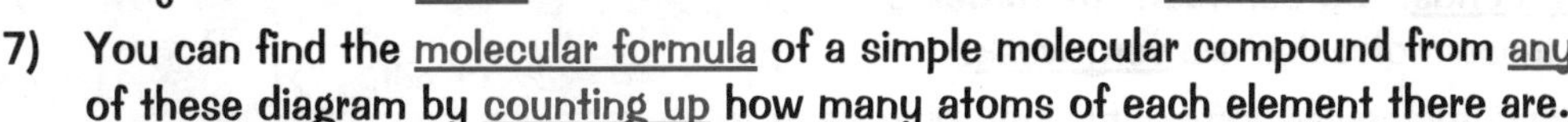

7) You can find the molecular formula of a simple molecular compound from any of these diagram by counting up how many atoms of each element there are.

A molecular formula shows you how many atoms of each element are in a molecule.

A diagram of the molecule ethane is shown on the right. Use the diagram to find the molecular formula of ethane.

```
   H   H
   |   |
H—C—C—H
   |   |
   H   H
```

In the diagram, there are two carbon atoms and six hydrogen atoms. So the molecular formula is C_2H_6.

Sharing is caring...

There's a whole page of dot and cross diagrams for other covalent molecules yet to come, but make sure you can draw the different diagrams that can be used to show the bonding in ammonia on this page first.

Q1 Draw a dot and cross diagram to show the bonding in a molecule of ammonia (NH_3). [2 marks]

Simple Molecular Substances

These molecules might be simple, but you've still gotta know about them. I know, the world is a cruel place.

Learn These Examples of Simple Molecular Substances

Simple molecular substances are made up of molecules containing a few atoms joined together by covalent bonds. Here are some common examples that you should know...

Hydrogen, H_2

Hydrogen atoms have just one electron. They only need one more to complete the first shell...

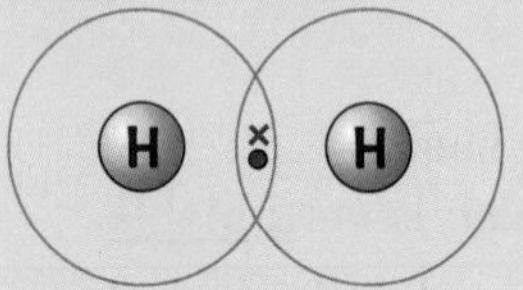

...so they often form single covalent bonds, either with other hydrogen atoms or with other elements, to achieve this.

Chlorine, Cl_2

Each chlorine atom needs just one more electron to complete the outer shell...

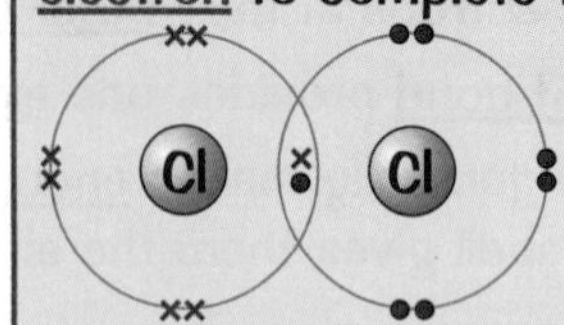

...so two chlorine atoms can share one pair of electrons and form a single covalent bond.

Oxygen, O_2

Each oxygen atom needs two more electrons to complete its outer shell...

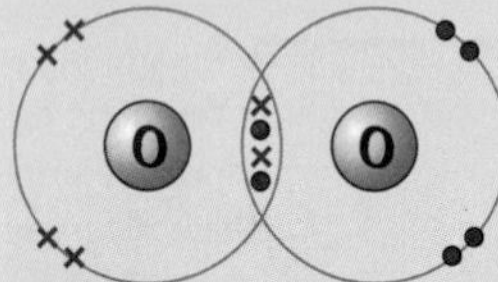

...so in oxygen gas two oxygen atoms share two pairs of electrons with each other making a double covalent bond.

Nitrogen, N_2

Nitrogen atoms need three more electrons...

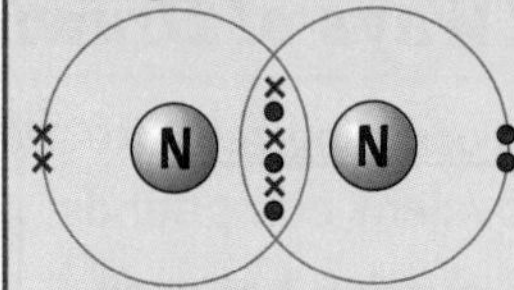

...so two nitrogen atoms share three pairs of electrons to fill their outer shells. This creates a triple bond.

Methane, CH_4

Carbon has four outer electrons, which is half a full shell.

It can form four covalent bonds with hydrogen atoms to fill up its outer shell.

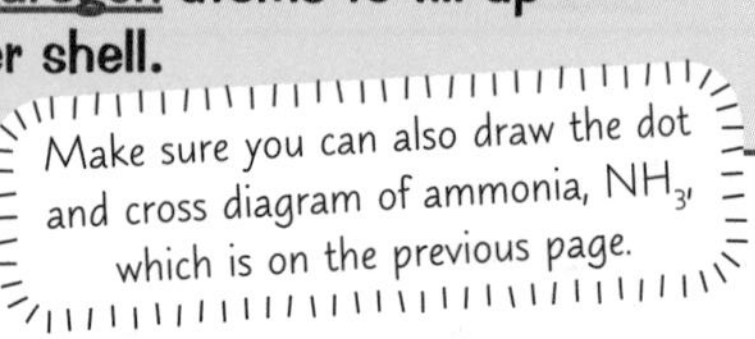

Make sure you can also draw the dot and cross diagram of ammonia, NH_3, which is on the previous page.

Water, H_2O

In water molecules, the oxygen shares a pair of electrons with two H atoms to form two single covalent bonds.

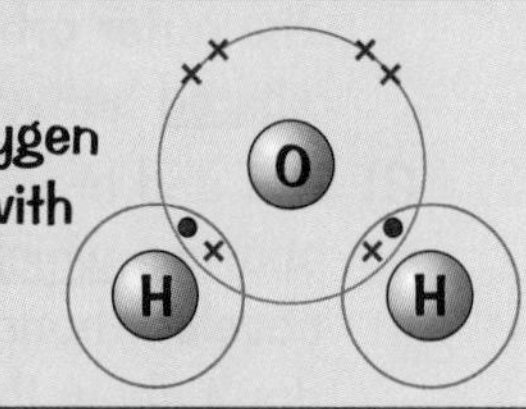

Hydrogen Chloride, HCl

This is very similar to H_2 and Cl_2. Again, both atoms only need one more electron to complete their outer shells.

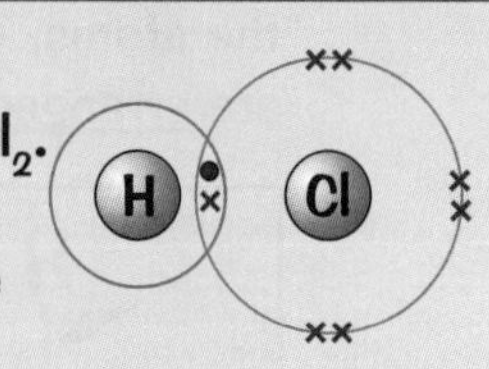

Properties of Simple Molecular Substances

Weak intermolecular forces

Chlorine

Oxygen

1) Substances containing covalent bonds usually have simple molecular structures, like the examples above.
2) The atoms within the molecules are held together by very strong covalent bonds. By contrast, the forces of attraction between these molecules are very weak.
3) To melt or boil a simple molecular compound, you only need to break these feeble intermolecular forces and not the covalent bonds. So the melting and boiling points are very low, because the molecules are easily parted from each other.
4) Most molecular substances are gases or liquids at room temperature.

5) As molecules get bigger, the strength of the intermolecular forces increases, so more energy is needed to break them, and the melting and boiling points increase.
6) Molecular compounds don't conduct electricity, simply because they aren't charged, so there are no free electrons or ions.

May the intermolecular force be with you...

Never forget that it's the weak forces between molecules that are broken when a simple molecular substance melts.

Q1 Explain why oxygen, O_2, is a gas at room temperature. [1 mark]

Q2 Explain why nitrogen, N_2, doesn't conduct electricity. [1 mark]

Polymers and Giant Covalent Structures

Wouldn't it be simply marvellous if only simple molecular substances had covalent bonds, and it was now time to put your feet up? Well it's not like that. Polymers and giant covalent substances also have covalent bonds.

Polymers Are Long Chains of Repeating Units

1) In a polymer, lots of small units are linked together to form a long molecule that has repeating sections.
2) All the atoms in a polymer are joined by strong covalent bonds.
3) Instead of drawing out a whole long polymer molecule (which can contain thousands or even millions of atoms), you can draw the shortest repeating section, called the repeating unit, like this:

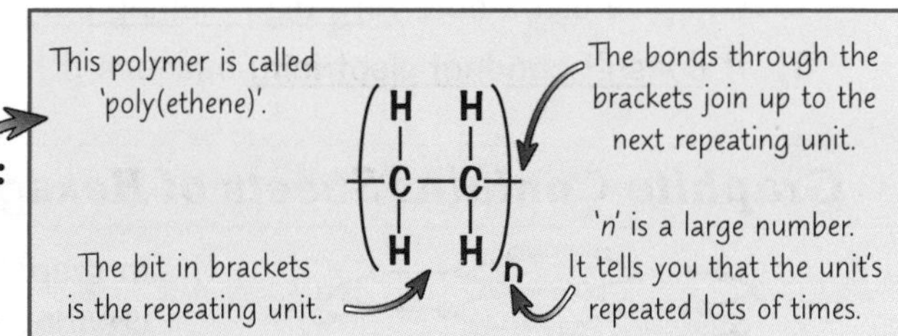

4) To find the molecular formula of a polymer, write down the molecular formula of the repeating unit in brackets, and put an 'n' outside.
5) So for poly(ethene), the molecular formula of the polymer is $(C_2H_4)_n$.
6) The intermolecular forces between polymer molecules are larger than between simple covalent molecules, so more energy is needed to break them. This means most polymers are solid at room temperature.
7) The intermolecular forces are still weaker than ionic or covalent bonds, so they generally have lower boiling points than ionic or giant molecular compounds.

Giant Covalent Structures Are Macromolecules

1) In giant covalent structures, all the atoms are bonded to each other by strong covalent bonds.
2) They have very high melting and boiling points as lots of energy is needed to break the covalent bonds between the atoms.
3) They don't contain charged particles, so they don't conduct electricity — not even when molten (except for a few weird exceptions such as graphite, see next page).
4) The main examples that you need to know about are diamond and graphite, which are both made from carbon atoms only, and silicon dioxide (silica).

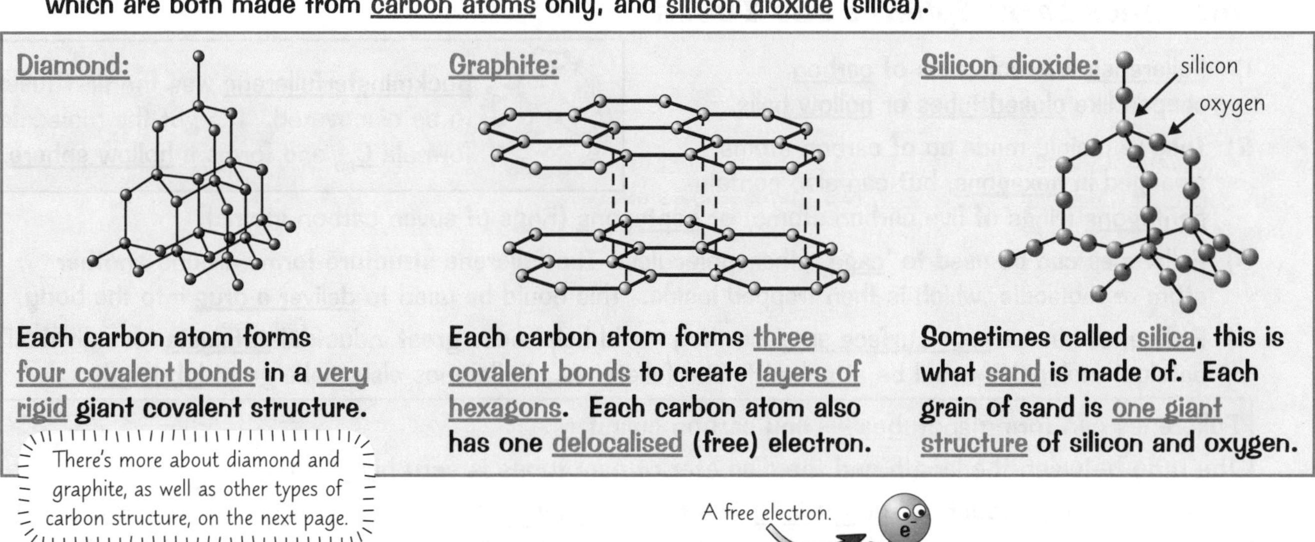

Diamond: Each carbon atom forms four covalent bonds in a very rigid giant covalent structure.

Graphite: Each carbon atom forms three covalent bonds to create layers of hexagons. Each carbon atom also has one delocalised (free) electron.

Silicon dioxide: Sometimes called silica, this is what sand is made of. Each grain of sand is one giant structure of silicon and oxygen.

There's more about diamond and graphite, as well as other types of carbon structure, on the next page.

A free electron.

What do you call a vehicle made of sand? Sili-car...

To melt or boil a simple molecular substance or a polymer, only the weakish intermolecular forces need to be broken. To melt or boil a giant covalent substance, you have to break very strong covalent bonds.

Q1 The repeating unit of poly(chloroethene) is shown on the right. What's the molecular formula of poly(chloroethene)? [1 mark]

(Cl H / —C—C— / H H)$_n$

Q2 Predict, with reasoning, whether diamond or poly(ethene) has a higher melting point. [3 marks]

Allotropes of Carbon

Allotropes are different structural forms of the same element in the same physical state. Carbon's got lots...

Diamond is Very Hard

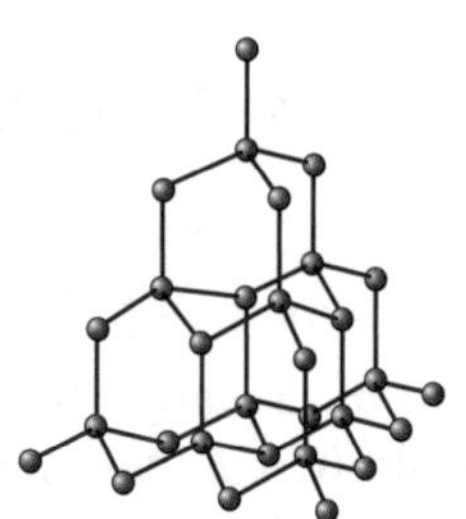

1) Diamond has a giant covalent structure, made up of carbon atoms that each form four covalent bonds. This makes diamond really hard.
2) Those strong covalent bonds take a lot of energy to break and give diamond a very high melting point.
3) It doesn't conduct electricity because it has no free electrons or ions.

Graphite Contains Sheets of Hexagons

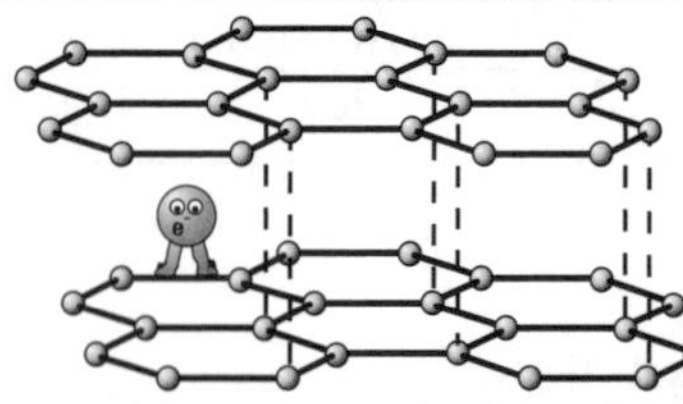

1) In graphite, each carbon atom only forms three covalent bonds, creating sheets of carbon atoms arranged in hexagons.
2) There aren't any covalent bonds between the layers — they're only held together weakly, so they're free to move over each other. This makes graphite soft and slippery, so it's ideal as a lubricating material.
3) Graphite's got a high melting point — the covalent bonds in the layers need loads of energy to break.
4) Only three out of each carbon's four outer electrons are used in bonds, so each carbon atom has one electron that's delocalised (free) and can move. So graphite conducts electricity and thermal energy.

Graphene is One Layer of Graphite

Graphene is a sheet of carbon atoms joined together in hexagons. The sheet is just one atom thick, making it a two-dimensional compound.

The network of covalent bonds makes it very strong. It's also incredibly light, so can be added to composite materials to improve their strength without adding much weight.

Like graphite, it contains delocalised electrons so can conduct electricity through the whole structure. This means it has the potential to be used in electronics.

Fullerenes Form Spheres and Tubes

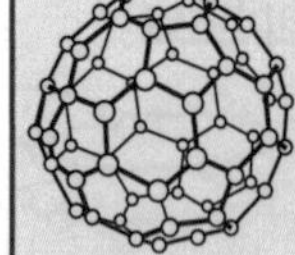

Buckminsterfullerene was the first fullerene to be discovered. It's got the molecular formula C_{60} and forms a hollow sphere.

1) Fullerenes are molecules of carbon, shaped like closed tubes or hollow balls.
2) They're mainly made up of carbon atoms arranged in hexagons, but can also contain pentagons (rings of five carbon atoms) or heptagons (rings of seven carbon atoms).
3) Fullerenes can be used to 'cage' other molecules. The fullerene structure forms around another atom or molecule, which is then trapped inside. This could be used to deliver a drug into the body.
4) Fullerenes have a huge surface area, so they could help make great industrial catalysts — individual catalyst molecules could be attached to the fullerenes. Fullerenes also make great lubricants.

Fullerenes can form nanotubes — tiny carbon cylinders.

The ratio between the length and the diameter of nanotubes is very high.

Nanotubes can conduct both electricity and thermal energy (heat).

They also have a high tensile strength (they don't break when they're stretched).

Technology that uses very small particles such as nanotubes is called nanotechnology. Nanotubes can be used in electronics or to strengthen materials without adding much weight, such as in tennis racket frames.

Greetings in the Caribbean — they're 'allo-tropical...

Before you go on, make sure you can explain the properties of all these allotropes of carbon.

Q1 Give three uses of fullerenes. [3 marks]

Metallic Bonding

Ever wondered what makes metals tick? Well, either way, this is the page for you.

Metallic Bonding Involves Delocalised Electrons

I don't think he's from round here.

1) Metals also consist of a giant structure.
2) The electrons in the outer shell of the metal atoms are delocalised (free to move around). There are strong forces of electrostatic attraction between the positive metal ions and the shared negative electrons.
3) These forces of attraction hold the atoms together in a regular structure and are known as metallic bonding. Metallic bonding is very strong.

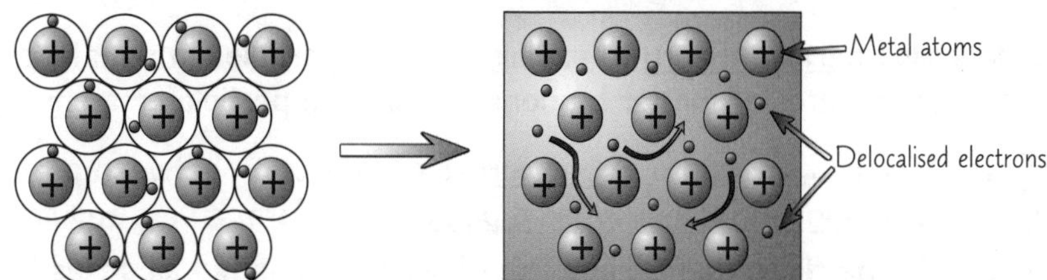

4) Substances that are held together by metallic bonding include metallic elements and alloys (see below).
5) It's the delocalised electrons in the metallic bonds which produce all the properties of metals.

Most Metals are Solid at Room Temperature

The electrostatic forces between the metal atoms and the delocalised sea of electrons are very strong, so need lots of energy to be broken.

This means that most compounds with metallic bonds have very high melting and boiling points, so they're generally solid at room temperature.

Metals are Good Conductors of Electricity and Heat

The delocalised electrons carry electrical current and thermal (heat) energy through the whole structure, so metals are good conductors of electricity and heat.

Most Metals are Malleable

The layers of atoms in a metal can slide over each other, making metals malleable — this means that they can be bent or hammered or rolled into flat sheets.

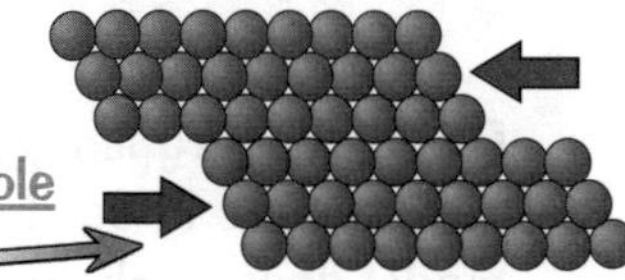

Alloys are Harder Than Pure Metals

1) Pure metals often aren't quite right for certain jobs — they're often too soft when they're pure so are mixed with other metals to make them harder. Most of the metals we use everyday are alloys — a mixture of two or more metals or a metal and another element. Alloys are harder and so more useful than pure metals.
2) Different elements have different sized atoms. So when another element is mixed with a pure metal, the new metal atoms will distort the layers of metal atoms, making it more difficult for them to slide over each other. This makes alloys harder than pure metals.

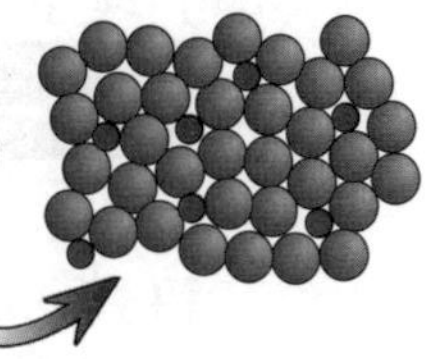

I saw a metal on the bus once — he was the conductor...

If your knowledge of metals is still feeling a bit delocalised, the questions below will help...

Q1 Copper is a metallic element. Describe and explain what property of copper makes it suitable for using in electrical circuits. [2 marks]

Q2 Suggest why an alloy of copper, rather than pure copper, is used to make hinges for doors [1 mark]

States of Matter

Better get your thinking hat on, as states of matter really... err.. matter. You'll need to imagine the particles in a substance as little snooker balls. Sounds strange, but it's useful for explaining lots of stuff in chemistry.

The Three States of Matter — Solid, Liquid and Gas

Materials come in three different forms — solid, liquid and gas. These are the three states of matter. Which state something is at a certain temperature (solid, liquid or gas) depends on how strong the forces of attraction are between the particles of the material. How strong the forces are depends on THREE THINGS:

a) the material (the structure of the substance and the type of bonds holding the particles together),

b) the temperature,

c) the pressure.

The particles could be atoms, ions or molecules.

You can use a model called particle theory to explain how the particles in a material behave in each of the three states of matter by considering each particle as a small, solid, inelastic sphere.

1) In solids, there are strong forces of attraction between particles, which holds them close together in fixed positions to form a very regular lattice arrangement.
2) The particles don't move from their positions, so all solids keep a definite shape and volume, and don't flow like liquids.
3) The particles vibrate about their positions — the hotter the solid becomes, the more they vibrate (causing solids to expand slightly when heated).

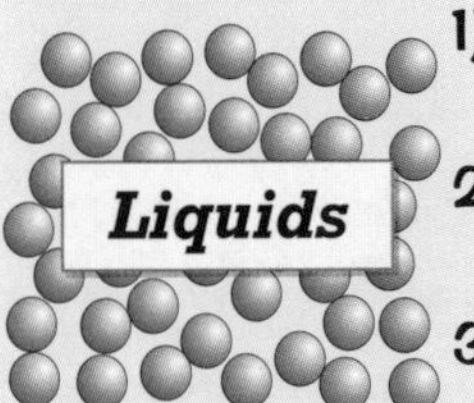

1) In liquids, there's a weak force of attraction between the particles. They're randomly arranged and free to move past each other, but they tend to stick closely together.
2) Liquids have a definite volume but don't keep a definite shape, and will flow to fill the bottom of a container.
3) The particles are constantly moving with random motion. The hotter the liquid gets, the faster they move. This causes liquids to expand slightly when heated.

1) In gases, the force of attraction between the particles is very weak — they're free to move and are far apart. The particles in gases travel in straight lines.
2) Gases don't keep a definite shape or volume and will always fill any container.
3) The particles move constantly with random motion. The hotter the gas gets, the faster they move. Gases either expand when heated, or their pressure increases.

Particle theory is a great model for explaining the three states of matter, but it isn't perfect. In reality, the particles aren't solid or inelastic and they aren't spheres — they're atoms, ions or molecules. Also, the model doesn't show the forces between the particles, so there's no way of knowing how strong they are.

State Symbols Tell You the State of a Substance in an Equation

You saw on page 99 how a chemical reaction can be shown using a word equation or symbol equation. Symbol equations can also include state symbols next to each substance — they tell you what physical state the reactants and products are in:

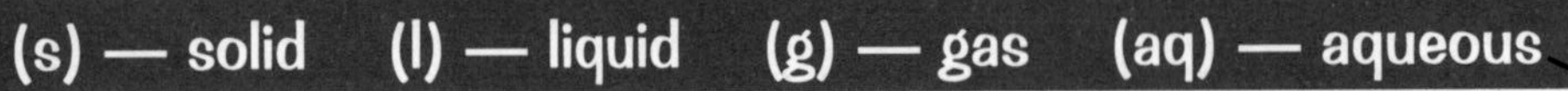

'Aqueous' means 'dissolved in water'.

For example, aqueous hydrochloric acid reacts with solid calcium carbonate to form aqueous calcium chloride, liquid water and carbon dioxide gas:

$$2HCl_{(aq)} + CaCO_{3(s)} \rightarrow CaCl_{2(aq)} + H_2O_{(l)} + CO_{2(g)}$$

Phew, what a page — particle-ularly gripping stuff...

I think it's pretty clever the way you can explain all the differences between solids, liquids and gases with just a page full of pink snooker balls. Anyway, that's the easy bit. The not-so-easy bit is learning it all.

Q1 Substance A does not have a definite shape or volume. What state is it in? [1 mark]

Changing State

This page is like a game show. To start, everyone seems nice and solid, but turn up the heat and it all changes.

Substances Can Change from One State to Another

Physical changes don't change the particles — just their arrangement or their energy.

1) When a solid is heated, its particles gain more energy.
2) This makes the particles vibrate more, which weakens the forces that hold the solid together.
3) At a certain temperature, called the melting point the particles have enough energy to break free from their positions. This is called MELTING and the solid turns into a liquid.
4) When a liquid is heated, again the particles get even more energy.
5) This energy makes the particles move faster, which weakens and breaks the bonds holding the liquid together.
6) At a certain temperature, called the boiling point, the particles have enough energy to break their bonds. This is BOILING (or evaporating). The liquid becomes a gas.

Solid

melting ↓ ↑ freezing

Liquid

boiling ↓ ↑ condensing

Gas

7) As a gas cools, the particles no longer have enough energy to overcome the forces of attraction between them.
8) Bonds form between the particles.
9) At the boiling point, so many bonds have formed between the gas particles that the gas becomes a liquid. This is called CONDENSING.
10) When a liquid cools, the particles have less energy, so move around less.

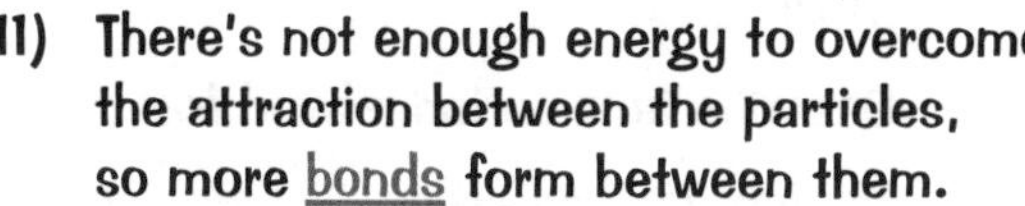

11) There's not enough energy to overcome the attraction between the particles, so more bonds form between them.

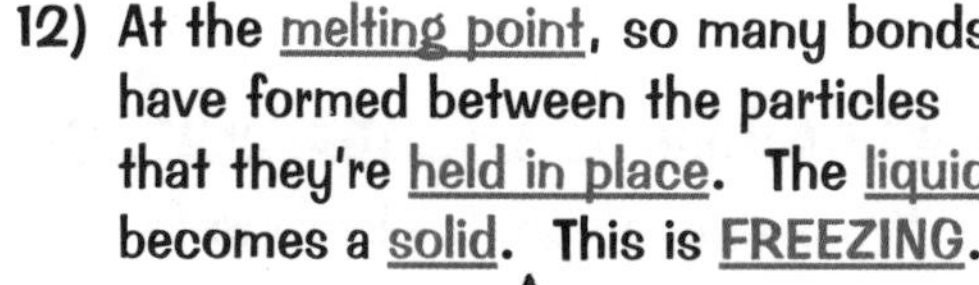

12) At the melting point, so many bonds have formed between the particles that they're held in place. The liquid becomes a solid. This is FREEZING.

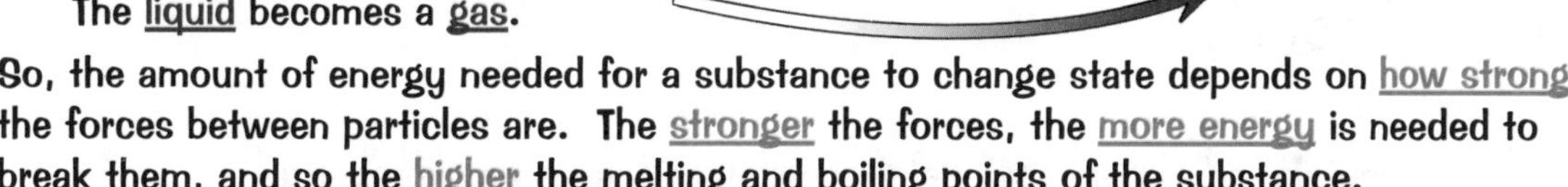

So, the amount of energy needed for a substance to change state depends on how strong the forces between particles are. The stronger the forces, the more energy is needed to break them, and so the higher the melting and boiling points of the substance.

You Have to be Able to Predict the State of a Substance

You might be asked to predict what state a substance is in at a certain temperature. If the temperature's below the melting point of substance, it'll be a solid. If it's above the boiling point, it'll be a gas. If it's in between the two points, then it's a liquid.

The bulk properties such as the melting point of a material depend on how lots of atoms interact together. An atom on its own doesn't have these properties.

EXAMPLE: Which of the molecular substances in the table is a liquid at room temperature (25 °C)?

	melting point	boiling point
oxygen	–219 °C	–183 °C
nitrogen	–210 °C	–196 °C
bromine	–7 °C	59 °C

Oxygen and nitrogen have boiling points below 25 °C, so will both be gases at room temperature.

So the answer's **bromine**. It melts at –7 °C and boils at 59 °C. So, it'll be a liquid at room temperature.

Some people are worth melting for...

Make sure you can describe what happens to particles, and the forces between them, as a substance is heated and cooled. Then learn all the technical terms, and you'll sound like a states of matter pro.

Q1 Ethanol melts at –114 °C and boils at 78 °C. Predict the state that ethanol is in at:
a) –150 °C b) 0 °C c) 25 °C d) 100 °C [4 marks]

Revision Questions for Topic C2

Now you've finished Topic C2, I bet I can guess what you're after next. A lovely set of questions to test how much of this lovely topic you can remember. I knew it...

- Try these questions and tick off each one when you get it right.
- When you've done all the questions under a heading and are completely happy with it, tick it off.

Ions and Ionic Compounds (p.112-114)

1) What type of ion do elements from each of the following groups form?
   a) Group 1
   b) Group 7
2) Describe how an ionic bond forms.
3) Sketch dot and cross diagrams to show the formation of:
   a) sodium chloride b) magnesium oxide c) magnesium chloride d) sodium oxide
4) Describe the structure of a crystal of sodium chloride.
5) List the main properties of ionic compounds.

Covalent Substances (p.115-118)

6) Describe how covalent bonds form.
7) Sketch dot and cross diagrams showing the bonding in a molecule of:
   a) hydrogen b) water c) hydrogen chloride
8) Explain why simple molecular compounds typically have low melting and boiling points.
9) Describe the structure of a polymer.
10) Give three examples of giant covalent substances.
11) Explain why graphite can conduct electricity.
12) Explain how fullerenes could be used to deliver drugs into the body.

Metallic Bonding (p.119)

13) What is metallic bonding?
14) List three properties of metals and explain how metallic structure causes each property.
15) Explain why alloys are harder than pure metals.

States of Matter (p.120-121)

16) Name the three states of matter.
17) What is the state symbol of an aqueous substance?
18) What is the name of the temperature at which a liquid becomes a gas?
19) How does the strength of the forces between particles influence the temperature at which a substance changes state?

Relative Formula Mass

Calculating relative formula mass is straight forward enough, but things can get a bit more confusing when you start working out the percentage compositions of compounds. Best get cracking, I suppose...

Compounds Have a Relative Formula Mass, M_r

If you have a compound like $MgCl_2$ then it has a relative formula mass, M_r, which is just the relative atomic masses of all the atoms in the molecular formula added together.

You can find the relative atomic mass (A_r) of an element from the periodic table — it's the same as its mass number. See page 97 for more.

EXAMPLE:

Find the relative formula mass of $MgCl_2$.

1) Look up the relative atomic masses of all the elements in the compound on the periodic table. (In the exams, you might be given the A_r you need in the question.)
A_r of Mg = 24 and the A_r of Cl = 35.5.
2) Add up all the relative atomic masses of the atoms in the compound.
Mg + (2 × Cl) = 24 + (2 × 35.5) = 95 So M_r of $MgCl_2$ = 95

There are two chlorine atoms in $MgCl_2$, so the relative atomic mass of chlorine needs to be multiplied by 2.

You Can Calculate the % Mass of an Element in a Compound

This is actually dead easy — so long as you've learnt this formula:

$$\text{Percentage mass of an element in a compound} = \frac{A_r \times \text{number of atoms of that element}}{M_r \text{ of the compound}} \times 100$$

EXAMPLE:

Find the percentage mass of sodium in sodium carbonate, Na_2CO_3.

A_r of sodium = 23, A_r of carbon = 12, A_r of oxygen = 16

M_r of Na_2CO_3 = (2 × 23) + 12 + (3 × 16) = 106

$$\text{Percentage mass of sodium} = \frac{A_r \times \text{number of atoms of that element}}{M_r \text{ of the compound}} \times 100 = \frac{23 \times 2}{106} \times 100 = 43\%$$

You might also come across more complicated questions where you need to work out the percentage mass.

EXAMPLE:

A mixture contains 20% iron ions by mass. What mass of iron chloride ($FeCl_2$) would you need to provide the iron ions in 50 g of the mixture? A_r of Fe = 56, A_r of Cl = 35.5.

1) Find the mass of iron in the mixture.
The mixture contains 20% iron by mass, so in 50 g there will be $50 \times \frac{20}{100} = 10$ g of iron.

2) Calculate the percentage mass of iron in iron chloride.

$$\text{Percentage mass of iron} = \frac{A_r \times \text{number of atoms of that element}}{M_r \text{ of the compound}} \times 100 = \frac{56}{56 + (2 \times 35.5)} \times 100 = 44.09...\%$$

3) Calculate the mass of iron chloride that contains 10 g of iron.
Iron chloride contains 44.09% iron by mass, so there will be 10 g of iron in $10 \div \frac{44.09...}{100} = 23$ g

So you need 23 g of iron chloride to provide the iron in 50 g of the mixture.

Relative mass — when you go to church with your parents...

The best way to get to grips with all this stuff is by practising. Start by having a go at these questions...

Q1 Calculate the relative formula mass (M_r) of: a) H_2O b) LiOH c) H_2SO_4 [3 marks]

Q2 Calculate the percentage composition by mass of potassium in potassium hydroxide (KOH). [2 marks]

The Mole

Moles can be pretty confusing. It's probably the word that puts people off. It's difficult to see the relevance of the word "mole" to anything but a small burrowing animal.

"The Mole" is Simply the Name Given to an Amount of a Substance

1) Just like "a million" is this many: 1 000 000; or "a billion" is this many: 1 000 000 000, so "the Avogadro constant" is this many: 602 000 000 000 000 000 000 000 or 6.02×10^{23}. And that's all it is. Just a number.
2) One mole of any substance is just an amount of that substance that contains an Avogadro number of particles — so 6.02×10^{23} particles. The particles could be atoms, molecules, ions or electrons.
3) The burning question, of course, is why is it such a silly long number like that, and with a 6 at the front?
4) The answer is that the mass of that number of atoms or molecules of any substance is exactly the same number of grams as the relative atomic mass (A_r) or relative formula mass (M_r) of the element or compound.

5) In other words, one mole of atoms or molecules of any substance will have a mass in grams equal to the relative formula mass (A_r or M_r) for that substance. Here are some examples:

Carbon has an A_r of 12.	So one mole of carbon weighs exactly 12 g.
Nitrogen gas, N_2, has an M_r of 28 (2 × 14).	So one mole of N_2 weighs exactly 28 g.
Carbon dioxide, CO_2, has an M_r of 44 (12 + [2 × 16]).	So one mole of CO_2 weighs exactly 44 g.

6) This means that 12 g of carbon, or 28 g of N_2, or 44 g of CO_2, all contain the same number of particles, namely one mole or 6.023×10^{23} atoms or molecules.

Nice Formula to Find the Number of Moles in a Given Mass:

$$\text{Number of moles} = \frac{\text{mass in g (of an element or compound)}}{M_r \text{ (of the element or compound)}}$$

EXAMPLE: How many moles are there in 66 g of carbon dioxide (CO_2)?

1) Calculate the M_r of carbon dioxide. M_r of CO_2 = 12 + (16 × 2) = 44
2) Use the formula above to find out how many moles there are. No. of moles = Mass (g) ÷ M_r = 66 ÷ 44 = 1.5 mol

Easy Peasy.

'mol' is the symbol for the unit 'moles'.

You can rearrange the equation above using this handy formula triangle. You could use it to find the mass of a known number of moles of a substance, or to find the M_r of a substance from a known mass and number of moles. Just cover up the thing you want to find with your finger and write down what's left showing.

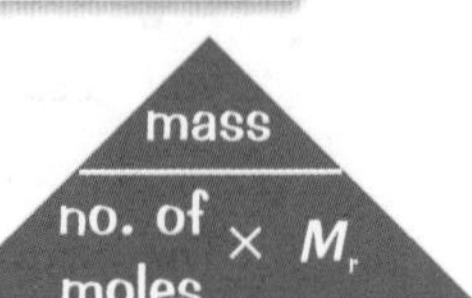

EXAMPLE: What mass of carbon is there in 4 moles of carbon dioxide?

There are 4 moles of carbon in 4 moles of CO_2.

Cover up 'mass' in the formula triangle. That leaves you with 'no. of moles × M_r'.

So the mass of 4 moles of carbon = 4 × 12 = **48 g**

What do moles have for pudding? Jam moly-poly...

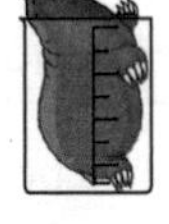

Calculations involving moles can send some people into a spin. Don't be one of those people — there's really no need to freak out about moles. Go back over this page until you've got your head round it all.

Q1 Calculate the number of moles in 90 g of water (H_2O). A_r(O) = 16, A_r(H) = 1. [2 marks]

Q2 Calculate the mass of 0.20 mol of potassium bromide (KBr). A_r(K) = 39, A_r(Br) = 80. [2 marks]

Conservation of Mass

You've probably realised by now that you can't magic stuff out of thin air, and you can't make it magically disappear, either. This fact is pretty useful for working out the amounts of substances in chemical reactions.

In a Chemical Reaction, Mass is Always Conserved

1) During a chemical reaction no atoms are destroyed and no atoms are created.
2) This means there are the same number and types of atoms on each side of a reaction equation.
3) Because of this, no mass is lost or gained — we say that mass is conserved during a reaction.
   E.g.

   $$2Li + F_2 \rightarrow 2LiF$$

   In this reaction, there are 2 lithium atoms and 2 fluorine atoms on each side of the equation.
4) By adding up the relative formula masses of the substances on each side of a balanced symbol equation, you can see that mass is conserved. The total M_r of all the reactants equals the total M_r of the products.

There's more about balanced symbol equations on p.99.

EXAMPLE:

Show that mass is conserved in this reaction: $2Li + F_2 \rightarrow 2LiF$.

1) Add up the relative formula masses on the left-hand side of the equation.
   $2 \times M_r(Li) + 2 \times M_r(F) = (2 \times 7) + (2 \times 19) = 14 + 38 = 52$
2) Add up the relative formula masses on the right-hand side of the equation.
   $2 \times M_r(LiF) = 2 \times (7 + 19) = 2 \times 26 = 52$

The total M_r on the left hand side of the equation is equal to the total M_r on the right hand side, so mass is conserved.

If the Mass Seems to Change, There's Usually a Gas Involved

In some experiments, you might observe a change of mass of an unsealed reaction vessel during a reaction. There are usually two explanations for this:

Explanation 1: If the mass increases, it's probably because one of the reactants is a gas that's found in air (e.g. oxygen) and all the products are solids, liquids or aqueous.

- Before the reaction, the gas is floating around in the air. It's there, but it's not contained in the reaction vessel, so you can't account for its mass.
- When the gas reacts to form part of the product, it becomes contained inside the reaction vessel — so the total mass of the stuff inside the reaction vessel increases.

For example, when a metal reacts with oxygen in an unsealed container, the mass of the container increases. The mass of the metal oxide produced equals the total mass of the metal and the oxygen that reacted from the air.

$$\text{metal}_{(s)} + \text{oxygen}_{(g)} \rightarrow \text{metal oxide}_{(s)}$$

Explanation 2: If the mass decreases, it's probably because one of the products is a gas and all the reactants are solids, liquids or aqueous.

- Before the reaction, all the reactants are contained in the reaction vessel.
- If the vessel isn't enclosed, then the gas can escape from the reaction vessel as it's formed. It's no longer contained in the reaction vessel, so you can't account for its mass — the total mass of the stuff inside the reaction vessel decreases.

For example, when a metal carbonate thermally decomposes to form a metal oxide and carbon dioxide gas, the mass of the reaction vessel will decrease if it isn't sealed. But in reality, the mass of the metal oxide and the carbon dioxide produced will equal the mass of the metal carbonate that decomposed.

$$\text{metal carbonate}_{(s)} \rightarrow \text{metal oxide}_{(s)} + \text{carbon dioxide}_{(g)}$$

Remember from the particle model on page 120 that a gas will expand to fill any container it's in. So if the reaction vessel isn't sealed, the gas expands out from the vessel, and escapes into the air around.

Leaving all the potatoes on your plate — that's mash conservation...

Never, ever forget that, in a reaction, the total mass of reactants is the same as the total mass of products.

Q1 Using the balanced equation, show that mass is conserved in the following reaction:

$H_2SO_{4(aq)} + 2NaOH_{(aq)} \rightarrow Na_2SO_{4(aq)} + 2H_2O_{(l)}$ $A_r(H) = 1, A_r(O) = 16, A_r(Na) = 23, A_r(S) = 32$ [5 marks]

The Mole and Equations

This is the moment where the 'number of moles = mass ÷ M_r' equation from page 124 comes into its own.

You Can Use Moles to Calculate Masses in Reactions

Remember those balanced equations back on page 99? Well, the big numbers in front of the chemical formulas of the reactants and products tell you how many moles of each substance takes part or is formed during the reaction.

The little numbers tell you how many atoms of each element there are in each of the substances.

For example:

$$Mg_{(s)} + 2HCl_{(aq)} \rightarrow MgCl_{2(aq)} + H_{2(g)}$$

In this reaction, 1 mole of magnesium and 2 moles of hydrochloric acid react together to form 1 mole of magnesium chloride and 1 mole of hydrogen gas.

You Can Balance Equations Using Reacting Masses

If you know the masses of the reactants and products that took part in a reaction, you can work out the balanced symbol equation for the reaction. Here are the steps you should take:

1) Divide the mass of each substance by its relative formula mass to find the number of moles.
2) Divide the number of moles of each substance by the smallest number of moles in the reaction.
3) If any of the numbers aren't whole numbers, multiply all the numbers by the same amount so that they all become whole numbers.
4) Write the balanced symbol equation for the reaction by putting these numbers in front of the chemical formulas.

EXAMPLE:

8.1 g of zinc oxide (ZnO) reacts completely with 0.60 g of carbon to form 2.2 g of carbon dioxide and 6.5 g of zinc. Write a balanced symbol equation for this reaction. $A_r(C) = 12$, $A_r(O) = 16$, $A_r(Zn) = 65$.

1) Work out M_r for each of the substances in the reaction:
   ZnO: 65 + 16 = 81 C: 12 CO_2: 12 + (2 × 16) = 44 Zn: 65
2) Divide the mass of each substance by its M_r to calculate how many moles of each substance reacted or were produced:
   ZnO: $\frac{8.1}{81} = 0.10$ mol C: $\frac{0.60}{12} = 0.050$ mol
   CO_2: $\frac{2.2}{44} = 0.050$ mol Zn: $\frac{6.5}{65} = 0.10$
3) Divide by the smallest number of moles, which is 0.050:
   ZnO: $\frac{0.10}{0.050} = 2.0$ C: $\frac{0.050}{0.050} = 1.0$
   CO_2: $\frac{0.050}{0.050} = 1.0$ Zn: $\frac{0.10}{0.050} = 2.0$
   These numbers give the ratio of the amounts of each substance in the reaction equation.
4) The numbers are all whole numbers, so you can write out the balanced symbol equation straight away:
   $$2ZnO + C \rightarrow CO_2 + 2Zn$$

Where do moles live? Edinburrow...

The calculations on this page have lots of steps, so the best way to learn how to do them is by practising. Luckily, there are some questions below to get you started. Don't say I don't spoil you. Better get cracking...

Q1 84 g of N_2 reacts completely with 18 g of H_2 to produce 102 g of NH_3. $M_r(N_2) = 28$, $M_r(H_2) = 2$, $M_r(NH_3) = 17$.

a) Calculate how many moles of each substance reacted or was produced. [3 marks]

b) Use your answer to part a) to write a balanced symbol equation for this reaction. [2 marks]

Limiting Reactants

Reactions don't go on forever — you need stuff in the reaction flask that can react. If one reactant gets completely used up in a reaction before the rest, then the reaction will stop. That reactant's called limiting.

Reactions Stop When One Reactant is Used Up

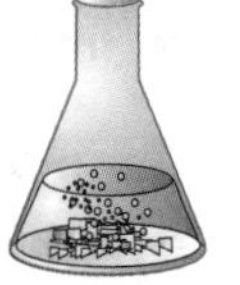

When some magnesium carbonate ($MgCO_3$) is placed into a beaker of hydrochloric acid, you can tell a reaction is taking place because you see lots of bubbles of gas being given off. After a while, the amount of fizzing slows down and the reaction eventually stops...

1) The reaction stops when all of one of the reactants is used up. Any other reactants are in excess. They're usually added in excess to make sure that the other reactant is used up.
2) The reactant that's used up in a reaction is called the limiting reactant (because it limits the amount of product that's formed).
3) The amount of product formed is directly proportional to the amount of limiting reactant. For example, if you halve the amount of limiting reactant the amount of product formed will also halve. If you double the amount of limiting reactant the amount of product will double (as long as it is still the limiting reactant).
4) This is because if you add more reactant there will be more reactant particles to take part in the reaction, which means more product particles.

The Amount of Product Depends on the Limiting Reactant

You can calculate the mass of a product formed in a reaction by using the mass of the limiting reactant and the balanced reaction equation.

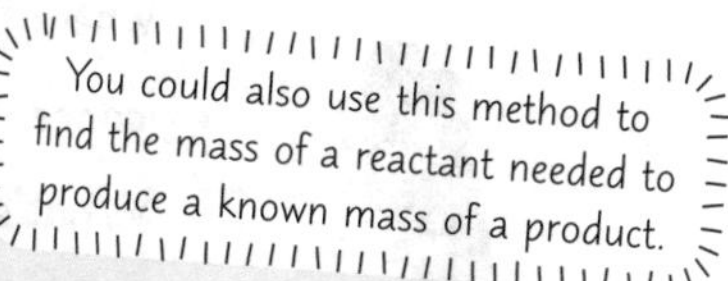

1) Write out the balanced equation.
2) Work out relative formula masses (M_r) of the reactant and product you want.
3) Find out how many moles there are of the substance you know the mass of.
4) Use the balanced equation to work out how many moles there'll be of the other substance. In this case, that's how many moles of product will be made of this many moles of reactant.
5) Use the number of moles to calculate the mass.

EXAMPLE: Calculate the mass of aluminium oxide formed when 135 g of aluminium is burned in air.

1) Write out the balanced equation: $4Al + 3O_2 \rightarrow 2Al_2O_3$
2) Calculate the relative formula masses: Al: 27 Al_2O_3: (2 × 27) + (3 × 16) = 102
3) Calculate the number of moles of aluminium in 135 g: Moles = $\frac{\text{mass}}{M_r} = \frac{135}{27} = 5$ — You don't have to find M_r of oxygen because it's in excess.
4) Look at the ratio of moles in the equation: 4 moles of Al react to produce 2 moles of Al_2O_3 — half the number of moles are produced. So 5 moles of Al will react to produce 2.5 moles of Al_2O_3

   If the question asked for the number of moles of aluminium oxide formed, you'd stop here.
5) Calculate the mass of 2.5 moles of aluminium oxide: mass = moles × M_r = 2.5 × 102 = 255 g

'A Rush of Mud to the Head' — my favourite album by Moldplay...

I've said it before, I'll say it again — practice makes perfect. So before you get distracted by a cute picture of a kitten, or wander off to have a cup of tea, have a go at the question below.

Q1 The balanced equation for the reaction between chlorine and potassium bromide is:

$$Cl_2 + 2KBr \rightarrow Br_2 + 2KCl$$

Calculate the mass of potassium chloride produced when 23.8 g of potassium bromide reacts in an excess of chlorine. A_r(K) = 39, A_r(Br) = 80, A_r(Cl) = 35.5. [4 marks]

Concentrations of Solutions

I can't promise that this page has all the answers to life, but there are quite a lot of solutions. Time to discover how you can work out the mass of a solute in a solution. Hold onto your hats and concentrate...

Concentration is a Measure of How Crowded Things Are

1) Lots of reactions in chemistry take place between substances that are dissolved in a solution. The amount of a substance (e.g. the mass or the number of moles) in a certain volume of a solution is called its concentration.
2) The more solute (the substance that's dissolved) there is in a given volume, the more concentrated the solution.

Concentration can be Measured in g/dm³

1) One way to measure the concentration of a solution is by calculating the mass of a substance in a given volume of solution. The units will be units of mass/units of volume. Here's how to calculate the concentration of a solution in g/dm³:

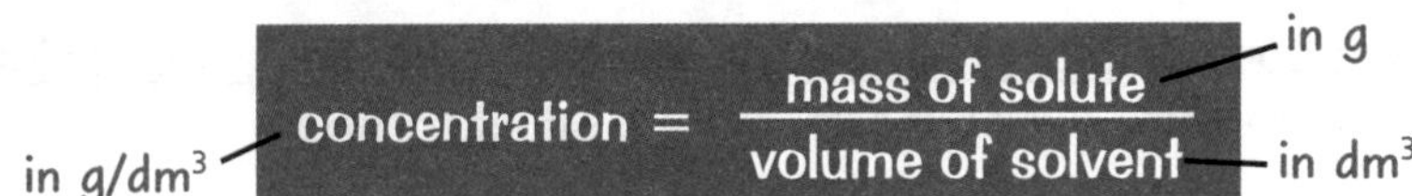

EXAMPLES:

1) What's the concentration in g/dm³ of a solution of sodium chloride where 30 g of sodium chloride is dissolved in 0.2 dm³ of water?

$$\text{concentration} = \frac{30}{0.2} = 150 \text{ g/dm}^3$$

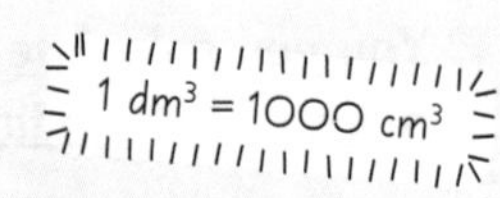

2) What's the concentration, in g/dm³, of a solution with 15 g of salt in 500 cm³?
   - Convert the volume to dm³ by dividing by 1000: 500 cm³ ÷ 1000 = 0.5 dm³
   - Now you've got the mass and the volume in the right units, just stick them in the formula: $\text{Concentration} = \frac{15}{0.5} = 30 \text{ g/dm}^3$

Gavin wasn't great at concentration.

2) You can rearrange the equation above to find the mass of solute in a given volume of solution if you know its concentration. Here's a handy formula triangle to help with rearranging the equation:

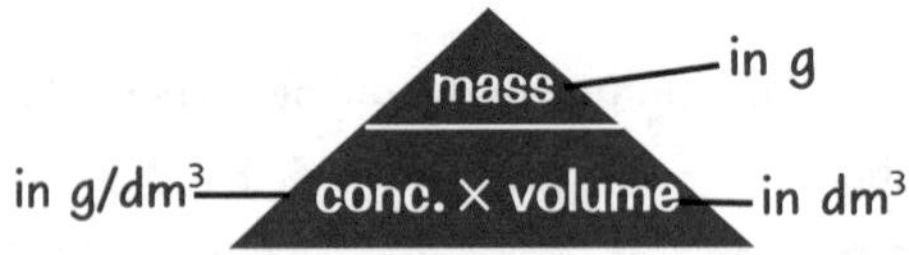

EXAMPLE:

What mass of a salt would you need to dissolve in 0.40 dm³ of water to make a solution with a concentration of 24 g/dm³?

- Use the formula triangle to rearrange the equation to make mass the subject: mass = concentration × volume
- Use this equation to calculate the mass: mass = 24 × 0.40 = 9.6 g

Remember — all measurements have some uncertainty to them. For repeated measurements, you can calculate the average (mean) and also the range of your results (see page 6). The range can be used to give you an idea of how uncertain the mean value is (see page 10).

CGP Revision Guides — not from concentrate...

Learning that formula could be a useful way to spend a couple of minutes. As could eating a biscuit. Why not kill two birds with one stone and write out the formula with one hand whilst holding a digestive in the other?

Q1 What is the mass of solute in 0.25 dm³ of solution with a concentration of 32 g/dm³? [1 mark]

Q2 Calculate the concentration of a solution that contains 0.6 g of salt in 15 cm³ of solvent. [2 marks]

Acids and Bases

Testing the pH of a solution means using an indicator — and that means pretty colours...

The pH Scale Goes From 0 to 14

1) The pH scale is a measure of how acidic or alkaline a solution is.
2) The lower the pH of a solution, the more acidic it is. The higher the pH of a solution, the more alkaline it is.
3) A neutral substance (e.g. pure water) has pH 7.

pH 0 1 2 3 4 5 6 7 8 9 10 11 12 13 14

ACIDS — NEUTRAL — ALKALIS

car battery acid, stomach acid; vinegar, lemon juice; acid rain; normal rain; pure water; washing-up liquid; pancreatic juice; soap powder; bleach; caustic soda (drain cleaner)

You Can Measure the pH of a Solution

1) An indicator is a dye that changes colour depending on whether it's above or below a certain pH. Some indicators contain a mixture of dyes that means they gradually change colour over a broad range of pH. These are called wide range indicators and they're useful for estimating the pH of a solution. For example, universal indicator gives the colours shown above.
2) A pH probe attached to a pH meter can also be used to measure pH electronically. The probe is placed in the solution you are measuring and the pH is given on a digital display as a numerical value, meaning it's more accurate than an indicator.

10.25

Acids and Bases Neutralise Each Other

1) An acid is a substance that forms aqueous solutions with a pH of less than 7. Acids form H^+ ions in water.
2) A base is a substance with a pH greater than 7.
3) An alkali is a base that dissolves in water to form a solution with a pH greater than 7. Alkalis form OH^- ions in water.

I have literally no idea what I'm doing.

The reaction between acids and bases is called neutralisation:

acid + base → salt + water

Neutralisation between acids and alkalis can be seen in terms of H^+ and OH^- ions like this:

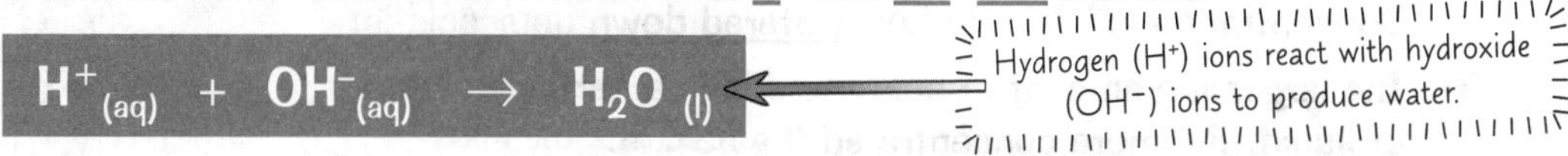

When an acid neutralises a base (or vice versa), the products are neutral, i.e. they have a pH of 7. An indicator can be used to show that a neutralisation reaction is over.

This page should have all bases covered...

pHew, you finished the page... This stuff isn't too bad really, and pH is worth knowing about — it's important to the chemistry in our bodies. For example, here's an interesting(ish) fact — your skin is slightly acidic (pH 5.5).

Q1 A student uses universal indicator to test the pH of some lemon juice. What colour would you expect the indicator to turn? [1 mark]

Q2 The pH of an unknown solution is found to be 8. Is the solution acidic or alkaline? [1 mark]

Strong Acids and Weak Acids

I like strong acids, and I also like weak acids. But which is better? There's only one way to find out...

Acids Produce Protons in Water

The thing about acids is that they ionise in aqueous solution — they produce hydrogen ions, H^+.
For example:

An H^+ ion is just a proton.

$HCl \rightarrow H^+ + Cl^-$
$HNO_3 \rightarrow H^+ + NO_3^-$

These acids don't produce hydrogen ions until they meet water. So, for example, hydrogen chloride gas isn't acidic.

Acids Can be Strong or Weak

1) Strong acids (e.g. sulfuric, hydrochloric and nitric acids) ionise completely in water. All acid particles dissociate to release H^+ ions.
2) Weak acids (e.g. ethanoic, citric and carbonic acids) do not fully ionise in solution. Only a small proportion of acid particles dissociate to release H^+ ions.
3) The ionisation of a weak acid is a reversible reaction, which sets up an equilibrium between the undissociated and dissociated acid. Since only a few of the acid particles release H^+ ions, the position of equilibrium lies well to the left.

For more on equilibria turn to p.147.

Strong acid: $HCl \longrightarrow H^+ + Cl^-$
Weak acid: $CH_3COOH \rightleftharpoons H^+ + CH_3COO^-$

4) Reactions of acids involve the H^+ ions reacting with other substances. If the concentration of H^+ ions is higher, the rate of reaction will be faster, so strong acids will be more reactive than weak acids of the same concentration.

pH is a Measure of the Concentration of Hydrogen Ions

1) The pH of an acid or alkali is a measure of the concentration of H^+ ions in the solution.
2) For every decrease of 1 on the pH scale, the concentration of H^+ ions increases by a factor of 10. So, an acid that has a pH of 4 has 10 times the concentration of H^+ ions of an acid that has a pH of 5. For a decrease of 2 on the pH scale, the concentration of H^+ ions increases by a factor of 100. The general rule for this is:

$$\text{Factor } H^+ \text{ ion concentration changes by } = 10^{-X}$$

X is the difference in pH. So if pH falls from 7 to 4 the difference is −3, and the factor the H^+ ion concentration has increased by is $10^{-(-3)} = 10^3$.

3) So the pH of a strong acid is always less than the pH of a weaker acid if they have the same concentration.

Don't Confuse Strong Acids with Concentrated Acids

1) Acid strength (i.e. strong or weak) tells you what proportion of the acid molecules ionise in water.
2) The concentration of an acid is different. Concentration measures how much acid there is in a certain volume of water. Concentration is basically how watered down your acid is.
3) The larger the amount of acid there is in a certain volume of liquid, the more concentrated the acid is.

Concentration describes the total number of dissolved acid molecules — not the number of molecules that are ionised to produce hydrogen ions at any given moment.

4) So you can have a dilute (not very concentrated) but strong acid, or a concentrated but weak acid.
5) pH will decrease with increasing acid concentration regardless of whether it's a strong or weak acid.

Weak acid or strong acid? I know which goes better with chips...

Acids are acidic because of H^+ ions. And strong acids are strong because they let go of all their H^+ ions at the drop of a hat... Well, at the drop of a drop of water.

Q1 Name a strong acid. [1 mark]

Q2 A student added strong acid to a weakly acidic solution of pH 6. The pH of the new solution was found to be pH 3. By how many times did the concentration of H^+ increase? [1 mark]

Reactions of Acids

Remember neutralisation from page 129? Well, there's more stuff on neutralisation reactions coming up...

Metal Oxides and Metal Hydroxides are Bases

1) Some metal oxides and metal hydroxides dissolve in water. These soluble compounds are alkalis. As you saw on page 129, alkalis react with acids in neutralisation reactions.
2) Even bases that won't dissolve in water will still take part in neutralisation reactions with acids.
3) So, all metal oxides and metal hydroxides react with acids to form a salt and water.

Acid + Metal Oxide → Salt + Water **Acid + Metal Hydroxide → Salt + Water**

The salt that's produced depends upon the acid and the metal ion in the oxide or hydroxide:

hydrochloric acid	+	copper oxide	→	copper chloride	+	water
2HCl	+	CuO	→	$CuCl_2$	+	H_2O
sulfuric acid	+	potassium hydroxide	→	potassium sulfate	+	water
H_2SO_4	+	2KOH	→	K_2SO_4	+	$2H_2O$
nitric acid	+	sodium hydroxide	→	sodium nitrate	+	water
HNO_3	+	NaOH	→	$NaNO_3$	+	H_2O

To work out the formula of an ionic compound, you need to balance the charges of the positive and negative ions so the overall charge of a compound is neutral. For more on ionic formulas, see p.114.

Acids and Metal Carbonates Produce Carbon Dioxide

Metal carbonates are also bases. They react with acids to produce a salt, water and carbon dioxide.

Acid + Metal Carbonate → Salt + Water + Carbon Dioxide

hydrochloric acid	+	sodium carbonate	→	sodium chloride	+	water	+	carbon dioxide
2HCl	+	Na_2CO_3	→	2NaCl	+	H_2O	+	CO_2
sulfuric acid	+	calcium carbonate	→	calcium sulfate	+	water	+	carbon dioxide
H_2SO_4	+	$CaCO_3$	→	$CaSO_4$	+	H_2O	+	CO_2

You can Make Soluble Salts Using an Insoluble Base

PRACTICAL

1) You need to pick the right acid and insoluble base, such as an insoluble metal oxide, hydroxide, or carbonate. E.g. if you want to make copper chloride, you could mix hydrochloric acid and copper oxide. $CuO_{(s)} + 2HCl_{(aq)} \rightarrow CuCl_{2\,(aq)} + H_2O_{(l)}$

You could also react the acid with a metal.

2) Gently warm the dilute acid using a Bunsen burner, then turn off the Bunsen burner.
3) Add the insoluble base to the acid a bit at a time, until no more reacts (i.e. the base is in excess). You'll know when all the acid has been neutralised because, even after stirring, the excess solid will just sink to the bottom of the flask.
4) Then filter out the excess solid to get the salt solution (see p.101).
5) To get pure, solid crystals of the salt, gently heat the solution using a water bath or an electric heater to evaporate some of the water (to make it more concentrated) and then stop heating it and leave the solution to cool. Crystals of the salt should form, which can be filtered out of the solution and then dried. This is called crystallisation (p.101).

filter paper

filter funnel

AHHHHH so many reactions...

In the exam you could get asked to describe how you would go about making a pure, dry sample of a given soluble salt. Make sure you understand the method and what reactants to use.

Q1 Calcium carbonate is added to hydrochloric acid.
Write a word equation for the reaction that occurs. [2 marks]

The Reactivity Series

You can place metals in order of reactivity. This can be a lot more useful than it sounds, promise.

The Reactivity Series — How Well a Metal Reacts

1) The reactivity series lists metals in order of their reactivity towards other substances.
2) For metals, their reactivity is determined by how easily they lose electrons — forming positive ions. The higher up the reactivity series a metal is, the more easily they form positive ions. Make sure you learn this list:
3) When metals react with water or acid, they lose electrons and form positive ions. So, the higher a metal is in the reactivity series, the more easily it reacts with water or acid.
4) If you compare the relative reactivity of different metals with either an acid or water and put them in order from most reactive to the least reactive, the order you get is the reactivity series.

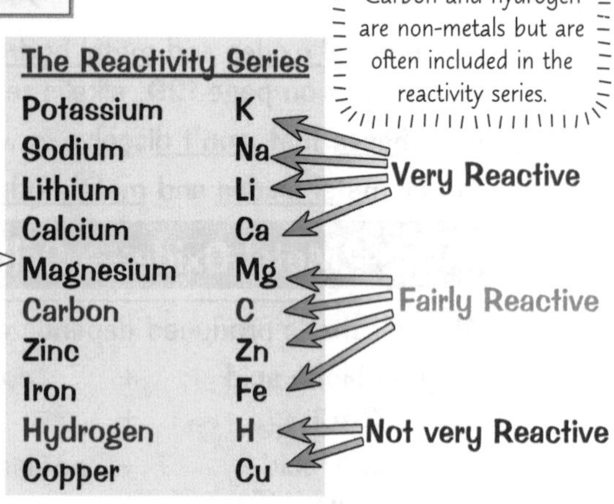

How Metals React With Acids Tells You About Their Reactivity

Some metals react with acids to produce a salt and hydrogen gas.

Acid + Metal → Salt + Hydrogen

1) The speed of reaction is indicated by the rate at which the bubbles of hydrogen are given off.
2) The more reactive the metal, the faster the reaction will go. Very reactive metals like potassium, sodium, lithium and calcium react explosively, but less reactive metals such as magnesium, zinc and iron react less violently. In general, copper won't react with cold, dilute acids.

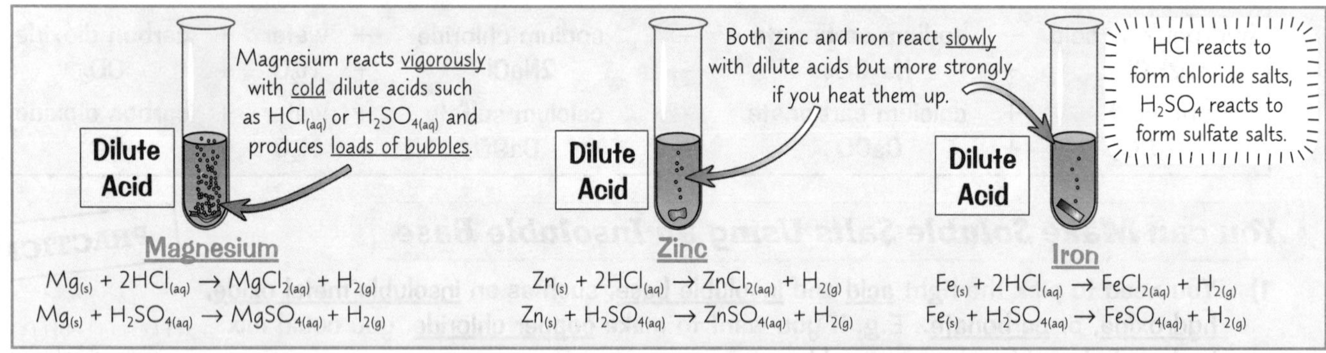

3) You can also investigate the reactivity of metals by measuring the temperature change of the reaction with an acid or water over a set time period. If you use the same mass and surface area of metal each time, then the more reactive the metal, the greater the temperature change should be.

Metals Also React with Water

The reactions of metals with water also show the reactivity of metals.

You can see more on the reactions of Group 1 metals with water on page 108.

Metal + Water → Metal Hydroxide + Hydrogen

For example, calcium: $Ca_{(s)} + 2H_2O_{(l)} \rightarrow Ca(OH)_{2(aq)} + H_{2(g)}$

1) The metals potassium, sodium, lithium and calcium will all react with water.
2) Less reactive metals like zinc, iron and copper won't react with water.

I AM NOT HIGHLY REACTIVE — OK...

See, experiments aren't just for fun — they can give you a thrilling insight into the relative reactivities of elements.

Q1 Give the balanced equation, including state symbols, for the reaction of sodium and water. [3 marks]

Separating Metals from Metal Oxides

Most metals are not found in the earth as pure lumps. Instead, you have to extract them from a compound meaning more work is required. Thanks for nothing nature...

Metals Often Have to be Separated from their Oxides

1) Lots of common metals, like iron and aluminium, react with oxygen to form oxides. This process is an example of oxidation. These oxides are often the ores that the metals need to be extracted from.
2) A reaction that separates a metal from its oxide is called a reduction reaction.

An ore is a type of rock that contains metal compounds.

FORMATION OF METAL ORE:

Oxidation = Gain of Oxygen

E.g. magnesium is oxidised to make magnesium oxide.

$$2Mg + O_2 \rightarrow 2MgO$$

EXTRACTION OF METAL:

Reduction = Loss of Oxygen

E.g. copper oxide is reduced to copper.

$$2CuO + C \rightarrow 2Cu + CO_2$$

Some Metals can be Extracted by Reduction with Carbon

1) Some metals can be extracted from their ores chemically by reduction using carbon.
2) In this reaction, the ore is reduced as oxygen is removed from it, and carbon gains oxygen so is oxidised. For example...

$2Fe_2O_3$	+	3C	→	4Fe	+	$3CO_2$
iron(III) oxide	+	carbon	→	iron	+	carbon dioxide

3) The position of the metal in the reactivity series determines whether it can be extracted by reduction with carbon.

- Metals higher than carbon in the reactivity series have to be extracted using electrolysis (p.135), which is expensive.
- Metals below carbon in the reactivity series can be extracted by reduction using carbon. For example, iron oxide is reduced in a blast furnace to make iron.
- This is because carbon can only take the oxygen away from metals which are less reactive than carbon itself is.

The Reactivity Series		
Potassium	K	Extracted using electrolysis.
Sodium	Na	
Lithium	Li	
Calcium	Ca	
Magnesium	Mg	
Carbon	C	
Zinc	Zn	Extracted by reduction using carbon.
Iron	Fe	
Copper	Cu	

More Reactive → Less Reactive

Some metals are so unreactive they are in the earth as the metal itself. For example, gold is mined as its elemental form.

Make sure you can explain how and why different metals are extracted in different ways.

Are you going to revise this page, ore what?

Metals are great aren't they? Loads of uses. Shame extracting them's not always cheap. Make sure you know the difference between reduction and oxidation and why carbon can be used to extract some metals but not others.

Q1 Write a balanced equation for the reduction of zinc oxide, ZnO, by carbon, C. [2 marks]

Q2 A mining company tried to extract calcium from its ore by reduction with carbon. The process did not work. Explain why. [1 mark]

Redox Reactions

In chemistry, oxidation doesn't just mean gain of oxygen. No, that would be far too easy.

If Electrons are Transferred, It's a Redox Reaction

1) Oxidation can mean the addition of oxygen (or a reaction with it), and reduction can be the removal of oxygen, but on this page we're looking at oxidation and reduction in terms of electrons.
2) A loss of electrons is called oxidation. A gain of electrons is called reduction. A handy way to remember this is by the mnemonic OIL RIG — Oxidation Is Loss, Reduction Is Gain.
3) REDuction and OXidation happen at the same time — hence the term "REDOX".

- Iron atoms are oxidised to Fe^{2+} ions when they react with dilute acid: $Fe + 2H^+ \rightarrow Fe^{2+} + H_2$
- The iron atoms lose electrons. They're oxidised by the hydrogen ions: $Fe - 2e^- \rightarrow Fe^{2+}$
- The hydrogen ions gain electrons. They're reduced by the iron atoms: $2H^+ + 2e^- \rightarrow H_2$

All reactions of metals and acids on p.132 are redox reactions.

Displacement Reactions are Redox Reactions

1) Displacement reactions involve one metal kicking another one out of a compound. Here's the rule:

A MORE REACTIVE metal will displace a LESS REACTIVE metal from its compound.

2) If you put a reactive metal into the solution of a dissolved metal compound, the reactive metal will replace the less reactive metal in the compound (see the reactivity series on p.132).

If you put iron in a solution of copper sulfate ($CuSO_4$) the more reactive iron will 'kick out' the less reactive copper from the solution. You end up with iron sulfate solution ($FeSO_4$) and copper metal.

iron + copper sulfate → iron sulfate + copper

$$Fe_{(s)} + CuSO_{4(aq)} \rightarrow FeSO_{4(aq)} + Cu_{(s)}$$

In this reaction the iron loses 2 electrons to become a 2+ ion — it's oxidised.
The copper ion gains these 2 electrons to become a copper atom — it's reduced.

$$Fe \rightarrow Fe^{2+} + 2e^-$$

$$Cu^{2+} + 2e^- \rightarrow Cu$$

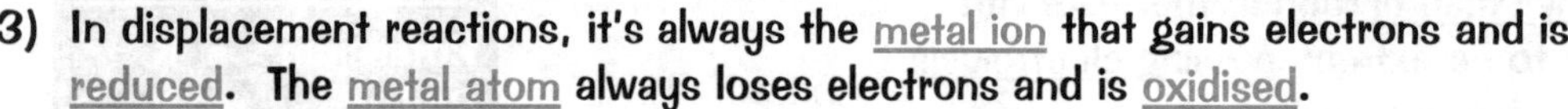

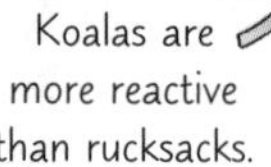

Koalas are more reactive than rucksacks.

3) In displacement reactions, it's always the metal ion that gains electrons and is reduced. The metal atom always loses electrons and is oxidised.
4) In the exam you could be asked to write word or symbol equations to show displacement reactions.

Ionic Equations Show Just the Useful Bits of Reactions

1) In an ionic equation only the particles that react and the products they form are shown. For example: $Mg_{(s)} + Zn^{2+}_{(aq)} \rightarrow Mg^{2+}_{(aq)} + Zn_{(s)}$
2) This just shows the displacement of zinc ions by magnesium metal.
Here's what the full equation of the above reaction would be if you'd started off with zinc chloride:

$$Mg_{(s)} + ZnCl_{2(aq)} \rightarrow MgCl_{2(aq)} + Zn_{(s)}$$

3) If you write out the equations so you can see all the ions, you'll see that the chloride ions don't change in the reaction — they're spectator ions. They're of no interest here so can be crossed out.

$$Mg_{(s)} + Zn^{2+}_{(aq)} + 2Cl^-_{(aq)} \rightarrow Mg^{2+}_{(aq)} + 2Cl^-_{(aq)} + Zn_{(s)}$$

4) Instead, the ionic equation for this displacement reaction just concentrates on the substances which are oxidised or reduced.

REDOX — great for bubble baths. Oh no, wait...

Ionic equations are hugely important in chemistry. Better practice until you can do them in your sleep.

Q1 The equation for the reaction of zinc and iron sulfate is: $Zn_{(s)} + FeSO_{4(aq)} \rightarrow ZnSO_{4(aq)} + Fe_{(s)}$

a) Write an ionic equation for the reaction. [1 mark]

b) State which species is being reduced and which is being oxidised. [2 marks]

Electrolysis

Electrolysis uses an electrical current to cause a reaction. It's actually pretty cool. No, really...

Electrolysis Means 'Splitting Up with Electricity'

1) During electrolysis, an electric current is passed through an electrolyte (a molten or dissolved ionic compound). The ions move towards the electrodes, where they react, and the compound decomposes.
2) The positive ions in the electrolyte will move towards the cathode (-ve electrode) and gain electrons (they are reduced).
3) The negative ions in the electrolyte will move towards the anode (+ve electrode) and lose electrons (they are oxidised).
4) This creates a flow of charge through the electrolyte as ions travel to the electrodes.
5) As ions gain or lose electrons, they form the uncharged element and are discharged from the electrolyte.

An electrolyte is just a liquid or solution that can conduct electricity. An electrode is a solid that conducts electricity and is submerged in the electrolyte

Electrolysis of Molten Ionic Solids Forms Elements

The electrodes should be inert so they don't react with the electrolyte.

1) An ionic solid can't be electrolysed because the ions are in fixed positions and can't move.
2) Molten ionic compounds can be electrolysed because the ions can move freely and conduct electricity.
3) Molten ionic liquids, e.g. lead bromide, are always broken up into their elements.
4) Positive metal ions are reduced to the element at the cathode: $Pb^{2+} + 2e^- \rightarrow Pb$
5) Negative non-metal ions are oxidised to the element at the anode: $2Br^- \rightarrow Br_2 + 2e^-$

Metals can be Extracted From Their Ores Using Electrolysis

If a metal is too reactive to be reduced with carbon (page 133) or reacts with carbon, then electrolysis can be used to extract it. Extracting metals via this method is very expensive as lots of energy is required to melt the ore and produce the required current.

1) Aluminium is extracted from the ore bauxite by electrolysis. Bauxite contains aluminium oxide, Al_2O_3.
2) Aluminium oxide has a very high melting temperature so it's mixed with cryolite to lower the melting point.
3) The molten mixture contains free ions — so it'll conduct electricity.
4) The positive Al^{3+} ions are attracted to the negative electrode where they each pick up three electrons and turn into neutral aluminium atoms. These then sink to the bottom of the electrolysis tank.
5) The negative O^{2-} ions are attracted to the positive electrode where they each lose two electrons. The neutral oxygen atoms will then combine to form O_2 molecules.

Cryolite is an aluminium based compound with a lower melting point than aluminium oxide.

At the negative electrode:

Reduction — a gain of electrons:

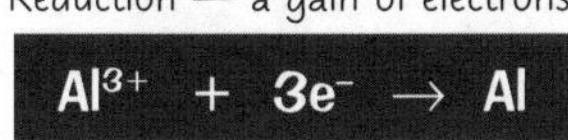

$Al^{3+} + 3e^- \rightarrow Al$

Metals form positive ions, so they're attracted to the negative electrode.

Aluminium is produced at the negative electrode.

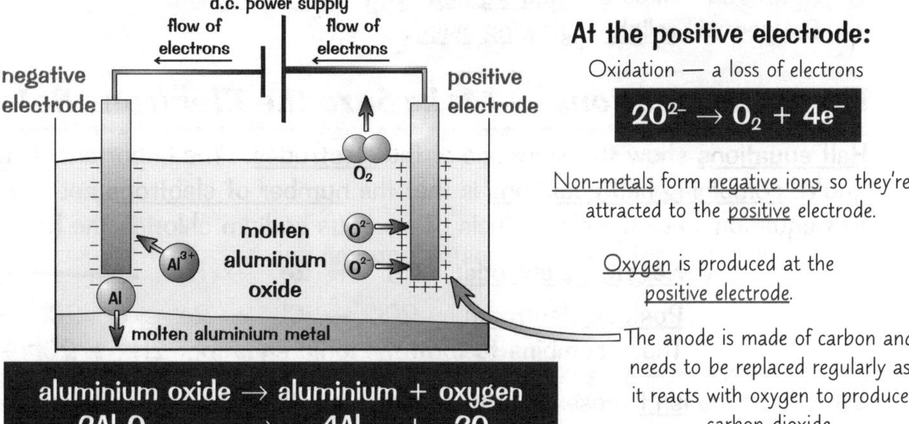

At the positive electrode:

Oxidation — a loss of electrons

$2O^{2-} \rightarrow O_2 + 4e^-$

Non-metals form negative ions, so they're attracted to the positive electrode.

Oxygen is produced at the positive electrode.

The anode is made of carbon and needs to be replaced regularly as it reacts with oxygen to produce carbon dioxide.

Overall Equation:

aluminium oxide → aluminium + oxygen

$2Al_2O_{3(l)} \rightarrow 4Al_{(l)} + 3O_{2(g)}$

Faster shopping at the supermarket — use Electrolleys...

It might be jolly useful for your exams to learn the products of electrolysis of molten lead bromide...

Q1 A student carries out electrolysis on molten sodium chloride. What is produced at:
a) the anode? b) the cathode? [2 marks]

Electrolysis of Aqueous Solutions

When you electrolyse an aqueous solution, you also have to factor in the ions in the water.

It May be Easier to Discharge Ions from Water than the Solute

1) In aqueous solutions, as well as the ions from the ionic compound, there will be hydrogen ions (H^+) and hydroxide ions (OH^-) from the water: $H_2O_{(l)} \rightleftharpoons H^+_{(aq)} + OH^-_{(aq)}$
2) At the cathode, if H^+ ions and metal ions are present, hydrogen gas will be produced if the metal ions form an elemental metal that is more reactive than hydrogen (e.g. sodium ions). If the metal ions form an elemental metal that is less reactive than hydrogen (e.g. copper ions), a solid layer of the pure metal will be produced instead.
3) At the anode, if OH^- and halide ions (Cl^-, Br^-, I^-) are present, molecules of chlorine, bromine or iodine will be formed. If no halide ions are present, then the OH^- ions are discharged and oxygen will be formed.

A solution of copper(II) sulfate ($CuSO_4$) contains four different ions: Cu^{2+}, SO_4^{2-}, H^+ and OH^-.

- Copper metal is less reactive than hydrogen. So at the cathode, copper metal is produced and coats the electrode.

$$Cu^{2+} + 2e^- \rightarrow Cu$$

- There aren't any halide ions present. So at the anode oxygen and water are produced. The oxygen can be seen as bubbles.

$$4OH^- \rightarrow O_2 + 2H_2O + 4e^-$$

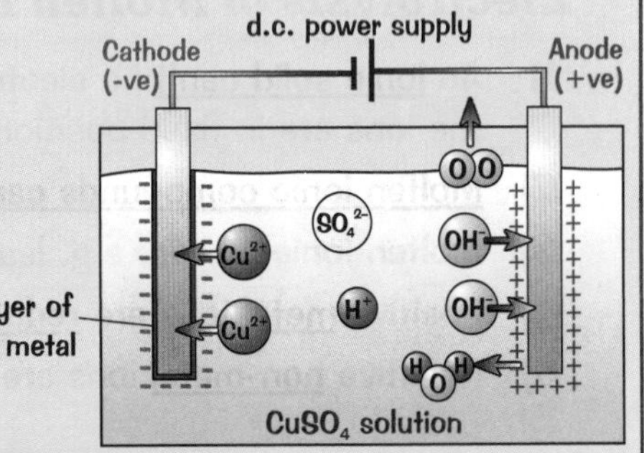

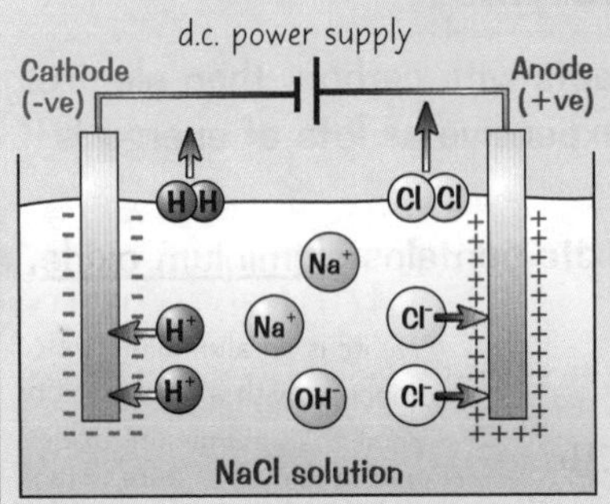

A solution of sodium chloride (NaCl) contains four different ions: Na^+, Cl^-, OH^- and H^+.

- Sodium metal is more reactive hydrogen. So at the cathode, hydrogen gas is produced.

$$2H^+ + 2e^- \rightarrow H_2$$

- Chloride ions are present in the solution. So at the anode chlorine gas is produced.

$$2Cl^- \rightarrow Cl_2 + 2e^-$$

If you're drawing the apparatus for an electrolysis experiment, remember to include a d.c. power supply, wires and labels for the anode and the cathode. The anode is the electrode on the same side as the longer line of the d.c. power supply symbol.

PRACTICAL

You can set up an electrolysis experiment in the lab like the set-up on page 236. Once the experiment is finished you can test any gaseous products to work out what was produced.

- Chlorine bleaches damp litmus paper, turning it white.
- Hydrogen makes a "squeaky pop" with a lighted splint.
- Oxygen will relight a glowing splint.

For more on tests for gases, turn to page 155.

The Half Equations — Make Sure the Electrons Balance

Half equations show the reactions at the electrodes. The important thing to remember when you're combining half equations is that the number of electrons needs to be the same for each half equation. For the electrolysis of aqueous sodium chloride the half equations are:

Negative Electrode: $2H^+ + 2e^- \rightarrow H_2$

Positive Electrode: $2Cl^- \rightarrow Cl_2 + 2e^-$ or $2Cl^- - 2e^- \rightarrow Cl_2$

These combine to form the ionic equation: $2H^+ + 2Cl^- \rightarrow H_2 + Cl_2$

The electrons on each side of the half equations balance, so they can be cancelled out in the full ionic equation.

When a halide isn't present in the aqueous solution, the half equation for the anode is:

$$4OH^- \rightarrow O_2 + 2H_2O + 4e^- \quad \text{or} \quad 4OH^- - 4e^- \rightarrow O_2 + 2H_2O$$

I wrote a poem about my tabby — it was a cat ode...

So it's kinda confusing this electrolysis malarkey — you need to take it slow and make sure you get it.

Q1 An aqueous solution of copper chloride, $CuCl_2$, is electrolysed using inert electrodes. Give the half equations for the anode and the cathode. [2 marks]

Revision Questions for Topics C3 & C4

Well, that wraps up Topic C4. Time to find out how much you really know from Topics C3 and C4.

- Try these questions and tick off each one when you get it right.
- When you've done all the questions under a heading and are completely happy with it, tick it off.

Moles and Equations (p.123-127)

1) How do you calculate the relative formula mass, M_r of a substance?
2) State the value of the Avogadro constant.
3) What is the formula that relates the number of moles of a substance to its mass and M_r?
4) What does conservation of mass mean?
5) Suggest why the mass of a reaction vessel might decrease during a reaction.
6) How can you determine the number of moles of each substance that would react together from the balanced reaction equation?
7) Explain what is meant by the term 'limiting reactant'.

Concentrations of Solutions (p.128)

8) What is concentration?
9) Give the equation for working out the concentration of a solution in g/dm^3.

Acids and their Reactions (p.129-131)

10) State whether the following pH values are acidic, alkaline or neutral.
    a) 9 b) 2 c) 7 d) 6
11) Give the general word equation for the reaction between an acid and a base.
12) What type of reagent could be used to show that an acid or base has been completely neutralised?
13) What is a strong acid?
14) Write a balanced equation for the reaction between hydrochloric acid and sodium carbonate.

The Reactivity Series (p. 132)

15) Is zinc more or less reactive than iron?
16) What is the general word equation for the reaction of a metal with an acid?
17) Give the balanced equation for the reaction of calcium with water.

Reduction and Oxidation (p.133-134)

18) What product forms in the oxidation of magnesium by oxygen?
19) Explain how you decide whether a metal can be extracted from its oxide by reduction with carbon.
20) In terms of electrons, give the definition of oxidation.
21) In a displacement reaction, does the metal atom get reduced or oxidised?

Electrolysis (p.135-136)

22) During electrolysis, which electrode are the positive ions attracted to?
23) Why can ionic solids not undergo electrolysis?
24) Do ions get reduced or oxidised at the anode?
25) During the manufacture of aluminium from bauxite, which electrode is aluminium formed at?
26) In what situation will hydrogen gas be given out during the electrolysis of an aqueous solution of an ionic solid?
27) If halide ions are present in an aqueous solution of an ionic solid will oxygen gas be released?

Exothermic and Endothermic Reactions

Whenever chemical reactions occur, there are changes in energy. This means that when chemicals get together, things either hot up or cool right off. I'll give you a heads up — this page is a good 'un.

Energy is Moved Around in Chemical Reactions

1) Chemicals store a certain amount of energy — and different chemicals store different amounts.
2) If the products of a reaction store more energy than the original reactants, then they must have taken in the difference in energy between the products and reactants from the surroundings during the reaction.
3) But if they store less, then the excess energy was transferred to the surroundings during the reaction.
4) The overall amount of energy doesn't change. This is because energy is conserved in reactions — it can't be created or destroyed, only moved around. This means the amount of energy in the universe always stays the same.

In an Exothermic Reaction, Heat is Given Out

1) An EXOTHERMIC reaction is one which transfers energy to the surroundings, usually by heating. This is shown by a rise in temperature.
2) The best example of an exothermic reaction is burning fuels — also called COMBUSTION. This gives out a lot of energy — it's very exothermic.
3) Neutralisation reactions (acid + alkali) are also exothermic.
4) Many oxidation reactions are exothermic. For example, adding sodium to water releases energy, so it must be exothermic — see page 108. The reaction releases energy and the sodium moves about on the surface of the water as it is oxidised.

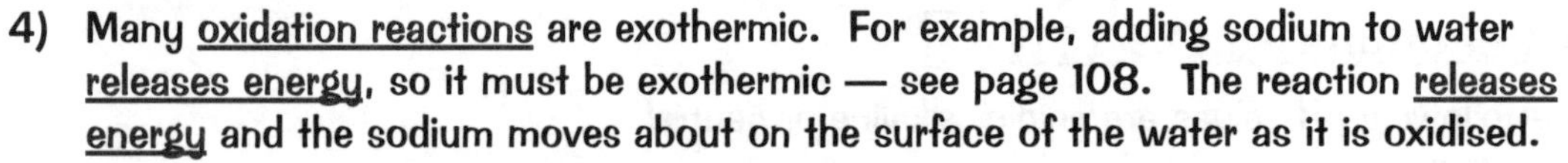

5) Exothermic reactions have lots of everyday uses. For example:

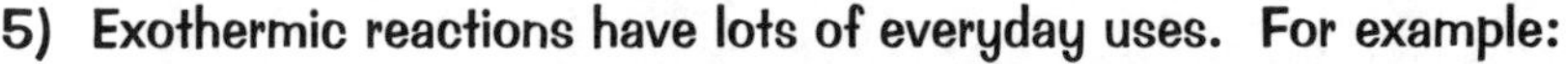

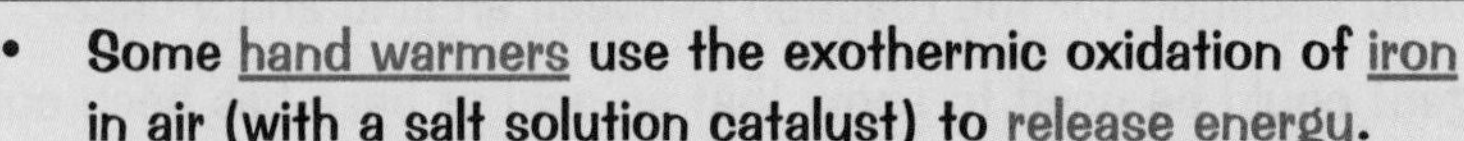

- Some hand warmers use the exothermic oxidation of iron in air (with a salt solution catalyst) to release energy.
- Self heating cans of hot chocolate and coffee also rely on exothermic reactions between chemicals in their bases.

In an Endothermic Reaction, Heat is Taken In

Physical processes can also take in or release energy. E.g. freezing is an exothermic process, melting is endothermic.

1) An ENDOTHERMIC reaction is one which takes in energy from the surroundings. This is shown by a fall in temperature.
2) Endothermic reactions are much less common than exothermic reactions, but they include:
   - The reaction between citric acid and sodium hydrogencarbonate.
   - Thermal decomposition — e.g. heating calcium carbonate causes it to decompose into calcium oxide (also called quicklime) and carbon dioxide:

Calcium carbonate — $CaCO_3$ (+ HEAT) → CO_2 + CaO — Quicklime

3) Endothermic reactions also have everyday uses. For example:

Endothermic reactions are used in some sports injury packs — the chemical reaction allows the pack to become instantly cooler without having to put it in the freezer.

Right, so burning gives out heat — really...

Remember, "exo-" = exit, "-thermic" = heat, so an exothermic reaction is one that gives out heat — and endothermic means just the opposite. To make sure you really understand these terms, try this question.

Q1 A student prepares a flask containing ethanoic acid and measures its temperature as 22.5 °C. He then adds dilute potassium hydroxide solution which is 21 °C. After 2 minutes the temperature of the reaction mixture is 28.5 °C. Is the reaction exothermic or endothermic? [1 mark]

More Exothermic and Endothermic Reactions

Sometimes it's not enough to just know if a reaction is endothermic or exothermic. You may also need to know how much energy is absorbed or released — you can do experiments to find this out. Fun, fun, fun...

Energy Transfer can be Measured

PRACTICAL

1) You can measure the amount of energy released by a chemical reaction (in solution) by taking the temperature of the reagents, mixing them in a polystyrene cup and measuring the temperature of the solution at the end of the reaction. Easy.
2) The biggest problem with energy measurements is the amount of energy lost to the surroundings.
3) You can reduce it a bit by putting the polystyrene cup into a beaker of cotton wool to give more insulation, and putting a lid on the cup to reduce energy lost by evaporation.
4) This method works for neutralisation reactions or reactions between metals and acids, or carbonates and acids.
5) You can also use this method to investigate what effect different variables have on the amount of energy transferred — e.g. the mass or concentration of the reactants used.
6) Here's how you could test the effect of acid concentration on the energy released in a neutralisation reaction between hydrochloric acid (HCl) and sodium hydroxide (NaOH):

1) Put 25 cm^3 of 0.25 mol/dm^3 of hydrochloric acid and sodium hydroxide in separate beakers.
2) Place the beakers in a water bath set to 25 °C until they are both at the same temperature (25 °C).
3) Add the HCl followed by the NaOH to a polystyrene cup with a lid — as in the diagram above.
4) Take the temperature of the mixture every 30 seconds, and record the highest temperature.
5) Repeat steps 1-4 using 0.5 mol/dm^3 and then 1 mol/dm^3 of hydrochloric acid.

Reaction profiles are sometimes called energy level diagrams.

Reaction Profiles Show Energy Changes

Reaction profiles are diagrams that show the relative energies of the reactants and products in a reaction, and how the energy changes over the course of the reaction.

1) This shows an exothermic reaction — the products are at a lower energy than the reactants. The difference in height represents the overall energy change in the reaction (the energy given out) per mole.
2) The initial rise in energy represents the energy needed to start the reaction. This is the activation energy (E_a).
3) The activation energy is the minimum amount of energy the reactants need to collide with each other and react. The greater the activation energy, the more energy needed to start the reaction — this has to be supplied, e.g. by heating the reaction mixture.

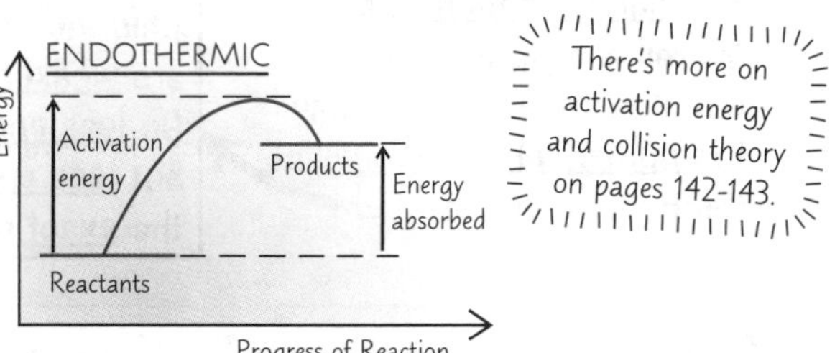

There's more on activation energy and collision theory on pages 142-143.

1) This shows an endothermic reaction because the products are at a higher energy than the reactants.
2) The difference in height represents the overall energy change during the reaction (the energy taken in) per mole.

Energy transfer — make sure you take it all in...

Don't get confused by these diagrams. In an exothermic reaction the particles release energy to their surroundings — even though the reaction mixture gets warmer, the particles themselves have lost energy.

Q1 Here is the equation for the combustion of methane in air: $CH_{4(g)} + 2O_{2(g)} \rightarrow CO_{2(g)} + 2H_2O_{(g)}$
Draw a reaction profile for this reaction. [3 marks]

Bond Energies

So you know that chemical reactions can take in or release energy — this page is about what causes these energy changes. Hint — it's all to do with making and breaking chemical bonds.

There's more on energy transfer on page 138.

Energy Must Always be Supplied to Break Bonds

1) During a chemical reaction, old bonds are broken and new bonds are formed.
2) Energy must be supplied to break existing bonds — so bond breaking is an endothermic process.
3) Energy is released when new bonds are formed — so bond formation is an exothermic process.

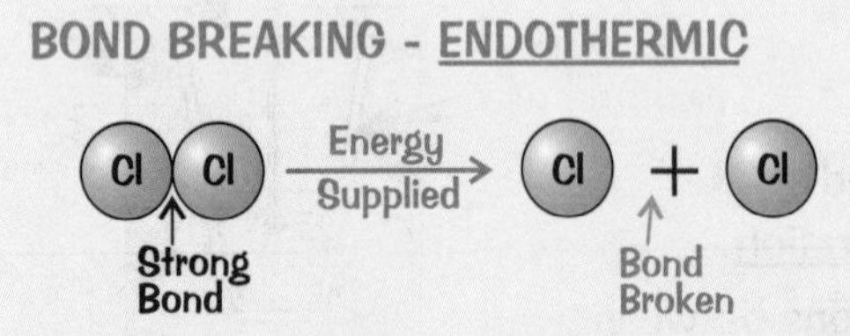

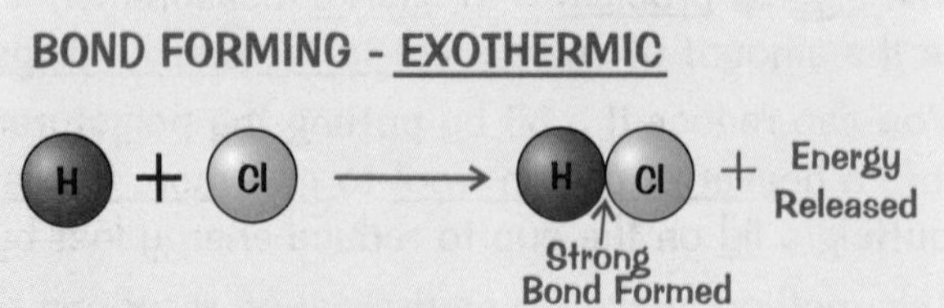

4) In exothermic reactions the energy released by forming bonds is greater than the energy used to break them. In endothermic reactions the energy used to break bonds is greater than the energy released by forming them.

Bond Energy Calculations — Need to be Practised

Bond forming

Every chemical bond has a particular bond energy associated with it.
This bond energy varies slightly depending on the compound the bond occurs in.

You can use these known bond energies to calculate the overall energy change for a reaction. The overall energy change is the sum of the energies needed to break bonds in the reactants minus the energy released when the new bonds are formed in the products. You need to practise a few of these, but the basic idea is really very simple...

EXAMPLE:

Using the bond energies given below, calculate the energy change for the reaction between H_2 and Cl_2 forming HCl:

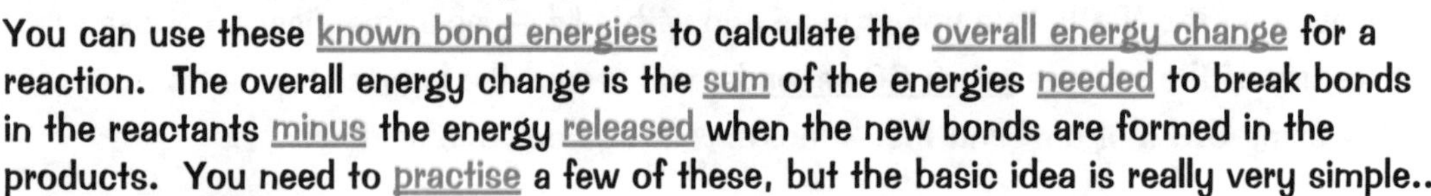

The bond energies you need are: H–H: +436 kJ/mol; Cl–Cl: +242 kJ/mol; H–Cl: +431 kJ/mol.

1) Find the energy required to break the original bonds:
   (1 × H–H) + (1 × Cl–Cl) = 436 kJ/mol + 242 kJ/mol = 678 kJ/mol
2) Find the energy released by forming the new bonds.
   2 × H–Cl = 2 × 431 kJ/mol = 862 kJ/mol
3) Find the overall energy change for the reaction using this equation:
   Overall energy change = energy required to break bonds – energy released by forming bonds
   = 678 kJ/mol – 862 kJ/mol = –184 kJ/mol

You can't compare the overall energy changes of reactions unless you know the numerical differences in the bond energies.

Chlorine and bromine react with hydrogen in a similar way. Br–Br bonds are weaker than Cl-Cl bonds and H–Br bonds are weaker than H–Cl bonds. So less energy is needed to break the bonds in the reaction with bromine, but less energy is released when the new bonds form. So unless you know the exact difference, you can't say which reaction releases more energy.

A student and their bed — a bond that can never be broken...

This stuff might look hard at the moment, but with a bit of practice it's dead easy and it'll win you easy marks if you understand all the theory behind it. See how you get on with this question:

Q1 N_2 reacts with H_2 in the following reaction: $N_2 + 3H_2 \rightarrow 2NH_3$
The bond energies for these molecules are:
N≡N: 941 kJ/mol; H–H: 436 kJ/mol; N–H: 391 kJ/mol.
Calculate the overall energy change for this reaction [3 marks]

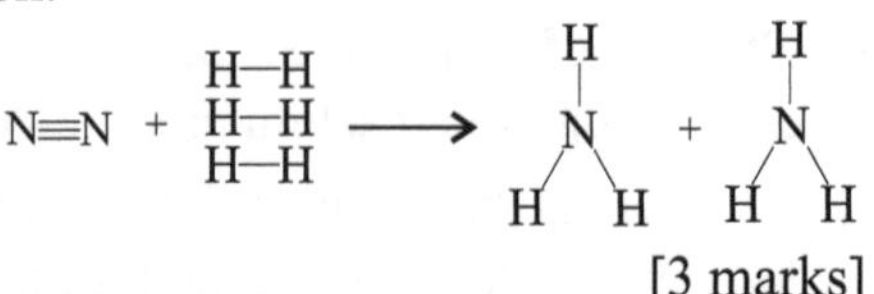

Revision Questions for Topic C5

Right, lets see how much you can remember — don't worry though, you can flick back if you get stuck.

- Try these questions and tick off each one when you get it right.
- When you've done all the questions under a heading and are completely happy with it, tick it off.

Exothermic and Endothermic Reactions (p.138-139) ☐

1) In an exothermic reaction is heat transferred to or from the surroundings? ☐
2) Name two different types of reaction which are exothermic. ☐
3) Define what is meant by an endothermic reaction. ☐
4) Write down the equation for the thermal decomposition of calcium carbonate. ☐
5) What is the purpose of putting the reaction container into a beaker containing cotton wool during an experiment to investigate the temperature change of an exothermic reaction? ☐
6) Sketch an energy level diagram for an endothermic reaction. ☐
7) What is the activation energy of a reaction? ☐
8) Is the following statement true or false? In an endothermic reaction, the products of the reaction have more energy than the reactants. ☐

Bond Energies (p.140) ☐

9) For the following sentences, use either endothermic or exothermic to fill in the blanks:
   a) Bond breaking is an __________ process.
   b) Bond forming is an __________ process.
   c) In an __________ reaction, the energy released by forming bonds is greater than the energy used to break them. ☐
10) What three steps would you use to find the overall energy change in a reaction if you were given the known bond enthalpies for the bonds present in the reactants and products? ☐

Rates of Reaction

Rates of reaction are pretty important. In the chemical industry, the faster you make chemicals, the faster you make money (and the faster everyone gets to go home for tea).

Reactions Can Go at All Sorts of Different Rates

1) The rate of a chemical reaction is how fast the reactants are changed into products.
2) One of the slowest is the rusting of iron (it's not slow enough though — what about my little Mini).
3) Other slow reactions include chemical weathering — like acid rain damage to limestone buildings.
4) An example of a moderate speed reaction would be the metal magnesium reacting with an acid to produce a gentle stream of bubbles.
5) Burning is a fast reaction, but explosions are even faster and release a lot of gas. Explosive reactions are all over in a fraction of a second.

You Need to Understand Graphs for the Rate of Reaction

1) You can find the speed of a reaction by recording the amount of product formed, or the amount of reactant used up over time (see page 144).
2) The steeper the line on the graph, the faster the rate of reaction. Over time the line becomes less steep as the reactants are used up.
3) The quickest reactions have the steepest lines and become flat in the least time.
4) The plot below uses the amount of product formed over time to show how the speed of a particular reaction varies under different conditions.

For more on the conditions that affect the rate of reaction — see next page.

- Graph 1 represents the original reaction.
- Graphs 2 and 3 represent the reaction taking place quicker, but with the same initial amounts of reactants. The slopes of the graphs are steeper than for graph 1.
- Graphs 1, 2 and 3 all converge at the same level, showing that they all produce the same amount of product although they take different times to produce it.
- Graph 4 shows more product and a faster reaction. This can only happen if more reactant(s) are added at the start.

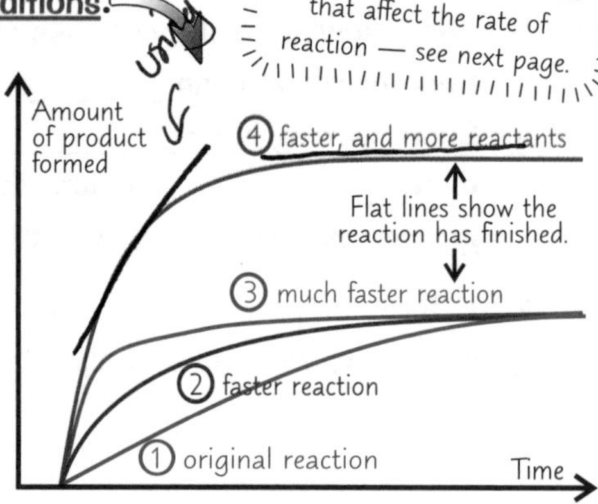

Particles Must Collide with Enough Energy in Order to React

Reaction rates are explained perfectly by collision theory. It's simple really.
The rate of a chemical reaction depends on:

1) The collision frequency of reacting particles (how often they collide). The more collisions there are the faster the reaction is. E.g. doubling the frequency of collisions doubles the rate.
2) The energy transferred during a collision. Particles have to collide with enough energy for the collision to be successful.

A successful collision is a collision that ends in the particles reacting to form products.

You might remember from page 139 that the minimum amount of energy that particles need to react is called the activation energy. Particles need this much energy to break the bonds in the reactants and start the reaction.

Factors that increase the number of collisions (so that a greater proportion of reacting particles collide) or the amount of energy particles collide with will increase the rate of the reaction (see next page for more).

Get a fast, furious reaction — tickle your teacher...

Collision theory's essential for understanding how different factors affect the rate of reaction — so make sure you understand it before moving on to the rest of Topic C6.

Q1 What is meant by the term activation energy? [1 mark]

Factors Affecting Rates of Reaction

I'd ask you to guess what this page is about, but the title pretty much says it all really. Read on...

The Rate of Reaction Depends on Four Things

1) Temperature.
2) The concentration of a solution or the pressure of gas.
3) Surface area — this changes depending on the size of the lumps of a solid.
4) The presence of a catalyst.

More Collisions Increases the Rate of Reaction

All four methods of increasing the rate of a reaction can be explained in terms of increasing the number of successful collisions between the reacting particles:

Increasing the Temperature Increases the Rate

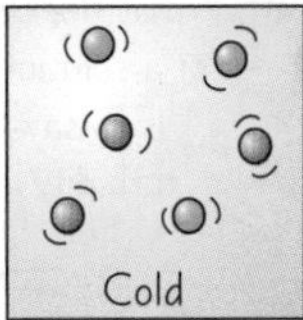

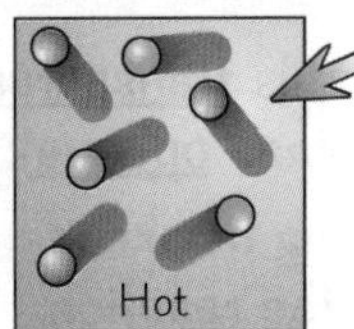

1) When the temperature is increased, the particles all move faster.
2) If they're moving faster, they're going to collide more frequently.
3) Also the faster they move the more energy they have, so more of the collisions will have enough energy to make the reaction happen.

Increasing the Concentration or Pressure Increases the Rate

1) If a solution is made more concentrated, it means there are more particles knocking about in the same volume of water (or other solvent).
2) Similarly, when the pressure of a gas is increased, it means that the same number of particles occupies a smaller space.
3) This makes collisions between the reactant particles more frequent.

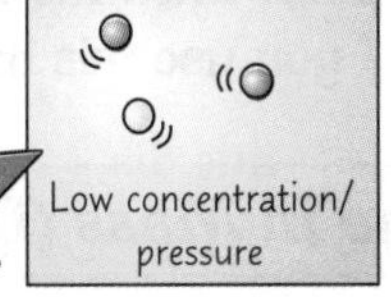

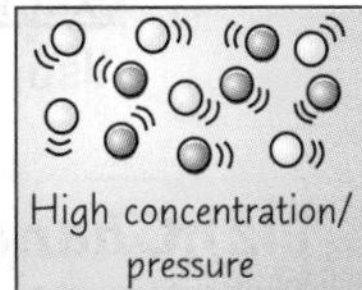

Increasing the Surface Area Increases the Rate

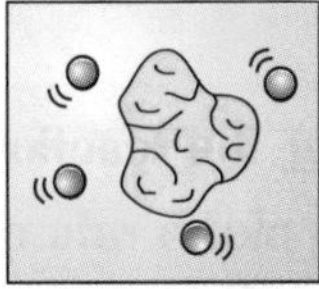

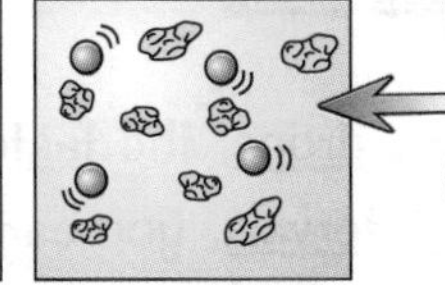

1) If one of the reactants is a solid, then breaking it up into smaller pieces will increase its surface area to volume ratio.
2) This means that for the same volume of the solid, the particles around it will have more area to work on — so there will be collisions more frequently.

Using a Catalyst Increases the Rate

1) A catalyst is a substance that speeds up a reaction, without being used up in the reaction itself. This means it's not part of the overall reaction equation.
2) Different catalysts are needed for different reactions, but they all work by decreasing the activation energy needed for the reaction to occur. They do this by providing an alternative reaction pathway with a lower activation energy.
3) Enzymes are biological catalysts — they catalyse reactions in living things.

This is a reaction profile. There's more on these on p.139.

Energy
Without Catalyst
With Catalyst
Reactants
Activation energy without a catalyst
Activation energy with a catalyst
Products
Progress of Reaction

Increase your concentration — burn through that exam paper...

Catalysts are really useful — they don't get used up so you can use them over and over again. Brilliant.

Q1 For each of the following pairs of reactions, state which one would have the fastest rate (A or B) and why:
a) A: A 2 g solid strip of magnesium with water. B: 2 g of powdered magnesium with water. [2 marks]
b) A: 2 mol/dm^3 HCl with excess ethanoic acid. B: 4 mol/dm^3 HCl with excess ethanoic acid. [2 marks]

→ Ignore all Anomalous results when calculating a mean.

PRACTICAL Measuring Rates of Reaction

All this talk about rates of reactions is fine and dandy, but it's no good if you can't measure it.

Here Are Three Ways to Measure the Rate of a Reaction

The rate of a reaction can be observed either by how quickly the reactants are used up or how quickly the products are formed:

$$\text{Rate of Reaction} = \frac{\text{Amount of reactant used or amount of product formed}}{\text{Time}}$$

This is the mean rate of reaction. To find the rate of a reaction at a particular time, you'll need to plot a graph and find the gradient at that time (see page 146).

When the product or reactant is a gas you usually measure the amount in cm^3. If it's a solid, then you use grams (g). Time is often measured in seconds (s). This means that the units for rate may be in cm^3/s or in g/s. You can also measure the amount of product or reactant in moles — so the units of rate could also be mol/s. Here are three different ways of measuring the rate of a reaction:

1) Precipitation and Colour Change

1) You can record the visual change in a reaction if the initial solution is transparent and the product is a precipitate which clouds the solution (it becomes opaque).
2) You can observe a mark through the solution and measure how long it takes for it to disappear — the faster the mark disappears, the quicker the reaction.
3) If the reactants are coloured and the products are colourless (or vice versa), you can time how long it takes for the solution to lose (or gain) its colour.
4) The results are very subjective — different people might not agree over the exact point when the mark 'disappears' or the solution changes colour. Also, if you use this method, you can't plot a rate of reaction graph from the results.

A posh way of saying that the cloudiness of a solution changes is to say that its 'turbidity' changes.

2) Change in Mass (Usually Gas Given Off)

1) Measuring the speed of a reaction that produces a gas can be carried out using a mass balance.
2) As the gas is released, the mass disappearing is measured on the balance.
3) The quicker the reading on the balance drops, the faster the reaction.
4) If you take measurements at regular intervals, you can plot a rate of reaction graph and find the rate quite easily (see page 146 for more).
5) This is the most accurate of the three methods described on this page because the mass balance is very accurate. But it has the disadvantage of releasing the gas straight into the room.

3) The Volume of Gas Given Off

1) This involves the use of a gas syringe to measure the volume of gas given off.
2) The more gas given off during a given time interval, the faster the reaction.
3) Gas syringes usually give volumes accurate to the nearest cm^3, so they're quite accurate. You can take measurements at regular intervals and plot a rate of reaction graph using this method too. You have to be quite careful though — if the reaction is too vigorous, you can easily blow the plunger out of the end of the syringe.

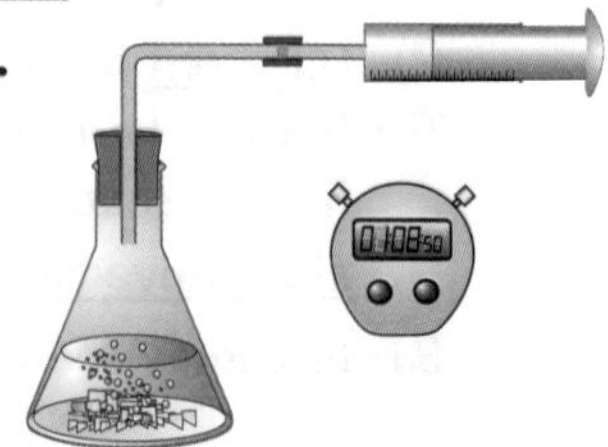

OK, have you got your stopwatch ready... *BANG!* — oh...

Make sure you've learnt the three different methods on this page, then have a go at this question:

Q1 The reaction between solid Na_2CO_3 and aqueous HCl releases CO_2 (a gas).

a) Describe an experiment that would allow you to measure the rate of this reaction. [3 marks]

b) Suggest units that would be appropriate for expressing the rate of this reaction. [1 mark]

Two Rates Experiments

PRACTICAL

Here's a lovely page on practical investigations into the effect of concentration on the rate of a reaction. It's particularly lovely because it's got two methods that you could use. Get your safety goggles on and let's go...

Magnesium and HCl React to Produce H_2 Gas

1) Start by adding a set volume of dilute hydrochloric acid to a conical flask and carefully place on a mass balance.
2) Now add some magnesium ribbon to the acid and quickly plug the flask with cotton wool.
3) Start the stopwatch and record the mass on the balance. Take readings of the mass at regular intervals.

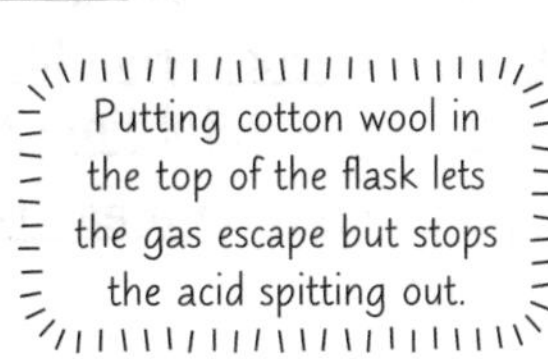

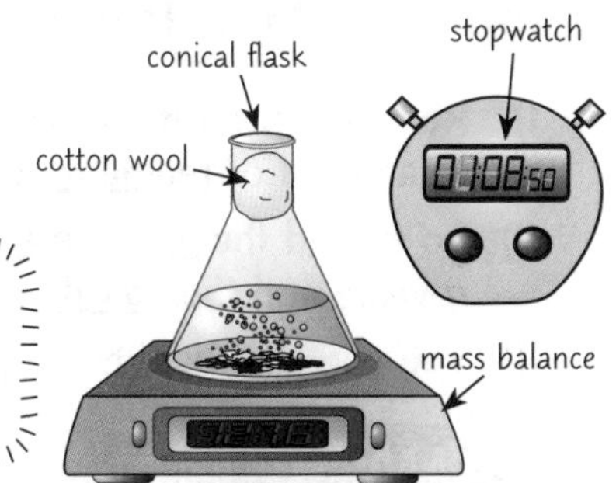

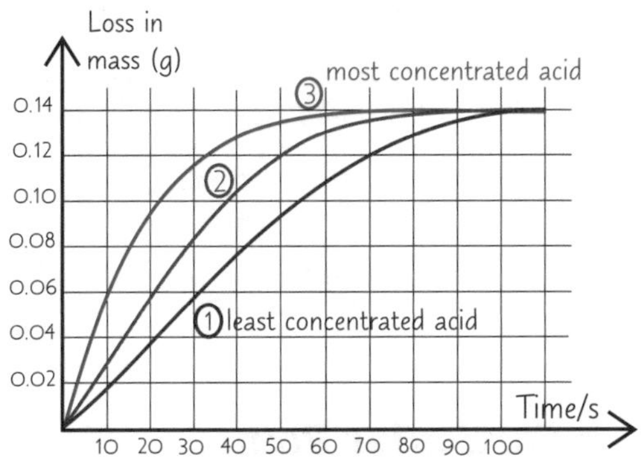

4) Plot the results in a table and work out the mass lost for each reading. Now you can plot a graph with time on the *x*-axis and loss of mass on the *y*-axis.
5) Repeat with more concentrated acid solutions. Variables such as the amount of magnesium ribbon and the volume of acid used should be kept the same each time — only change the acid's concentration. This is to make your experiment a fair test — see p.4.
6) The three graphs show that a higher concentration of acid gives a faster rate of reaction.

You could also measure the gas released using a gas syringe, as on the previous page.

Sodium Thiosulfate and HCl Produce a Cloudy Precipitate

1) These two chemicals are both clear solutions. They react together to form a yellow precipitate of sulfur.
2) Start by adding a set volume of dilute sodium thiosulfate to a conical flask.
3) Place the flask on a piece of paper with a black cross drawn on it. Add some dilute HCl to the flask and start the stopwatch.
4) Now watch the black cross disappear through the cloudy sulfur and time how long it takes to go.
5) The reaction can be repeated with solutions of either reactant at different concentrations. (Only change the concentration of one reactant at a time though). The depth of the liquid must be kept the same each time.
6) These results show the effect of increasing the concentration of HCl on the rate of reaction, when added to an excess of sodium thiosulfate.

This reaction releases sulfur dioxide, so the experiment should be carried out in a well-ventilated place.

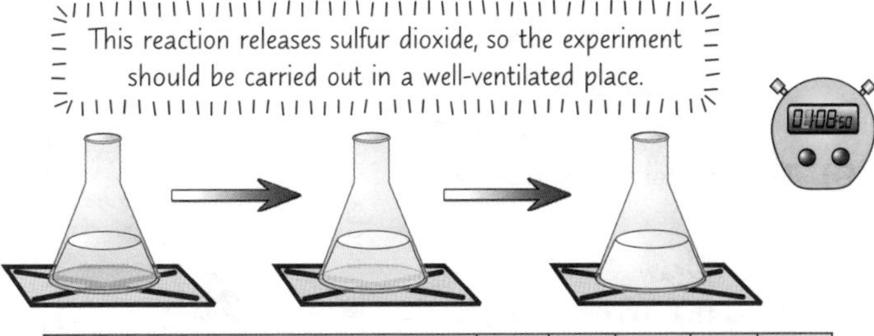

Concentration of HCl (mol/dm^3)	0.5	1	1.5	2	2.5
Time taken for mark to disappear (s)	193	184	178	171	164

7) The higher the concentration, the quicker the reaction and therefore the less time it takes for the mark to disappear.
8) One sad thing about this reaction is that it doesn't give a set of graphs. Well I think it's sad. All you get is a set of readings of how long it took till the mark disappeared for each concentration. Boring.

Although you could draw a graph of concentration against 1/time which will give you an approximate rate.

Bubbling acid, sulfurous clouds — proper witchcraft this is...

You should learn the methods involved in these experiments — but remember, other reactions can also be used to investigate the four factors that affect rate. You might see different experiments in your exams, or the same ones but measuring a different factor — so watch out.

Q1 A student carried out an experiment investigating the effect of changing the HCl concentration on the rate of reaction between HCl and Mg. State two factors that he should have kept constant. [2 marks]

Finding Reaction Rates from Graphs

You might remember a bit about how to interpret graphs on reaction rate from page 142 — well this page shows you how to use them to calculate rates.

You can Calculate the Mean Reaction Rate from a Graph

1) Remember, a rate of reaction graph shows the amount of product formed or amount of reactant used up on the y-axis and time on the x-axis.
2) So to find the mean rate for the whole reaction, you just work out the overall change in the y-value and then divide this by the total time taken for the reaction.
3) You can also use the graph to find the mean rate of reaction between any two points in time:

The graph shows the volume of gas released by a reaction, measured at regular intervals. Find the mean rate of reaction between 20 s and 40 s.

Mean rate of reaction = change in y ÷ change in x
= (19 cm³ – 15 cm³) ÷ 20 s.
= 0.2 cm³/s

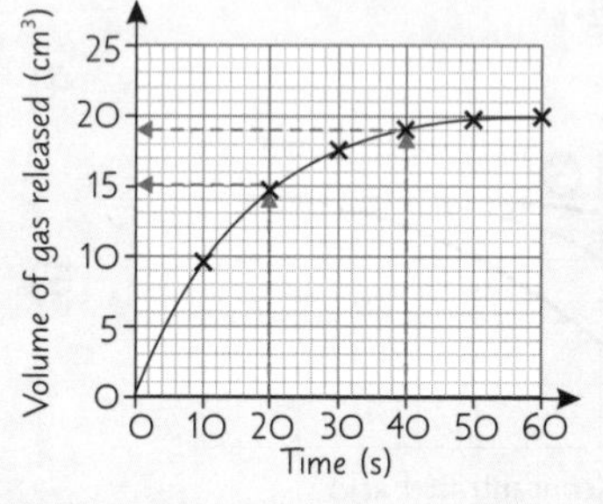

If you're asked to find the mean rate of reaction for the whole reaction, remember that the reaction finishes as soon as the line on the graph goes flat.

Draw a Tangent to Find the Reaction Rate at a Particular Point

If you want to find the rate of the reaction at a particular point in time, you need to find the gradient (slope) of the curve at that point. The easiest way to do this is to draw a tangent to the curve — a straight line that touches the curve at one point and doesn't cross it. You then work out the gradient of the tangent. It's simpler than it sounds, honest...

EXAMPLE:

The graph below shows the mass of reactant used up measured at regular intervals during a chemical reaction. What is the rate of reaction at 3 minutes?

1) Position a ruler on the graph at the point where you want to know the rate — here it's 3 minutes.
2) Adjust the ruler until the space between the ruler and the curve is equal on both sides of the point.
3) Draw a line along the ruler to make the tangent. Extend the line right across the graph.

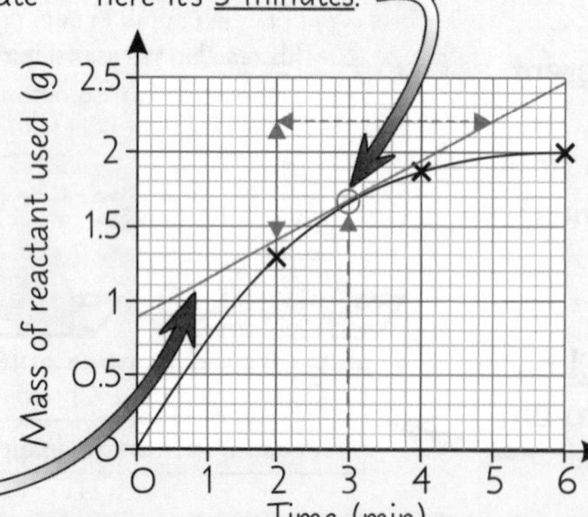

4) Pick two points on the line that are easy to read. Use them to calculate the gradient of the tangent in order to find the rate:

gradient = change in y ÷ change in x
= (2.2 – 1.4) ÷ (5.0 – 2.0)
= 0.8 ÷ 3.0
= 0.27

So, the rate of reaction at 3 minutes was 0.27 g/min.

Calculate your reaction to this page. Boredom? How dare you...

There's only one way to learn this stuff properly — practise. So you'd better get going with this question.

Q1 Calcium carbonate powder was added to a conical flask containing dilute HCl. CO_2 was produced and collected in a gas syringe. The volume of gas released was recorded at 10 second intervals in the following table:

Time (s)	10	20	30	40	50	60
Volume of CO_2 (cm³)	24	32	36	38	39	40

a) Plot these results on a graph and draw a line of best fit. [3 marks]

b) Find the rate of the reaction at time = 25 s. [4 marks]

Reversible Reactions

Some reactions can go backwards. Honestly, that's all you need...

The ⇌ shows the reaction goes both ways.

Reversible Reactions Will Reach Equilibrium

This equation shows a reversible reaction — the products (C and D) can react to form the reactants (A and B) again:

$$A + B \rightleftharpoons C + D$$

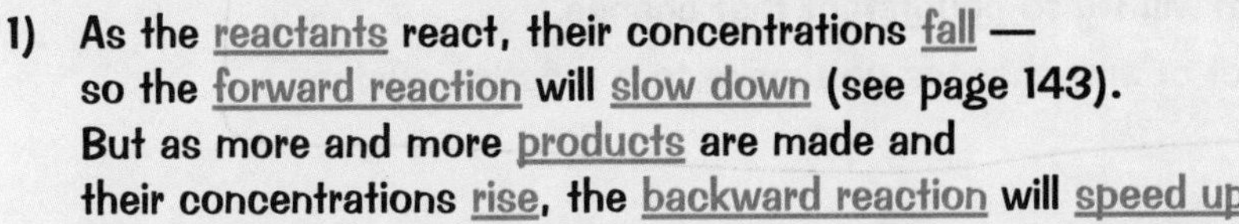

1) As the reactants react, their concentrations fall — so the forward reaction will slow down (see page 143). But as more and more products are made and their concentrations rise, the backward reaction will speed up.
2) After a while the forward reaction will be going at exactly the same rate as the backward one — the system is at equilibrium.
3) At equilibrium, both reactions are still happening, but there's no overall effect (it's a dynamic equilibrium). This means the concentrations of reactants and products have reached a balance and won't change.
4) Equilibrium is only reached if the reversible reaction takes place in a 'closed system'. A closed system just means that none of the reactants or products can escape and nothing else can get in.

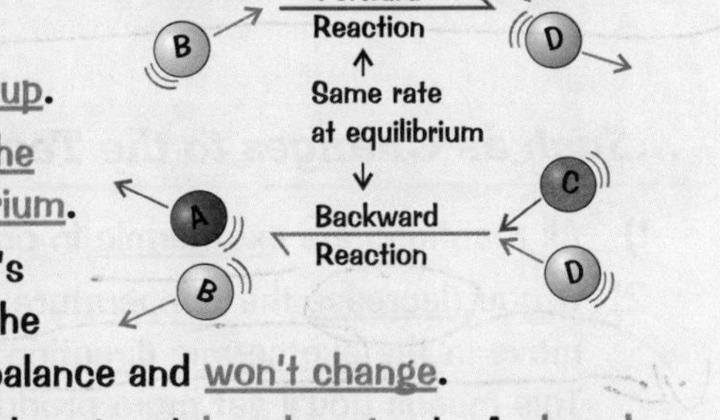

The Position of Equilibrium Can be on the Right or the Left

1) When a reaction's at equilibrium it doesn't mean the amounts of reactants and products are equal.
2) If the equilibrium lies to the right, the concentration of products is greater than that of the reactants.
3) If the equilibrium lies to the left, the concentration of reactants is greater than that of the products.
4) The position of equilibrium depends on the following conditions (as well as the reaction itself):
   - the temperature,
   - the pressure (this only affects equilibria involving gases),
   - the concentration of the reactants and products.

E.g. ammonium chloride ⇌ ammonia + hydrogen chloride
Heating this reaction moves the equilibrium to the right (more ammonia and hydrogen chloride) and cooling it moves it to the left (more ammonium chloride).

The next page tells you why these things affect equilibrium position.

Reversible Reactions Can Be Endothermic and Exothermic

1) In reversible reactions, if the reaction is endothermic in one direction, it will be exothermic in the other.
2) The energy transferred from the surroundings by the endothermic reaction is equal to the energy transferred to the surroundings during the exothermic reaction.
3) A good example is the thermal decomposition of hydrated copper sulfate:

See page 138 for more on endothermic and exothermic reactions.

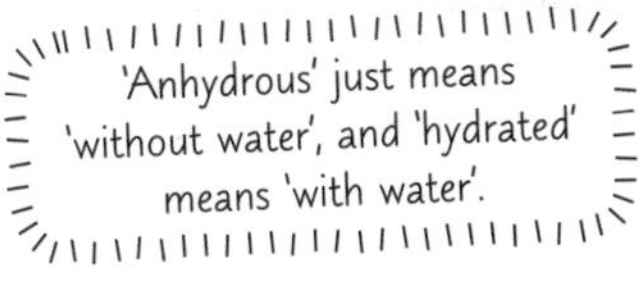

hydrated copper sulfate ⇌ anhydrous copper sulfate + water (forward: endothermic; backward: exothermic)

If you heat blue hydrated copper(II) sulfate crystals, it drives the water off and leaves white anhydrous copper(II) sulfate powder. This is endothermic.

If you then add a couple of drops of water to the white powder you get the blue crystals back again. This is exothermic.

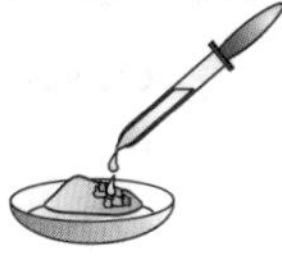

Dynamic equilibrium — lots of activity, but not to any great effect.*

Make sure you understand everything on this page before you move on to the next one. Trust me, it'll help.

Q1 What does it mean if a system is at equilibrium? [1 mark]

* Much like the England football team.

Le Chatelier's Principle

Reversible reactions don't like being messed around — so if you change something, the system will respond to undo the change. Sneaky.

Reversible Reactions Try to Counteract Changes...

1) Le Chatelier's Principle is the idea that if you change the conditions of a reversible reaction at equilibrium, the system will try to counteract that change.
2) It can be used to predict the effect of any changes you make to a reaction system.

...Such as Changes to the Temperature...

1) All reactions are exothermic in one direction and endothermic in the other (see previous page).
2) If you decrease the temperature, the equilibrium will move in the exothermic direction to produce more heat. This means you'll get more products for the exothermic reaction and fewer products for the endothermic reaction.
3) If you raise the temperature, the equilibrium will move in the endothermic direction to try and decrease it. You'll now get more products for the endothermic reaction and fewer products for the exothermic reaction.

$N_2 + 3H_2 \rightleftharpoons 2NH_3$

Here the forward reaction is exothermic — a decrease in temperature moves equilibrium to the right (more NH_3).

...Pressure...

1) Changing the pressure only affects an equilibrium involving gases.
2) If you increase the pressure, the equilibrium tries to reduce it — it moves in the direction where there are fewer molecules of gas.
3) If you decrease the pressure, the equilibrium tries to increase it — it moves in the direction where there are more molecules of gas.
4) You can use the balanced symbol equation for a reaction to see which side has more molecules of gas.

$N_2 + 3H_2 \rightleftharpoons 2NH_3$

There are 4 moles on the left (1 of N_2 and 3 of H_2) but only 2 on the right. So, if you increase the pressure, the equilibrium shifts to the right (more NH_3).

...or Concentration

1) If you change the concentration of either the reactants or the products, the system will no longer be at equilibrium.
2) So the system responds to bring itself back to equilibrium again.
3) If you increase the concentration of the reactants the system tries to decrease it by making more products.
4) If you decrease the concentration of products the system tries to increase it again by reducing the amount of reactants.

$N_2 + 3H_2 \rightleftharpoons 2NH_3$

If more N_2 or H_2 is added, the forward reaction increases to produce more NH_3.

An equilibrium is like a particularly stubborn mule...

It's good science this stuff. You do one thing, and the reaction does the other. On the face of it, that sounds like it'd be pretty annoying, but in reality it's what gives you control of what happens in a reversible reaction. And in industry, control is what makes the whole shebang profitable. Mmmm... Money.

Q1 For the following reactions, state the effect of an increase in pressure on the amount of products at equilibrium.

a) $N_2O_{4(g)} \rightleftharpoons 2NO_{2(g)}$ [1 mark]

b) $ClNO_{2(g)} + NO_{(g)} \rightleftharpoons NO_{2(g)} + ClNO_{(g)}$ [1 mark]

c) $2CO_{(g)} + O_{2(g)} \rightleftharpoons 2CO_{2(g)}$ [1 mark]

Revision Questions for Topic C6

We'll you've almost made it — you're just one more page away from a lovely cup of tea and a biscuit...

- Try these questions and tick off each one when you get it right.
- When you've done all the questions under a heading and are completely happy with it, tick it off.

Rates of Reaction and Factors Affecting Them (p.142-143)

1) On a rate of reaction graph, what does the line getting steeper show?
2) What does a flat line on a graph of amount of products against time show?
3) What two factors relating to the collisions between particles influence the rate of a reaction?
4) What are the four factors that affect the rate of a chemical reaction?
5) Why does increasing the temperature of a reaction mixture increase the rate of a reaction?
6) Other than increasing the temperature, describe two ways of increasing the rate of reaction between a solution and a solid.
7) What is a catalyst?
8) How does a catalyst increase the rate of a reaction?

Measuring and Calculating Rates of Reaction (p.144-146)

9) State the equation that could be used to calculate the mean rate of a reaction.
10) Give three possible units for the rate of a chemical reaction.
11) How would you measure the rate of a reaction between two clear solutions, in which the product formed was a precipitate?
12) Explain why measuring a mass change during a reaction is an accurate method of measuring rate.
13) Describe how you could investigate the effect of increasing HCl concentration on the rate of reaction between HCl and Mg.
14) Describe how you could use a graph to find the mean rate of a reaction between two points in time.
15) What is a tangent?
16) How would you use a tangent to find the gradient of a curve at a particular point?

Reversible Reactions and Le Chatelier's Principle (p.147-148)

17) Which one of the following statements is true?
    a) In a reaction at equilibrium, there is the same amount of products as reactants.
    b) If the forward reaction in a reversible reaction is exothermic, then the reverse reaction is endothermic.
    c) If the equilibrium of a system lies to the right, then the concentration of products is less than the concentration of reactants.
18) What effect will decreasing the temperature have on a reversible reaction in which the forward reaction is exothermic?
19) How can you predict the effect of changing the pressure of a gaseous reaction?
20) According to Le Chatelier's Principle, what will the effect of decreasing the concentration of the products for the forward reaction have on a reversible reaction?

Hydrocarbons

Organic chemistry is about compounds that contain carbon. Hydrocarbons are the simplest organic compounds. As you're about to discover, the properties of hydrocarbons make them really useful.

Hydrocarbons Only Contain Hydrogen and Carbon Atoms

A hydrocarbon is any compound that is formed from carbon and hydrogen atoms only.
So $C_{10}H_{22}$ (decane, an alkane) is a hydrocarbon, but $CH_3COOC_3H_7$ (an ester) is not — it contains oxygen.

Alkanes Have All C–C Single Bonds

1) Alkanes are the simplest type of hydrocarbon you can get. They have the general formula C_nH_{2n+2}.
2) The alkanes are a homologous series — a group of organic compounds that react in a similar way.
3) Alkanes are saturated compounds — each carbon atom forms four single covalent bonds.
4) The first four alkanes are methane, ethane, propane and butane.

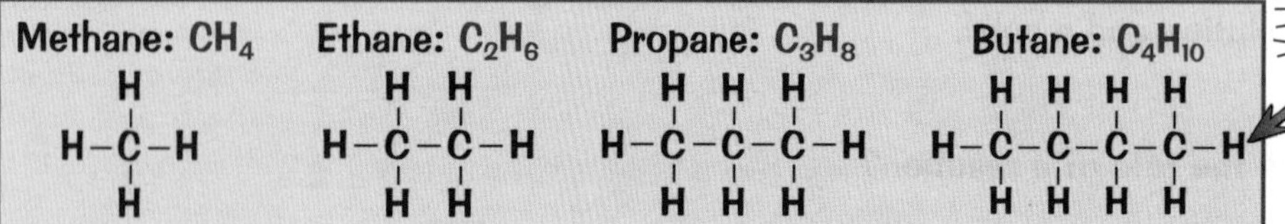

Hydrocarbon Properties Change as the Chain Gets Longer

As the length of the carbon chain changes, the properties of the hydrocarbon change.

1) The shorter the carbon chain, the more runny a hydrocarbon is — that is, the less viscous (gloopy) it is.
2) Hydrocarbons with shorter carbon chains are also more volatile, i.e. they have lower boiling points.
3) Also, the shorter the carbon chain, the more flammable (easier to ignite) the hydrocarbon is.
4) The properties of hydrocarbons affect how they're used for fuels. E.g. short chain hydrocarbons with lower boiling points are used as 'bottled gases' — stored under pressure as liquids in bottles.

Complete Combustion Occurs When There's Plenty of Oxygen

1) The complete combustion of any hydrocarbon in oxygen releases lots of energy. The only waste products are carbon dioxide and water vapour.

   hydrocarbon + oxygen → carbon dioxide + water (+ energy)

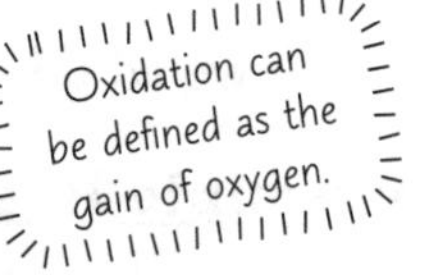

2) During combustion, both carbon and hydrogen from the hydrocarbon are oxidised.
3) Hydrocarbons are used as fuels due to the amount of energy released when they combust completely.
4) You need to be able to give a balanced symbol equation for the complete combustion of a simple hydrocarbon fuel when you're given its molecular formula. It's pretty easy — here's an example:

EXAMPLE: Write a balanced equation for the complete combustion of methane (CH_4).

See p.99 for more on balancing equations.

1) On the left hand side, there's one carbon atom, so only one molecule of CO_2 is needed to balance this. $CH_4 + ?O_2 \rightarrow CO_2 + ?H_2O$
2) On the left hand side, there are four hydrogen atoms, so two water molecules are needed to balance them. $CH_4 + ?O_2 \rightarrow CO_2 + 2H_2O$
3) There are four oxygen atoms on the right hand side of the equation. Two oxygen molecules are needed on the left to balance them. $CH_4 + 2O_2 \rightarrow CO_2 + 2H_2O$

The name's bond — single covalent bond...

So hydrocarbons only contain two ingredients — carbon and hydrogen. Jamie Oliver would not be happy.

Q1 A student has two alkanes, C_5H_{12} and $C_{10}H_{22}$. Compare the following properties of the alkanes:
a) viscosity b) boiling point c) flammability [3 marks]

Q2 Write a balanced symbol equation for the complete combustion of propane, C_3H_8. [2 marks]

Fractional Distillation

Crude oil can be used to make loads of useful things, such as fuels. But you can't just put crude oil in your car. First, the different hydrocarbons have to be separated. That's where fractional distillation comes in.

Crude Oil is Made Over a Long Period of Time

1) Crude oil is a fossil fuel. It's formed from the remains of plants and animals, mainly plankton, that died millions of years ago and were buried in mud. Over millions of years, with high temperature and pressure, the remains turn to crude oil, which can be drilled up from the rocks where it's found.
2) Fossil fuels like coal, oil and gas are called non-renewable fuels as they take so long to make that they're being used up much faster than they're being formed. They're finite resources (see p.161) — one day they'll run out.

Fractional Distillation can be Used to Separate Hydrocarbon Fractions

Crude oil is a mixture of lots of different hydrocarbons, most of which are alkanes. The different compounds in crude oil are separated by fractional distillation.

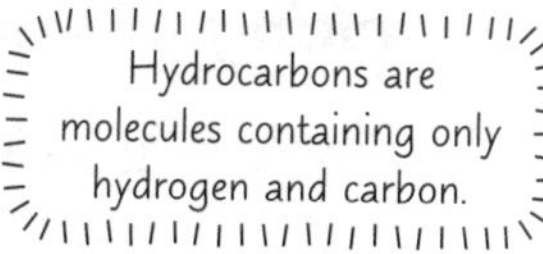

Here's how it works:

1) The oil is heated until most of it has turned into gas. The gases enter a fractionating column (and the liquid bit is drained off).
2) In the column there's a temperature gradient (it's hot at the bottom and gets cooler as you go up).
3) The longer hydrocarbons have high boiling points. They condense back into liquids and drain out of the column early on, when they're near the bottom. The shorter hydrocarbons have lower boiling points. They condense and drain out much later on, near to the top of the column where it's cooler.
4) You end up with the crude oil mixture separated out into different fractions. Each fraction contains a mixture of hydrocarbons that all contain a similar number of carbon atoms, so have similar boiling points.

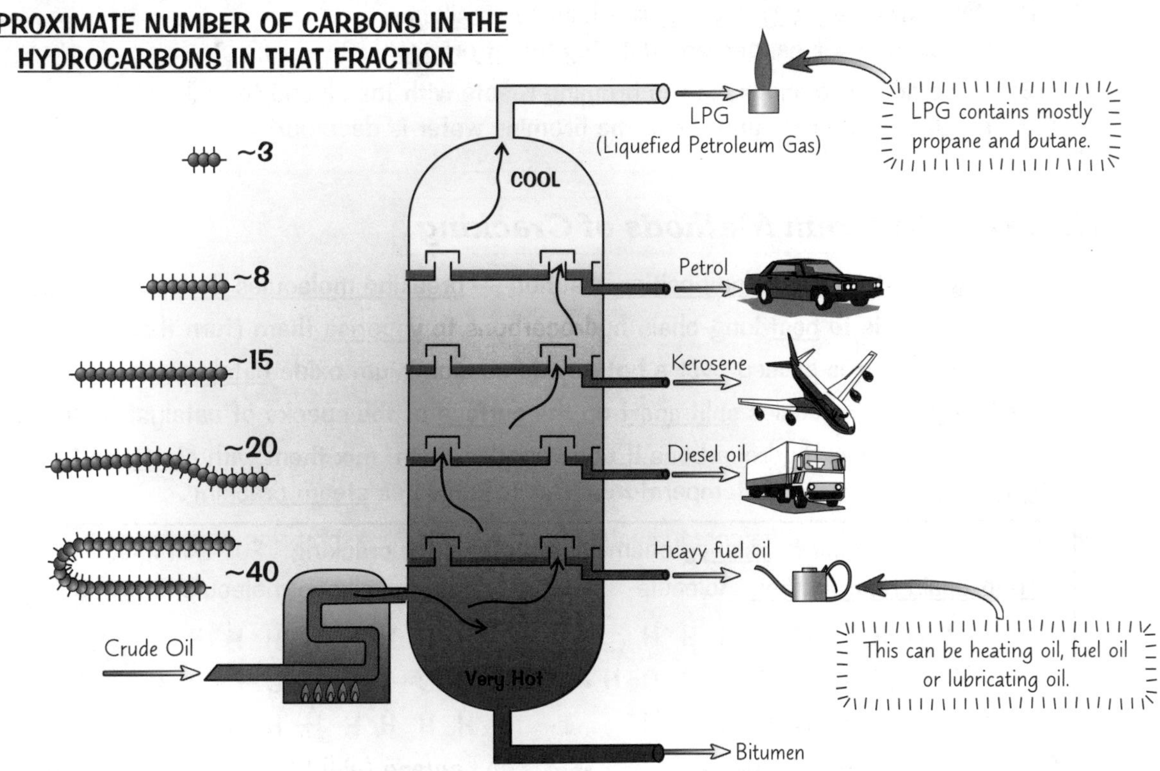

How much petrol is there in crude oil? Just a fraction...

Make sure you understand how fractional distillation works — it might just save your life... OK, maybe not.

Q1 Petrol drains further up a fractionating column than diesel. What does this suggest about the boiling points of the hydrocarbons which make up petrol compared to those in diesel? [1 mark]

Q2 Describe the temperature gradient in a fractionating column used for fractional distillation. [1 mark]

Uses and Cracking of Crude Oil

Crude oil has fuelled modern civilisation — it would be a very different world if we hadn't discovered oil.

Crude Oil has Various Uses Important in Modern Life

1) Oil provides the fuel for most modern transport — cars, trains, planes, the lot. Diesel oil, kerosene, heavy fuel oil and LPG (liquid petroleum gas) all come from crude oil.
2) The petrochemical industry uses some of the hydrocarbons from crude oil as a feedstock to make new compounds for use in things like polymers, solvents, lubricants, and detergents.
3) All the products you get from crude oil are examples of organic compounds (compounds containing carbon atoms). The reason you get such a large variety of products is because carbon atoms can bond together to form different groups called homologous series. These groups contain similar compounds with many properties in common. Alkanes and alkenes are both examples of homologous series.

Cracking Means Splitting Up Long-Chain Hydrocarbons

1) Short-chain hydrocarbons are flammable so make good fuels and are in high demand. However, long-chain hydrocarbons form thick gloopy liquids like tar which aren't all that useful, so...
2) ...a lot of the longer alkane molecules produced from fractional distillation are turned into smaller, more useful ones by a process called cracking.
3) Some of the products of cracking are useful as fuels, e.g. petrol for cars and paraffin for jet fuel.
4) As well as alkanes, cracking also produces another type of hydrocarbon called alkenes. Alkenes are a lot more reactive than alkanes. They're used as a starting material when making lots of other compounds and can be used to make polymers.

Bromine water can be used to test for alkenes:

1) When orange bromine water is added to an alkane, no reaction will happen and it'll stay bright orange.
2) If it's added to an alkene the bromine reacts with the alkene to make a colourless compound — so the bromine water is decolourised.

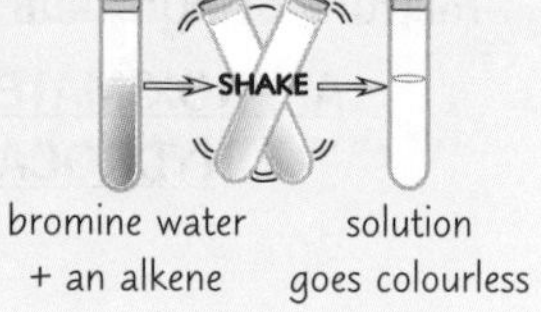

There are Different Methods of Cracking

1) Cracking is a thermal decomposition reaction — breaking molecules down by heating them.
2) The first step is to heat long-chain hydrocarbons to vaporise them (turn them into a gas).
3) Then the vapour is passed over a hot powdered aluminium oxide catalyst.
4) The long-chain molecules split apart on the surface of the specks of catalyst — this is catalytic cracking.
5) You can also crack hydrocarbons if you vaporise them, mix them with steam and then heat them to a very high temperature. This is known as steam cracking.

You need to be able to balance chemical equations for cracking. For example:

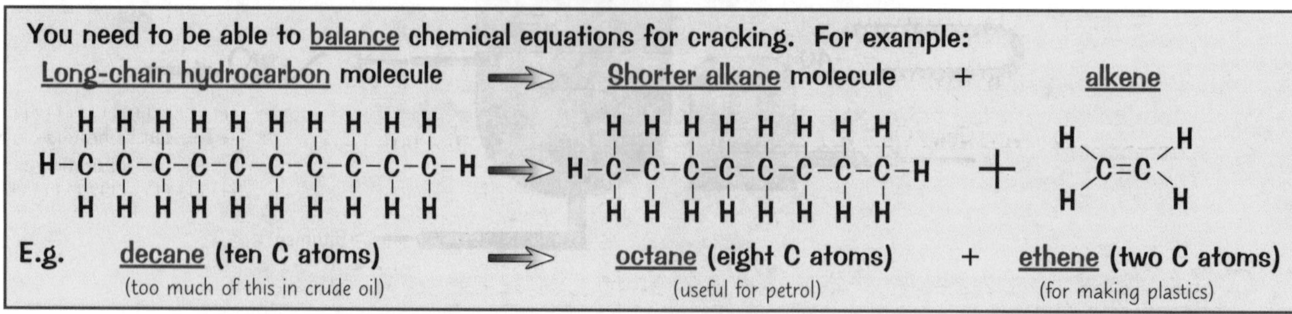

This page is tough — better get cracking...

We use lots of oil — we're dependent on it for loads of things. So we could be in a proper pickle when it runs out.

Q1 Pentane, C_5H_{12}, can be cracked into ethene, C_2H_4, and one other hydrocarbon. Give the formula of the other hydrocarbon. [1 mark]

Purity and Formulations

In an ideal world, every compound a chemist made would be 100% pure. Unfortunately, in the real world it doesn't always work out like that — but luckily, there are ways to find out how pure a substance is.

Purity is Defined Differently in Chemistry to Everyday

1) Usually when you refer to a substance as being pure you mean that nothing has been added to it, so it's in its natural state. For example: pure milk or beeswax.
2) In chemistry, a pure substance is something that only contains one compound or element throughout — not mixed with anything else.

The Boiling or Melting Point Tells You How Pure a Substance Is

1) A chemically pure substance will melt or boil at a specific temperature.
2) You can test the purity of a sample by measuring its melting or boiling point and comparing it with the melting or boiling point of the pure substance (which you can find from a data book).
3) The closer your measured value is to the actual melting or boiling point, the purer your sample is.
4) Impurities in your sample will lower the melting point and increase the melting range of your substance.
5) Impurities in your sample will also increase the boiling point and may result in your sample boiling at a range of temperatures.

Formulations are Mixtures with Exact Amounts of Components

1) Formulations are useful mixtures with a precise purpose that are made by following a 'formula' (a recipe). Each component in a formulation is present in a measured quantity, and contributes to the properties of the formulation so that it meets its required function.

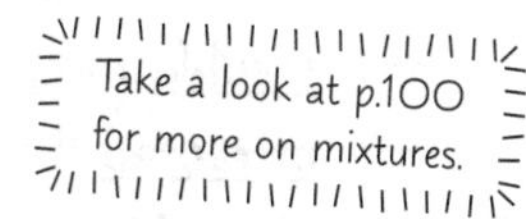

> For example, paints are formulations composed of:
> - Pigment — gives the paint colour, for example titanium oxide is used as a pigment in white paints.
> - Solvent — used to dissolve the other components and alter the viscosity.
> - Binder (resin) — forms a film that holds the pigment in place after it's been painted on.
> - Additives — added to further change the physical and chemical properties of the paint.
>
> Depending on the purpose of the paint, the chemicals used and their amounts will be changed so the paint produced is right for the job.

2) Formulations are really important in the pharmaceutical industry. For example, by altering the formulation of a pill, chemists can make sure it delivers the drug to the correct part of the body at the right concentration, that it's consumable and has a long enough shelf life.
3) In everyday life, formulations can be found in cleaning products, fuels, cosmetics, fertilisers, metal alloys and even food and drink.
4) When you buy a product, you might find that it has information about its composition on the packaging. For example, the ratio or percentage of each component. This tells you the product's a formulation. It also lets you choose a formulation with the right composition for your particular use.

Cake and tea are key to the revision success formula...

Knowing how pure a product is can be vital in industries such as pharmaceuticals and the food industry. Luckily for us, chemists have lots of different ways to make sure they're making exactly what they want.

Q1 The melting point of a sample of aspirin made by a student is measured as being between 128-132 °C. The melting point and boiling point of pure aspirin are 136 °C and 140 °C respectively.

a) Give two reasons why the melting point measured shows that the sample is not pure. [2 marks]

b) Suggest a value for the boiling point of the sample. [1 mark]

Paper Chromatography

You met chromatography on page 100. Now it's time to see how it works. Careful — things might get crazy...

Chromatography uses Two Phases

Chromatography is an analytical method used to separate the substances in a mixture. You can then use it to identify the substances. There are different types of chromatography, but they all have two 'phases':

- A mobile phase — where the molecules can move. This is always a liquid or a gas.
- A stationary phase — where the molecules can't move. This can be a solid or a really thick liquid.

1) During a chromatography experiment, the substances in the sample constantly move between the mobile and the stationary phases — an equilibrium is formed between the two phases.
2) The mobile phase moves through the stationary phase, and anything dissolved in the mobile phase moves with it. How quickly a chemical moves depends on how it's 'distributed' between the two phases — whether it spends more time in the mobile phase or the stationary phase.
3) The chemicals that spend more time in the mobile phase than the stationary phase will move further through the stationary phase.
4) The components in a mixture will normally separate through the stationary phase, so long as all the components spend different amounts of time in the mobile phase. The number of spots may change in different solvents as the distribution of the chemical will change depending on the solvent. A pure substance will only ever form one spot in any solvent as there is only one substance in the sample.

During paper chromatography the stationary phase is the chromatography paper (often filter paper) and the mobile phase is the solvent (e.g ethanol or water).
The amount of time the molecules spend in each phase depends on two things:

- How soluble they are in the solvent.
- How attracted they are to the paper.

Molecules with a higher solubility in the solvent, and which are less attracted to the paper, will spend more time in the mobile phase — and they'll be carried further up the paper.

The method for carrying out paper chromatography is on page 100.

You can Calculate the R_f Value for Each Chemical

PRACTICAL

1) The result of chromatography analysis is called a chromatogram.
2) An R_f value is the ratio between the distance travelled by the dissolved substance (the solute) and the distance travelled by the solvent. The further through the stationary phase a substance moves, the larger the R_f value. You can calculate R_f values using the formula:

$$R_f = \frac{\text{distance travelled by substance (B)}}{\text{distance travelled by solvent (A)}}$$

This is the distance from the baseline to the centre of the spot.

3) Chromatography is often carried out to see if a certain substance is present in a mixture. To do this, you run a pure sample of that substance (a reference) alongside the unknown mixture. If the R_f values of the reference and one of the spots in the mixture match, the substance may be present (although you haven't yet proved they're the same).
4) The R_f value is dependent on the solvent — if you change the solvent the R_f value for a substance will change. You can test both the mixture and the reference in a number of different solvents. If the R_f value of the reference compound matches the R_f value of one of the spots in the mixture in all the solvents, then it's likely the reference compound is present in the mixture. If the spots in the mixture and the spot in the reference only have the same R_f value in some of the solvents, then the reference compound isn't present in the mixture.

Chromatography revision — it's a phase you have to get through...

You can't see the chemicals moving between the two phases, but it does happen. You'll just have to trust me.

Q1 Explain how paper chromatography separates mixtures. [4 marks]

Tests for Gases

Ahh... tests, glorious tests. Luckily, these aren't the kind of tests you have to revise for, but you should probably revise these tests for your exam — it's swings and roundabouts really...

There are Tests for 4 Common Gases

1) Chlorine

Chlorine bleaches damp litmus paper, turning it white. (It may turn red for a moment first though — that's because a solution of chlorine is acidic.)

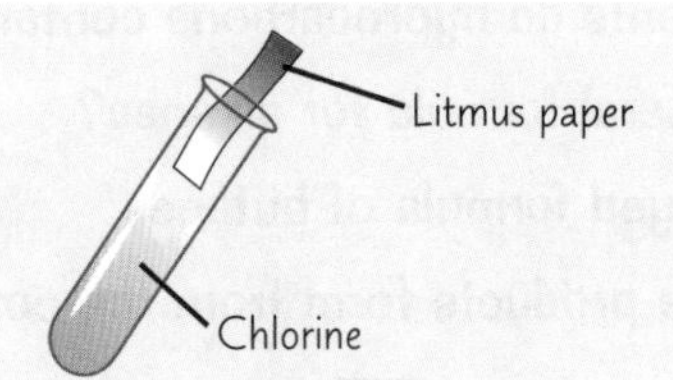

2) Oxygen

If you put a glowing splint inside a test tube containing oxygen, the oxygen will relight the glowing splint.

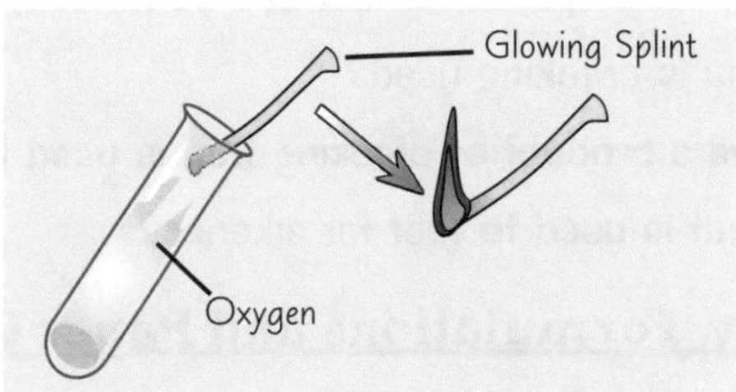

3) Carbon Dioxide

Bubbling carbon dioxide through (or shaking carbon dioxide with) an aqueous solution of calcium hydroxide (known as limewater) causes the solution to turn cloudy.

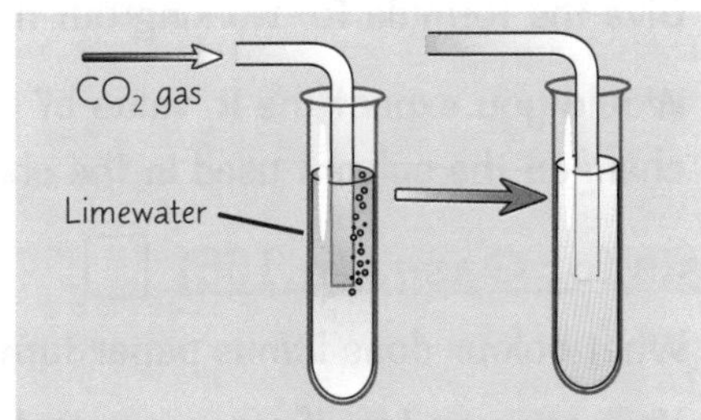

4) Hydrogen

If you hold a lit splint at the open end of a test tube containing hydrogen, you'll get a "squeaky pop". (The noise comes from the hydrogen burning quickly with the oxygen in the air to form H_2O.)

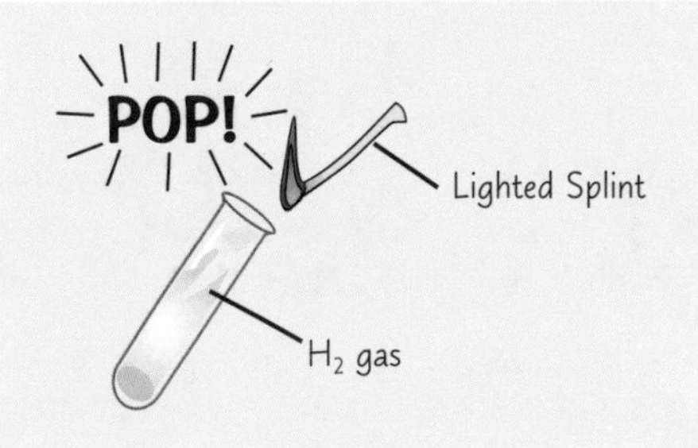

Hopefully this page won't be too testing for you...

Tests for gases are brilliant. You might think it's because you get to do a nice experiment to do in class, but I like them because you get to write 'squeaky pop' as a real scientific observation.

Q1 A student collects the gas given off during a reaction and bubbles it through limewater. The limewater goes cloudy. Identify the gas produced. [1 mark]

Revision Questions for Topics C7 & C8

Well, that's it for Topics C7 & C8 — I think they were my favourite so far. Or maybe it was C1... or C2...

- Try these questions and tick off each one when you get it right.
- When you've done all the questions under a heading and are completely happy with it, tick it off.

Hydrocarbons (p.150)

1) What two elements do hydrocarbons contain?
2) What is the general formula for alkanes?
3) Draw the displayed formula of butane.
4) What two waste products form from the complete combustion of hydrocarbons?

Crude Oil (p.151-152)

5) How is crude oil formed?
6) Where are the shortest carbon chains found in the fractional distillation column?
7) Give three products that can be made from crude oil.
8) Why is cracking used?
9) Give a product of cracking that is used for making plastics.
10) What is used to test for alkenes?

Purity, Formulations and Paper Chromatography (p.153-154)

11) What is a formulation?
12) What are the two phases called in chromatography?
13) In paper chromatography, how many spots will a pure substance form on the paper?
14) Give the formula for working out the R_f value of a substance.
15) Would you expect the R_f value of a substance to change if you changed the solvent used in the chromatography experiment?

Tests for Gases (p.155)

16) What colour does litmus paper turn in the presence of chlorine?
17) How can you test if a gas in a test tube is oxygen?

The Evolution of the Atmosphere

Theories for how the Earth's atmosphere evolved have changed a lot over the years — it's hard to gather evidence from such a long time period and from so long ago (4.6 billion years). Here's one idea we've got:

Phase 1 — Volcanoes Gave Out Gases

1) The first billion years of Earth's history were pretty explosive — the surface was covered in volcanoes that erupted and released lots of gases. We think this was how the early atmosphere was formed.
2) The early atmosphere was probably mostly carbon dioxide, with virtually no oxygen. This is quite like the atmospheres of Mars and Venus today.
3) Volcanic activity also released nitrogen, which built up in the atmosphere over time, as well as water vapour and small amounts of methane and ammonia.

Phase 2 — Oceans, Algae and Green Plants Absorbed Carbon Dioxide

1) When the water vapour in the atmosphere condensed, it formed the oceans.
2) Lots of carbon dioxide was removed from the early atmosphere as it dissolved in the oceans. This dissolved carbon dioxide then went through a series of reactions to form carbonate precipitates that formed sediments on the seabed.
3) Green plants and algae evolved and absorbed some of the carbon dioxide so that they could carry out photosynthesis (see below). Later, marine animals evolved. Their shells and skeletons contained carbonates from the oceans.
4) Some of the carbon these organisms took in from the atmosphere and oceans became locked up in rocks and fossil fuels after the organisms died.

- When plants, plankton and marine animals die, they fall to the seabed and get buried by layers of sediment. Over millions of years, they become compressed and form sedimentary rocks, oil and gas — trapping the carbon within them and helping to keep carbon dioxide levels in the atmosphere reduced.
- Things like coal, crude oil and natural gas that are made by this process are called 'fossil fuels'.
- Crude oil and natural gas are formed from deposits of plankton. These fossil fuels form reservoirs under the seabed when they get trapped in rocks.
- Coal is a sedimentary rock made from thick plant deposits.
- Limestone is also a sedimentary rock. It's mostly made of calcium carbonate deposits from the shells and skeletons of marine organisms.

Phase 3 — Green Plants and Algae Produced Oxygen

1) As well as absorbing the carbon dioxide in the atmosphere, green plants and algae produced oxygen by photosynthesis — this is when plants use light to convert carbon dioxide and water into sugars:
2) Algae evolved first — about 2.7 billion years ago. Then over the next billion years or so, green plants also evolved.

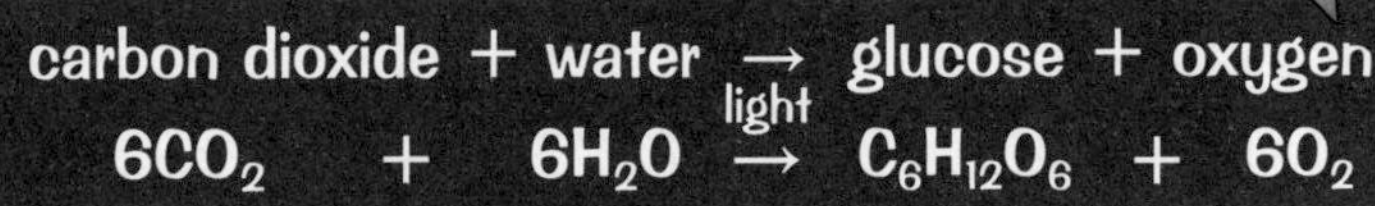

carbon dioxide + water $\xrightarrow{\text{light}}$ glucose + oxygen

$$6CO_2 + 6H_2O \xrightarrow{\text{light}} C_6H_{12}O_6 + 6O_2$$

3) As oxygen levels built up in the atmosphere over time, more complex life (like animals) could evolve.
4) Eventually, about 200 million years ago, the atmosphere reached a composition similar to what it is today: approximately 80% nitrogen, 20% oxygen and small amounts of other gases (each only makes up less than 1% of the atmosphere), mainly carbon dioxide, noble gases and water vapour.

The atmosphere's evolving — shut the window will you...

We've learnt about the atmosphere from Antarctic ice cores. Each year, a layer of ice forms with bubbles of air trapped in it. The deeper the ice, the older the air, so examining air in different layers shows us how it's changed.

Q1 Describe how sedimentary rocks are formed. [2 marks]

Greenhouse Gases and Climate Change

Greenhouse gases are important but can also cause problems — it's all about keeping a delicate balance.

Carbon Dioxide is a Greenhouse Gas

1) Greenhouse gases like carbon dioxide, methane and water vapour act like an insulating layer in the Earth's atmosphere — this, amongst other factors, allows the Earth to be warm enough to support life.
2) All particles absorb certain frequencies of radiation. Greenhouse gases don't absorb the incoming short wavelength radiation from the sun — but they do absorb the long wavelength radiation that gets reflected back off the Earth. Then they re-radiate it in all directions — including back towards the Earth. The longwave radiation is thermal radiation, so it results in warming of the surface of the Earth. This is the greenhouse effect.

Short wavelength radiation

Long wavelength radiation

Greenhouse gases

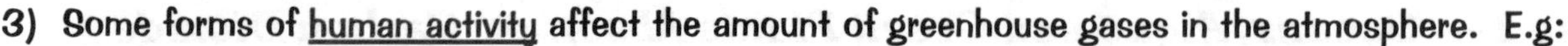

3) Some forms of human activity affect the amount of greenhouse gases in the atmosphere. E.g:

- Deforestation: fewer trees means less CO_2 is removed from the atmosphere via photosynthesis.
- Burning fossil fuels: carbon that was 'locked up' in these fuels is released as CO_2.
- Agriculture: more farm animals produce more methane through their digestive processes.
- Creating waste: more landfill sites and more waste from agriculture means more CO_2 and methane released by decomposition of waste.

Increasing Carbon Dioxide is Linked to Climate Change

1) The Earth's temperature varies naturally, but recently the average temperature of the Earth's surface has been increasing. Most scientists agree that the extra carbon dioxide from human activity is causing this increase and that this will lead to climate change.
2) Evidence for this has been peer-reviewed (see page 1) — so you know that the information out there is reliable.
3) Unfortunately, it's hard to fully understand the Earth's climate — this is because it's so complex, and there are so many variables, that it's very hard to make a model that isn't oversimplified.
4) This has led to speculation, particularly in the media — where stories may be biased or only some of the information given.

See page 2 for more on science in the media.

Climate Change Could Have Dangerous Consequences

The Earth's climate is complex, but it's still important to make predictions about the consequences of climate change so that policy-makers can make decisions now. For example:

1) An increase in global temperature could lead to polar ice caps melting — causing a rise in sea levels, increased flooding in coastal areas and coastal erosion.
2) Changes in rainfall patterns (the amount, timing and distribution) may cause some regions to get too much or too little water. This, along with changes in temperature, may affect the ability of certain regions to produce food.
3) The frequency and severity of storms may also increase.
4) Changes in temperature and the amount of water available in a habitat may affect wild species, leading to differences in their distribution.

Eee, problems, problems — there's always summat goin' wrong...

Everyone's talking about climate change these days — it's pretty scary stuff, so make sure you get it.

Q1 Describe three potential consequences of climate change. [3 marks]

Carbon Footprints

It's generally accepted that greenhouse gas emissions from human activities is causing climate change. Knowing what leads to a lot of emissions of carbon dioxide could be useful for stopping it happening.

Carbon Footprints are Tricky to Measure

1) Carbon footprints are basically a measure of the amount of carbon dioxide and other greenhouse gases released over the full life cycle of something. That can be a service (e.g. the school bus), an event (e.g. the Olympics), a product (e.g. a toastie maker) — almost anything.
2) Measuring the total carbon footprint of something can be really hard, though — or even impossible.
3) That's because there are so many different factors to consider — for example, you would have to count the emissions released as a result of sourcing all the parts of your toastie maker and in making it, not to mention the emissions produced when you actually use it and finally dispose of it. Eugh, complicated...
4) Still, a rough calculation can give a good idea of what the worst emitters are — so that people can avoid them in the future.

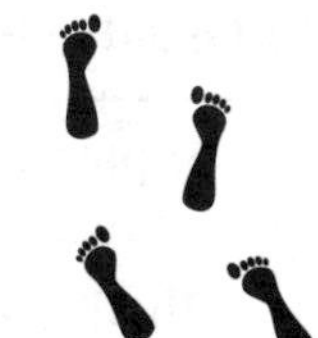

There are Ways of Reducing Carbon Footprints

You can't always measure a carbon footprint exactly, but there are always methods to try and reduce it. Anything that reduces the amount of greenhouse gases (e.g. carbon dioxide or methane) given out by a process will also reduce its carbon footprint. Here are some things that can be done:

- Renewable energy sources or nuclear energy could be used instead of fossil fuels.
- Using more efficient processes could conserve energy and cut waste. Lots of waste decomposes to release methane, so this will reduce methane emissions.
- Governments could tax companies or individuals based on the amount of greenhouse gases they emit — e.g. taxing cars based on the amount of carbon dioxide they emit over a set distance could mean that people choose to buy ones that are more fuel-efficient and so less polluting.
- Governments can also put a cap on emissions of all greenhouse gases that companies make — then sell licences for emissions up to that cap.
- There's also technology that captures the CO_2 produced by burning fossil fuels before it's released into the atmosphere — it can then be stored deep underground in cracks in the rock such as old oil wells.

But Making Reductions is Still Difficult

1) It's easy enough saying that we should cut emissions, but actually doing it — that's a different story.
2) For a start, there's still a lot of work to be done on alternative technologies that result in lower CO_2 emissions.
3) A lot of governments are also worried that making these changes will impact on the economic growth of communities — which could be bad for people's well-being. This is particularly important for countries that are still developing.
4) Because not everyone is on board, it's hard to make international agreements to reduce emissions. Most countries don't want to sacrifice their economic development if they think that others won't do the same.
5) It's not just governments, though — individuals in developed countries need to make changes to their lifestyles. But it might be hard to get people to make changes if they don't want to and if there isn't enough education provided about why the changes are necessary and how to make them.

Who has the biggest carbon footprint then? Clowns of course...

Carbon footprints are a game of 'fortunately/unfortunately'. Unfortunately, carbon emissions can lead to global warming. Fortunately, there are steps we can take to cut our carbon dioxide emissions. Unfortunately, not everyone's on board. Fortunately, as time goes on, people are doing more to reduce their emissions. And so on...

Q1 State two things governments can do to try to reduce the greenhouse gas emissions of businesses. [2 marks]

Air Pollution

Increasing carbon dioxide is causing climate change. But CO_2 isn't the only gas released when fossil fuels burn — you also get other nasties like oxides of nitrogen, sulfur dioxide and carbon monoxide.

Combustion of Fossil Fuels Releases Gases and Particles

Hydrocarbons are compounds that only contain hydrogen and carbon (see page 150).

1) Fossil fuels, such as crude oil and coal, contain hydrocarbons. During combustion, the carbon and hydrogen in these compounds are oxidised so that carbon dioxide and water vapour are released into the atmosphere.
2) When there's plenty of oxygen, all the fuel burns — this is called complete combustion.
3) If there's not enough oxygen, some of the fuel doesn't burn — this is called incomplete combustion. Under these conditions, solid particles (called particulates) of soot (carbon) and unburnt fuel are released and carbon monoxide can be produced as well as carbon dioxide.
4) Particulates in the air can cause all sorts of problems:

There's more about complete combustion on p.150.

- If particulates are inhaled, they can get stuck in the lungs and cause damage. This can then lead to respiratory problems.
- They're also bad for the environment — they themselves, or the clouds they help to produce, reflect sunlight back into space. This means that less light reaches the Earth — causing global dimming.

5) It's not just particulates from incomplete combustion that cause problems. Carbon monoxide is pretty nasty too.

- Carbon monoxide (CO) is really dangerous because it can stop your blood from doing its proper job of carrying oxygen around the body.
- It does this by binding to the haemoglobin in your blood that normally carries O_2 — so less oxygen is able to be transported round your body.
- A lack of oxygen in the blood can lead to fainting, a coma or even death.
- Carbon monoxide doesn't have any colour or smell, so it's very hard to detect. This makes it even more dangerous.

Sulfur Dioxide and Oxides of Nitrogen Can be Released

1) Sulfur dioxide (SO_2) is released during the combustion of fossil fuels, such as coal, that contain sulfur impurities — the sulfur in the fuel becomes oxidised.
2) Nitrogen oxides are created from a reaction between the nitrogen and oxygen in the air, caused by the heat of the burning. (This can happen in the internal combustion engines of cars.)
3) When these gases mix with clouds they form dilute sulfuric acid or dilute nitric acid. This then falls as acid rain.
4) Acid rain kills plants and damages buildings and statues. It also makes metal corrode. It's shocking.
5) Not only that, but sulfur dioxide and nitrogen oxides can also be bad for human health — they cause respiratory problems if they're breathed in.

SO_2 gas reacts with water to form sulfuric acid. You can test for sulfur impurities in a fuel by bubbling the gases from combustion through a solution containing Universal indicator — if the fuel contains sulfur, the gases will contain SO_2 which will form sulfuric acid and turn the Universal indicator red.

Revision and pollution — the two bugbears of modern life...

Eeee.... cars and fossil fuels — they're nowt but trouble. But at least this topic is kind of interesting, what with its relevance to everyday life and all. Just think... you could see this kind of stuff on TV.

Q1 Name three potential pollutants that could be released as a result of incomplete combustion of hydrocarbons, that wouldn't be released as a result of complete combustion. [3 marks]

Finite and Renewable Resources

There are lots of different resources that humans use to provide energy for things like heating or travelling, as well as for building materials and food. Some of these resources get replaced, some don't.

Natural Resources Come From the Earth, Sea and Air

1) Natural resources form without human input. They include anything that comes from the earth, sea or air. For example, cotton for clothing or oil for fuel.
2) Some of these natural products can be replaced by synthetic products or improved upon by man-made processes. For example, rubber is a natural product that can be extracted from the sap of a tree, however man-made polymers have now been made which can replace rubber in uses such as tyres.
3) Agriculture provides conditions where natural resources can be enhanced for our needs. E.g. the development of fertilisers have meant we can produce a high yield of crops.

Some Natural Resources will Run Out

1) Renewable resources reform at a similar rate to, or faster than, we use them.
2) For example, timber is a renewable resource as trees can be planted following a harvest and only take a few years to regrow. Other examples of renewable resources include fresh water and food.
3) Finite (non-renewable) resources, aren't formed quickly enough to be considered replaceable.
4) Finite resources include fossil fuels and nuclear fuels such as uranium and plutonium. Minerals and metals found in ores in the earth are also non-renewable materials.
5) After they've been extracted, many finite resources undergo man-made processes to provide fuels and materials necessary for modern life. For example, fractional distillation (see p.151) is used to produce usable products such as petrol from crude oil and metal ores are reduced to produce a pure metal (see p.133).

Tables, Charts and Graphs can Give You an Insight Into Different Resources

You may be asked to interpret information about resources in the exam.

The table below shows information for two resources, coal and timber. Identify which resource is which.

	Energy Density (MJ/m^3)	Time it takes to form
Resource 1	7600-11400	10 years
Resource 2	23000-26000	10^6 years

The time it takes for Resource 1 to reform is 10^5 times shorter than Resource 2 suggesting it is a renewable resource. Resource 1 is also a far less energetic fuel than Resource 2, so is more likely to be timber than coal. Resource 1 is timber and Resource 2 is coal.

10^6 is a shorthand way of showing 1000000. This is because $10^6 = 10 \times 10 \times 10 \times 10 \times 10 \times 10 = 1000000$.

Extracting Finite Resources has Risks

1) Many modern materials are made from raw, finite resources, for example most plastics, metals and building materials.
2) People have to balance the social, economic and environmental effects of extracting finite resources.
3) For example, mining metal ores is good because useful products can be made. It also provides local people with jobs and brings money into the area. However, mining ores is bad for the environment as it uses loads of energy, scars the landscape, produces lots of waste and destroys habitats.

This book is a renewable resource — a gift that keeps on giving...

Unfortunately we can't just run around using every resource we get our hands on — we have to consider the impacts of our actions. If you ever start a major mining project think... What would David Attenborough do?

Q1 Using examples, state the difference between a finite and renewable resource. [2 marks]

Reuse and Recycling

Many materials used in the modern world are limited. Once they're finished with, it's usually far better to recycle them than to use new finite resources which will eventually run out.

Chemistry is Improving Sustainability

1) Sustainable development is an approach to development that takes account of the needs of present society while not damaging the lives of future generations.
2) As you saw on the last page, not all resources are renewable so it's unsustainable to keep using them.
3) As well as using resources, extracting resources can be unsustainable due to the amount of energy used and waste produced. Processing the resources into useful materials, such as glass or bricks, can be unsustainable too, as the processes often use energy that's made from finite resources.
4) One way of reducing the use of finite resources is for people to use less. This doesn't just reduce the use of that resource but also anything needed to produce it.
5) We can't stop using finite resources altogether, but chemists can develop and adapt processes that use lower amounts of finite resources and reduce damage to the environment. For example, chemists have developed catalysts that reduce the amount of energy required for certain industrial processes.

Copper-Rich Ores are in Short Supply

1) Copper is a finite resource. One way to improve its sustainability is by extracting it from low-grade ores (ores without much copper in). Scientists are looking into new ways of doing this:

These methods can be used to extract other metals too.

- Bioleaching — bacteria are used to convert copper compounds in the ore into soluble copper compounds, separating out the copper from the ore in the process. The leachate (the solution produced by the process) contains copper ions, which can be extracted, e.g. by electrolysis (see p.135) or displacement (see p.134) with a more reactive metal, e.g. scrap iron.
- Phytomining — this involves growing plants in soil that contains copper. The plants can't use or get rid of the copper so it gradually builds up in the leaves. The plants can be harvested, dried and burned in a furnace. The ash contains soluble copper compounds from which copper can be extracted by electrolysis or displacement using scrap iron.

2) Traditional methods of copper mining are pretty damaging to the environment. These new methods of extraction have a much smaller impact, but the disadvantage is that they're slow.

Recycling Metals is Important

Recycling is way to reduce our need for copper rich ores.

1) Mining and extracting metals takes lots of energy, most of which comes from burning fossil fuels.
2) Recycling metals often uses much less energy than is needed to mine and extract new metal, conserves the finite amount of each metal in the earth and cuts down on the amount of waste getting sent to landfill.
3) Metals are usually recycled by melting them and then casting them into the shape of the new product.
4) Depending on what the metal will be used for after recycling, the amount of separation required for recyclable metals can change. For example, waste steel and iron can be kept together as they can both be added to iron in a blast furnace to reduce the amount of iron ore required.

A blast furnace is used to extract iron from its ore at a high temperature using carbon.

Glass can Also be Recycled

Glass recycling can help sustainability by reducing the amount of energy needed to make new glass products, and also the amount of waste created when used glass is thrown away.

1) Glass bottles can often be reused without reshaping.
2) Other forms of glass can't be reused so they're recycled instead. Usually the glass is separated by colour and chemical composition before being recycled.
3) The glass is crushed and then melted to be reshaped for use in glass products such as bottles or jars. It might also be used for a different purpose such as insulating glass wool for wall insulation in homes.

CGP Jokes — 85% recycled since 1996...

Recycling is really handy — as well as saving limited finite materials it also saves energy.

Q1 Give three positive effects of recycling metals. [3 marks]

Life Cycle Assessments

If a company wants to manufacture a new product, they carry out a life cycle assessment (LCA).

Life Cycle Assessments Show Total Environmental Costs

A life cycle assessment (LCA) looks at every stage of a product's life to assess the impact it would have on the environment.

1 Getting the Raw Materials:

1) Extracting raw materials needed for a product can damage the local environment, e.g. mining metals. Extraction can also result in pollution due to the amount of energy needed.
2) Raw materials often need to be processed to extract the desired materials and this often needs large amounts of energy. E.g. extracting metals from ores or fractional distillation of crude oil.

2 Manufacture and Packaging:

1) Manufacturing products and their packaging can use a lot of energy resources and can also cause a lot of pollution, e.g. harmful fumes such as carbon monoxide or hydrogen chloride.
2) You also need to think about any waste products and how to dispose of them. The chemical reactions used to make compounds from their raw materials can produce waste products. Some waste can be turned into other useful chemicals, reducing the amount that ends up polluting the environment.

3 Using the Product:

1) The use of a product can damage the environment. For example, burning fuels releases greenhouse gases and other harmful substances. Fertilisers can leach into streams and rivers causing damage to ecosystems.
2) How long a product is used for or how many uses it gets is also a factor — products that need lots of energy to produce but are used for ages mean less waste in the long run.

4 Product Disposal:

1) Products are often disposed of in landfill sites. This takes up space and pollutes land and water, e.g. if paint washes off a product and gets into rivers.
2) Energy is used to transport waste to landfill, which causes pollutants to be released into the atmosphere.
3) Products might be incinerated (burnt), which causes air pollution.

You Can Compare Life Cycle Assessments for Plastic and Paper Bags

Life Cycle Assessment Stage	Plastic Bag	Paper Bag
Raw Materials	Crude oil	Timber
Manufacturing and Packaging	The compounds needed to make the plastic are extracted from crude oil by fractional distillation, followed by cracking and then polymerisation. Waste is reduced as the other fractions of crude oil have other uses.	Pulped timber is processed using lots of energy. Lots of waste is made.
Using the Product	Can be reused. Can be used for other things as well as shopping, for example bin liners.	Usually only used once.
Product Disposal	Recyclable but not biodegradable and will take up space in landfill and pollute land.	Biodegradable, non-toxic and can be recycled.

Life cycle assessments have shown that even though plastic bags aren't biodegradable, they take less energy to make and have a longer lifespan than paper bags, so may be less harmful to the environment.

There are Problems with Life Cycle Assessments

1) The use of energy, some natural resources and the amount of certain types of waste produced by a product over it's lifetime can be easily quantified. But the effect of some pollutants is harder to give a numerical value to. E.g. it's difficult to apply a value to the negative visual effects of plastic bags in the environment compared to paper ones.
2) So, producing an LCA is not an objective method as it takes into account the values of the person carrying out the assessment. This means LCAs can be biased.
3) Selective LCAs, which only show some of the impacts of a product on the environment can also be biased as they can be written to deliberately support the claims of a company, in order to give them positive advertising.

Need exercise? Go life-cycling then...

In the exam you may be asked to evaluate the use of different materials for a particular product, using an LCA.

Q1 What are the four stages that need to be considered to conduct a life cycle assessment? [4 marks]

Potable Water

We all need safe drinking water. The way that water's made safe depends on local conditions.

Potable Water is Water You Can Drink

1) Potable water is water that's been treated or is naturally safe for humans to drink — it's essential for life.
2) Chemists wouldn't call it pure, though. Pure water only contains H_2O molecules whereas potable water can contain lots of other dissolved substances.
3) The important thing is that the levels of dissolved salts aren't too high, that it has a pH between 6.5 and 8.5 and also that there aren't any nasties (like bacteria or other microbes) swimming around in it.

The Way that Potable Water is Produced Depends on Where You Are

1) Rainwater is a type of fresh water. Fresh water is water that doesn't have much dissolved in it.
2) When it rains, water can either collect as surface water (in lakes, rivers and reservoirs) or as groundwater (in rocks called aquifers that trap water underground).
3) In the UK, the source of fresh water used depends on location. Surface water tends to dry up first, so in warm areas, e.g. the south-east, most of the domestic water supply comes from groundwater.
4) Even though it only has low levels of dissolved substances, water from these fresh water sources still needs to be treated to make it safe before it can be used. This process includes:

- Filtration — a wire mesh screens out large twigs etc, and then gravel and sand beds filter out any other solid bits.
- Sterilisation — the water is sterilised to kill any harmful bacteria or microbes. This can be done by bubbling chlorine gas through it or by using ozone or ultraviolet light.

mesh

sand and gravel filtration

sterilisation

5) In some very dry countries, e.g. Kuwait, there's not enough surface or groundwater and instead seawater must be treated by desalination to provide potable water.
6) Distillation can be used to desalinate seawater.
7) You can test and purify a sample of water in the lab using distillation:

Chemicals can also be added to the water supply, such as fluoride (which is good for teeth). This is controversial, because people aren't given any choice over whether they consume them or not.

PRACTICAL

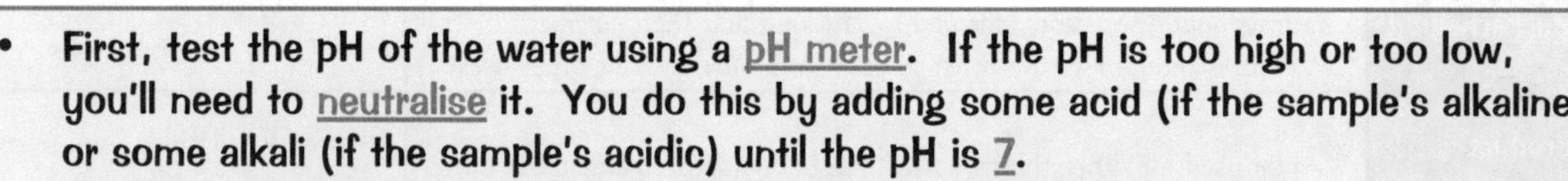

- First, test the pH of the water using a pH meter. If the pH is too high or too low, you'll need to neutralise it. You do this by adding some acid (if the sample's alkaline) or some alkali (if the sample's acidic) until the pH is 7.
- Set up the equipment as shown in the diagram on the right.
- As the water in the flask heats up, it'll evaporate (become a gas) and will enter the condenser as steam.
- The drop in temperature inside the condenser, due to the cold water around it, will cause the steam to condense back into liquid water.
- Collect the water running out of the condenser in a beaker.
- Retest the pH of the water with a pH meter to check it's neutral.
- You can tell whether there were salts in your initial sample by looking to see whether there are any crystals in the round bottomed flask once the water's been distilled.

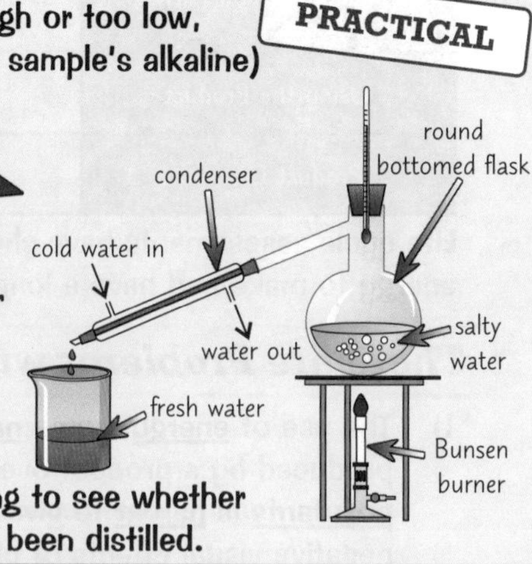

8) Seawater can also be treated by processes that use membranes — like reverse osmosis. The salty water is passed through a membrane that only allows water molecules to pass through. Ions and larger molecules are trapped by the membrane so separated from the water.
9) Both distillation and reverse osmosis need loads of energy, so they're really expensive and not practical for producing large quantities of fresh water.

Potable water — nothing to do with gardening...

Distilling salty water could be useful if you ever end up stranded on a desert island. Oh, and for your exams too.

Q1 Describe the steps you could take to treat water from a groundwater source to make it potable. [2 marks]

Waste Water Treatment

It might not be pretty, but dealing with our waste is really important to ensure that we don't pollute the natural environment — it also means that we can access nice clean water. Super.

Waste Water Comes from Lots of Different Sources

1) We use water for lots of things at home — like having a bath, going to the toilet, doing the washing-up, etc. When you flush this water down the drain, it goes into the sewers and towards sewage treatment plants.
2) Agricultural systems also produce a lot of waste water including nutrient run-off from fields and slurry from animal farms.
3) Sewage from domestic or agricultural sources has to be treated to remove any organic matter and harmful microbes before it can be put back into freshwater sources like rivers or lakes. Otherwise it would make them very polluted and would pose health risks.
4) Industrial processes also produce a lot of waste water that has to be collected and treated.
5) As well as organic matter, industrial waste water can also contain harmful chemicals — so it has to undergo additional stages of treatment before it is safe to release it into the environment.

Sewage Treatment Happens in Several Stages

Some of the processes involved in treating waste water at sewage treatment plants include:

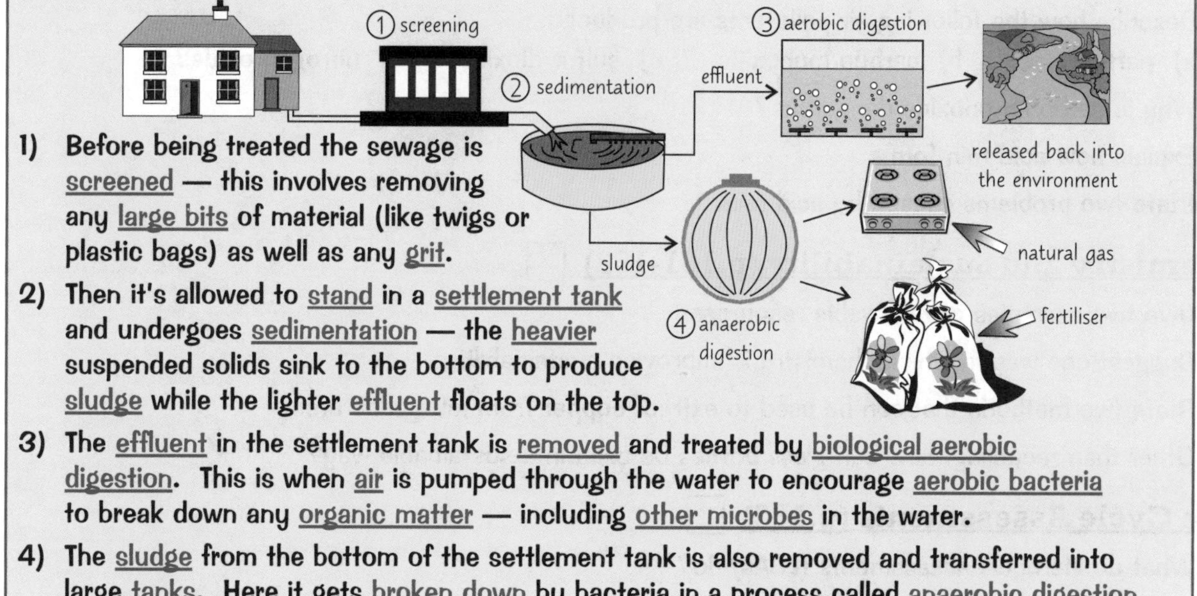

1) Before being treated the sewage is screened — this involves removing any large bits of material (like twigs or plastic bags) as well as any grit.
2) Then it's allowed to stand in a settlement tank and undergoes sedimentation — the heavier suspended solids sink to the bottom to produce sludge while the lighter effluent floats on the top.
3) The effluent in the settlement tank is removed and treated by biological aerobic digestion. This is when air is pumped through the water to encourage aerobic bacteria to break down any organic matter — including other microbes in the water.
4) The sludge from the bottom of the settlement tank is also removed and transferred into large tanks. Here it gets broken down by bacteria in a process called anaerobic digestion.
5) Anaerobic digestion breaks down the organic matter in the sludge, releasing methane gas in the process. The methane gas can be used as an energy source and the remaining digested waste can be used as a fertiliser.
6) For waste water containing toxic substances, additional stages of treatment may involve adding chemicals (e.g. to precipitate metals), UV radiation or using membranes.

Aerobic just means with oxygen, whereas anaerobic means without oxygen.

Sewage treatment requires more processes than treating fresh water but uses less energy than the desalination of salt water, so could be used as an alternative in areas where there's not much fresh water. For example, Singapore is treating waste water and recycling it back into drinking supplies. However, people don't like the idea of drinking water that used to be sewage.

Is it just me, or does this page stink? Phew...

Modern sewage systems have done wonders to make life in developed countries much less... well... smelly.

Q1 List three stages of treatment that domestic sewage undergoes at a sewage treatment plant. [3 marks]

Revision Questions for Topics C9 & C10

That's all for Topics C9 and C10, but before you breathe a sigh of relief, there are some questions to try.

- Try these questions and tick off each one when you get it right.
- When you've done all the questions under a heading and are completely happy with it, tick it off.

The Evolution of the Atmosphere (p.157)

1) How do scientists think the atmosphere was formed during the first billion years or so of Earth's history?
2) Name five gases that scientists think were present in the early atmosphere.
3) Describe how the levels of carbon dioxide in the atmosphere were reduced.
4) Write the balanced chemical equation for photosynthesis.
5) State the approximate composition of the atmosphere today.

Pollution and Climate Change (p.158-160)

6) Name three greenhouse gases.
7) Explain how the greenhouse effect works to keep the Earth warm.
8) State three ways in which human activity is leading to an increase in carbon dioxide in the atmosphere.
9) What is a carbon footprint?
10) Explain why reducing carbon dioxide emissions can be a difficult issue.
11) Describe how the following air pollutants are produced:
    a) particulates, b) carbon monoxide, c) sulfur dioxide, d) nitrogen oxides.
12) Why is carbon monoxide dangerous?
13) Explain how acid rain forms.
14) State two problems caused by acid rain.

Chemistry and Sustainability (p.161-162)

15) Give two examples of renewable resources.
16) Suggest one way in which chemistry is improving sustainability.
17) State two methods that can be used to extract copper from low grade ores.
18) Other than recycling, how can glass bottles be used in a sustainable way?

Life Cycle Assessments (p.163)

19) What do life cycle assessments (LCAs) do?
20) Give one problem of life cycle assessments.

Potable Water (p.164)

21) What is potable water?
22) Suggest a source of fresh water.
23) Describe how you could distil seawater in the lab.
24) What other method could you use for making sea water potable?

Waste Water Treatment (p.165)

25) Name three different sources of waste water.
26) Why is it important to treat waste water before releasing it into the environment?
27) What type of waste water could contain harmful chemicals?
28) What two products can be obtained by the anaerobic digestion of sewage sludge?

Energy Stores and Systems

Energy is never used up. Instead it's just transferred between different energy stores and different objects...

Energy is Transferred Between Stores

When energy is transferred to an object, the energy is stored in one of the object's energy stores.

The energy stores you need to know are:

1) Thermal energy stores
2) Kinetic energy stores
3) Gravitational potential energy stores
4) Elastic potential energy stores
5) Chemical energy stores
6) Magnetic energy stores
7) Electrostatic energy stores
8) Nuclear energy stores

Energy is transferred mechanically (by a force doing work), electrically (work done by moving charges), by heating or by radiation (e.g. light, p.220, or sound).

You may also see thermal energy stores called internal energy stores.

When a System Changes, Energy is Transferred

1) A system is just a fancy word for a single object (e.g. the air in a piston) or a group of objects (e.g. two colliding vehicles) that you're interested in.
2) When a system changes, energy is transferred. It can be transferred into or away from the system, between different objects in the system or between different types of energy stores.
3) Closed systems are systems where neither matter nor energy can enter or leave. The net change in the total energy of a closed system is always zero.

Energy can be Transferred by Heating...

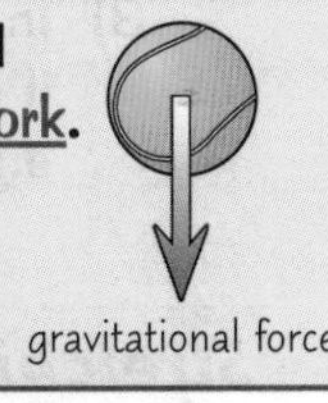

1) Take the example of boiling water in a kettle — you can think of the water as the system. Energy is transferred to the water (from the kettle's heating element) by heating, into the water's thermal energy store (causing the temperature of the water to rise).
2) You could also think of the kettle's heating element and the water together as a two-object system. Energy is transferred electrically to the thermal energy store of the kettle's heating element, which transfers energy by heating to the water's thermal energy store.

...or by Doing Work

1) Work done is just another way of saying energy transferred — they're the same thing.
2) Work can be done when current flows (work is done against resistance in a circuit, see p.179) or by a force moving an object (there's more on this on page 203).

The initial force exerted by a person to throw a ball upwards does work. It causes an energy transfer from the chemical energy store of the person's arm to the kinetic energy store of the ball and arm.

A ball dropped from a height is accelerated by gravity. The gravitational force does work. It causes energy to be transferred from the ball's gravitational potential energy store to its kinetic energy store.

gravitational force

The friction between a car's brakes and its wheels does work as it slows down. It causes an energy transfer from the wheels' kinetic energy stores to the thermal energy store of the surroundings.

frictional forces cause a transfer of energy

In a collision between a car and a stationary object, the normal contact force between the car and the object does work. It causes energy to be transferred from the car's kinetic energy store to other energy stores, e.g. the elastic potential and thermal energy stores of the object and the car body. Some energy might also be transferred away by sound waves.

All this work, I can feel my energy stores being drained...

Energy stores pop up everywhere in physics, the pesky scoundrels — make sure you've got to grips with them.

Q1 Describe the energy transfers that occur when the wind causes a windmill to spin. [3 marks]

Kinetic and Potential Energy Stores

Now you've got your head around energy stores, it's time to see how you can calculate the amount of energy in three of the most common ones — kinetic, gravitational potential and elastic potential energy stores.

Movement Means Energy in an Object's Kinetic Energy Store

1) Anything that is moving has energy in its kinetic energy store. Energy is transferred to this store when an object speeds up and is transferred away from this store when an object slows down.
2) The energy in the kinetic energy store depends on the object's mass and speed. The greater its mass and the faster it's going, the more energy there will be in its kinetic energy store.
3) There's a slightly tricky formula for it, so you have to concentrate a little bit harder for this one.

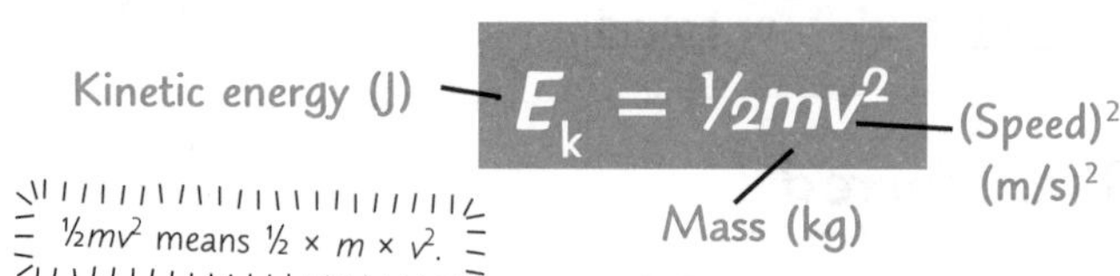

A car of mass 2500 kg is travelling at 20 m/s. Calculate the energy in its kinetic energy store.

E_k = ½ × 2500 × 20^2 = 500 000 J

Raised Objects Store Energy in Gravitational Potential Energy Stores

1) Lifting an object in a gravitational field requires work. This causes a transfer of energy to the gravitational potential energy (g.p.e.) store of the raised object. The higher the object is lifted, the more energy is transferred to this store.
2) The amount of energy in a g.p.e. store depends on the object's mass, its height and the strength of the gravitational field the object is in (p.202).
3) You can use this equation to find the change in energy in an object's gravitational potential energy store for a change in height, h.

$$E_p = mgh$$

g.p.e (J) — E_p; Mass (kg) — m; Gravitational field strength (N/kg) — g; Height (m) — h

Falling Objects Also Transfer Energy

1) When something falls, energy from its gravitational potential energy store is transferred to its kinetic energy store.
2) For a falling object when there's no air resistance:

Energy lost from the g.p.e. store = Energy gained in the kinetic energy store

3) In real life, air resistance (p.210) acts against all falling objects — it causes some energy to be transferred to other energy stores, e.g. the thermal energy stores of the object and surroundings.

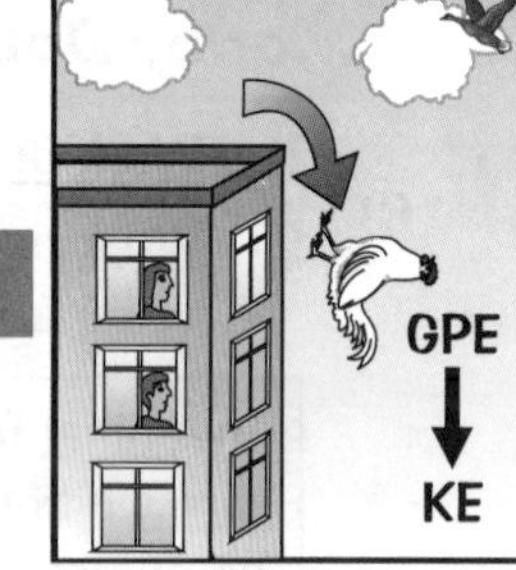

Stretching can Transfer Energy to Elastic Potential Energy Stores

Stretching or squashing an object can transfer energy to its elastic potential energy store.
So long as the limit of proportionality has not been exceeded (p.205) energy in the elastic potential energy store of a stretched spring can be found using:

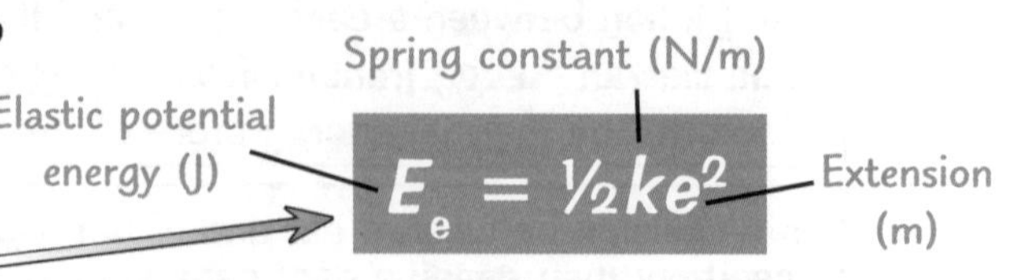

Make the most of your potential — jump on your bed...

Wow, that's a lot of energy equations. Make sure you know how to use them all, and remember that the energy in an object's kinetic energy store only changes if it's changing its speed. Now have a crack at this delightful question...

Q1 A 2.0 kg object is dropped from a height of 10 m. Calculate the speed of the object after it has fallen 5.0 m, assuming there is no air resistance. Give your answer to two significant figures. g = 9.8 N/kg. [5 marks]

Specific Heat Capacity

Specific heat capacity is really just a sciencey way of saying how hard it is to heat something up...

Different Materials Have Different Specific Heat Capacities

1) More energy needs to be transferred to the thermal energy store of some materials to increase their temperature than others. E.g. you need 4200 J to warm 1 kg of water by 1 °C, but only 139 J to warm 1 kg of mercury by 1 °C.
2) Materials that need to gain lots of energy in their thermal energy stores to warm up also transfer loads of energy when they cool down again. They can 'store' a lot of energy.
3) Specific heat capacity is the amount of energy needed to raise the temperature of 1 kg of a substance by 1 °C.
4) Here's the equation that links energy transferred to specific heat capacity: (the Δ's just mean "change in").

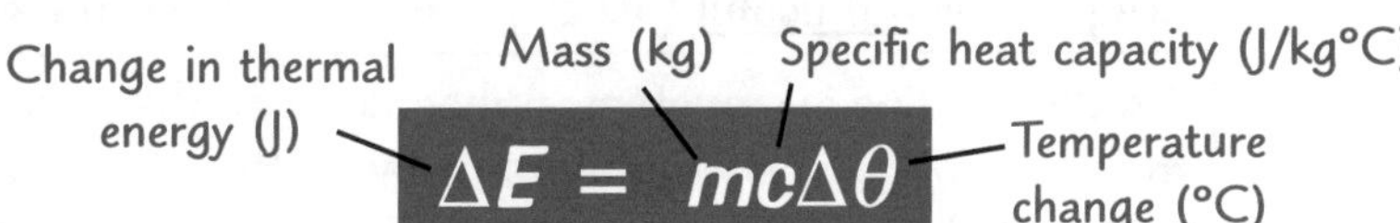

You Can Investigate Specific Heat Capacities

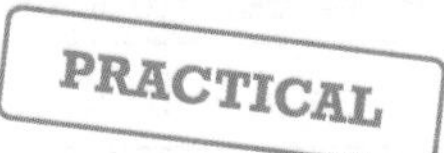

1) To investigate a solid material (e.g. copper), you'll need a block of the material with two holes in it (for the heater and thermometer to go into, see below).
2) Measure the mass of the block, then wrap it in an insulating layer (e.g. a thick layer of newspaper) to reduce the energy transferred from the block to the surroundings. Insert the thermometer and heater as shown on the right.
3) Measure the initial temperature of the block and set the potential difference, V, of the power supply to be 10 V. Turn on the power supply and start a stop watch.
4) When you turn on the power, the current in the circuit (i.e. the moving charges) does work on the heater, transferring energy electrically from the power supply to the heater's thermal energy store. This energy is then transferred to the material's thermal energy store by heating, causing the material's temperature to increase.
5) As the block heats up, take readings of the temperature and current, I, every minute for 10 minutes. You should find that the current through the circuit doesn't change as the block heats up.
6) When you've collected enough readings (10 should do it), turn off the power supply. Using your measurement of the current, and the potential difference of the power supply, you can calculate the power supplied to the heater, using $P = VI$ (p.188). You can use this to calculate how much energy, E, has been transferred to the heater at the time of each temperature reading using the formula $E = Pt$, where t is the time in seconds since the experiment began.
7) If you assume all the energy supplied to the heater has been transferred to the block, you can plot a graph of energy transferred to the thermal energy store of the block against temperature. It should look something like this: (you may or may not get the curved bit at the beginning, don't worry about it).

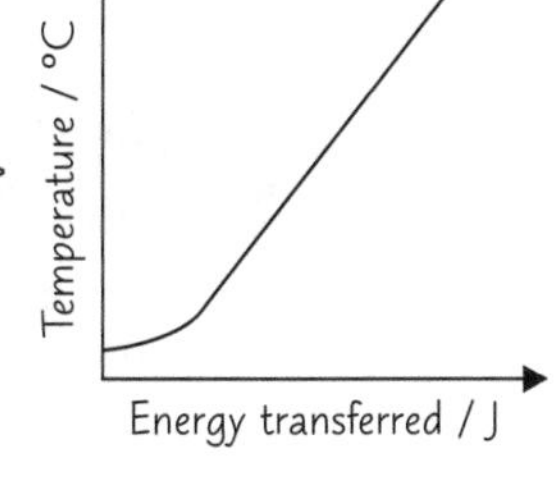

8) Find the gradient of the straight part of the graph. This is $\Delta\theta \div \Delta E$. You know from the equation above that $\Delta E = mc\Delta\theta$. So the specific heat capacity of the material of the block is: $1 \div$ (gradient $\times$ the mass of the block).
9) You can repeat this experiment with different materials to see how their specific heat capacities compare.

You can also investigate the specific heat capacity of liquids — just place the heater and thermometer in an insulated beaker filled with a known mass of the liquid.

I've eaten five sausages — I have a high specific meat capacity...

The specific heat capacity equation looks a bit tricky, but like all equations, it's easy to use when you know how.

Q1 Find the final temperature of 5 kg of water, at an initial temperature of 5 °C, after 50 kJ of energy has been transferred to it. The specific heat capacity of water is 4200 J/kg°C. [3 marks]

Conservation of Energy and Power

Repeat after me: energy is NEVER destroyed. Make sure you learn that fact, it's really important.

You Need to Know the Conservation of Energy Principle

1) The conservation of energy principle is that energy is always conserved:

   Energy can be transferred usefully, stored or dissipated, but can never be created or destroyed.

2) When energy is transferred between stores, not all of the energy is transferred usefully into the store that you want it to go to. Some energy is always dissipated when an energy transfer takes place.
3) Dissipated energy is sometimes called 'wasted energy' because the energy is being stored in a way that is not useful (usually energy has been transferred into thermal energy stores).

   A mobile phone is a system. When you use the phone, energy is usefully transferred from the chemical energy store of the battery in the phone. But some of this energy is dissipated in this transfer to the thermal energy store of the phone (you may have noticed your phone feels warm if you've been using it for a while).

4) You also need to be able to describe energy transfers for closed systems:

   A cold spoon is dropped into an insulated flask of hot soup, which is then sealed. You can assume that the flask is a perfect thermal insulator so the spoon and the soup form a closed system. Energy is transferred from the thermal energy store of the soup to the useless thermal energy store of the spoon (causing the soup to cool down slightly). Energy transfers have occurred within the system, but no energy has left the system — so the net change in energy is zero, p.167.

Power is the 'Rate of Doing Work' — i.e. How Much per Second

1) Power is the rate of energy transfer, or the rate of doing work.
2) Power is measured in watts. One watt = 1 joule of energy transferred per second.
3) You can calculate power using these equations:

$$P = \frac{E}{t}$$

Power (W), Energy transferred (J), Time (s)

$$P = \frac{W}{t}$$

Power (W), Work done (J), Time (s)

4) A powerful machine is not necessarily one which can exert a strong force (although it usually ends up that way). A powerful machine is one which transfers a lot of energy in a short space of time.

Take two cars that are identical in every way apart from the power of their engines. Both cars race the same distance along a straight race track to a finish line. The car with the more powerful engine will reach the finish line faster than the other car — i.e. it will transfer the same amount of energy but over less time.

EXAMPLE:

It takes 8000 J of work to lift a stunt performer to the top of a building. Motor A can lift the stunt performer to the correct height in 50 s. Motor B would take 300 s to lift the performer to the same height. Which motor is most powerful? Calculate the power of this motor.

1) Both motors transfer the same amount of energy, but motor A would do it quicker than motor B. So, motor A is the more powerful motor.
2) Plug the time taken and work done for motor A into the equation $P = W \div t$ and find the power.
   $P = W \div t = 8000 \div 50 = 160$ W

Energy can't be created or destroyed — only talked about a lot...

Remember, when energy is wasted it's not destroyed — it still exists, it just isn't stored usefully anymore.

Q1 A motor transfers 4.8 kJ of energy in 2 minutes. Calculate its power output. [3 marks]

Reducing Unwanted Energy Transfers

There are a few ways you can reduce the amount of energy scampering off to a completely useless store — lubrication and thermal insulation are the ones you need to know about. Read on...

Lubrication Reduces Frictional Forces

1) Whenever something moves, there's usually at least one frictional force acting against it (p.210). This causes some energy in the system to be dissipated (p.170), e.g. air resistance can transfer energy from a falling object's kinetic energy store to its thermal energy store.
2) For objects that are being rubbed together, lubricants can be used to reduce the friction between the objects' surfaces when they move. Lubricants are usually liquids (like oil), so they can flow easily between objects and coat them.

Streamlining reduces air resistance too, see p.210.

Heating Can Occur by Conduction and Convection

1) When an object is heated, energy is transferred to the kinetic energy stores of its particles.
2) This causes the particles to vibrate more and to collide with each other. During these collisions, energy is transferred between the particles' kinetic energy stores. This is conduction.
3) Thermal conductivity is a measure of how quickly energy is transferred through a material in this way. Materials with a high thermal conductivity transfer energy between their particles at a faster rate.
4) If the particles are free to move (e.g. in a gas or a liquid) the particles moving faster means that the space between individual particles increases. This causes the density (p.192) of the region being heated to decrease.
5) Because liquids and gases can flow, the warmer and less dense region will rise above denser, cooler regions. So energetic particles move away from hotter to cooler regions — this is convection.

Insulation Reduces the Rate of Energy Transfer by Heating

The last thing you want when you've made your house nice and toasty is for that energy to escape outside. There are a few things you can do to prevent energy losses through heating:

- Have thick walls that are made from a material with a low thermal conductivity. The thicker the walls and the lower their thermal conductivity, the slower the rate of energy transfer will be (so the building will cool more slowly).
- Use thermal insulation. Here are some examples:

Reducing the difference between the temperature inside and outside the house will also reduce the rate of energy transfer.

1) Some houses have cavity walls, made up of an inner and an outer wall with an air gap in the middle. The air gap reduces the amount of energy transferred by conduction through the walls. Cavity wall insulation, where the cavity wall air gap is filled with a foam, can also reduce energy transfer by convection in the wall cavity.
2) Loft insulation can reduce convection currents (a cycle where air particles are constantly being heated, rising, cooling and then sinking) being created in lofts.

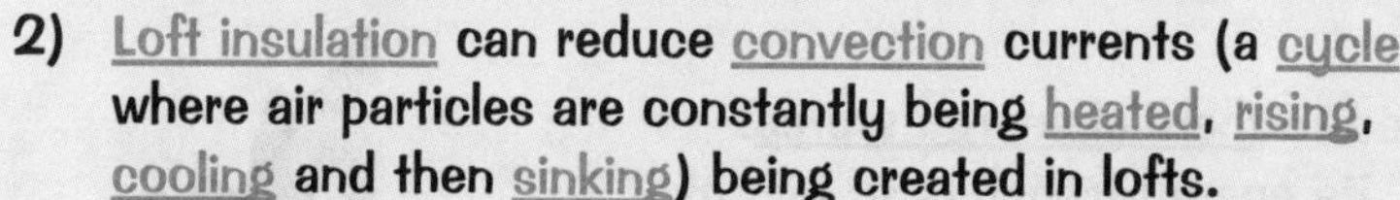

3) Double-glazed windows work in the same way as cavity walls — they have an air gap between two sheets of glass to prevent energy transfer by conduction through the windows.
4) Draught excluders around doors and windows reduce energy transfers by convection.

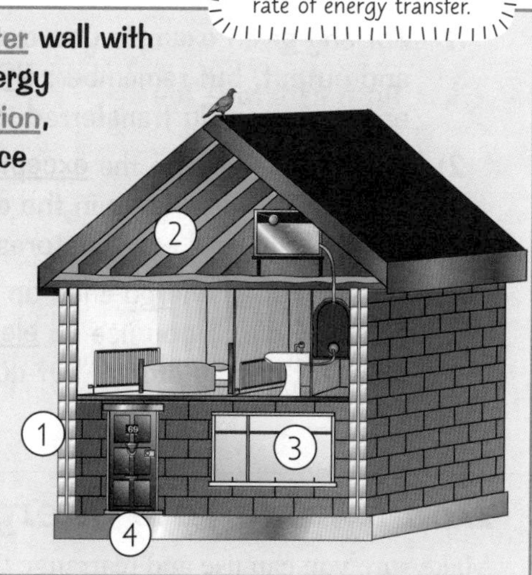

Bundle your brew in newspaper to stop it going cold...

Understanding conduction and convection is really useful, especially when explaining how to stop unwanted transfers. Have a go at naming as many methods for reducing energy transfers as you can, then try this question.

Q1 Explain how cavity wall insulation reduces the amount of energy transferred out of a house. [3 marks]

Efficiency

More! More! Tell me more about energy transfers please! Oh go on then, since you insist...

Most Energy Transfers Involve Some Waste Energy

1) Useful devices are only useful because they can transfer energy from one store to another.
2) As you'll probably have gathered by now, some of the input energy is usually wasted by being transferred to a useless energy store — usually a thermal energy store.
3) The less energy that is 'wasted' in this energy store, the more efficient the device is said to be.
4) You can improve the efficiency of energy transfers by insulating objects, lubricating them or making them more streamlined (see pages 171 and 210).
5) The efficiency for any energy transfer can be worked out using this equation:

$$\text{Efficiency} = \frac{\text{Useful output energy transfer}}{\text{Total input energy transfer}}$$

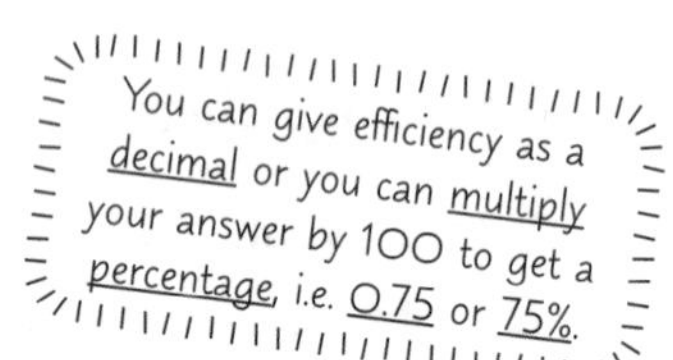

6) You might not know the energy inputs and outputs of a device, but you can still calculate its efficiency as long as you know the power input and output:

$$\text{Efficiency} = \frac{\text{Useful power output}}{\text{Total power input}}$$

A blender is 70% efficient. It has a total input power of 600 W. Calculate the useful output power.

1) Change the efficiency from a percentage to a decimal. efficiency = 70% = 0.7
2) Rearrange the equation for useful power output. useful power output = efficiency × total power input
3) Stick in the numbers you're given. = 0.7 × 600 = 420 W

Useful Energy Input Isn't Usually Equal to Total Energy Output

1) For any given example you can talk about the types of energy being input and output, but remember: NO device is 100% efficient and the wasted energy is usually transferred to useless thermal energy stores.
2) Electric heaters are the exception to this. They're usually 100% efficient because all the energy in the electrostatic energy store is transferred to "useful" thermal energy stores.
3) Ultimately, all energy ends up transferred to thermal energy stores. For example, if you use an electric drill, its energy transfers to lots of different energy stores, but quickly ends up all in thermal energy stores.

Don't waste your energy — turn the TV off while you revise...

Make sure you can use and rearrange the equations for efficiency, then have a go at these questions.

Q1 A motor in a remote-controlled car transfers 300 J of energy into the car's energy stores. 225 J are transferred to the car's kinetic energy stores. Calculate the efficiency of the motor. [2 marks]

Q2 A machine has a useful power output of 900 W and a total power input of 1200 W. In a given time, 72 kJ of energy is transferred to the machine. Calculate the amount of energy usefully transferred by the machine in this time. [4 marks]

Energy Resources and Their Uses

Energy resources, both renewable and non-renewable, are mostly used to generate electricity.
There's loads more on how over the next few pages, but two other major uses are transport and heating.

Non-Renewable Energy Resources Will Run Out One Day

Non-renewable energy resources are fossil fuels and nuclear fuel (uranium and plutonium). Fossil fuels are natural resources that form underground over millions of years. They are typically burnt to provide energy. The three main fossil fuels are:

1) Coal
2) Oil
3) (Natural) Gas

- These will all 'run out' one day.
- They all do damage to the environment.
- But they provide most of our energy.

Renewable Energy Resources Will Never Run Out

Renewable energy resources are:

1) The Sun (Solar)
2) Wind
3) Water waves
4) Hydro-electricity
5) Bio-fuel
6) Tides
7) Geothermal

- These will never run out — the energy can be 'renewed' as it is used.
- Most of them do damage the environment, but in less nasty ways than non-renewables.
- The trouble is they don't provide much energy and some of them are unreliable because they depend on the weather.

Energy Resources can be Used for Transport...

Transport is one of the most obvious places where fuel is used. Here are a few transportation methods that use either renewable or non-renewable energy resources:

Electricity can also be used to power vehicles, (e.g. trains and some cars). It can be generated using renewable or non-renewable energy resources (p.174-176).

NON-RENEWABLE ENERGY RESOURCES

- Petrol and diesel powered vehicles (including most cars) use fuel created from oil.
- Coal is used in some old-fashioned steam trains to boil water to produce steam.

RENEWABLE ENERGY RESOURCES

Vehicles that run on pure bio-fuels (p.176) or a mix of a bio-fuel and petrol or diesel (only the bio-fuel bit is renewable, though).

...And for Heating

Energy resources are also needed for heating things like your home.

NON-RENEWABLE ENERGY RESOURCES

- Natural gas is the most widely used fuel for heating homes in the UK. The gas is used to heat water, which is then pumped into radiators throughout the home.
- Coal is commonly burnt in fireplaces.
- Electric heaters (sometimes called storage heaters) which use electricity generated from non-renewable energy resources.

RENEWABLE ENERGY RESOURCES

- A geothermal (or ground source) heat pump uses geothermal energy resources (p.174) to heat buildings.
- Solar water heaters work by using the sun to heat water which is then pumped into radiators in the building.
- Burning bio-fuel or using electricity generated from renewable resources can also be used for heating.

I'm pretty sure natural gas is renewable — I make enough of it...

You need to know the difference between the two different types of energy resource, so get cracking.

Q1 Write down whether each of the following are renewable or non-renewable energy resources.
a) Tidal power b) Natural gas c) Nuclear power d) Bio-fuel [4 marks]

Wind, Solar and Geothermal

Renewable energy resources, like wind, solar and geothermal resources, will not run out. They don't generate as much electricity as non-renewables though — if they did we'd all be using solar-powered toasters by now.

Wind Power — Lots of Little Wind Turbines

1) This involves putting lots of wind turbines up in exposed places like on moors or round coasts.
2) Each turbine has a generator inside it — the rotating blades turn the generator and produce electricity.
3) There's no pollution (except for a little bit when they're manufactured).
4) But they do spoil the view. You need about 1500 wind turbines to replace one coal-fired power station and 1500 of them cover a lot of ground — which would have a big effect on the scenery.
5) And they can be very noisy, which can be annoying for people living nearby.
6) There's also the problem of the turbines stopping when the wind stops or if the wind is too strong, and it's impossible to increase supply when there's extra demand. On average, wind turbines produce electricity 70-85% of the time.
7) The initial costs are quite high, but there are no fuel costs and minimal running costs.
8) There's no permanent damage to the landscape — if you remove the turbines, you remove the noise and the view returns to normal.

Solar Cells — Expensive but No Environmental Damage

(well, there may be a bit caused by making the cells)

1) Solar cells generate electric currents directly from sunlight. Solar cells are often the best source of energy to charge batteries in calculators and watches which don't use much electricity.
2) Solar power is often used in remote places where there's not much choice (e.g. the Australian outback) and to power electric road signs and satellites.
3) There's no pollution. (Although they do use quite a lot of energy to manufacture in the first place.)
4) In sunny countries solar power is a very reliable source of energy — but only in the daytime. Solar power can still be cost-effective even in cloudy countries like Britain though.
5) Like wind, you can't increase the power output when there is extra demand (p.189).
6) Initial costs are high but after that the energy is free and running costs almost nil.
7) Solar cells are usually used to generate electricity on a relatively small scale.

Time to recharge.

Geothermal Power — Energy in Underground Thermal Energy Stores

1) This is possible in volcanic areas or where hot rocks lie quite near to the surface. The source of much of the energy is the slow decay of various radioactive elements, including uranium, deep inside the Earth.
2) This is actually brilliant free energy that's reliable and does very little damage to the environment.
3) Geothermal power can be used to generate electricity, or to heat buildings directly.
4) The main drawbacks with geothermal power are that there aren't very many suitable locations for power plants, and that the cost of building a power plant is often high compared to the amount of energy it produces.

People love the idea of wind power — just not in their back yard...

There are pros and cons to all energy resources. Make sure you know them for solar, wind and geothermal.

Q1 Explain why geothermal power is more reliable than wind power. [2 marks]

Hydro-electricity, Waves and Tides

Good ol' water. Not only can we drink it, we can also use it to generate electricity. It's easy to get confused between wave and tidal power as they both involve the seaside — but don't. They are completely different.

Hydro-electric Power Uses Falling Water

1) Hydro-electric power usually requires the flooding of a valley by building a big dam. Water is allowed out through turbines. There is no pollution (as such).
2) But there is a big impact on the environment due to the flooding of the valley (rotting vegetation releases methane and CO_2) and possible loss of habitat for some species (sometimes the loss of whole villages). The reservoirs can also look very unsightly when they dry up. Putting hydroelectric power stations in remote valleys tends to reduce their impact on humans.
3) A big advantage is it can provide an immediate response to an increased demand for electricity.
4) There's no problem with reliability except in times of drought — but remember this is Great Britain we're talking about.
5) Initial costs are high, but there are no fuel costs and minimal running costs.
6) It can be a useful way to generate electricity on a small scale in remote areas.

Wave Power — Lots of Little Wave-Powered Turbines

1) You need lots of small wave-powered turbines located around the coast. Like with wind power (p.174) the moving turbines are connected to a generator.
2) There is no pollution. The main problems are disturbing the seabed and the habitats of marine animals, spoiling the view and being a hazard to boats.
3) They are fairly unreliable, since waves tend to die out when the wind drops.
4) Initial costs are high, but there are no fuel costs and minimal running costs. Wave power is never likely to provide energy on a large scale, but it can be very useful on small islands.

Tidal Barrages — Using the Sun and Moon's Gravity

1) Tides are used in lots of ways to generate electricity. The most common method is building a tidal barrage.
2) Tidal barrages are big dams built across river estuaries, with turbines in them. As the tide comes in it fills up the estuary. The water is then allowed out through turbines at a controlled speed.
3) Tides are produced by the gravitational pull of the Sun and Moon.
4) There is no pollution. The main problems are preventing free access by boats, spoiling the view and altering the habitat of the wildlife, e.g. wading birds, sea creatures and beasties who live in the sand.
5) Tides are pretty reliable in the sense that they happen twice a day without fail, and always near to the predicted height. The only drawback is that the height of the tide is variable so lower (neap) tides will provide significantly less energy than the bigger 'spring' tides. They also don't work when the water level is the same either side of the barrage — this happens four times a day because of the tides.
6) Initial costs are moderately high, but there are no fuel costs and minimal running costs. Even though it can only be used in some of the most suitable estuaries tidal power has the potential for generating a significant amount of energy.

The hydro-electric power you're supplying — it's electrifying...

Learn the differences between all of these water-based resources before having a go at this question.

Q1 Give one negative environmental impact of wave power. [1 mark]

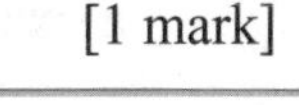

Bio-fuels and Non-renewables

And the energy resources just keep on coming. It's over soon, I promise. Just a few more to go.

Bio-fuels are Made from Plants and Waste

1) Bio-fuels are renewable energy resources created from either plant products or animal dung. They can be solid, liquid or gas and can be burnt to produce electricity or run cars in the same way as fossil fuels.
2) They are supposedly carbon neutral, although there is some debate about this as it's only really true if you keep growing plants at the rate that you're burning things.
3) Bio-fuels are fairly reliable, as crops take a relatively short time to grow and different crops can be grown all year round. However, they cannot respond to immediate energy demands. To combat this, bio-fuels are continuously produced and stored for when they are needed.
4) The cost to refine bio-fuels is very high and some worry that growing crops specifically for bio-fuels will mean there isn't enough space or water to meet the demands for crops that are grown for food.
5) In some regions, large areas of forest have been cleared to make room to grow bio-fuels, resulting in lots of species losing their natural habitats. The decay and burning of this vegetation also increases CO_2 and methane emissions.

Non-Renewables are Reliable...

1) Fossil fuels and nuclear energy are reliable. There's enough fossil and nuclear fuels to meet current demand, and they are extracted from the Earth at a fast enough rate that power plants always have fuel in stock. This means that the power plants can respond quickly to changes in demand (p.189).
2) However, these fuels are slowly running out. If no new resources are found, some fossil fuel stocks may run out within a hundred years.
3) While the set-up costs of power plants can be quite high compared to some other energy resources, the running costs aren't that expensive. Combined with fairly low fuel extraction costs, using fossil fuels is a cost effective way to produce energy (which is why it's so popular).

...But Create Environmental Problems

1) Coal, oil and gas release CO_2 into the atmosphere when they're burned. All this CO_2 adds to the greenhouse effect, and contributes to global warming.
2) Burning coal and oil also releases sulfur dioxide, which causes acid rain — which can be harmful to trees and soils and can have far-reaching effects in ecosystems.
3) Acid rain can be reduced by taking the sulfur out before the fuel is burned, or cleaning up the emissions.
4) Coal mining makes a mess of the landscape, especially "open-cast mining". As with many energy resources, the view can be spoilt by fossil fuel power plants.
5) Oil spillages cause serious environmental problems, affecting mammals and birds that live in and around the sea. We try to avoid them, but they'll always happen.
6) Nuclear power is clean but the nuclear waste is very dangerous and difficult to dispose of.
7) Nuclear fuel (e.g. uranium) is relatively cheap but the overall cost of nuclear power is high due to the cost of the power plant and final decommissioning.
8) Nuclear power always carries the risk of a major catastrophe like the Fukushima disaster in Japan.

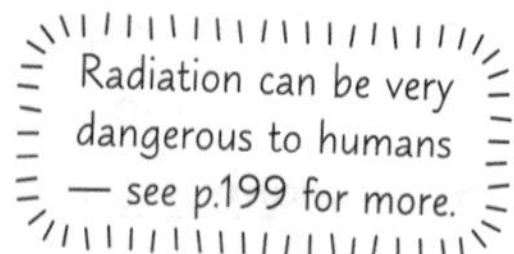

Bio-fuels are great — but don't burn your biology notes just yet...

Make sure you can talk about the reliability and any environmental issues of using bio-fuels or non-renewables.

Q1 Give two benefits of power plants that use fossil fuels. [2 marks]

Q2 Describe the environmental impact of using oil as an energy resource for generating electricity. [3 marks]

Trends in Energy Resource Use

Over time, the types of energy resources we use change. There are lots of reasons for this — breakthroughs in technology, understanding more about how they affect the environment or changes in cost are just a few.

Currently we Still Depend on Fossil Fuels

See p.189 for more about the supply and demand of electricity.

1) Over the 20th century, the electricity use of the UK hugely increased as the population grew and people began to use electricity for more and more things.
2) Since the beginning of the 21st century, electricity use in the UK has been decreasing (slowly), as we get better at making appliances more efficient (p.172) and become more careful with energy use in our homes.
3) Most of our electricity is produced using fossil fuels (mostly coal and gas) and from nuclear power.
4) Generating electricity isn't the only reason we burn fossil fuels — oil (diesel and petrol) is used to fuel cars, and gas is used to heat homes and cook food.
5) However, we are trying to increase our use of renewable energy resources (the UK aims to use renewable resources to provide 15% of its total yearly energy by 2020). This move towards renewable energy resources has been triggered by many things...

People Want to use More Renewable Energy Resources

1) We now know that burning fossil fuels is very damaging to the environment (p.176). This makes many people want to use more renewable energy resources that affect the environment less.
2) People and governments are also becoming increasingly aware that non-renewables will run out one day. Many people think it's better to learn to get by without non-renewables before this happens.
3) Pressure from other countries and the public has meant that governments have begun to introduce targets for using renewable resources. This in turn puts pressure on energy providers to build new power plants that use renewable resources to make sure they do not lose business and money.
4) Car companies have also been affected by this change in attitude towards the environment. Electric cars and hybrids (cars powered by two fuels, e.g. petrol and electricity) are already on the market and their popularity is increasing.

The Use of Renewables is Limited by Reliability, Money and Politics

1) There's a lot of scientific evidence supporting renewables, but although scientists can give advice, they don't have the power to make people, companies or governments change their behaviour (see p.2).
2) Building new renewable power plants costs money, so some energy providers are reluctant to do this, especially when fossil fuels are so cost effective. The cost of switching to renewable power will have to be paid, either by customers in their bills, or through government and taxes. Some people don't want to or can't afford to pay, and there are arguments about whether it's ethical to make them.
3) Even if new power plants are built, there are arguments over where to put them. E.g. many people don't want to live next to a wind farm, causing protests. There are arguments over whether it's ethical to make people put up with wind farms built next to them when they may not agree with the reasons for their use.
4) Some energy resources like wind power are not as reliable as traditional fossil fuels, whilst others cannot increase their power output on demand. This would mean either having to use a combination of different power plants (which would be expensive) or researching ways to improve reliability.
5) Research on improving the reliability and cost of renewables takes time and money — it may be years before improvements are made even with funding. Until then, we need dependable, non-renewable power.
6) Making personal changes can also be quite expensive. Hybrid cars are generally more expensive than equivalent petrol cars and things like solar panels for your home are still quite pricey. The cost of these things is slowly going down, but they are still not an option for many people.

Going green is on-trend this season...

So with more people wanting to help the environment, others not wanting to be inconvenienced and greener alternatives being expensive to set up, the energy resources we use are changing. Just not particularly quickly.

Q1 Give two reasons why we currently do not use more renewable energy resources in the UK. [2 marks]

Revision Questions for Topic P1

Well, that wraps up Topic P1 — time to put yourself to the test and find out how much you really know.

- Try these questions and tick off each one when you get it right.
- When you've done all the questions for a topic and are completely happy with it, tick off the topic.

Energy Stores and Systems (p.167-168)

1) Write down four energy stores.
2) Describe the energy transfers that occur as a ball falls to the ground.
3) Give the equation for finding the energy in an object's kinetic energy store.
4) If energy is transferred to an object's kinetic energy store, what happens to its speed?
5) Give the equation for finding the energy in an object's gravitational potential energy store.
6) What kind of energy store is energy transferred to when you compress a spring?

Specific Heat Capacity (p.169)

7) What is the definition of the specific heat capacity of a material?
8) Give the equation that relates energy transferred and specific heat capacity.
9) Describe an experiment to find the specific heat capacity of a material.

Conservation of Energy and Power (p.170)

10) State the conservation of energy principle.
11) Define power and give two equations to calculate power.
12) What are the units of power?

Reducing Unwanted Energy Transfers and Improving Efficiency (p.171-172)

13) How can you reduce unwanted energy transfers in a machine with moving, touching components?
14) True or false? A high thermal conductivity means there is a high rate of energy transfer.
15) Give four ways to prevent unwanted energy transfers in a home.
16) True or false? Thicker walls make a house cool down quicker.
17) What is the efficiency of an energy transfer? Give the equation that relates efficiency to power.

Energy Resources and Trends in their Use (p.173-177)

18) Name four renewable energy resources and four non-renewable energy resources.
19) What is the difference between renewable and non-renewable energy resources?
20) Give an example of how a renewable energy resource is used in everyday life.
21) Explain why solar power is considered to be a fairly reliable energy resource.
22) True or false? Tidal barrages are useful for storing energy to be used during times of high demand.
23) Give two ways in which the environment can be damaged when using fossil fuels.
24) Give one environmental benefit of using nuclear power.
25) Explain why the UK plans to use more renewable energy resources in the future.

Current and Circuit Symbols

It's pretty bad news if the word current makes you think of delicious cakes instead of physics. Learn what it means, as well as some handy symbols to show items like batteries and switches in a circuit.

Current is the Flow of Electrical Charge

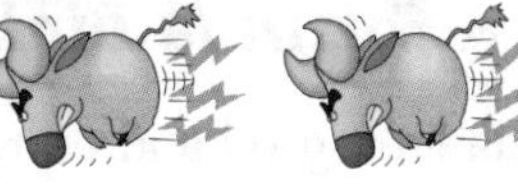

1) Electric current is a flow of electrical charge. Electrical charge will only flow round a complete (closed) circuit if there is a potential difference, so a current can only flow if there's a source of potential difference. The unit of current is the ampere, A.
2) In a single, closed loop (like the one on the right) the current has the same value everywhere in the circuit (see p.183).
3) Potential difference (or voltage) is the driving force that pushes the charge round. Its unit is the volt, V.
4) Resistance is anything that slows the flow down. Unit: ohm, Ω.
5) The current flowing through a component depends on the potential difference across it and the resistance of the component (p.180).

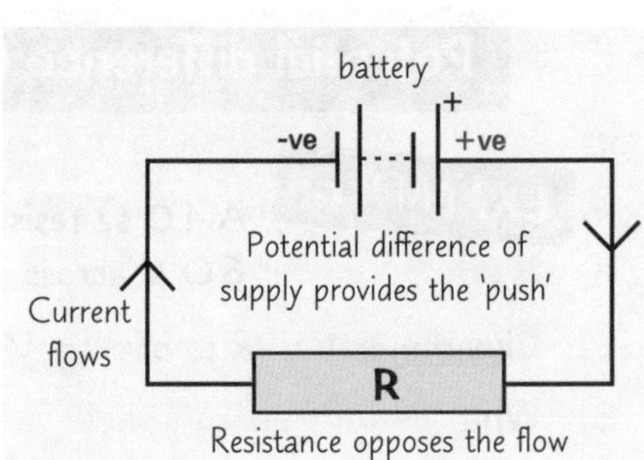

The greater the resistance across a component, the smaller the current that flows (for a given potential difference across the component).

Total Charge Through a Circuit Depends on Current and Time

The size of the current is the rate of flow of charge. When current flows past a point in a circuit for a length of time then the charge that has passed is given by this formula:

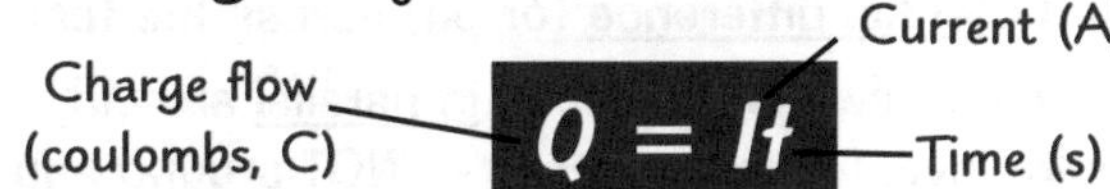

More charge passes around the circuit when a larger current flows.

EXAMPLE:

A battery charger passes a current of 2.0 A through a cell over a period of 2.5 hours. How much charge is transferred to the cell?

$Q = It = 2.0 \times (2.5 \times 60 \times 60)$
$= 18\ 000$ C

Learn these Circuit Diagram Symbols

You need to be able to understand circuit diagrams and draw them using the correct symbols. Make sure all the wires in your circuit are straight lines and that the circuit is closed, i.e. you can follow a wire from one end of the power supply, through any components, to the other end of the supply (ignoring any switches).

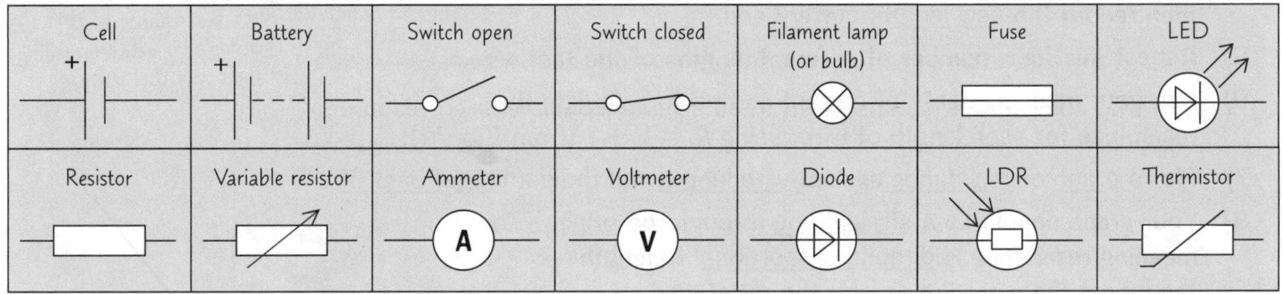

I think it's about time you took charge...

You've no doubt seen some of those circuit symbols before, but take a good look at all of them and practise drawing them. It's no good if you get asked to draw a circuit diagram and you can't tell a resistor from a fuse.

Q1 A laptop charger passes a current of 8.0 A through a laptop battery. Calculate how long the charger needs to be connected to the battery for 28 800 C of charge to be transferred to the laptop. [3 marks]

Q2 A student creates a simple circuit containing a battery, a switch and a bulb. He connects them all in a single, closed loop. Draw the circuit diagram for this circuit. [3 marks]

Resistance and V = IR

Ooh experiments, you've gotta love 'em. Here's a simple experiment for investigating resistance.

There's a Formula Linking Potential Difference and Current

The formula linking pd and current is very useful (and pretty common):

Potential difference (V) = Current (A) × Resistance (Ω)

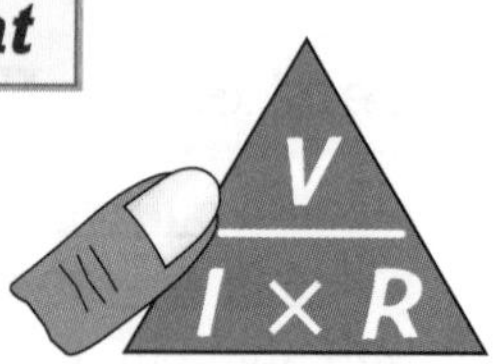

Use this formula triangle to rearrange. Just cover up the thing you're trying to find, and what's left visible is the formula you're after.

A 4.0 Ω resistor in a circuit has a potential difference of 6.0 V across it. What is the current through the resistor?

Rearrange $V = IR$ to give $I = V \div R$, then substitute in the values you have. $I = 6.0 \div 4.0 = 1.5$ A

You Can Investigate the Factors Affecting Resistance

PRACTICAL

The resistance of a circuit can depend on a number of factors, like whether components are in series or parallel, p.185, or the length of wire used in the circuit. You can investigate the effect of wire length using the circuit below.

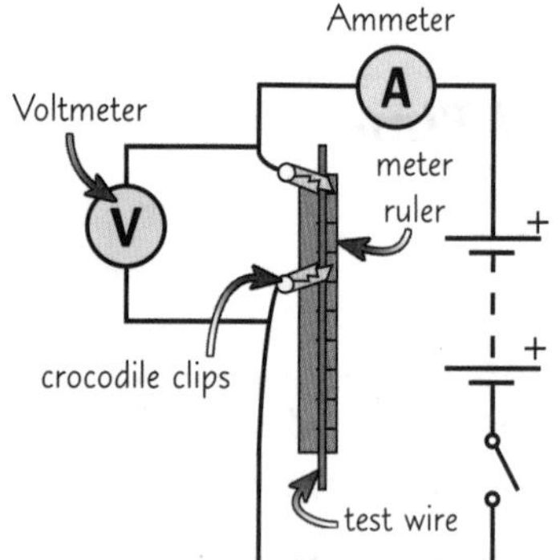

The Ammeter

1) Measures the current (in amps) flowing through the test wire.
2) The ammeter must always be placed in series with whatever you're investigating.

See p.183-184 for more on series and parallel circuits.

The Voltmeter

1) Measures the potential difference (or pd) across the test wire (in volts).
2) The voltmeter must always be placed in parallel around whatever you're investigating (p.184) — NOT around any other bit of the circuit, e.g. the battery.

A thin wire will give you the best results. Make sure it's as straight as possible so your length measurements are accurate.

1) Attach a crocodile clip to the wire level with 0 cm on the ruler.
2) Attach the second crocodile clip to the wire, e.g. 10 cm away from the first clip. Write down the length of the wire between the clips.
3) Close the switch, then record the current through the wire and the pd across it.
4) Open the switch, then move the second crocodile clip, e.g. another 10 cm, along the wire. Close the switch again, then record the new length, current and pd.
5) Repeat this for a number of different lengths of the test wire.
6) Use your measurements of current and pd to calculate the resistance for each length of wire, using $R = V \div I$ (from $V = IR$).
7) Plot a graph of resistance against wire length and draw a line of best fit.
8) Your graph should be a straight line through the origin, meaning resistance is directly proportional to length — the longer the wire, the greater the resistance.
9) If your graph doesn't go through the origin, it could be because the first clip isn't attached exactly at 0 cm, so all of your length readings are a bit out. This is a systematic error (p.5).

The wire may heat up during the experiment, which will affect its resistance (p.181). Leave the switch open for a bit between readings to let the circuit cool down.

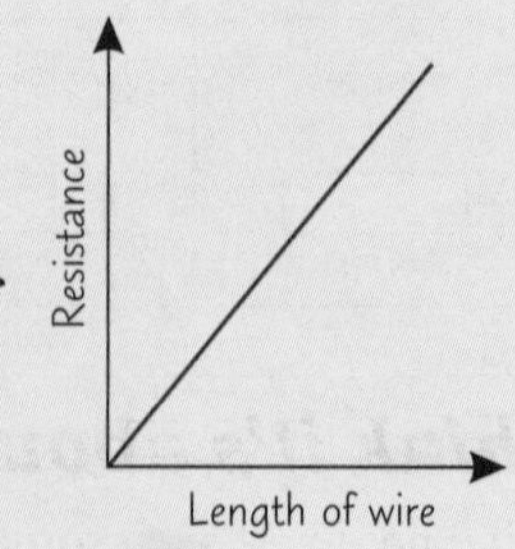

Measure gymnastics — use a vaultmeter...

You could also investigate the effect of diameter or material on the resistance of a wire. What fun.

Q1 An appliance is connected to a 230 V source. Calculate the resistance of the appliance if a current of 5.0 A is flowing through it. [3 marks]

Resistance and I-V Characteristics

There are three different graphs to learn on this page — you have to know how you get them too.

Ohmic Conductors Have a Constant Resistance

For some components, as the current through them is changed, the resistance of the component changes as well.

1) The resistance of ohmic conductors (e.g. a wire or a resistor) doesn't change with the current. At a constant temperature, the current flowing through an ohmic conductor is directly proportional to the potential difference across it. (R is constant in $V = IR$, previous page.)
2) The resistance of some resistors and components DOES change, e.g. a diode or a filament lamp.
3) When an electrical charge flows through a filament lamp, it transfers some energy to the thermal energy store of the filament (p.167), which is designed to heat up. Resistance increases with temperature, so as the current increases, the filament lamp heats up more and the resistance increases.
4) For diodes, the resistance depends on the direction of the current. They will happily let current flow in one direction, but have a very high resistance if it is reversed.

Three Very Important I-V Characteristics

PRACTICAL

This type of circuit uses direct current (dc) (p.186) and is a series circuit (p.183).

The term '*I-V* characteristic' refers to a graph which shows how the current (*I*) flowing through a component changes as the potential difference (*V*) across it is increased.
Linear components have an *I-V* characteristic that's a straight line (e.g. a fixed resistor).
Non-linear components have a curved *I-V* characteristic (e.g. a filament lamp or a diode).

You can do this experiment to find a component's *I-V* characteristic:

1) Set up the test circuit shown on the right.
2) Begin to vary the variable resistor. This alters the current flowing through the circuit and the potential difference across the component.
3) Take several pairs of readings from the ammeter and voltmeter to see how the potential difference across the component varies as the current changes. Repeat each reading twice more to get an average pd at each current.

4) Swap over the wires connected to the cell, so the direction of the current is reversed.

5) Plot a graph of current against voltage for the component.
6) The *I-V* characteristics you get for an ohmic conductor, filament lamp and diode should look like this:

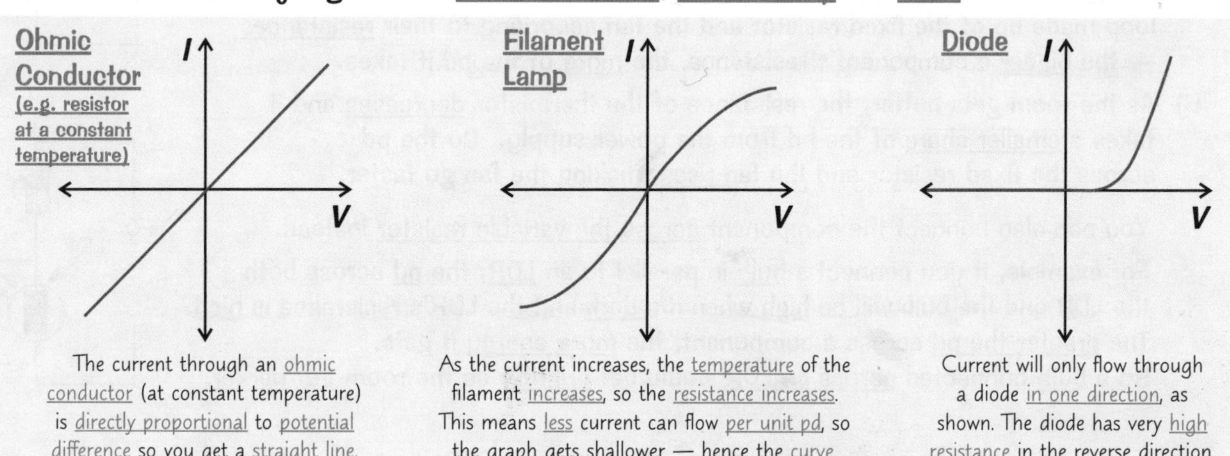

The current through an ohmic conductor (at constant temperature) is directly proportional to potential difference so you get a straight line.

As the current increases, the temperature of the filament increases, so the resistance increases. This means less current can flow per unit pd, so the graph gets shallower — hence the curve.

Current will only flow through a diode in one direction, as shown. The diode has very high resistance in the reverse direction.

Since $V = IR$, you can calculate the resistance at any point on the *I-V* characteristic by calculating $R = V/I$.

In the end you'll have to learn this — resistance is futile...

Draw out those graphs until you're sketching them in your sleep and make sure you can tell whether they're showing a linear or non-linear component.

Q1 Draw the *I-V* characteristic for: a) an ohmic conductor b) a filament lamp [4 marks]

Circuit Devices

The fun doesn't stop with filament bulbs. As well as temperature, resistance can depend on things like light intensity, which is how LDRs work. They're really useful for circuits that sense changes in light levels.

LDR is Short for Light Dependent Resistor

1) An LDR is a resistor that is dependent on the intensity of light. Simple really.
2) In bright light, the resistance falls.
3) In darkness, the resistance is highest.
4) They have lots of applications including automatic night lights, outdoor lighting and burglar detectors.

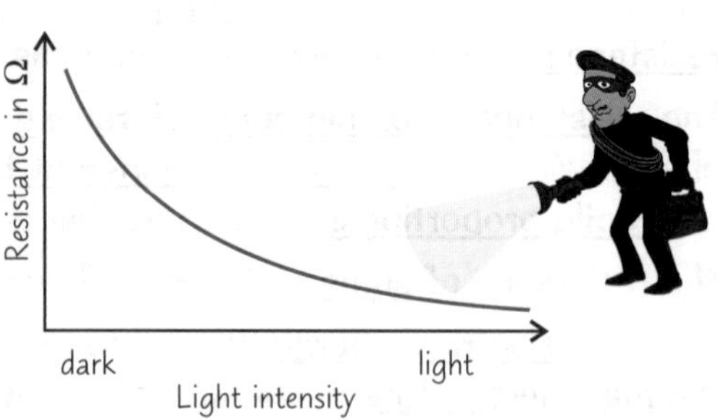

The Resistance of a Thermistor Depends on Temperature

1) A thermistor is a temperature dependent resistor.
2) In hot conditions, the resistance drops.
3) In cool conditions, the resistance goes up.
4) Thermistors make useful temperature detectors, e.g. car engine temperature sensors and electronic thermostats.

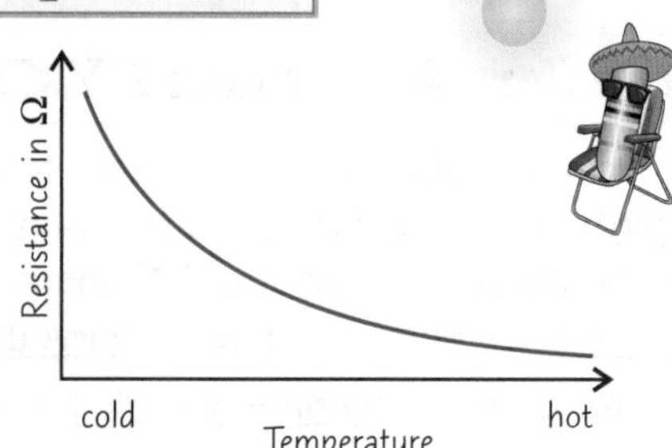

You Can Use LDRs and Thermistors in Sensing Circuits

1) Sensing circuits can be used to turn on or increase the power to components depending on the conditions that they are in.
2) The circuit on the right is a sensing circuit used to operate a fan in a room.
3) The fixed resistor and the fan will always have the same potential difference across them (because they're connected in parallel — see p.184).
4) The pd of the power supply is shared out between the thermistor and the loop made up of the fixed resistor and the fan according to their resistances — the bigger a component's resistance, the more of the pd it takes.
5) As the room gets hotter, the resistance of the thermistor decreases and it takes a smaller share of the pd from the power supply. So the pd across the fixed resistor and the fan rises, making the fan go faster.

You can also connect the component across the variable resistor instead. For example, if you connect a bulb in parallel to an LDR, the pd across both the LDR and the bulb will be high when it's dark and the LDR's resistance is high. The greater the pd across a component, the more energy it gets. So a bulb connected across an LDR would get brighter as the room got darker.

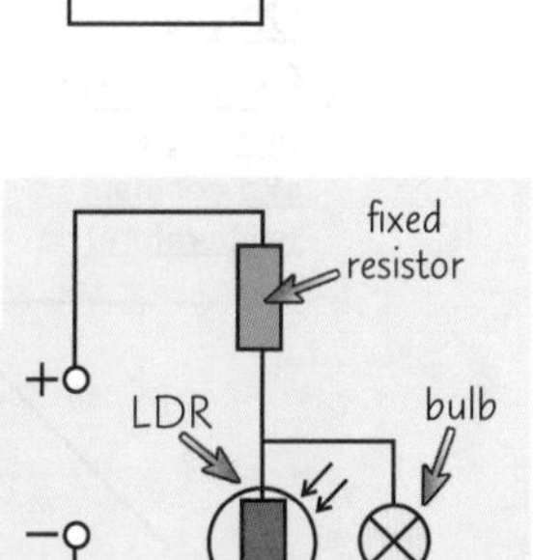

LDRs — Light Dependent Rabbits...

More odd circuit symbols, but at least we're getting into how different components are used in daily life — the next time your heating turns on automatically, you can be smug in your knowledge of thermistors.

Q1 Describe one everyday use for the following components:
a) a LDR b) a thermistor [2 marks]

Series Circuits

There's a difference between connecting components in series and parallel. Make sure you learn it, and know the rules about what happens to current, pd and resistance in each case — read on for more series fun.

Series Circuits — All or Nothing

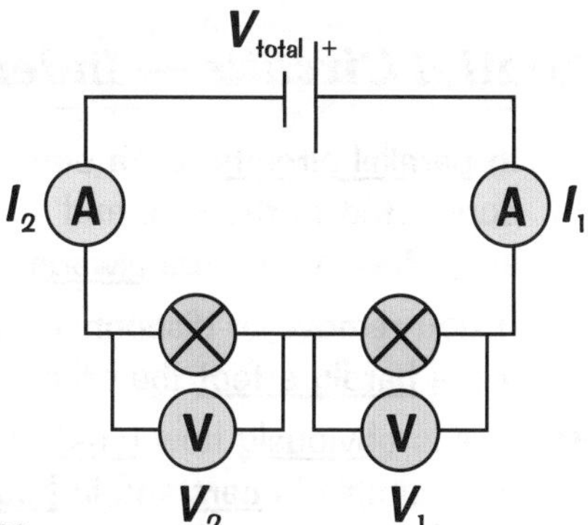

1) In series circuits, the different components are connected in a line, end to end, between the +ve and –ve of the power supply (except for voltmeters, which are always connected in parallel, but they don't count as part of the circuit).
2) If you remove or disconnect one component, the circuit is broken and they all stop. This is generally not very handy, and in practice very few things are connected in series.
3) You can use the following rules to design series circuits to measure quantities and test components (e.g. the test circuit on p.181 and the sensor circuits on p.182).

Potential Difference is Shared

In series circuits the total pd of the supply is shared between the various components. So the potential differences round a series circuit always add up to equal the source pd:

$$V_{total} = V_1 + V_2 + \ldots$$

Current is the Same Everywhere

1) In series circuits the same current flows through all components, i.e.:

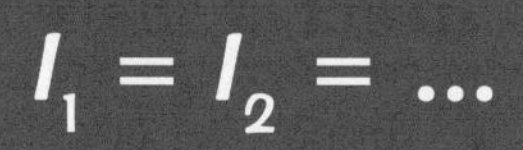

$$I_1 = I_2 = \ldots$$

2) The size of the current is determined by the total pd of the cells and the total resistance of the circuit: i.e. $I = V \div R$.

Resistance Adds Up

1) In series circuits the total resistance of two components is just the sum of their resistances:

$$R_{total} = R_1 + R_2$$

2) This is because by adding a resistor in series, the two resistors have to share the total pd.
3) The potential difference across each resistor is lower, so the current through each resistor is also lower. In a series circuit, the current is the same everywhere so the total current in the circuit is reduced when a resistor is added. This means the total resistance of the circuit increases.
4) The bigger a component's resistance, the bigger its share of the total potential difference.

For the circuit diagram below, calculate the current passing through the circuit.

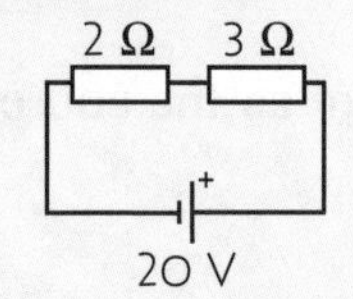

1) First find the total resistance by adding together the resistance of the two resistors. $R_{total} = 2 + 3 = 5\ \Omega$
2) Then rearrange $V = IR$ and substitute in the values you have. $I = V \div R = 20 \div 5 = 4$ A

Cell Potential Differences Add Up

1) There is a bigger pd when more cells are in series, if they're all connected the same way.
2) For example when two cells with a potential difference of 1.5 V are connected in series they supply 3 V between them.

Series circuits — they're no laughing matter...

Get those rules straightened out in your head, then have a quick go at this question to test what you can remember.

Q1 Two 12 V cells are connected in series with a 2 Ω resistor, a 3 Ω resistor and a 7 Ω resistor. Calculate the current through the circuit. [5 marks]

Parallel Circuits

Parallel circuits are much more sensible than series circuits and so they're much more common in real life. All the electrics in your house will be wired in parallel circuits.

Parallel Circuits — Independence and Isolation

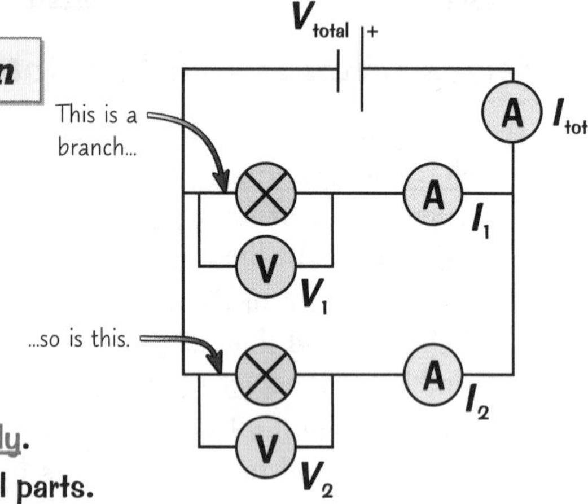

1) In parallel circuits, each component is separately connected to the +ve and –ve of the supply (except ammeters, which are always connected in series).
2) If you remove or disconnect one of them, it will hardly affect the others at all.
3) This is obviously how most things must be connected, for example in cars and in household electrics. You have to be able to switch everything on and off separately.
4) Everyday circuits often include a mixture of series and parallel parts.

Potential Difference is the Same Across All Components

$$V_1 = V_2 = \ldots$$

1) In parallel circuits all components get the full source pd, so the potential difference is the same across all components:
2) This means that identical bulbs connected in parallel will all be at the same brightness.

Current is Shared Between Branches

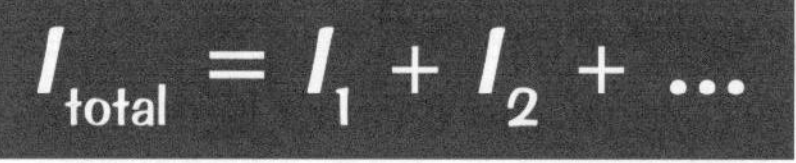

1) In parallel circuits the total current flowing around the circuit is equal to the total of all the currents through the separate components.
2) In a parallel circuit, there are junctions where the current either splits or rejoins. The total current going into a junction has to equal the total current leaving.
3) If two identical components are connected in parallel then the same current will flow through each component.

The currant is shared between branches

Adding a Resistor in Parallel Reduces the Total Resistance

1) If you have two resistors in parallel, their total resistance is less than the resistance of the smallest of the two resistors.
2) This can be tough to get your head around, but think about it like this:

- In parallel, both resistors have the same potential difference across them as the source.
- This means the 'pushing force' making the current flow is the same as the source pd for each resistor that you add.
- But by adding another loop, the current has more than one direction to go in.
- This increases the total current that can flow around the circuit. Using $V = IR$, an increase in current means a decrease in the total resistance of the circuit.

A current shared (between identical components) — is a current halved...

Parallel circuits are a bit more complicated, but they're much more useful than series circuits, so get learning them.

Q1 Explain what happens to the current and resistance in a circuit containing a cell and a resistor when a second resistor is added in parallel. [2 marks]

Q2 Draw a circuit diagram for two filament lamps connected in parallel to a battery. Both of the lamps can be switched on and off without affecting each other. [3 marks]

Investigating Resistance

PRACTICAL

You saw on page 180 how the length of the wire affects its resistance. Now it's time to do an experiment to see how placing resistors in series or in parallel can affect the resistance of the whole circuit.

You Can Investigate Adding Resistors in Series...

1) First, you'll need to find at least four identical resistors.
2) Then build the circuit shown on the right using one of the resistors. Make a note of the potential difference of the battery (V).
3) Measure the current through the circuit using the ammeter. Use this to calculate the resistance of the circuit using $R = V \div I$.
4) Add another resistor, in series with the first.
5) Again, measure the current through the circuit and use this and the potential difference of the battery to calculate the overall resistance of the circuit.

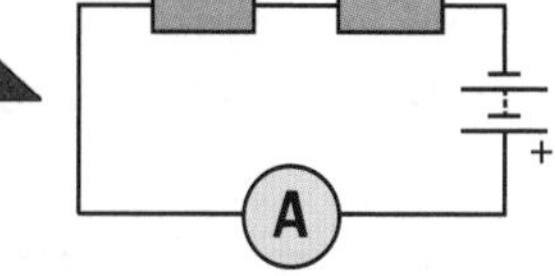

6) Repeat steps 4 and 5 until you've added all of your resistors.
7) Plot a graph of the number of resistors against the total resistance of the circuit (see below).

... or in Parallel

1) Using the same equipment as before (so the experiment is a fair test), build the same initial circuit.
2) Measure the total current through the circuit and calculate the resistance of the circuit using $R = V \div I$ (again, V is the potential difference of the battery).
3) Next, add another resistor, in parallel with the first.

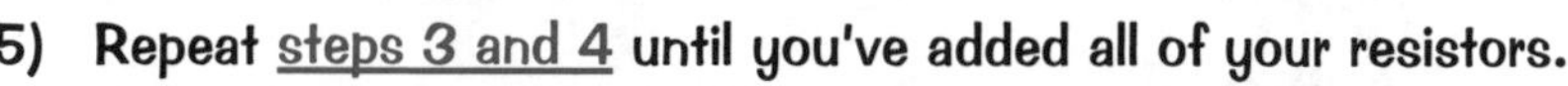

4) Measure the total current through the circuit and use this and the potential difference of the battery to calculate the overall resistance of the circuit.
5) Repeat steps 3 and 4 until you've added all of your resistors.
6) Plot a graph of the number of resistors in the circuit against the total resistance.

Your Results Should Match the Resistance Rules

1) You should find that adding resistors in series increases the total resistance of the circuit (adding a resistor decreases the total current through the circuit).
2) The more resistors you add, the larger the resistance of the whole circuit.
3) When you add resistors in parallel, the total current through the circuit increases — so the total resistance of the circuit has decreased.
4) The more resistors you add, the smaller the overall resistance becomes — as shown by the graph on the right.
5) These results agree with what you learnt about resistance in series and parallel circuits on pages 183 and 184.

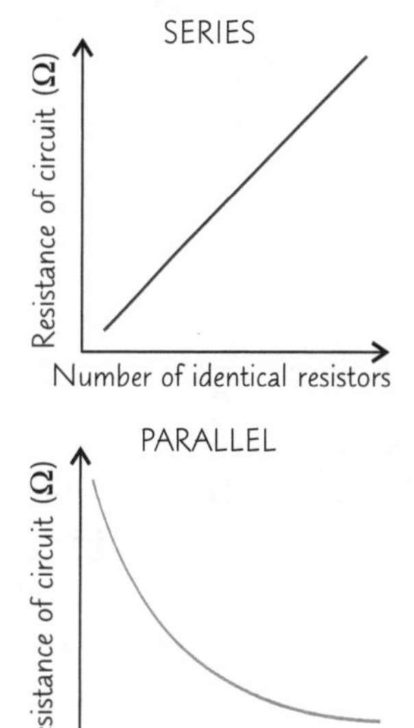

I can't resist a good practical...

Nothing too hard on this page, which makes a nice change from all of those rules about circuits. Make sure you're completely happy building circuits from diagrams, before moving on to the fun world of mains electricity... wooo...

Q1 Draw a diagram of a single circuit that could be used to investigate the effect of adding resistors in parallel. Your circuit should include switches. [1 mark]

Electricity in the Home

There are two types of electricity supply — alternating and direct currents. Read on for more about both...

Mains Supply is ac, Battery Supply is dc

1) There are two types of electricity supplies — alternating current (ac) and direct current (dc).
2) In ac supplies the current is constantly changing direction. Alternating currents are produced by alternating voltages in which the positive and negative ends keep alternating.
3) The UK mains supply (the electricity in your home) is an ac supply at around 230 V.
4) The frequency of the ac mains supply is 50 cycles per second or 50 Hz (hertz).
5) By contrast, cells and batteries supply direct current (dc).
6) Direct current is a current that is always flowing in the same direction. It's created by a direct voltage.

Most Cables Have Three Separate Wires

1) Most electrical appliances are connected to the mains supply by three-core cables. This means that they have three wires inside them, each with a core of copper and a coloured plastic coating.
2) The colour of the insulation on each cable shows its purpose.
3) The colours are always the same for every appliance. This is so that it is easy to tell the different wires apart.
4) You need to know the colour of each wire, what each of them is for and what their pd is:

1) LIVE WIRE — brown. The live wire provides the alternating potential difference (at about 230 V) from the mains supply.

2) NEUTRAL WIRE — blue. The neutral wire completes the circuit and carries away current — electricity normally flows in through the live wire and out through the neutral wire. It is around 0 V.

3) EARTH WIRE — green and yellow. It is for protecting the wiring, and for safety — it stops the appliance casing from becoming live. It doesn't usually carry a current — only when there's a fault. It's also at 0 V.

The Live Wire Can Give You an Electric Shock

1) Your body (just like the earth) is at 0 V. This means that if you touch the live wire, a large potential difference is produced across your body and a current flows through you.
2) This causes a large electric shock which could injure or even kill you.
3) Even if a plug socket or a light switch is turned off (i.e. the switch is open) there is still a danger of an electric shock. A current isn't flowing but there's still a pd in the live wire. If you made contact with the live wire, your body would provide a link between the supply and the earth, so a current would flow through you.
4) Any connection between live and earth can be dangerous. If the link creates a low resistance path to earth, a huge current will flow, which could result in a fire.

Why are earth wires green and yellow — when mud is brown..?

Electricity is very useful, but it can also be very dangerous. Make sure you know the risks.

Q1 State the potential difference of: a) the live wire b) the neutral wire c) the earth wire. [3 marks]

Power of Electrical Appliances

Energy is transferred between stores electrically (like you saw on page 167) by electrical appliances.

Energy is Transferred from Cells and Other Sources

1) You know from page 167 that a moving charge transfers energy. This is because the charge does work against the resistance of the circuit. (Work done is the same as energy transferred, p.203.)
2) Electrical appliances are designed to transfer energy to components in the circuit when a current flows.

Kettles transfer energy electrically from the mains ac supply to the thermal energy store of the heating element inside the kettle.

Energy is transferred electrically from the battery of a handheld fan to the kinetic energy store of the fan's motor.

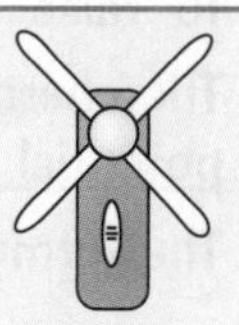

3) Of course, no appliance transfers all energy completely usefully. The higher the current, the more energy is transferred to the thermal energy stores of the components (and then the surroundings). You can calculate the efficiency of any electrical appliance — see p.172.

Energy Transferred Depends on the Power

1) The total energy transferred by an appliance depends on how long the appliance is on for and its power.
2) The power of an appliance is the energy that it transfers per second. So the more energy it transfers in a given time, the higher its power.
3) The amount of energy transferred by electrical work is given by:

This equation should be familiar from page 170.

Energy transferred (J) = Power (W) × Time (s) $E = Pt$

EXAMPLE:

A 600 W microwave is used for 5 minutes. How long (in minutes) would a 750 W microwave take to do the same amount of work?

1) Calculate the energy transferred by the 600 W microwave in five minutes. $E = Pt = 600 \times (5 \times 60) = 180\,000$ J
2) Rearrange $E = Pt$ and sub in the energy you calculated and the power of the 750 W microwave. $t = E \div P = 180\,000 \div 750 = 240$ s
3) Convert the time back to minutes. $240 \div 60 = 4$ minutes

Remember that the time must be in seconds.

So the 750 W microwave would take 4 minutes to do the same amount of work.

4) Appliances are often given a power rating — they're labelled with the maximum safe power that they can operate at. You can usually take this to be their maximum operating power.
5) The power rating tells you the maximum amount of energy transferred between stores per second when the appliance is in use.
6) This helps customers choose between models — the lower the power rating, the less electricity an appliance uses in a given time and so the cheaper it is to run.
7) But, a higher power doesn't necessarily mean that it transfers more energy usefully. An appliance may be more powerful than another, but less efficient, meaning that it might still only transfer the same amount of energy (or even less) to useful stores (see p.170).

Transfer this page to your useful knowledge store...

Get that equation for power hard-wired into your brain and then become a powerful physicist by practising it:

Q1 An appliance transfers 6000 J of energy in 30 seconds. Calculate its power. [2 marks]

Q2 Calculate the difference in the amount of energy transferred by a 250 W TV and a 375 W TV when they are both used for two hours. [4 marks]

More on Power

And we're not done yet. There are even more power equations for you to get your head around, how fun.

Potential Difference is Energy Transferred per Charge Passed

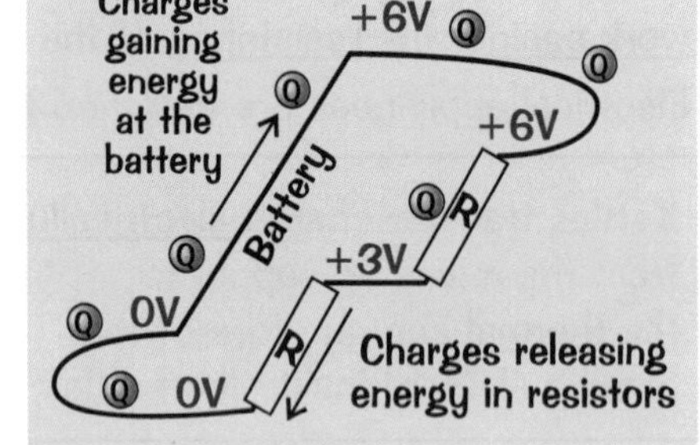

1) When an electrical charge goes through a change in potential difference, then energy is transferred.
2) Energy is supplied to the charge at the power source to 'raise' it through a potential.
3) The charge gives up this energy when it 'falls' through any potential drop in components elsewhere in the circuit.
4) The formula is real simple:

5) That means that a battery with a bigger pd will supply more energy to the circuit for every coulomb of charge which flows round it, because the charge is raised up "higher" at the start.

The motor in an electric toothbrush is attached to a 3 V battery. 140 C of charge passes through the circuit as it is used. Calculate the energy transferred.

$E = QV = 140 \times 3 = 420$ J

This energy is transferred to the kinetic energy store of the motor, as well as to the thermal energy stores of the surroundings.

Power Also Depends on Current and Potential Difference

1) As well as energy transferred in a given time, the power of an appliance can be found with:

Power (W) = Potential difference (V) × Current (A) $\quad P = VI$

A 1.0 kW hair dryer is connected to a 230 V supply. Calculate the current through the hair dryer. Give your answer to two significant figures.

1) Rearrange the equation for current. $I = P \div V$
2) Make sure your units are correct. 1.0 kW = 1000 W
3) Then just stick in the numbers that you have. $I = 1000 \div 230 = 4.34... = 4.3$ A (to 2 s.f.)

2) You can also find the power if you don't know the potential difference. To do this, stick $V = IR$ from page 180 into $P = VI$, which gives you:

$$P = I^2R$$

Resistance (Ω)

You have the power — now use your potential...

I'm afraid the best way to learn all of this is to just practise using those equations again and again. Sorry.

Q1 Calculate the energy transferred from a 200 V source as 10 000 C of charge passes. [2 marks]

Q2 An appliance is connected to a 12 V source. A current of 4.0 A flows through it. Calculate the power of the appliance. [2 marks]

Q3 An appliance is connected to a 230 V mains supply and has a current of 10.0 A flowing through it. Calculate the resistance of the appliance. [5 marks]

The National Grid

The national grid is a giant web of wires that covers the whole of Britain, getting electricity from power stations to homes everywhere. Whoever you pay for your electricity, it's the national grid that gets it to you.

Electricity is Distributed via the National Grid

1) The national grid is a giant system of cables and transformers that covers the UK and connects power stations to consumers (anyone who is using electricity).
2) The national grid transfers electrical power from power stations anywhere on the grid (the supply) to anywhere else on the grid where it's needed (the demand) — e.g. homes and industry.

Electricity Production has to Meet Demand

1) Throughout the day, electricity usage (the demand) changes. Power stations have to produce enough electricity for everyone to have it when they need it.
2) They can predict when the most electricity will be used though. Demand increases when people get up in the morning, come home from school or work and when it starts to get dark or cold outside. Popular events like a sporting final being shown on TV could also cause a peak in demand.
3) Power stations often run at well below their maximum power output, so there's spare capacity to cope with a high demand, even if there's an unexpected shut-down of another station.
4) Lots of smaller power stations that can start up quickly are also kept in standby just in case.

The National Grid Uses a High Pd and a Low Current

Remember that power is the energy transferred in a given time, so a higher power means more energy transferred.

1) To transmit the huge amount of power needed, you need either a high potential difference or a high current (as $P = VI$, from the previous page).
2) The problem with a high current is that you lose loads of energy as the wires heat up and energy is transferred to the thermal energy store of the surroundings.
3) It's much cheaper to boost the pd up really high (400 000 V) and keep the current as low as possible.
4) For a given power, increasing the pd decreases the current, which decreases the energy lost by heating the wires and the surroundings. This makes the national grid an efficient way of transferring energy.

Potential Difference is Changed by a Transformer

1) To get the potential difference to 400 000 V to transmit power requires transformers as well as big pylons with huge insulators — but it's still cheaper.
2) The transformers have to step the potential difference up at one end, for efficient transmission, and then bring it back down to safe, usable levels at the other end.

3) The potential difference is increased ('stepped up') using a step-up transformer.
4) It's then reduced again ('stepped down') for domestic use using a step-down transformer.

Transformers — NOT robots in disguise...

Transformers can be a little tricky, but what's important here is that you understand how they're used in the national grid to reduce energy losses during transmission. Have a go at this question to test what you've learnt.

Q1 Explain why the national grid is efficient at transferring energy. Refer to the potential difference and current during transmission. [4 marks]

Revision Questions for Topic P2

And that's the end of Topic P2 — here's some revision questions to see how much has stuck in your head.

- Try these questions and tick off each one when you get it right.
- When you've done all the questions for a topic and are completely happy with it, tick off the topic.

Circuit Basics (p.179-185) ☐

1) Define current and state an equation that links current, charge and time, with units for each. ☐
2) What is meant by potential difference and resistance in a circuit? ☐
3) Draw the circuit diagram symbols for a resistor, a voltmeter, an LED and a diode. ☐
4) What is the equation that links potential difference, current and resistance? ☐
5) Explain how you would investigate how the length of a wire affects its resistance. ☐
6) Name one linear component and one non-linear component. ☐
7) Draw the *I-V* characteristic for an ohmic conductor, a filament lamp and a diode. ☐
8) True or false? The resistance of an LDR increases with light intensity. ☐
9) What happens to the resistance of a thermistor as it gets hotter? ☐
10) True or false? Potential difference is shared between components in a series circuit. ☐
11) How does the current through each component vary in a series circuit? ☐
12) True or false? Current is shared between the branches of a parallel circuit. ☐
13) A resistor is in series with a cell. A second resistor is added in parallel to the first. How does the overall resistance of the circuit change? ☐
14) Describe an experiment to investigate how adding resistors in series and parallel affects the total resistance of the circuit. ☐

Electricity in the Home (p.186) ☐

15) True or false? Mains supply electricity is an alternating current. ☐
16) What is the potential difference and the frequency of the UK mains supply? ☐
17) Name and give the colours of the three wires in a three-core cable. Why are they colour coded? ☐
18) Explain why touching a live wire is dangerous. ☐

Power and the National Grid (p.187-189) ☐

19) Describe the energy transfers that occur for a battery-powered fan. ☐
20) What is the power rating of an appliance? ☐
21) State three equations that can be used to calculate electrical power. ☐
22) What is the national grid? ☐
23) Explain why electricity is transferred by the national grid at a high pd but low current. ☐
24) What are the functions of step-up and step-down transformers? ☐

The Particle Model and Motion in Gases

The particle model of matter says that everything is made up of lots of tiny particles. It's dead useful.

All Matter is Made up of Particles

In particle theory, you can think of the particles that make up matter as tiny balls. You can explain the ways that matter behaves in terms of how these tiny balls move, and the forces between them. The three states of matter are solid (e.g. ice), liquid (e.g. water) and gas (e.g. water vapour). The particles of a substance in each state are the same — only the arrangement and energy of the particles are different.

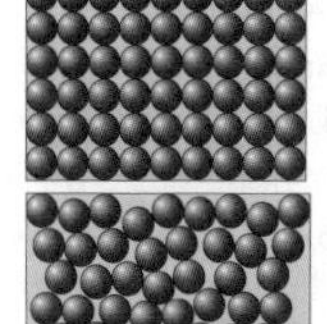

SOLIDS — strong forces of attraction hold the particles close together in a fixed, regular arrangement. The particles don't have much energy so they can only vibrate about their fixed positions.

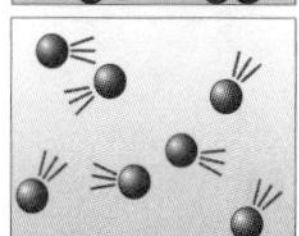

LIQUIDS — there are weaker forces of attraction between the particles. The particles are close together, but can move past each other, and form irregular arrangements. They have more energy than the particles in a solid — they move in random directions at low speeds.

GASES — there are almost no forces of attraction between the particles. The particles have more energy than in liquids and solids — they're free to move, and are constantly moving with random directions and speeds.

Colliding Gas Particles Create Pressure

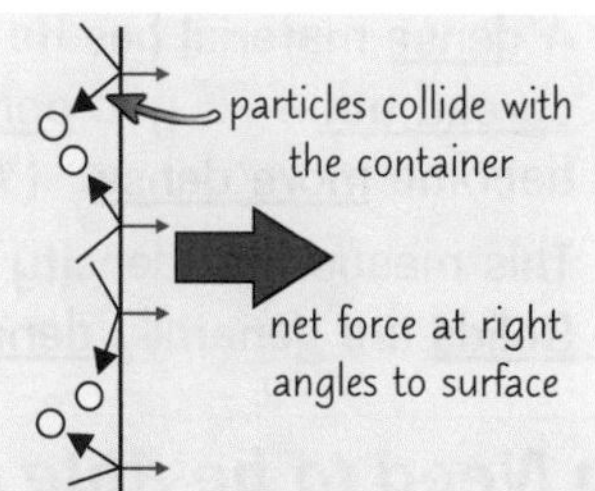

1) Particles in gases (and liquids to a certain extent, but you don't need to worry about them) are free to move around. As they move, they bang into each other and whatever else happens to get in the way (like the sides of the container they're being kept in).
2) When they collide with something, they exert a force on it.
3) Pressure is the force exerted per unit area.
4) So in a sealed container, the outward gas pressure is the total force exerted by all of the particles in the gas on a unit area of the container walls.

Increasing the Temperature of a Gas Can Increase its Pressure

1) If you increase the temperature of a gas, you transfer energy into the kinetic energy stores of its particles (there's more about this on p.193).
2) The temperature of a gas is related to the average energy in the kinetic energy stores of the particles in the gas. The higher the temperature, the higher the average energy.
3) So as you increase the temperature of a gas, the average speed of its particles increases. This is because the energy in the particles' kinetic energy stores is $\frac{1}{2}mv^2$ — p.168.
4) This means that, for a gas at a constant volume, increasing its temperature increases its pressure.

- As the particles are travelling quicker, it means that they hit the sides of the container more often in a given amount of time.
- Each particle also has a larger momentum (p.216) which means that they exert a larger force when they collide with the container.

These factors both increase the total force exerted on a unit area, and so increase the pressure.

Don't let the pressure of exams get to you...

Get your head around the ideas behind the particle model before you tackle the rest of the topic.

Q1 Explain why decreasing the temperature of a fixed volume of gas decreases its pressure. [3 marks]

Density of Materials

The density of an object tells you how many of its particles have been squished into a given space.

The Particle Model can also Explain Density

Density is a measure of the 'compactness' of a substance. It relates the mass of a substance to how much space it takes up (i.e. it's a substance's mass per unit volume).

The units of density are kg/m³ (the mass is in kg and the volume is in m³).

You might also see density given in g/cm³. (1 g/cm³ = 1000 kg/m³)

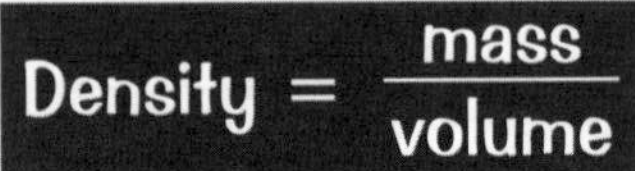

$$\text{Density} = \frac{\text{mass}}{\text{volume}}$$

The symbol for density is a Greek letter rho (ρ) — it looks like a p but it isn't.

m / ρ × V

This number is given in standard form — a way of writing very large or small numbers quickly: $6.3 \times 10^{-4} = 0.00063$

EXAMPLE: A gold bar has a mass of 12 kg and a volume of 6.3×10^{-4} m³. Calculate the density of the gold bar. Give your answer to two significant figures.

1) First, plug the numbers you've been given into the equation for density.

Density = mass ÷ volume
= 12 ÷ (6.3×10^{-4}) = 19047.6...

2) Then round your answer to two significant figures.

Density = 19 000 kg/m³ (to 2 s.f.)

3) Check your units match what's given in the question.

1) The density of an object depends on what it's made of and how its particles are arranged.
2) A dense material has its particles packed tightly together. The particles in a less dense material are more spread out — if you compressed the material, its particles would move closer together, and it would become more dense. (You wouldn't be changing its mass, but you would be decreasing its volume.)
3) This means that density varies between different states of matter (see previous page). Solids are generally denser than liquids, and gases are usually less dense than liquids.

You Need to be Able to Measure Density in Different Ways

PRACTICAL

To find the density of a solid object

1) Use a balance to measure its mass (see p.232).
2) If it's a regular solid, start by measuring its length, width and height with an appropriate piece of equipment (e.g. a ruler). Then calculate its volume using the relevant formula for that shape.
3) For an irregular solid, you can find its volume by submerging it in a eureka can filled with water. The water displaced by the object will be transferred to the measuring cylinder:

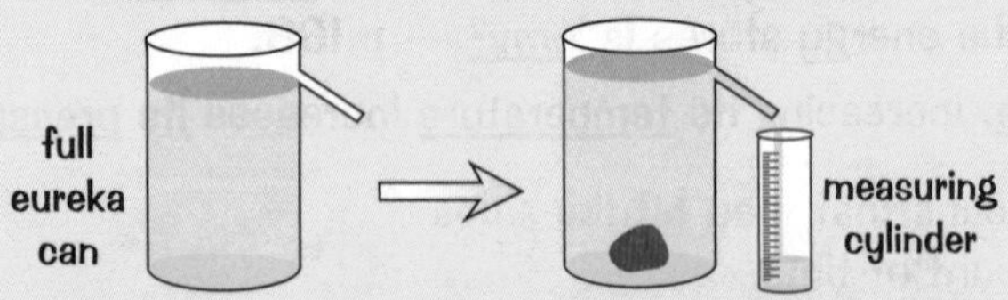

4) Record the volume of water in the measuring cylinder. This is the volume of the object.
5) Plug the object's mass and volume into the formula above to find its density.

To find the density of a liquid

1) Place a measuring cylinder on a balance and zero the balance.
2) Pour 10 ml of the liquid into the measuring cylinder (see p.232) and record the liquid's mass.
3) Pour another 10 ml into the measuring cylinder, repeating the process until the cylinder is full and recording the total volume and mass each time.
4) For each measurement, use the formula to find the density. (Remember that 1 ml = 1 cm³.)
5) Finally, take an average of your calculated densities. This will give you a value for the density of the liquid.

The volume of a cube is equal to length × width × height. Make sure you know the formulas for basic shapes.

Who can measure volume — the eureka can can, oh the eureka can can...

Remember — density is all about how tightly packed the particles in a substance are. Nice and simple really.

Q1 A cube has edges of length 1.5 cm and average density 3500 kg/m³. What is its mass? [5 marks]

Internal Energy and Changes of State

This page is all about heating things. Take a look at your specific heat capacity notes (p.169) before you start — you need to understand it and be able to use $\Delta E = mc\Delta\theta$ for this topic too I'm afraid.

Internal Energy is the Energy Stored by the Particles That Make Up a System

1) The particles in a system vibrate or move around — they have energy in their kinetic energy stores.
2) They also have energy in their potential energy stores due to their positions.
3) The energy stored in a system is stored by its particles (atoms and molecules). The internal energy of a system is the total energy that its particles have in their kinetic and potential energy stores.
4) Heating the system transfers energy to its particles (they gain energy in their kinetic stores and move faster), increasing the internal energy.
5) This leads to a change in temperature or a change in state. If the temperature changes, the size of the change depends on the mass of the substance, what it's made of (its specific heat capacity) and the energy input. Make sure you remember all of the stuff on specific heat capacity from p.169, particularly how to use the formula.
6) A change in state occurs if the substance is heated enough — the particles will have enough energy in their kinetic energy stores to break the bonds holding them together.

A Change of State Conserves Mass

1) When you heat a liquid, it boils (or evaporates) and becomes a gas. When you heat a solid, it melts and becomes a liquid. These are both changes of state.
2) The state can also change due to cooling. The particles lose energy and form bonds.
3) The changes of state are:

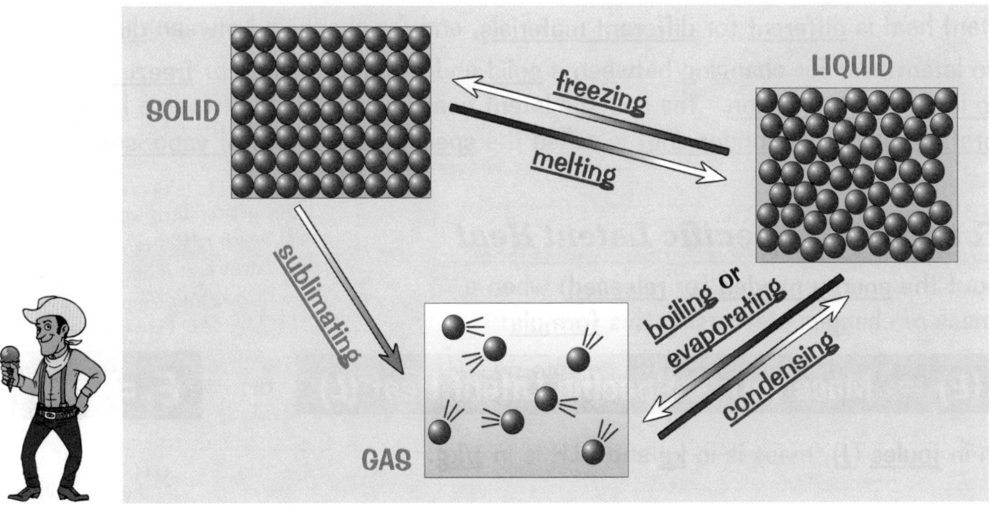

4) A change of state is a physical change (rather than a chemical change). This means you don't end up with a new substance — it's the same substance as you started with, just in a different form.
5) If you reverse a change of state (e.g. freeze a substance that has been melted), the substance will return to its original form and get back its original properties.
6) The number of particles doesn't change — they're just arranged differently. This means mass is conserved — none of it is lost when the substance changes state.

Breaking Bonds — Blofeld never quite manages it...

I'll say it one more time — have a look back over your specific heat capacity notes. They'll really help you understand all this stuff on temperature changes and internal energy. Now don't say I didn't warn you...

Q1 During an experiment, a solid is heated until it melts into a liquid. Explain how heating the solid causes this change of state. [3 marks]

Specific Latent Heat

If you heat up a pan of water on the stove, the water never gets any hotter than 100 °C. You can carry on heating it up, but the temperature won't rise. How come, you say? It's all to do with latent heat...

A Change of State Requires Energy

1) When a substance is melting or boiling, you're still putting in energy and so increasing the internal energy, but the energy's used for breaking intermolecular bonds rather than raising the temperature. There are flat spots on the heating graph where energy is being transferred by heating but not being used to change the temperature.

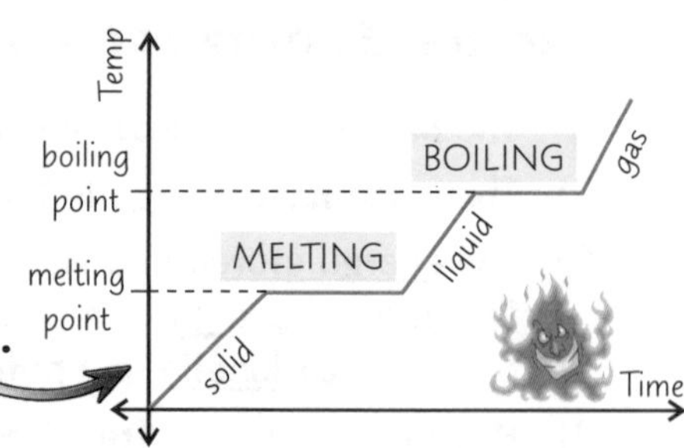

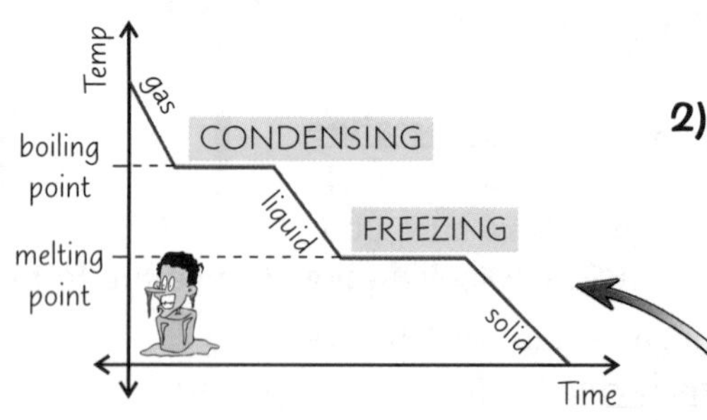

2) When a substance is condensing or freezing, bonds are forming between particles, which releases energy. This means the internal energy decreases, but the temperature doesn't go down until all the substance has turned to liquid (condensing) or a solid (freezing). The flat parts of the graph show this energy transfer.

3) The energy needed to change the state of a substance is called latent heat.

Specific Latent Heat is the Energy Needed to Change the State of a 1 kg Mass

1) The specific latent heat (SLH) of a substance is the amount of energy needed to change 1 kg of it from one state to another without changing its temperature.
2) For cooling, specific latent heat is the energy released by a change in state.
3) Specific latent heat is different for different materials, and for changing between different states.
4) The specific latent heat for changing between a solid and a liquid (melting or freezing) is called the specific latent heat of fusion. The specific latent heat for changing between a liquid and a gas (evaporating, boiling or condensing) is called the specific latent heat of vaporisation.

There's a Formula for Specific Latent Heat

You can work out the energy needed (or released) when a substance of mass m changes state using this formula:

Don't get confused with specific heat capacity (p.169), which relates to a temperature rise of 1 °C. Specific latent heat is about changes of state where there's no temperature change.

Energy (E) = Mass (m) × Specific Latent Heat (L) or: $E = mL$

Energy is given in joules (J), mass is in kg and SLH is in J/kg.

The specific latent heat of vaporisation for water (boiling) is 2 260 000 J/kg. How much energy is needed to completely boil 1.50 kg of water at 100 °C?

1) Just plug the numbers into the formula.
2) The units are joules because it's energy.

$E = mL$
$= 1.50 \times 2\,260\,000$
$= 3\,390\,000$ J

If you're finding mass or SLH, you'll need to rearrange. Here's the formula triangle.

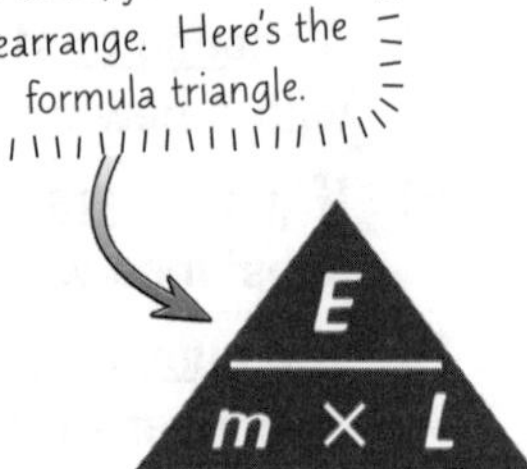

My specific latent heat of revision* is 500 J/kg...

When it comes to the specific latent heat of vaporisation and fusion, the formula's the same, but the process is different. Make sure you understand which process you're actually looking at — you don't want to get caught out.

Q1 The SLH of fusion for a particular substance is 120 000 J/kg. How much energy is needed to melt 250 g of the substance when it is already at its melting temperature? [2 marks]

*the amount of energy required to turn 1 kg of revision notes into a top grade

Developing the Model of the Atom

All this started with a Greek fella called Democritus in the 5th Century BC. He thought that all matter, whatever it was, was made up of identical lumps called "atomos". And that's as far as it got until the 1800s...

Rutherford Replaced the Plum Pudding Model with the Nuclear Model...

1) In 1804 John Dalton agreed with Democritus that matter was made up of tiny spheres ("atoms") that couldn't be broken up, but he reckoned that each element was made up of a different type of "atom".
2) Nearly 100 years later, J J Thomson discovered particles called electrons that could be removed from atoms. So Dalton's theory wasn't quite right. Thomson suggested atoms were spheres of positive charge with tiny negative electrons stuck in them like fruit in a plum pudding — the plum pudding model.
3) However, in 1909, scientists in Rutherford's lab tried firing a beam of alpha particles (see p.196) at thin gold foil — this was the alpha scattering experiment. From the plum pudding model, they expected the particles to pass straight through the gold sheet, or only be slightly deflected. But although most of the particles did go straight through the sheet, some were deflected more than expected, and a few were deflected back the way they had come — something the plum pudding model couldn't explain.
4) Because a few alpha particles were deflected back, the scientists realised that most of the mass of the atom must be concentrated at the centre in a tiny nucleus. This nucleus must also have a positive charge, since it repelled the positive alpha particles.
5) They also realised that because nearly all the alpha particles passed straight through, most of an atom is just empty space. This was the first nuclear model of the atom.

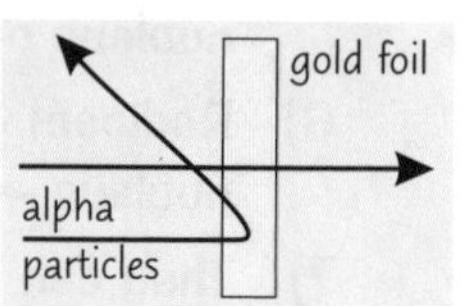

...Which Developed into the Current Model of the Atom

1) The nuclear model that resulted from the alpha particle scattering experiment was a positively charged nucleus surrounded by a cloud of negative electrons.
2) Niels Bohr said that electrons orbiting the nucleus do so at certain distances called energy levels. His theoretical calculations agreed with experimental data.
3) Evidence from further experiments changed the model to have a nucleus made up of a group of particles (protons) which all had the same positive charge that added up to the overall charge of the nucleus.

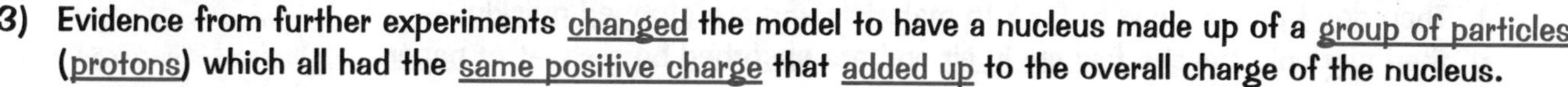

4) About 20 years after the idea of a nucleus was accepted, in 1932, James Chadwick proved the existence of the neutron, which explained the imbalance between the atomic and mass numbers (page 196).

nucleus
shells
electrons

The Current Model of the Atom

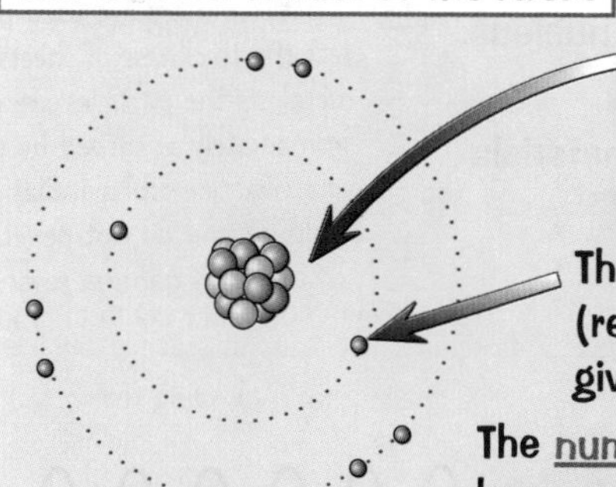

The nucleus is tiny but it makes up most of the mass of the atom. It contains protons (which are positively charged — they have a +1 relative charge) and neutrons (which are neutral, with a relative charge of 0) — which gives it an overall positive charge. Its radius is about 10 000 times smaller than the radius of the atom.

The rest of the atom is mostly empty space. Negative electrons (relative charge –1) whizz round the outside of the nucleus really fast. They give the atom its overall size — the radius of an atom is about 1×10^{-10} m.

The number of protons = the number of electrons, as protons and electrons have an equal but opposite charge and atoms have no overall charge.

Electrons in energy levels can move within (or sometimes leave) the atom. If they gain energy by absorbing EM radiation (p.220) they move to a higher energy level, further from the nucleus. If they release EM radiation, they move to a lower energy level that is closer to the nucleus. If one or more outer electrons leaves the atom, the atom becomes a positively charged ion.

We're currently pretty happy with this model, but there's no saying it won't change. Just like for the plum pudding, new experiments sometimes mean we have to change or completely get rid of current models.

These models don't have anything on my miniature trains...

This is science in action folks — as new evidence came along, the model of the atom was changed and updated.

Q1 a) Describe the current model of the atom. [4 marks]
b) State the radius of an atom and describe how this compares to the size of its nucleus. [2 marks]

Isotopes and Nuclear Radiation

Isotopes and ionisation. They sound similar, but they're totally different, so read this page carefully.

Isotopes are Different Forms of the Same Element

1) All atoms of each element have a set number of protons (so each nucleus has a given positive charge). The number of protons in an atom is its atomic number.
2) The mass number of an atom (the mass of the nucleus) is the number of protons + the number of neutrons in its nucleus.
3) Isotopes of an element are atoms with the same number of protons (the same atomic number, and so the same charge on the nucleus) but a different number of neutrons (a different mass number). E.g. $^{18}_{8}O$ is an isotope of oxygen.
4) All elements have different isotopes, but there are usually only one or two stable ones.
5) The other unstable isotopes tend to decay into other elements and give out radiation as they try to become more stable (they try to balance the number of protons and neutrons in their nucleus or get rid of any excess energy). This process is called radioactive decay.
6) Radioactive substances spit out one or more types of ionising radiation from their nucleus — the ones you need to know are alpha, beta and gamma radiation.
7) They can also release neutrons (n) when they decay to rebalance the number of protons and neutrons.
8) Ionising radiation is radiation that knocks electrons off atoms, creating positive ions. The ionising power of a radiation source is how easily it can do this.

Every oxygen atom has 8 protons.

Mass number — $^{16}_{8}O$ — Element symbol (oxygen)
Atomic number

All atoms can be shown with this notation.

$^{14}_{7}N$

Alpha Particles are Helium Nuclei

1) Alpha radiation is when an alpha particle (α) is emitted from the nucleus. An α-particle is two neutrons and two protons (like a helium nucleus).
2) They don't penetrate very far into materials and are stopped quickly — they can only travel a few cm in air and are absorbed by a sheet of paper.
3) Because of their size they are strongly ionising.

Alpha radiation is used in smoke detectors — it ionises air particles, causing a current to flow. If there is smoke in the air, it binds to the ions — meaning the current stops and the alarm sounds.

Beta Particles are High-Speed Electrons

e^-

1) A beta particle (β) is simply a fast-moving electron released by the nucleus. Beta particles have virtually no mass and a charge of –1.
2) They are moderately ionising. They penetrate moderately far into materials before colliding and have a range in air of a few metres. They are absorbed by a sheet of aluminium (around 5 mm).
3) For every beta particle emitted, a neutron in the nucleus has turned into a proton (page 197).

Beta emitters are used to test the thickness of sheets of metal, as the particles are not immediately absorbed by the material like alpha radiation would be and do not penetrate as far as gamma rays.

Gamma Rays are EM Waves with a Short Wavelength

1) Gamma rays (γ) are waves of electromagnetic radiation (p.220) released by the nucleus.
2) They penetrate far into materials without being stopped and will travel a long distance through air.
3) This means they are weakly ionising because they tend to pass through rather than collide with atoms. Eventually they hit something and do damage.
4) They can be absorbed by thick sheets of lead or metres of concrete.

Uses of gamma rays are on p.224.

Ionising radiation — good for getting creases out of your clothes...

Knowing different kinds of radiation and what can absorb them usually bags you a few easy marks in an exam.

Q1 In the medical industry, radiation is directed at medical equipment sealed in packaging. The radiation sterilises the equipment. Explain whether alpha radiation would be suitable for this use. [2 marks]

Nuclear Equations

Nuclear equations show radioactive decay and once you get the hang of them they're dead easy. Get going.

Mass and Atomic Numbers Have to Balance

1) Nuclear equations are a way of showing radioactive decay by using element symbols (p.196).
2) They're written in the form: atom before decay → atom after decay + radiation emitted.
3) There is one golden rule to remember:
   the total mass and atomic numbers must be equal on both sides.

Alpha Decay Decreases the Charge and Mass of the Nucleus $^{4}_{2}He$

1) Remember, alpha particles are made up of two protons and two neutrons. So when an atom emits an alpha particle, its atomic number reduces by 2 and its mass number reduces by 4.
2) A proton is positively charged and a neutron is neutral, so the charge of the nucleus decreases.
3) In nuclear equations, an alpha particle can be written as a helium nucleus: $^{4}_{2}He$.

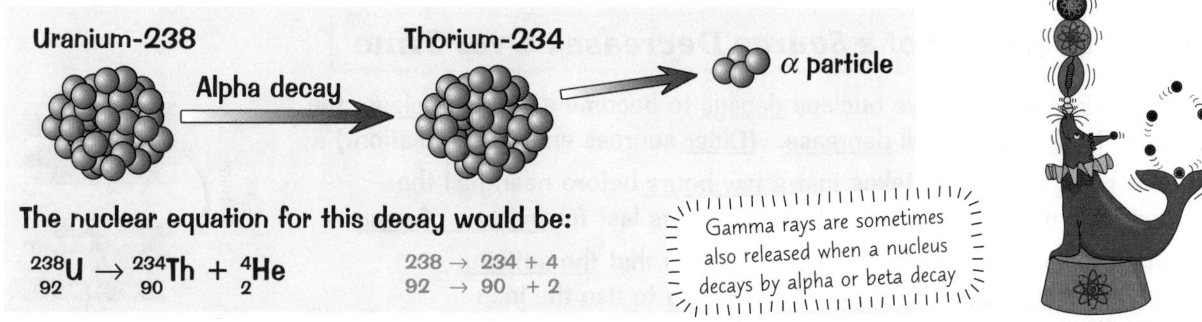

The nuclear equation for this decay would be:

$^{238}_{92}U \rightarrow\ ^{234}_{90}Th +\ ^{4}_{2}He$ $\quad$ $238 \rightarrow 234 + 4$, $92 \rightarrow 90 + 2$

Gamma rays are sometimes also released when a nucleus decays by alpha or beta decay

Beta Decay Increases the Charge of the Nucleus $^{0}_{-1}e$

1) When beta decay occurs, a neutron in the nucleus turns into a proton and releases a fast-moving electron (the beta particle).
2) The number of protons in the nucleus has increased by 1.
   This increases the positive charge of the nucleus (the atomic number).
3) Because the nucleus has lost a neutron and gained a proton during beta decay, the mass of the nucleus doesn't change (protons and neutrons have the same mass).
4) A beta particle is written as $^{0}_{-1}e$ in nuclear equations.

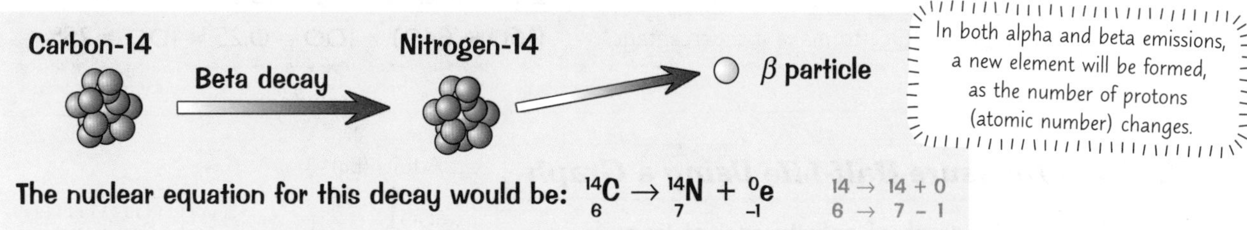

The nuclear equation for this decay would be: $^{14}_{6}C \rightarrow\ ^{14}_{7}N +\ ^{0}_{-1}e$ $\quad$ $14 \rightarrow 14 + 0$, $6 \rightarrow 7 - 1$

Gamma Rays Don't Change the Charge or Mass of the Nucleus

1) Gamma rays are a way of getting rid of excess energy from a nucleus.
2) This means that there is no change to the atomic mass or atomic number of the atom.

Keep balanced during revision and practise nuclear equations...

Nuclear equations are simple, but that doesn't mean you shouldn't practise them. Try these questions on for size.

Q1 What type of radiation is given off in this decay? $^{8}_{3}Li \rightarrow\ ^{8}_{4}Be$ + radiation. [1 mark]

Q2 Write the nuclear equation for $^{219}_{86}Rn$ decaying to polonium (Po) by emitting an alpha particle. [3 marks]

Half-life

How quickly unstable nuclei decay is measured using activity and half-life — two very important terms.

Radioactivity is a Totally Random Process

1) Radioactive substances give out radiation from the nuclei of their atoms — no matter what.
2) This radiation can be measured with a Geiger-Muller tube and counter, which records the count-rate — the number of radiation counts reaching it per second.
3) Radioactive decay is entirely random. So you can't predict exactly which nucleus in a sample will decay next, or when any one of them will decay.
4) But you can find out the time it takes for the amount of radiation emitted by a source to halve, this is known as the half-life. It can be used to make predictions about radioactive sources, even though their decays are random.
5) Half-life can be used to find the rate at which a source decays — its ACTIVITY. Activity is measured in becquerels, Bq (where 1 Bq is 1 decay per second).

The Radioactivity of a Source Decreases Over Time

1) Each time a radioactive nucleus decays to become a stable nucleus, the activity as a whole will decrease. (Older sources emit less radiation.)
2) For some isotopes it takes just a few hours before nearly all the unstable nuclei have decayed, whilst others last for millions of years.
3) The problem with trying to measure this is that the activity never reaches zero, which is why we have to use the idea of half-life to measure how quickly the activity drops off.

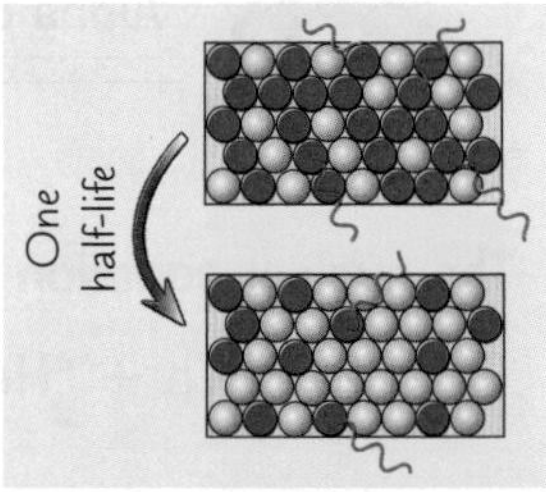

The half-life is the time taken for the number of radioactive nuclei in an isotope to halve.

4) Half-life can also be described as the time taken for the activity (and so count-rate) to fall to half of its initial value.

EXAMPLE: The initial activity of a sample is 640 Bq. Calculate the final activity as a percentage of the initial activity after two half-lives.

1) Find the activity after each half-life. — 1 half-life: 640 ÷ 2 = 320
2) Now divide the final activity by the initial activity, then multiply by 100 to make it a percentage. — 2 half-lives: 320 ÷ 2 = 160; (160 ÷ 640) × 100 = 0.25 × 100 = **25%**

Always double check what the question is asking for — it may want a fraction, ratio or a percentage.

You Can Measure Half-Life Using a Graph

1) If you plot a graph of activity against time, it will always be shaped like the one to the right.
2) The half-life is found from the graph by finding the time interval on the bottom axis corresponding to a halving of the activity on the vertical axis. Easy.

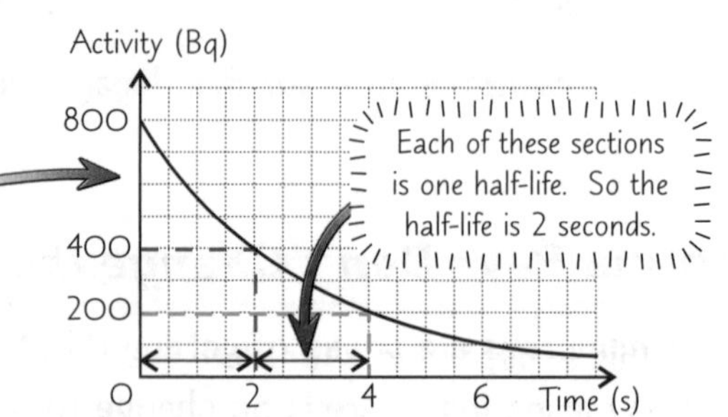

The half-life of a box of chocolates is about five minutes...

Half-life — the time for the number of radioactive nuclei, the activity or the count-rate to halve. Simple.

Q1 The initial count-rate of a sample is 40 cps.
Show that the ratio of its final count rate to its initial count rate is 1:8 after three half-lives. [3 marks]

Irradiation and Contamination

Time to find out how to reduce the risks associated with working with radioactive sources.

There are Risks to Using Radiation

Ionising radiation can enter living cells and ionise atoms within them. This can damage the cells (which can cause things like cancer) or kill them off completely. That's why it's important that you know the precautions to take when working with any sources of radiation.

Exposure to Radiation is called Irradiation

1) Objects near a radioactive source are irradiated by it. This simply means they're exposed to it.
2) Irradiating something does not make it radioactive (and won't turn you into a superhero).
3) Keeping sources in lead-lined boxes and standing behind barriers when using sources are common ways of reducing the effects of irradiation.
4) In some industries, the source may be in a different room and remote-controlled arms are used to handle it.

Contamination is Radioactive Particles Getting onto Objects

1) If unwanted radioactive atoms get onto or into an object, the object is said to be contaminated. E.g. if you touch a radioactive source without wearing gloves, your hands would be contaminated.
2) These contaminating atoms might then decay, releasing radiation which could cause you harm.
3) Contamination is especially dangerous because radioactive particles could get inside your body.
4) Gloves and tongs should be used when handling sources, to avoid particles getting stuck to your skin or under your nails.
5) Some industrial workers wear protective suits to stop them breathing in particles.

The Seriousness of Irradiation and Contamination Depends on the Source

Contamination or irradiation can cause different amounts of harm, based on the radiation type.

1) Outside the body, beta and gamma sources are the most dangerous.
2) This is because beta and gamma can penetrate the body and get to the delicate organs.
3) Alpha is less dangerous because it can't penetrate the skin and is easily blocked by a small air gap (p.196).
4) High levels of irradiation from all sources are dangerous, but especially from ones that emit beta and gamma.
5) Inside the body, alpha sources are the most dangerous, because they do all their damage in a very localised area. So contamination, rather than irradiation, is the major concern when working with alpha sources.
6) Beta sources are less damaging inside the body, as radiation is absorbed over a wider area, and some passes out of the body altogether. Gamma sources are the least dangerous inside the body, as they mostly pass straight out — they have the lowest ionising power, p.196.

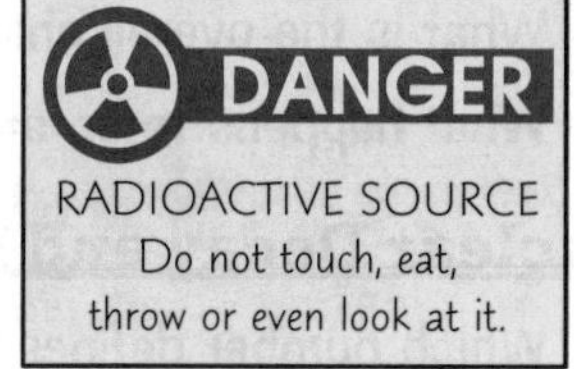

The more we understand how different types of radiation affect our bodies, the better we can protect ourselves when using them. This is why it's so important that research about this is published. The data is peer-reviewed (see p.1) and can quickly become accepted, leading to many improvements in our use of radioactive sources.

Top tip number 364 — if something is radioactive, don't lick it...

Make sure you can describe how to prevent irradiation and contamination, and why it's so important that you do.

Q1 State one way of preventing irradiation. [1 mark]

Q2 For a gamma source, is contamination or irradiation a larger concern? [1 mark]

Revision Questions for Topics P3 & P4

Well, that's the end of Topic P4 — hopefully it wasn't too painful. Time to see how much you've absorbed.

- Try these questions and tick off each one when you get it right.
- When you've done all the questions under a heading and are completely happy with it, tick it off.

The Particle Model and Motion in Gases (p.191)

1) What are the three states of matter?
2) For each state of matter, describe the arrangement of the particles.
3) Explain how a gas in a sealed container exerts a pressure on the walls of the container.

Density of Materials (p.192)

4) What is the formula for density? What are the units of density?
5) True or false? Solids are usually denser than gases.
6) Describe how you could find the volume of an irregular solid object.

Internal Energy and Changes of State (p.193-194)

7) What is internal energy?
8) What happens to the particles in a substance when that substance is heated?
9) Name the five changes of state.
10) True or false? Mass stays the same when a substance changes state.
11) Sketch a graph of temperature against time for a gas being cooled. Your graph should show the points that the gas turns into a liquid and that the liquid turns into a solid.
12) Define specific latent heat. Give a formula for specific latent heat.

The Atomic Model (p.195)

13) True or false? People used to believe that atoms were tiny spheres that couldn't be broken apart.
14) Describe Rutherford and Marsden's experiment which disproved the plum pudding model.
15) What happens to an electron in an atom if it releases EM radiation?
16) Who provided evidence to suggest the existence of the neutron?
17) True or false? Electrons make up most of the mass of an atom.
18) What is the overall charge of an atom?
19) What happens to an atom if it loses one or more of its electrons?

Nuclear Decay and Half-life (p.196-198)

20) Which number defines what element an atom is: the atomic number or the mass number?
21) What is the atomic number of an atom? What is the mass number of an atom?
22) What is an isotope? Are they usually stable?
23) For the three types of ionising radiation, give: a) their ionising power, b) their range in air.
24) Draw the symbols for both alpha and beta radiation in nuclear equations.
25) What is the activity of a source? How does activity relate to count-rate?
26) Define half-life and describe how to find a source's half-life, given a graph of its activity over time.

Dangers of Radiation (p.199)

27) Define irradiation and contamination.
28) Give two examples of how to protect against: a) contamination, b) irradiation.
29) Compare the hazards of being irradiated and contaminated by:
    a) an alpha source, b) a gamma source.

Contact and Non-Contact Forces

When you're talking about the forces acting on an object, it's not enough to just talk about the size of each force. You need to know their direction too — force is a vector, with a size and a direction.

Vectors Have Magnitude and Direction

1) Force is a vector quantity — vector quantities have a magnitude and a direction.
2) Lots of physical quantities are vector quantities:

   Vector quantities: force, velocity, displacement, acceleration, momentum, etc.

3) Some physical quantities only have magnitude and no direction. These are called scalar quantities:

   Scalar quantities: speed, distance, mass, temperature, time, etc.

4) Vectors are usually represented by an arrow — the length of the arrow shows the magnitude, and the direction of the arrow shows the direction of the quantity.

Velocity is a vector, but speed is a scalar quantity.
Both bikes are travelling at the same speed, v (the length of each arrow is the same).
They have different velocities because they are travelling in different directions.

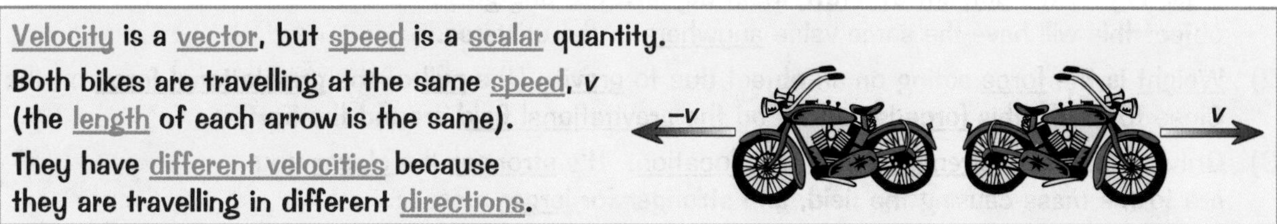

Forces Can be Contact or Non-Contact

1) A force is a push or a pull on an object that is caused by it interacting with something.
2) All forces are either contact or non-contact forces.
3) When two objects have to be touching for a force to act, that force is called a contact force.

   E.g. friction, air resistance, tension in ropes, normal contact force, etc.

4) If the objects do not need to be touching for the force to act, the force is a non-contact force.

   E.g. magnetic force, gravitational force, electrostatic force, etc.

5) When two objects interact, there is a force produced on both objects. An interaction pair is a pair of forces that are equal and opposite and act on two interacting objects. (This is basically Newton's Third Law — see p.212.)

The Sun and the Earth are attracted to each other by the gravitational force. This is a non-contact force. An equal but opposite force of attraction is felt by both the Sun and the Earth.

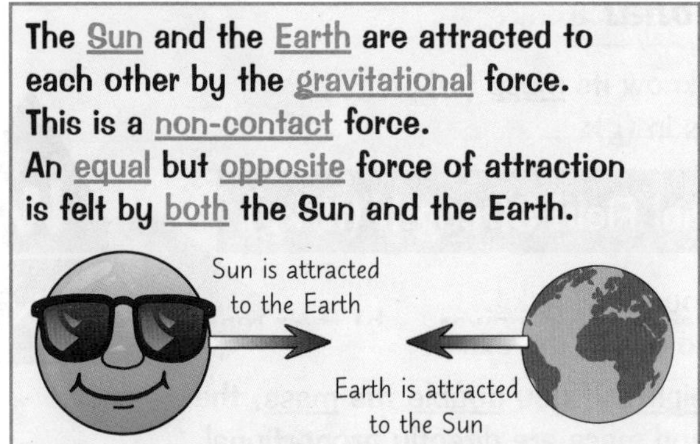

A chair exerts a force on the ground, whilst the ground pushes back at the chair with the same force (the normal contact force). Equal but opposite forces are felt by both the chair and the ground.

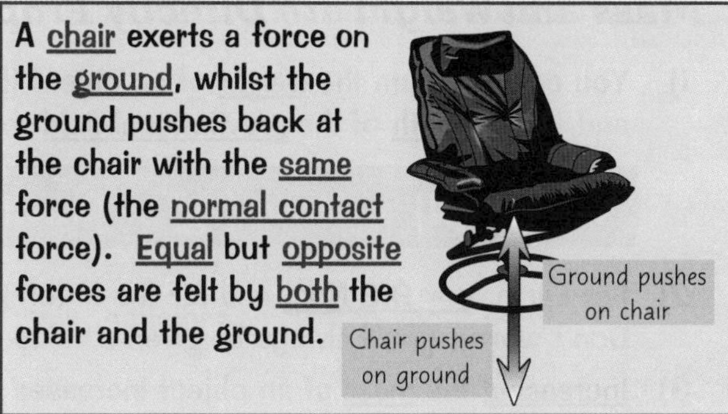

My life's feeling pretty scalar — I've no idea where I'm headed...

This all seems pretty basic, but it's vital you understand it if you want to make it through the rest of this topic.

Q1 A tennis ball is dropped from a height. Name one contact force and one non-contact force that act on the ball as it falls. [2 marks]

Q2 Name two examples of: a) a scalar quantity b) a vector quantity [4 marks]

Weight, Mass and Gravity

Now for something a bit more attractive — the force of gravity. Enjoy...

Gravitational Force is the Force of Attraction Between Masses

Gravity attracts all masses, but you only notice it when one of the masses is really really big, e.g. a planet. Anything near a planet or star is attracted to it very strongly.

This has two important effects:

1) On the surface of a planet, it makes all things fall towards the ground.
2) It gives everything a weight.

Weight and Mass are Not the Same

1) Mass is just the amount of 'stuff' in an object. For any given object this will have the same value anywhere in the universe.
2) Weight is the force acting on an object due to gravity (the pull of the gravitational force on the object). Close to Earth, this force is caused by the gravitational field around the Earth.
3) Gravitational field strength varies with location. It's stronger the closer you are to the mass causing the field, and stronger for larger masses.
4) The weight of an object depends on the strength of the gravitational field at the location of the object. This means that the weight of an object changes with its location.
5) For example, an object has the same mass whether it's on Earth or on the Moon — but its weight will be different. A 1 kg mass will weigh less on the Moon (about 1.6 N) than it does on Earth (about 9.8 N), simply because the gravitational field strength on the surface of the Moon is less.
6) Weight is a force measured in newtons. You can think of the force as acting from a single point on the object, called its centre of mass (a point at which you assume the whole mass is concentrated). For a uniform object (one that's the same density, p.192, throughout and is a regular shape), this will be at the centre of the object.
7) Weight is measured using a calibrated spring balance (or newtonmeter).
8) Mass is not a force. It's measured in kilograms with a mass balance (an old-fashioned pair of balancing scales).

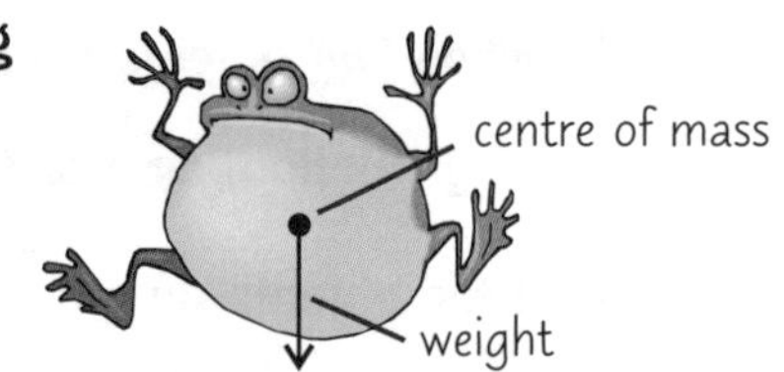

Mass and Weight are Directly Proportional

1) You can calculate the weight of an object if you know its mass (m) and the strength of the gravitational field that it is in (g):

Weight (N) = Mass (kg) × Gravitational Field Strength (N/kg)

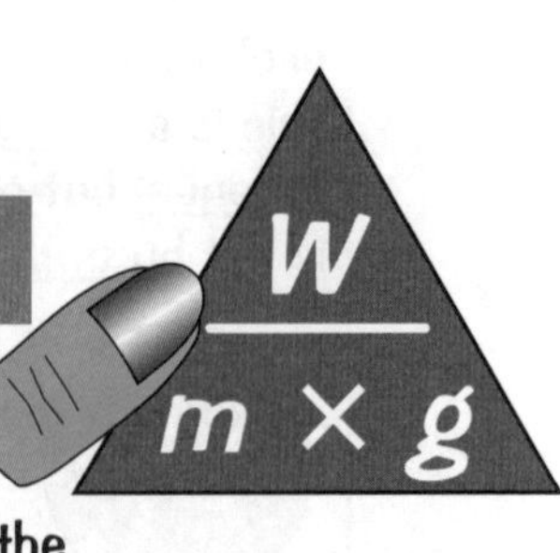

2) For Earth, $g \approx 9.8$ N/kg and for the Moon it's around 1.6 N/kg. Don't worry, you'll always be given a value of g to use in the exam.
3) Increasing the mass of an object increases its weight. If you double the mass, the weight doubles too, so you can say that weight and mass are directly proportional.
4) You can write this, using the direct proportionality symbol, as $W \propto m$.

I don't think you understand the gravity of this situation...

Remember that weight is a force due to gravity that acts from an object's centre of mass. It changes depending on the strength of the gravitational field the object is in (and is directly proportional to the mass of the object too).

Q1 Calculate the weight in newtons of a 5 kg mass:
a) on Earth ($g \approx 9.8$ N/kg) b) on the Moon ($g \approx 1.6$ N/kg) [4 marks]

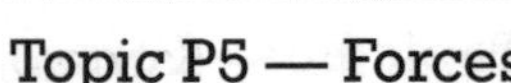

Resultant Forces and Work Done

I'm sure you're no stranger to doing work, but in physics it's all to do with overall forces and energy.

Free Body Diagrams Show All the Forces Acting on an Object

1) You need to be able to describe all the forces acting on an isolated object or a system (p.167) — i.e. every force acting on the object or system but none of the forces the object or system exerts on the rest of the world.
2) For example, a skydiver's weight acts on him pulling him towards the ground and drag (air resistance) also acts on him, in the opposite direction to his motion.
3) This can be shown using a free body diagram like the one on the right.
4) The sizes of the arrows show the relative magnitudes of the forces and the directions show the directions of the forces acting on the object.

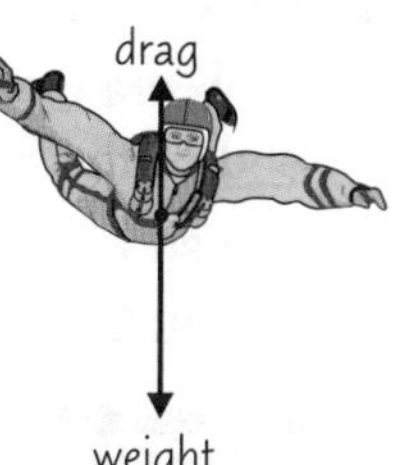

A Resultant Force is the Overall Force on a Point or Object

1) In most real situations there are at least two forces acting on an object along any direction.
2) If you have a number of forces acting at a single point, you can replace them with a single force (so long as the single force has the same effect as all the original forces together).
3) This single force is called the resultant force. (There's a downward resultant force acting on the skydiver above.)
4) If the forces all act along the same line (they're all parallel), the overall effect is found by adding those going in the same direction and subtracting any going in the opposite direction.

EXAMPLE: For the free body force diagram given, calculate the resultant force acting on the van.

1) Consider the horizontal and vertical directions separately.
2) State the size and direction of the resultant force.

Vertical: 1500 – 1500 = 0 N

Horizontal: 1200 – 1000 N = 200 N

The resultant force is 200 N to the left.

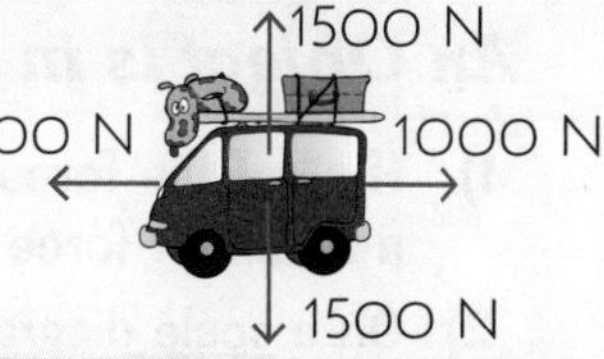

If A Resultant Force Moves An Object, Work is Done

When a force moves an object through a distance, ENERGY IS TRANSFERRED and WORK IS DONE on the object.

1) To make something move (or keep it moving if there are frictional forces), a force must be applied.
2) The thing applying the force needs a source of energy (like fuel or food).
3) The force does 'work' to move the object and energy is transferred from one store to another (p.167).
4) Whether energy is transferred 'usefully' (e.g. lifting a load) or is 'wasted' (p.170) you can still say that 'work is done'. Just like Batman and Bruce Wayne, 'work done' and 'energy transferred' are the same.

When you push something along a rough surface (like a carpet) you are doing work against frictional forces. Energy is being transferred to the kinetic energy store of the object because it starts moving, but some is also being transferred to thermal energy stores due to the friction. This causes the overall temperature of the object to increase. (Like rubbing your hands together to warm them up.)

5) You can find out how much work has been done using:
6) One joule of work is done when a force of one newton causes an object to move a distance of one metre. You need to be able to convert joules to newton metres: 1 J = 1 Nm.

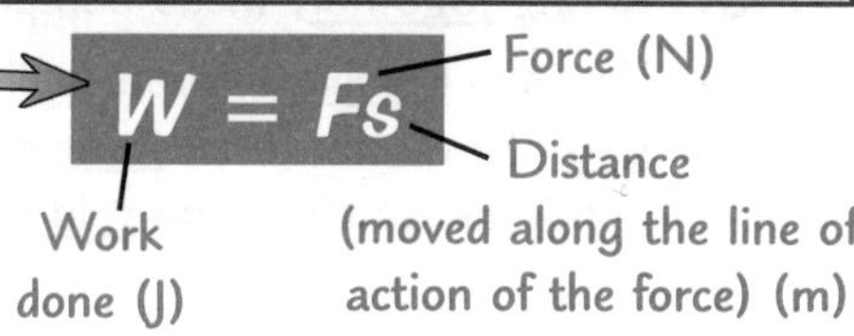

Consolidate all your forces into one easy-to-manage force...

Free body diagrams make most force questions easier, so start by sketching one. Then get to work.

Q1 A force of 20 N pushes an object 20 cm. Calculate the work done on the object. [3 marks]

Calculating Forces

Scale drawings are useful things — they can help you resolve forces or work out the resultant force.

Use Scale Drawings to Find Resultant Forces

1) Draw all the forces acting on an object, to scale, 'tip-to-tail'.
2) Then draw a straight line from the start of the first force to the end of the last force — this is the resultant force.
3) Measure the length of the resultant force on the diagram to find the magnitude and the angle to find the direction of the force.

EXAMPLE: A man is on an electric bicycle that has a driving force of 4 N north. However, the wind produces a force of 3 N east. Find the magnitude and direction of the resultant force.

1) Start by drawing a scale drawing of the forces acting.
2) Make sure you choose a sensible scale (e.g. 1 cm = 1 N).
3) Draw the resultant from the tail of the first arrow to the tip of the last arrow.
4) Measure the length of the resultant with a ruler and use the scale to find the force in N.
5) Use a protractor to measure the direction as a bearing.

A bearing is an angle measured clockwise from north, given as a 3 digit number, e.g. 10° = 010°.

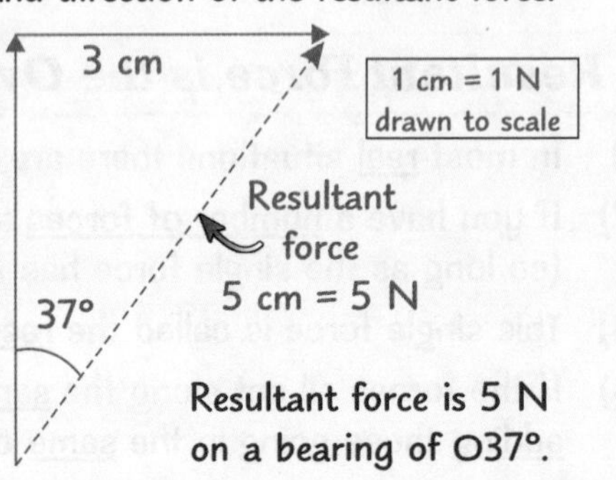

Resultant force is 5 N on a bearing of 037°.

An Object is in Equilibrium if the Forces on it are Balanced

1) If all of the forces acting on an object combine to give a resultant force of zero, the object is in equilibrium.
2) On a scale diagram, this means that the tip of the last force you draw should end where the tail of the first force you drew begins. E.g. for three forces, the scale diagram will form a triangle.
3) You might be given forces acting on an object and told to find a missing force, given that the object is in equilibrium. To do this, draw out the forces you do know (to scale and tip-to-tail), join the end of the last force to the start of the first force. This line is the missing force so you can measure its size and direction.

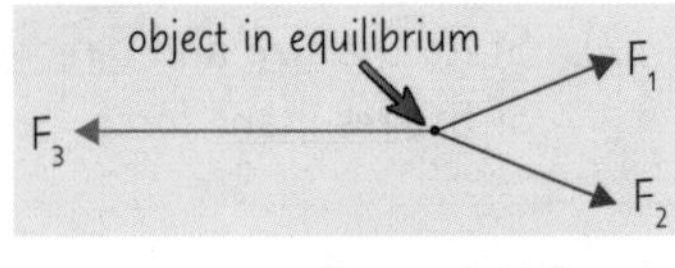

Tip-to-tail the forces join up...

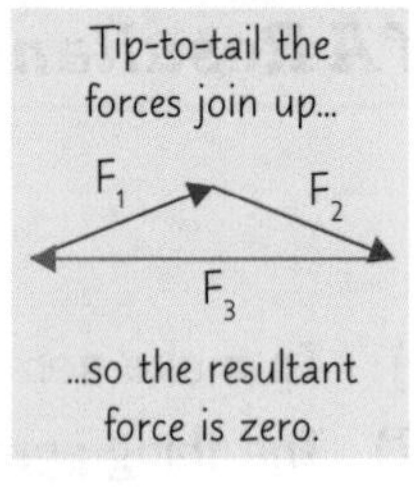

...so the resultant force is zero.

Make sure you draw the last force in the right direction. It's in the opposite direction to how you'd draw a resultant force.

You Can Split a Force into Components

1) Not all forces act horizontally or vertically — some act at awkward angles.
2) To make these easier to deal with, they can be split into two components at right angles to each other (usually horizontal and vertical).
3) Acting together, these components have the same effect as the single force.
4) You can resolve a force (split it into components) by drawing it on a scale grid. Draw the force to scale, and then add the horizontal and vertical components along the grid lines. Then you can just measure them.

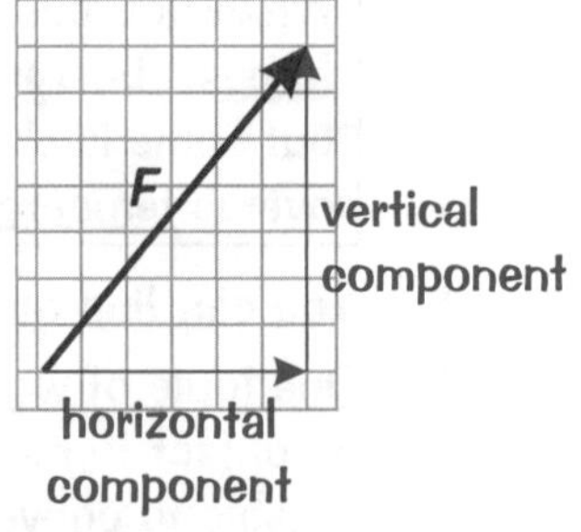

Don't blow things out of proportion — it's only scale drawings...

Keep those pencils sharp and those scale drawings accurate — or you'll end up with the wrong answer.

Q1 A toy boat crosses a stream. The motor provides a 12 N driving force to the north. The river's current causes a force of 5 N west to act on the boat. Find the magnitude of the resultant force. [2 marks]

Forces and Elasticity

You can use forces to stretch things too. The fun never ends...

Stretching, Compressing or Bending Transfers Energy

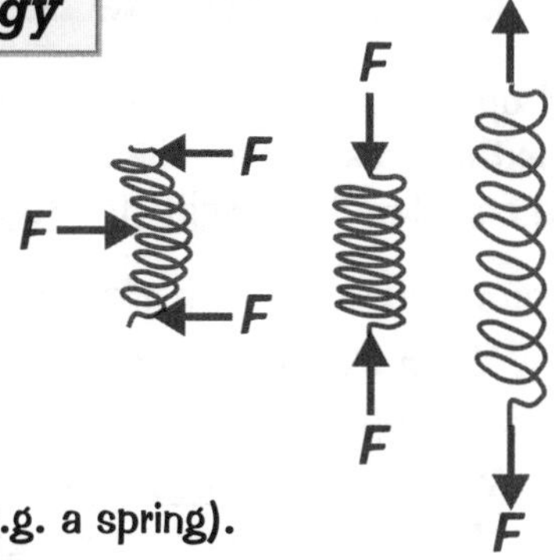

1) When you apply a force to an object you may cause it to stretch, compress or bend.
2) To do this, you need more than one force acting on the object (otherwise the object would simply move in the direction of the applied force, instead of changing shape).
3) An object has been elastically deformed if it can go back to its original shape and length after the force has been removed.
4) Objects that can be elastically deformed are called elastic objects (e.g. a spring).
5) An object has been inelastically deformed if it doesn't return to its original shape and length after the force has been removed.
6) Work is done when a force stretches or compresses an object and causes energy to be transferred to the elastic potential energy store of the object. If it is elastically deformed, ALL this energy is transferred to the object's elastic potential energy store (see p.168).

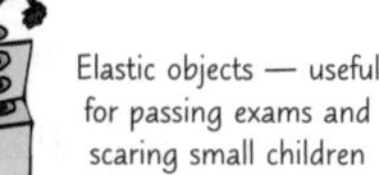

Elastic objects — useful for passing exams and scaring small children

Extension is Directly Proportional to Force...

If a spring is supported at the top and then a weight is attached to the bottom, it stretches.

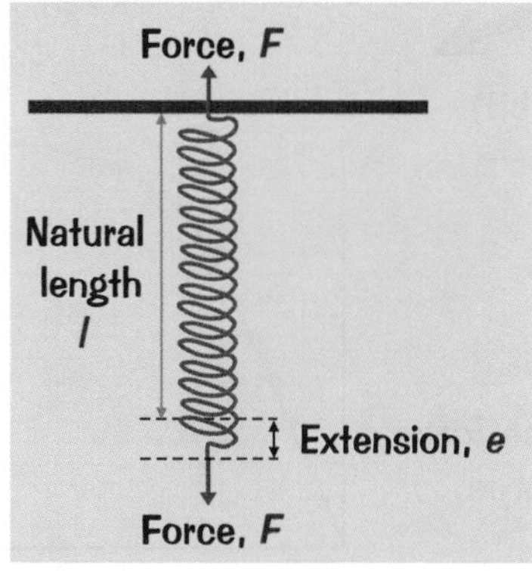

1) The extension of a stretched spring (or other elastic object) is directly proportional to the load or force applied — so $F \propto e$.
2) This is the equation:

$$F = ke$$

Force (N), Spring constant (N/m), Extension (m)

3) The spring constant depends on the material that you are stretching — a stiffer spring has a greater spring constant.
4) The equation also works for compression (where e is just the difference between the natural and compressed lengths — the compression).

...but this Stops Working when the Force is Great Enough

There's a limit to the amount of force you can apply to an object for the extension to keep on increasing proportionally.

1) The graph shows force against extension for an elastic object.
2) There is a maximum force above which the graph curves, showing that extension is no longer proportional to force. This is known as the limit of proportionality and is shown on the graph at the point marked P.
3) You might see graphs with these axes the other way around — extension-force graphs. The graph still starts has a straight part, but starts to curve upwards once you go past the limit of proportionality, instead of downwards.

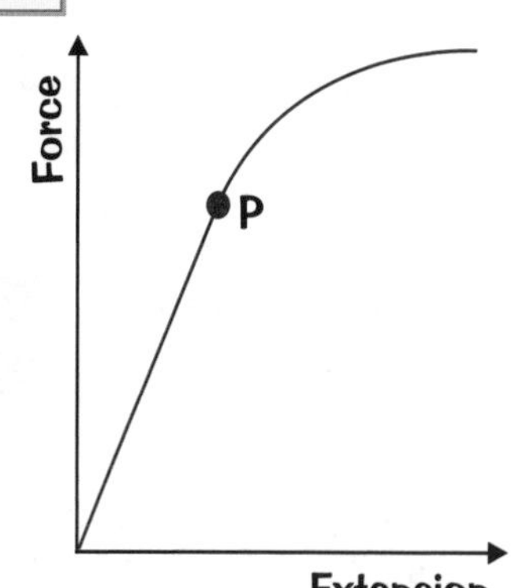

I could make a joke, but I don't want to stretch myself...

That equation is pretty simple, but that doesn't mean you can skip over it. Have a go at the question below.

Q1 A spring is fixed at one end and a force of 1 N is applied to the other end, causing it to stretch. The spring extends by 2 cm. Calculate the spring constant of the spring. [4 marks]

Investigating Springs

You can do an easy experiment to see exactly how adding masses to a spring causes it to stretch.

You Can Investigate the Link Between Force and Extension

PRACTICAL

Set up the apparatus as shown in the diagram. Make sure you have plenty of extra masses, then measure the mass of each (with a mass balance) and calculate its weight (the force applied) using $W = mg$ (p.202).

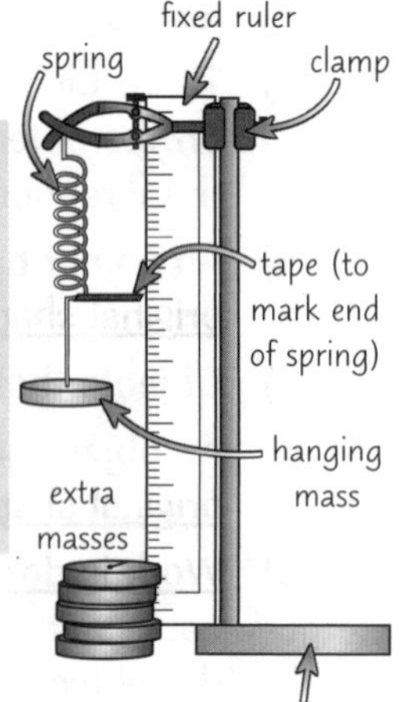

You could do a quick pilot experiment first to check your masses are a good size:

- Using an identical spring to the one you'll be testing, load it with masses one at a time up to a total of five. Measure the extension each time you add another mass.
- Work out the increase in the extension of the spring for each of your masses. If any of them cause a bigger increase than the previous masses, you've gone past the spring's limit of proportionality. If this happens, you'll need to use smaller masses, or else you won't get enough measurements for your graph.

1) Measure the natural length of the spring (when no load is applied) with a millimetre ruler clamped to the stand. Make sure you take the reading at eye level and add a marker (e.g. a thin strip of tape) to the bottom of the spring to make the reading more accurate.
2) Add a mass to the spring and allow it to come to rest. Record the mass and measure the new length of the spring. The extension is the change in length.
3) Repeat this process until you have enough measurements (no fewer than 6).
4) Plot a force-extension graph of your results. It will only start to curve if you exceed the limit of proportionality, but don't worry if yours doesn't (as long as you've got the straight line bit).

To check whether the deformation is elastic or inelastic, you can remove each mass temporarily and check the spring goes back to the previous extension.

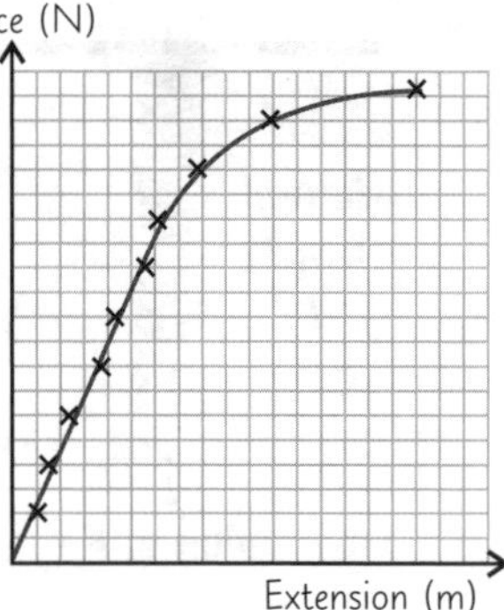

- When the line of best fit is a straight line it means there is a linear relationship between force and extension (they're directly proportional, see previous page). $F = ke$, so the gradient of the straight line is equal to k, the spring constant.
- When the line begins to bend, the relationship is now non-linear between force and extension — the spring stretches more for each unit increase in force.

You Can Work Out Energy Stored for Linear Relationships

1) As long as a spring is not stretched past its limit of proportionality, the work done in stretching (or compressing) a spring can be found using:

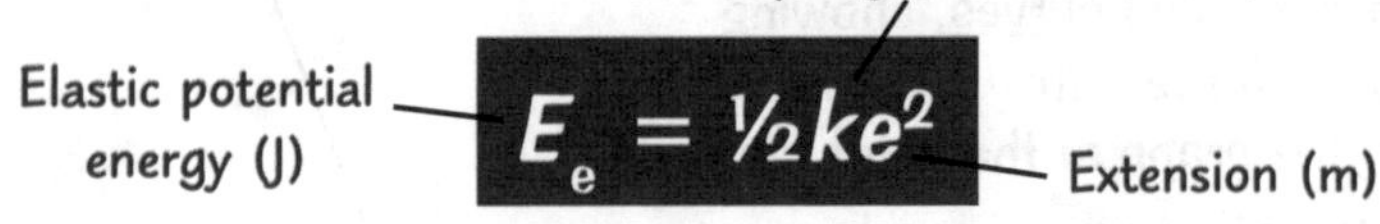

The energy in the elastic potential energy store of a stretched spring is equal to the area under a force-extension graph up to that point:

Force
Extension

2) For elastic deformation, this formula can be used to calculate the energy stored in a spring's elastic potential energy store. It's also the energy transferred to the spring as it's deformed (or transferred by the spring as it returns to its original shape).

Time to spring into action and learn all this...

Remember that you can only use the gradient to find the spring constant if the graph is linear (a straight line).

Q1 A spring with a spring constant of 40 N/m extends elastically by 2.5 cm. Calculate the amount of energy stored in its elastic potential energy store. [3 marks]

Distance, Displacement, Speed and Velocity

Time for a quick recap on distance and speed. You should race through this page. On your marks...

Distance is Scalar, Displacement is a Vector

1) Distance is just how far an object has moved. It's a scalar quantity (p.201) so it doesn't involve direction.
2) Displacement is a vector quantity. It measures the distance and direction in a straight line from an object's starting point to its finishing point — e.g. the plane flew 5 metres north. The direction could be relative to a point, e.g. towards the school, or a bearing (a three-digit angle from north, e.g. 035°).
3) If you walk 5 m north, then 5 m south, your displacement is 0 m but the distance travelled is 10 m.

Speed and Velocity are Both How Fast You're Going

1) Speed and velocity both measure how fast you're going, but speed is a scalar and velocity is a vector:

> Speed is just how fast you're going (e.g. 30 mph or 20 m/s) with no regard to the direction.
> Velocity is speed in a given direction, e.g. 30 mph north or 20 m/s, 060°.

2) This means you can have objects travelling at a constant speed with a changing velocity. This happens when the object is changing direction whilst staying at the same speed. An object moving in a circle at a constant speed has a constantly changing velocity, as the direction is always changing (e.g. a car going around a roundabout).
3) If you want to measure the speed of an object that's moving with a constant speed, you should time how long it takes the object to travel a certain distance, e.g. using a ruler and a stopwatch. You can then calculate the object's speed from your measurements using this formula:

$$s = vt$$

distance travelled (m) = speed (m/s) × time (s)

4) Objects rarely travel at a constant speed. E.g. when you walk, run or travel in a car, your speed is always changing. For these cases, the formula above gives the average (mean) speed during that time.

You Need to Know Some Typical Everyday Speeds

1) Whilst every person, train, car etc. is different, there is usually a typical speed that each object travels at. Remember these typical speeds for everyday objects:

A person walking — 1.5 m/s	A car — 25 m/s
A person running — 3 m/s	A train — 30 m/s
A person cycling — 6 m/s	A plane — 250 m/s

2) Lots of different things can affect the speed something travels at. For example, the speed at which a person can walk, run or cycle depends on their fitness, their age, the distance travelled and the terrain (what kind of land they're moving over, e.g. roads, fields) as well as many other factors.
3) It's not only the speed of objects that varies. The speed of sound (330 m/s in air) changes depending on what the sound waves are travelling through, and the speed of wind is affected by many factors.
4) Wind speed can be affected by things like temperature, atmospheric pressure and if there are any large buildings or structures nearby (e.g. forests reduce the speed of the air travelling through them).

Ah, speed equals distance over time — that old chestnut...

Remember those typical speeds of objects — you might need to use them to make estimates.

Q1 A sprinter runs 200 m in 25 s. Calculate his speed. [3 marks]

Q2 Marie walks her dog after school. She takes a route of 1500 m that starts at and returns to her house. State: a) the distance she travels b) her displacement [2 marks]

Acceleration

Uniform acceleration sounds fancy, but it's just speeding up (or slowing down) at a constant rate.

Acceleration is How Quickly You're Speeding Up

1) Acceleration is definitely not the same as velocity or speed.
2) Acceleration is the change in velocity in a certain amount of time.
3) You can find the average acceleration of an object using:

$$a = \frac{\Delta v}{t}$$

Acceleration (m/s²) — a; Change in velocity (m/s) — Δv; Time (s) — t

4) Deceleration is just negative acceleration (if something slows down, the change in velocity is negative).

EXAMPLE:

A cat accelerates at 2.5 m/s² from 2.0 m/s to 6.0 m/s. Find the time it takes to do this.

$t = \Delta v \div a$

$= (6.0 - 2.0) \div 2.5 = 1.6$ s

You Need to be Able to Estimate Accelerations

You might have to estimate the acceleration (or deceleration) of an object. To do this, you need the typical speeds from the previous page:

EXAMPLE:

A car is travelling along a road, when it collides with a tree and comes to a stop. Estimate the deceleration of the car.

1) First, give a sensible speed for the car to be travelling at. — The typical speed of a car is ~25 m/s.
2) Next, estimate how long it would take the car to stop. — The car comes to a stop in ~1 s.
3) Put these numbers into the acceleration equation. — $a = \Delta v \div t$ $= (-25) \div 1$ $= -25$ m/s²
4) The question asked for the deceleration, so you can lose the minus sign (which shows the car is slowing down): — So the deceleration is ~25 m/s²

The ~ symbol just means it's an approximate value (or answer).

Uniform Acceleration Means a Constant Acceleration

1) Constant acceleration is sometimes called uniform acceleration.
2) Acceleration due to gravity (g) is uniform for objects in free fall. It's roughly equal to 9.8 m/s² near the Earth's surface and has the same value as gravitational field strength (p.202).
3) You can use this equation for uniform acceleration:

$$v^2 - u^2 = 2as$$

Final velocity (m/s) — v; Initial velocity (m/s) — u; Acceleration (m/s²) — a; Distance (m) — s

Initial velocity is just the starting velocity of the object.

EXAMPLE:

A van travelling at 23 m/s starts decelerating uniformly at 2.0 m/s² as it heads towards a built-up area 112 m away. What will its speed be when it reaches the built-up area?

1) First, rearrange the equation so v^2 is on one side. — $v^2 = u^2 + 2as$
2) Now put the numbers in — remember a is negative because it's a deceleration. — $v^2 = 23^2 + (2 \times -2.0 \times 112)$ $= 81$
3) Finally, square root the whole thing. — $v = \sqrt{81} = 9$ m/s

Uniform problems — get a clip-on tie or use the equation above...

You might not be told what equation to use in the exam, so make sure you can spot when to use the equation for uniform acceleration. Make a list of the information you're given to help you see what to do.

Q1 A ball is dropped from a height, h, above the ground. The speed of the ball just before it hits the ground is 7 m/s. Calculate the height the ball is dropped from. (acceleration due to gravity ≈ 9.8 m/s²) [3 marks]

Distance-Time and Velocity-Time Graphs

You need to be able to draw and interpret distance and velocity-time graphs.

You Can Show Journeys on Distance-Time Graphs

If an object moves in a straight line, its distance travelled can be plotted on a distance-time graph.

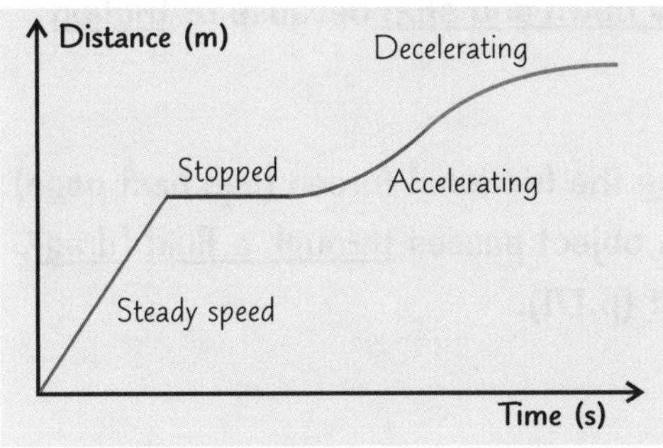

1) Gradient = speed. (The steeper the graph, the faster it's going.) This is because: speed = distance ÷ time = (change in vertical axis) ÷ (change in horizontal axis).
2) Flat sections are where it's stationary — it's stopped.
3) Straight uphill sections mean it is travelling at a steady speed.
4) Curves represent acceleration or deceleration (p.208)
5) A steepening curve means it's speeding up (increasing gradient).
6) A levelling off curve means it's slowing down.
7) If the object is changing speed (accelerating) you can find its speed at a point by finding the gradient of the tangent to the curve at that point, p.146.

You Can Also Show them on a Velocity-Time Graph

How an object's velocity changes as it travels can be plotted on a velocity-time graph.

1) Gradient = acceleration, since acceleration is change in velocity ÷ time.
2) Flat sections represent travelling at a steady speed.
3) The steeper the graph, the greater the acceleration or deceleration.
4) Uphill sections (/) are acceleration.
5) Downhill sections (\) are deceleration.
6) A curve means changing acceleration.
   If the graph is curved, you can use a tangent to the curve at a point to find the acceleration at that point.

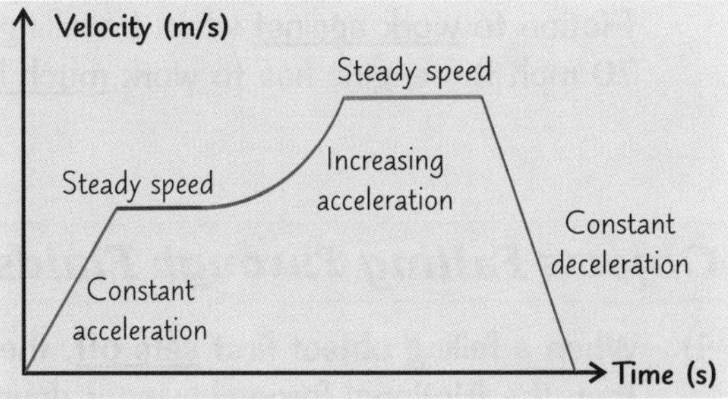

7) The area under any section of the graph (or all of it) is equal to the distance travelled in that time interval.
8) If the section under the graph is irregular, it's easier to find the area by counting the squares under the line and multiplying the number by the value of one square.

EXAMPLE:

The velocity-time graph of a car's journey is plotted.

a) Calculate the acceleration of the car over the first 10 s.
b) How far does the car travel in the first 15 s of the journey?

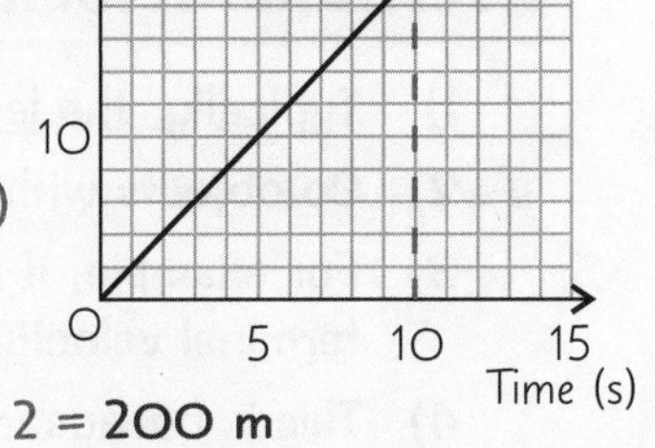

a) This is just the gradient of the line: $a = \Delta v \div t = 20 \div 10 = 2\ \text{m/s}^2$

b) Split the area into a triangle and a rectangle, then add together their areas.
Area = (½ × 10 × 20) + (5 × 20) = 200 m

Or find the value of one square, count the total number of squares under the line, and then multiply these two values together.

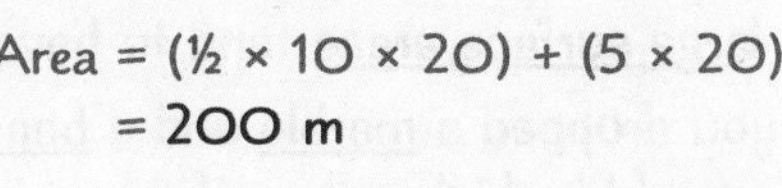

1 square = 2 m/s × 1 s = 2 m
Area = 100 squares = 100 × 2 = 200 m

Understanding motion graphs — it can be a real uphill struggle...

Make sure you know the difference between distance-time and velocity-time graphs, and how to interpret them.

Q1 Sketch the distance-time graph for an object that accelerates before travelling at a steady speed. [2 marks]

Q2 A stationary car starts accelerating increasingly for 10 s until it reaches a speed of 20 m/s. It travels at this speed for 20 s until the driver sees a hazard and brakes. He decelerates uniformly, coming to a stop 4 s after braking. Draw the velocity-time graph for this journey. [3 marks]

Terminal Velocity

Ever wondered why it's so hard to run into a hurricane whilst wearing a sandwich board? It's all to do with the air around you causing drag. Read on to find out more about drag and how it affects terminal velocity...

Friction is Always There to Slow Things Down

1) If an object has no force propelling it along it will always slow down and stop because of friction (unless you're in space where there's nothing to rub against).
2) Friction always acts in the opposite direction to movement.
3) To travel at a steady speed, the driving force needs to balance the frictional forces (see next page).
4) You get friction between two surfaces in contact, or when an object passes through a fluid (drag).
5) You can reduce friction between surfaces by using a lubricant (p.171).

Drag Increases as Speed Increases

1) Drag is the resistance you get in a fluid (a gas or a liquid). Air resistance is a type of drag.
2) The most important factor by far in reducing drag is keeping the shape of the object streamlined.
3) This is where the object is designed to allow fluid to flow easily across it, reducing drag. Parachutes work in the opposite way — they want as much drag as they can get.
4) Frictional forces from fluids always increase with speed. A car has much more friction to work against when travelling at 70 mph compared to 30 mph. So at 70 mph the engine has to work much harder just to maintain a steady speed.

Air flows easily over a streamlined car.

Objects Falling Through Fluids Reach a Terminal Velocity

1) When a falling object first sets off, the force of gravity is much more than the frictional force slowing it down, so it accelerates.
2) As the speed increases the friction builds up.
3) This gradually reduces the acceleration until eventually the frictional force is equal to the accelerating force (so the resultant force is zero).
4) It will have reached its maximum speed or terminal velocity and will fall at a steady speed.

Falling with style

Terminal Velocity Depends on Shape and Area

1) Typically, the less streamlined an object is, the lower its terminal velocity.
2) So objects with large surface areas tend to have lower terminal velocities.
3) For example, if you dropped a marble and a beach ball off a tall building, the marble's terminal velocity would be higher than the terminal velocity of the beach ball.
4) This is because there is more air resistance acting on the beach ball, at any given speed.
5) So the beach ball spends less time accelerating (and so doesn't speed up as much) before the air resistance is large enough to equal the accelerating force.

Learning about air resistance — it can be a real drag...

Frictional forces are pretty much everywhere and they crop up again and again in physics, so make sure you are comfortable talking about them. Then move on to explaining how drag affects an object's terminal velocity.

Q1 Explain why a ball falling from the top of a tall building reaches terminal velocity. [3 marks]

Newton's First and Second Laws

In the 1660s, a chap called Isaac Newton worked out his dead useful Laws of Motion. Here are the first two.

A Force is Needed to Change Motion

This may seem simple, but it's important. Newton's First Law says that a resultant force (p.203) is needed to make something start moving, speed up or slow down:

> If the resultant force on a stationary object is zero, the object will remain stationary. If the resultant force on a moving object is zero, it'll just carry on moving at the same velocity (same speed and direction).

So, when a train or car or bus or anything else is moving at a constant velocity, the resistive and driving forces on it must all be balanced. The velocity will only change if there's a non-zero resultant force acting on the object.

1) A non-zero resultant force will always produce acceleration (or deceleration) in the direction of the force.
2) This "acceleration" can take five different forms: starting, stopping, speeding up, slowing down and changing direction.
3) On a free body diagram, the arrows will be unequal.

Acceleration is Proportional to the Resultant Force

1) The larger the resultant force acting on an object, the more the object accelerates — the force and the acceleration are directly proportional. You can write this as $F \propto a$.
2) Acceleration is also inversely proportional to the mass of the object — so an object with a larger mass will accelerate less than one with a smaller mass (for a fixed resultant force).
3) There's an incredibly useful formula that describes Newton's Second Law:

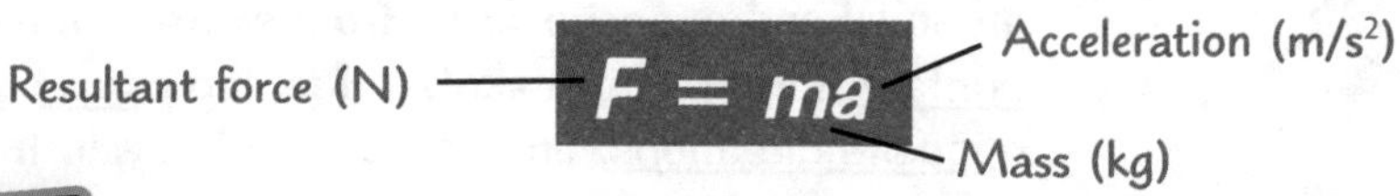

EXAMPLE: A van of mass of 2080 kg has an engine that provides a driving force of 5200 N. At 70 mph the drag force acting on the van is 5148 N. Find its acceleration at 70 mph.

1) Work out the resultant force on the van. (Drawing a free body diagram may help.)
   Resultant force = 5200 – 5148 = 52 N
2) Rearrange $F = ma$ and stick in the values you know.
   $a = F \div m$
   $= 52 \div 2080 = 0.025$ m/s²

You can use Newton's Second Law to get an idea of the forces involved in everyday transport. Large forces are needed to produce large accelerations:

EXAMPLE: Estimate the resultant force on a car as it accelerates from rest to a typical speed.

1) Estimate the acceleration of the car, using typical speeds from page 207. (The ~ means approximately.)
   A typical speed of a car is ~25 m/s.
   It takes ~10 s to reach this.
   So $a = \Delta v \div t = 25 \div 10 = 2.5$ m/s²
2) Estimate the mass of the car.
   Mass of a car is ~1000 kg.
3) Put these numbers into Newton's 2nd Law.
   So using $F = ma = 1000 \times 2.5 = 2500$ N
   So the resultant force is ~2500 N.

Accelerate your learning — force yourself to revise...

Short and sweet, just how I like my equations. Unfortunately you can't get away with just learning those symbols — make sure you've got your head around both of those laws, before moving on to Newton's third and final law.

Q1 Find the force needed for an 80 kg man on a 10 kg bike to accelerate at 0.25 m/s². [2 marks]

Inertia and Newton's Third Law

Inertia and Newton's Third Law can seem simple on the surface, but they can quickly get confusing. Make sure you really understand what's going on with it — especially if an object is in equilibrium.

Inertia is the Tendency for Motion to Remain Unchanged

1) Until acted upon by a resultant force, objects at rest stay at rest and objects moving at a steady speed will stay moving at that speed (Newton's First Law). This tendency to continue in the same state of motion is called inertia.
2) An object's inertial mass measures how difficult it is to change the velocity of an object.
3) Inertial mass can be found using Newton's Second Law of $F = ma$ (previous page). Rearranging this gives $m = F \div a$, so inertial mass is just the ratio of force over acceleration.

Newton's Third Law: Equal and Opposite Forces Act on Interacting Objects

Newton's Third Law says:

> When two objects interact, the forces they exert on each other are equal and opposite.

1) If you push something, say a shopping trolley, the trolley will push back against you, just as hard.
2) And as soon as you stop pushing, so does the trolley. Kinda clever really.
3) So far so good. The slightly tricky thing to get your head round is this — if the forces are always equal, how does anything ever go anywhere? The important thing to remember is that the two forces are acting on different objects.

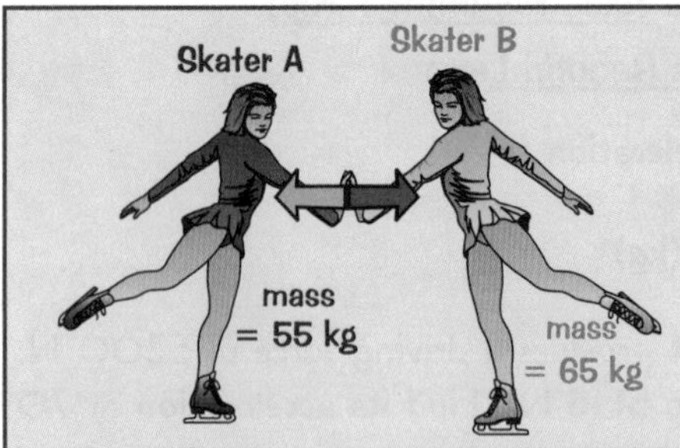

When skater A pushes on skater B (the 'action' force), she feels an equal and opposite force from skater B's hand (the 'normal contact' force). Both skaters feel the same sized force, in opposite directions, and so accelerate away from each other.

Skater A will be accelerated more than skater B, though, because she has a smaller mass — remember $a = F \div m$.

An example of Newton's Third Law in an equilibrium situation is a man pushing against a wall. As the man pushes the wall, there is a normal contact force acting back on him. These two forces are the same size. As the man applies a force and pushes the wall, the wall 'pushes back' on him with an equal force.

It can be easy to get confused with Newton's Third Law when an object is in equilibrium. A book resting on the ground is in equilibrium. The weight of the book is equal to the normal contact force.

But this is NOT Newton's Third Law because the two forces are different types, and both acting on the book.

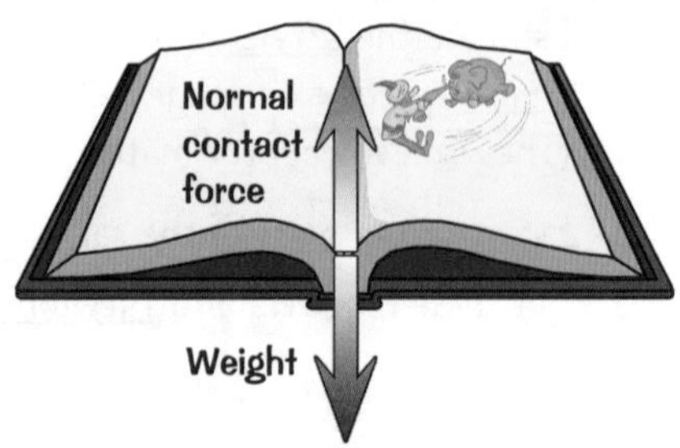

Newton's fourth law — revision must be done with tea...

Newton's 3rd law really trips people up, so make sure you understand exactly what the forces are acting on and how that results in movement (or lack of it). Then have a crack at this question to practise what you know.

Q1 Explain why you don't move when you lean on a wall, even though you are exerting a force. [3 marks]

Investigating Motion

Sure, you can learn the different laws of motion, but doing an experiment for yourself can really help you to understand what's going on. Read on for some snazzy ways to test how mass and force affect motion.

You can Investigate how Mass and Force Affect Acceleration

PRACTICAL

It's time for an experiment that tests Newton's 2nd law, $F = ma$ (p.211).

1) Set up the apparatus shown below. Set up the trolley so it holds a piece of card with a gap in the middle that will interrupt the signal on the light gate twice. If you measure the length of each bit of card that will pass through the light gate and input this into the software, the light gate can measure the velocity for each bit of card. It can use this to work out the acceleration of the trolley.
2) Connect the trolley to a piece of string that goes over a pulley and is connected on the other side to a hook (that you know the mass of and can add more masses to).
3) The weight of the hook and any masses attached to it will provide the accelerating force, equal to the mass of the hook (m) × acceleration due to gravity (g).
4) The weight of the hook and masses accelerates both the trolley and the masses, so you are investigating the acceleration of the system (the trolley and the masses together).
5) Mark a starting line on the table the trolley is on, so that the trolley always travels the same distance to the light gate.
6) Place the trolley on the starting line, holding the hook so the string is taut (not loose and touching the table), and release it.
7) Record the acceleration measured by the light gate as the trolley passes through it. This is the acceleration of the whole system.
8) Repeat this twice more to get an average acceleration.

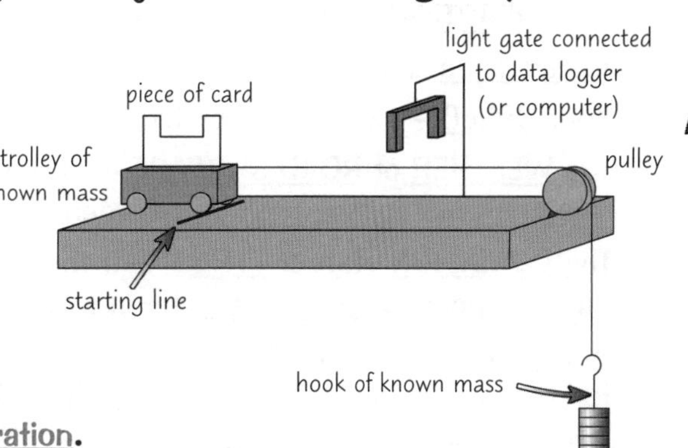

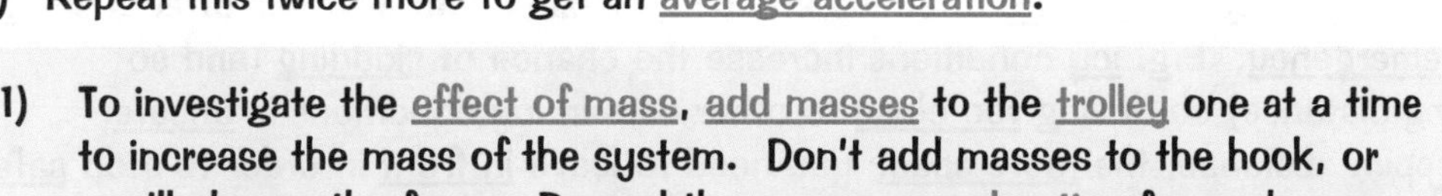

1) To investigate the effect of mass, add masses to the trolley one at a time to increase the mass of the system. Don't add masses to the hook, or you'll change the force. Record the average acceleration for each mass.
2) To investigate the effect of force, you need to keep the total mass of the system the same, but change the mass on the hook. To do this, start with all the masses loaded onto the trolley, and transfer the masses to the hook one at a time, to increase the accelerating force (the weight of the hanging masses). The mass of the system stays the same as you're only transferring the masses from one part of the system (the trolley) to another (the hook). Record the average acceleration for each force.

The friction between the trolley and the bench might affect your acceleration measurements. You could use an air track to reduce this friction (a track which hovers a trolley on jets of air).

Newton's Second Law Can Explain the Results

1) Newton's Second Law can be written as $F = ma$. Here, F = weight of the hanging masses, m = mass of the whole system and a = acceleration of the system.
2) By adding masses to the trolley, the mass of the whole system increases, but the force applied to the system stays the same. This should lead to a decrease in the acceleration of the trolley, as $a = F \div m$.
3) By transferring masses to the hook, you are increasing the accelerating force without changing the mass of the whole system. So increasing the force should lead to an increase in the acceleration of the trolley.

My acceleration increases with nearby cake...

Know the ins and outs of that experiment — you could be asked about any part of it or to describe the whole thing.

Q1 Explain how a light gate can be used to measure the acceleration of a trolley. [3 marks]

Stopping Distances

Knowing what affects stopping distances is especially useful for everyday life, as well as the exam.

Many Factors Affect Your Total Stopping Distance

1) In an emergency (e.g. a hazard ahead in the road), a driver may perform an emergency stop. This is where maximum force is applied by the brakes in order to stop the car in the shortest possible distance. The longer it takes to perform an emergency stop, the higher the risk of crashing into whatever's in front.
2) The distance it takes to stop a car in an emergency (its stopping distance) is found by:

   Stopping Distance = Thinking Distance + Braking Distance

   Where the THINKING DISTANCE is how far the car travels during the driver's reaction time (the time between the driver seeing a hazard and applying the brakes). And the BRAKING DISTANCE is the distance taken to stop under the braking force (once the brakes are applied). Typical car braking distances are: 14 m at 30 mph, 55 m at 60 mph and 75 m at 70 mph.

   Thinking distance is affected by:
   - Your SPEED — the faster you're going the further you'll travel during the time you take to react.
   - Your REACTION TIME — the longer your reaction time (see p.215), the longer your thinking distance.

   Braking distance is affected by:
   - Your SPEED — for a given braking force, the faster a vehicle travels, the longer it takes to stop.
   - The WEATHER or ROAD SURFACE — if it is wet or icy, or there are leaves or oil on the road, there is less grip (and so less friction) between a vehicle's tyres and the road, which can cause tyres to skid.
   - The CONDITION of your TYRES — if the tyres of a vehicle are bald (they don't have any tread left) then they cannot get rid of water in wet conditions. This leads to them skidding on top of the water.
   - How good your BRAKES are — if brakes are worn or faulty, they won't be able to apply as much force as well-maintained brakes, which could be dangerous when you need to brake hard.
3) You need to be able to describe the factors affecting stopping distance and how this affects safety — especially in an emergency. E.g. icy conditions increase the chance of skidding (and so increase the stopping distance) so driving too close to other cars in icy conditions is unsafe. The longer your stopping distance, the more space you need to leave in front in order to stop safely.
4) Speed limits are really important because speed affects the stopping distance so much.

Braking Relies on Friction Between the Brakes and Wheels

1) When the brake pedal is pushed, this causes brake pads to be pressed onto the wheels. This contact causes friction, which causes work to be done. The work done between the brakes and the wheels transfers energy from the kinetic energy stores of the wheels to the thermal energy stores of the brakes. The brakes increase in temperature.
2) The faster a vehicle is going, the more energy it has in its kinetic stores, so the more work needs to be done to stop it. This means that a greater braking force is needed to make it stop within a certain distance.
3) A larger braking force means a larger deceleration. Very large decelerations can be dangerous because they may cause brakes to overheat (so they don't work as well) or could cause the vehicle to skid.
4) You can estimate the forces involved in accelerations of vehicles using typical values:

EXAMPLE: A car travelling at a typical speed makes an emergency stop to avoid hitting a hazard 25 m ahead. Estimate the braking force needed to produce this deceleration.

1) Assume the deceleration is uniform, and rearrange $v^2 - u^2 = 2as$ to find the deceleration.
   $v = \sim 25$ m/s $m = \sim 1000$ kg.
   $a = (v^2 - u^2) \div 2s = (0^2 - 25^2) \div (2 \times 25) = -12.5$
2) Then use $F = ma$, with $m = \sim 1000$ kg.
   $F = 1000 \times 12.5 = 12\,500$ N, so F is $\sim 12\,500$ N

Stop right there — and learn this page...

Make sure you can calculate stopping distances and explain the factors that affect the braking distance.

Q1 Give one factor that affects braking distance. [1 mark]

Reaction Times

Go long! You need fast reaction times to avoid getting hit in the face when playing catch.

Reaction Times Vary From Person to Person

Everyone's reaction time is different, but a typical reaction time is between 0.2 and 0.9 s. This can be affected by tiredness, drugs or alcohol. Distractions can also affect your ability to react.

You can Measure Reaction Times with the Ruler Drop Test

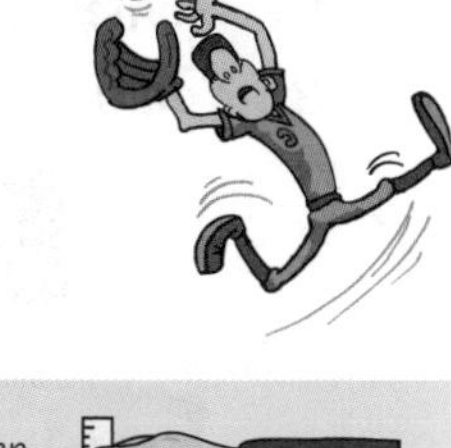

You can do simple experiments to investigate your reaction time, but as reaction times are so short, you haven't got a chance of measuring one with a stopwatch.

One way of measuring reaction times is to use a computer-based test (e.g. clicking a mouse when the screen changes colour).

Another is the ruler drop test:

1) Sit with your arm resting on the edge of a table (this should stop you moving your arm up or down during the test). Get someone else to hold a ruler so it hangs between your thumb and forefinger, lined up with zero. You may need a third person to be at eye level with the ruler to check it's lined up.
2) Without giving any warning, the person holding the ruler should drop it. Close your thumb and finger to try to catch the ruler as quickly as possible.

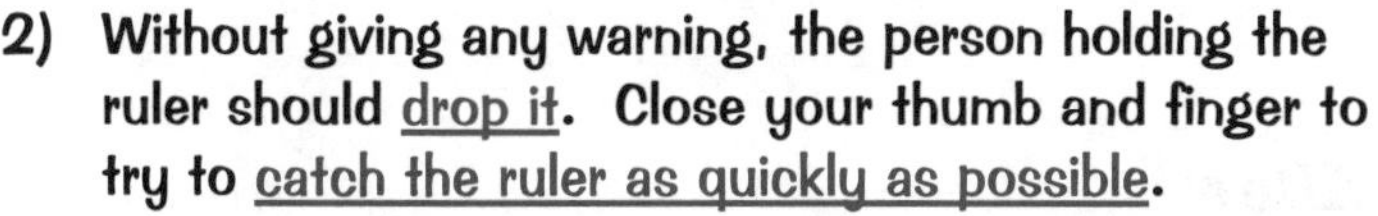

3) The measurement on the ruler at the point where it is caught is how far the ruler dropped in the time it takes you to react.
4) The longer the distance, the longer the reaction time.
5) You can calculate how long the ruler falls for (the reaction time) because acceleration due to gravity is constant (roughly 9.8 m/s^2).

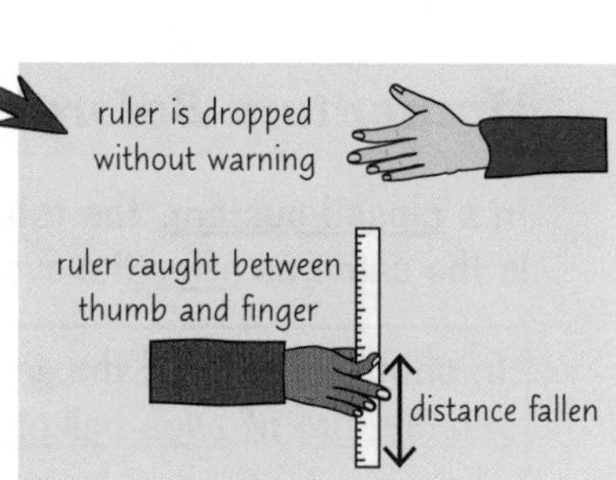

E.g. say you catch the ruler at 20 cm. From p.208 you know: $v^2 - u^2 = 2as$.

$u = 0$, $a = 9.8$ m/s^2 and $s = 0.2$ m, so: $v = \sqrt{2 \times 9.8 \times 0.2 + 0} = 1.97...$ m/s

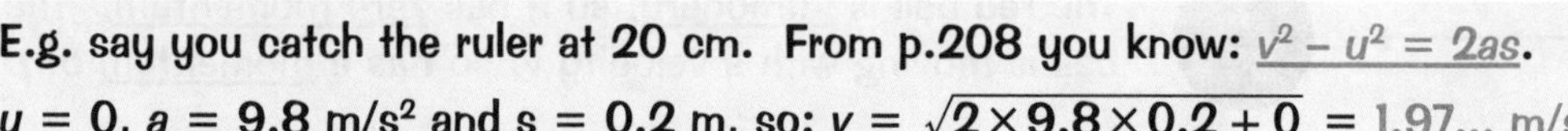

v is equal to the change in velocity of the ruler.

You also know: $a = \Delta v \div t$ so $t = \Delta v \div a = 1.97... \div 9.8 = 0.202...$ s $= 0.2$ s (to 1 s.f.).

This gives your reaction time.

6) It's pretty hard to do this experiment accurately, so you should do a lot of repeats and calculate an average reaction time. The results will be better if the ruler falls straight down — you might want to add a blob of modelling clay to the bottom to stop it from waving about.
7) Make sure it's a fair test — use the same ruler for each repeat, and have the same person dropping it.
8) You could try to investigate some factors affecting reaction time, e.g. you could introduce distractions by having some music playing or by having someone talk to you while the test takes place (see the previous page for more on the factors affecting reaction time).
9) Remember to still do lots of repeats and calculate the mean reaction time with distractions, which you can compare to the mean reaction time without distractions.

Test a friend's reaction time by throwing this book at them...

Not really. Instead re-read this page and make sure you can describe the experiment. Much more fun.

Q1 Mark's reaction time is tested using the ruler drop test. He is tested in the early afternoon and at night. In the afternoon, he catches the ruler after it has fallen a distance of 16.2 cm. At night, he catches the ruler after it has fallen 18.5 cm.

a) Calculate Mark's reaction time in the afternoon. Give your answer to 2 significant figures. [5 marks]

b) Explain why Mark's thinking distance might be longer when driving in the evening. [2 marks]

Momentum

A large rugby player running very fast has much more momentum than a skinny one out for a Sunday afternoon stroll. It's something that all moving objects have, so you better get your head around it.

Momentum = Mass × Velocity

Momentum is mainly about how much 'oomph' an object has. It's a property that all moving objects have.

1) The greater the mass of an object, or the greater its velocity, the more momentum the object has.
2) Momentum is a vector quantity — it has size and direction.
3) You can work out the momentum of an object using:

$$p = mv$$

momentum (kg m/s) = mass (kg) × velocity (m/s)

EXAMPLE:

A 50 kg cheetah is running at 60 m/s. Calculate its momentum.

$p = mv = 50 \times 60$
$= 3000$ kg m/s

EXAMPLE:

A boy has a mass of 30 kg and a momentum of 75 kg m/s. Calculate his velocity.

$v = p \div m = 75 \div 30 = 2.5$ m/s

Momentum Before = Momentum After

In a closed system, the total momentum before an event (e.g. a collision) is the same as after the event. This is called conservation of momentum.

A closed system is just a fancy way of saying that no external forces act.

In snooker, balls of the same size and mass collide with each other. Each collision is an event where the momentum of each ball changes, but the overall momentum stays the same (momentum is conserved).

Before: (m) —v→ (m)

The red ball is stationary, so it has zero momentum. The white ball is moving with a velocity v, so has a momentum of $p = mv$.

After: (m) → (m) ——→

The white ball hits the red ball, causing it to move. The red ball now has momentum. The white ball continues moving, but at a much smaller velocity (and so a much smaller momentum). The combined momentum of the red and white ball is equal to the original momentum of the white ball, mv.

A moving car hits into the back of a parked car. The crash causes the two cars to lock together, and they continue moving in the direction that the original moving car was travelling, but at a lower velocity.

Before: The momentum was equal to mass of moving car × its velocity.

After: The mass of the moving object has increased, but its momentum is equal to the momentum before the collision. So an increase in mass causes a decrease in velocity.

If the momentum before an event is zero, then the momentum after will also be zero. E.g. in an explosion, the momentum before is zero. After the explosion, the pieces fly off in different directions, so that the total momentum cancels out to zero.

Learn this stuff — it'll only take a moment... um...

Conservation of momentum is incredibly handy — make sure you get your head down and practise it.

Q1 Calculate the momentum of a 60 kg woman running at 3 m/s. [2 marks]

Q2 Describe how momentum is conserved by a gun recoiling (moving backwards) as it shoots a bullet. [4 marks]

Revision Questions for Topic P5

Well, that's Topic P5 over and done with — have a quick break then see how you've done with this summary.

- Try these questions and tick off each one when you get it right.
- When you've done all the questions under a heading and are completely happy with it, tick it off.

Forces and Work Done (p.201-204)

1) Explain the difference between scalar and vector quantities.
2) True or false? Time is a vector quantity.
3) What is the difference between contact and non-contact forces?
4) Explain the difference between mass and weight.
5) What is the formula for calculating the weight of an object?
6) What is a free body diagram?
7) What is a resultant force?
8) Give the formula for calculating the work done by a force, and explain what each symbol means.
9) How many joules of work does 1 Nm equal?
10) Describe the forces acting on an object in equilibrium.

Stretching (p.205-206)

11) What is the difference between an elastic and an inelastic deformation?
12) Give the equation that relates force, extension and the spring constant of an object.
13) What is the limit of proportionality?
14) Describe an experiment you could do to investigate the relationship between force and extension.
15) How do you find the following from a linear force-extension graph? a) spring constant, b) work done
16) Give the equation used to find the energy in an elastic object's elastic potential energy store.

Motion (p.207-213)

17) What is the difference between displacement and distance?
18) Define acceleration in terms of velocity and time.
19) What does the term 'uniform acceleration' mean?
20) What does the gradient represent for a) a distance-time graph? b) a velocity-time graph?
21) What is terminal velocity? What causes it?
22) State Newton's three laws of motion.
23) What is inertia?

Car Safety and Momentum (p.214-216)

24) What is the stopping distance of a vehicle? How can it be calculated?
25) State four things that can affect the braking distance of a vehicle.
26) Give two things that affect a person's reaction time.
27) What is an average reaction time?
28) Briefly describe an experiment you could do to compare people's reaction times.
29) State the formula used to calculate an object's momentum.

Transverse and Longitudinal Waves

Waves transfer energy from one place to another without transferring any matter (stuff).

Waves Transfer Energy in the Direction they are Travelling

When waves travel through a medium, the particles of the medium oscillate and transfer energy between each other (see p.167). BUT overall, the particles stay in the same place — only energy is transferred.

For example, if you drop a twig into a calm pool of water, ripples form on the water's surface. The ripples don't carry the water (or the twig) away with them though.

Similarly, if you strum a guitar string and create sound waves, the sound waves don't carry the air away from the guitar and create a vacuum.

1) The amplitude of a wave is the maximum displacement of a point on the wave from its undisturbed position.
2) The wavelength is the distance between the same point on two adjacent waves (e.g. between the trough of one wave and the trough of the wave next to it).
3) Frequency is the number of complete waves passing a certain point per second. Frequency is measured in hertz (Hz). 1 Hz is 1 wave per second.
4) From the frequency, you can find the period of a wave using: This is the amount of time it takes for a full cycle of the wave.
5) All waves are either transverse or longitudinal (see below).

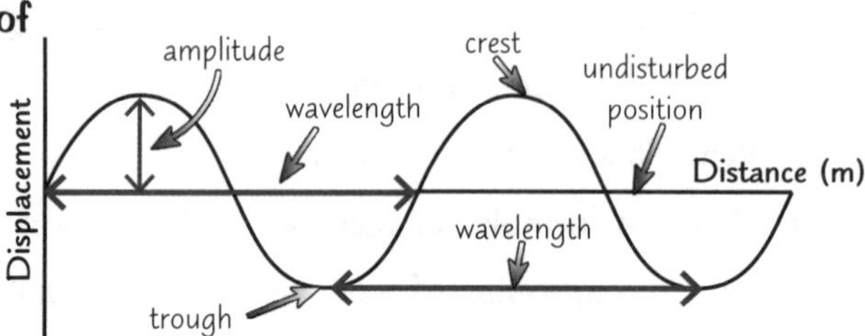

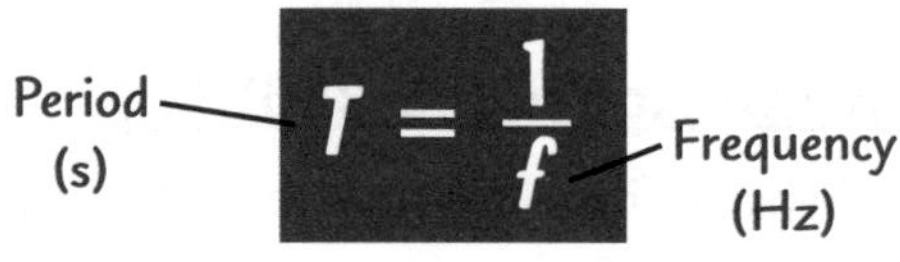

$$T = \frac{1}{f}$$

Transverse Waves Have Sideways Vibrations

In transverse waves, the oscillations (vibrations) are perpendicular (at 90°) to the direction of energy transfer. Most waves are transverse, including:

1) All electromagnetic waves, e.g. light (p.220).
2) Ripples and waves in water (see p.219).
3) A wave on a string.

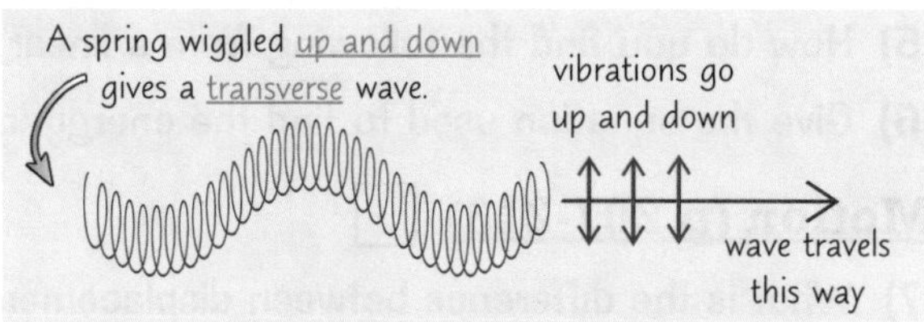

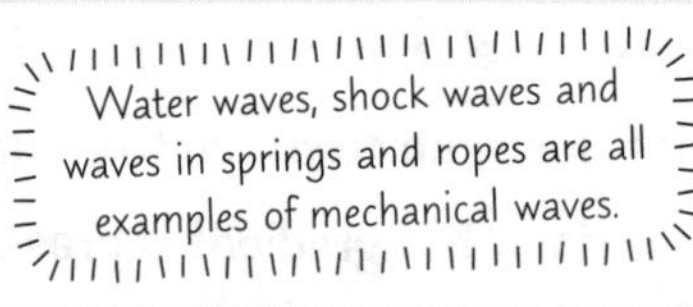

Longitudinal Waves Have Parallel Vibrations

In longitudinal waves, the oscillations are parallel to the direction of energy transfer. An example is sound waves in air.

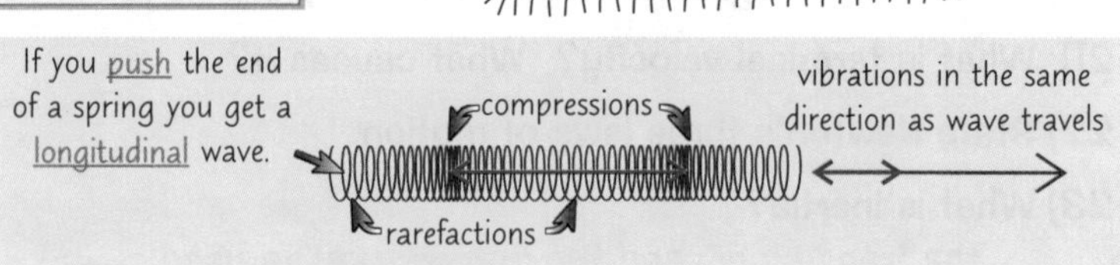

Wave Speed = Frequency × Wavelength

The wave speed is the speed at which energy is being transferred (or the speed the wave is moving at). The wave equation applies to all waves:

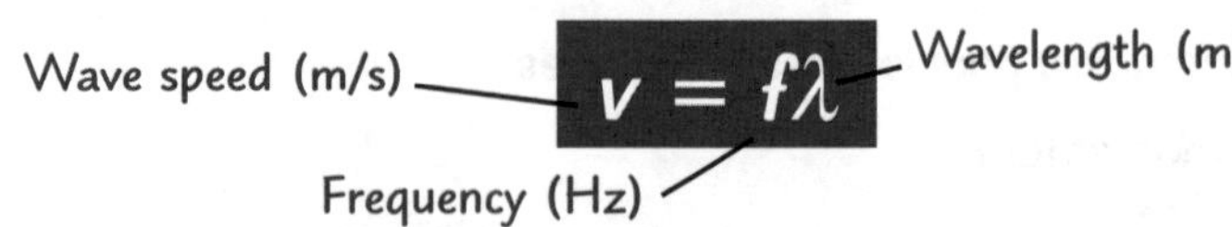

$$v = f\lambda$$

EXAMPLE:

A radio wave has a frequency of 12.0×10^6 Hz. Find its wavelength. (The speed of radio waves in air is 3.0×10^8 m/s.)

$\lambda = v \div f$

$= (3.0 \times 10^8) \div (12.0 \times 10^6) = 25$ m

So, that's the wave basics...

Make sure you've got all this clear in your head, otherwise the rest of the topic will just be a wavey blur of nonsense.

Q1 A wave has a speed of 0.15 m/s and a wavelength of 7.5 cm. Calculate its frequency. [4 marks]

Experiments With Waves

Time to experiment. Make sure you can choose suitable equipment to measure the speed of different waves.

Use an Oscilloscope to Measure the Speed of Sound

By attaching a signal generator to a speaker you can generate sounds with a specific frequency. You can use two microphones and an oscilloscope to find the wavelength of the sound waves generated.

1) Set up the oscilloscope so the detected waves at each microphone are shown as separate waves.
2) Start with both microphones next to the speaker, then slowly move one away until the two waves are aligned on the display, but have moved exactly one wavelength apart.
3) Measure the distance between the microphones to find one wavelength (λ).
4) You can then use the formula $v = f\lambda$ (p.218) to find the speed (v) of the sound waves passing through the air — the frequency (f) is whatever you set the signal generator to (around 1 kHz is sensible).
5) The speed of sound in air is around 330 m/s, so check your results roughly agree with this.

Measure the Speed of Water Ripples Using a Strobe Light

PRACTICAL

1) Using a signal generator attached to the dipper of a ripple tank you can create water waves at a set frequency.
2) Use a strobe light to see wave crests on a screen below the tank.
3) Increase the frequency of the strobe light until the wave pattern on the screen appears to 'freeze' and stop moving. This happens when the frequency of the strobe light is equal to the frequency of the waves.
4) The strobe is a good piece of equipment to use because it allows you to measure a still pattern instead of a constantly moving one.
5) The distance between each shadow line is equal to one wavelength. Measure the distance between shadow lines that are 10 wavelengths apart, then divide this distance by 10 to find the average wavelength. This is a good method for measuring small wavelengths (p.233).
6) Use $v = f\lambda$ to calculate the wave speed of the waves.

Make sure you dim the lights for this experiment.

You can Use the Wave Equation for Waves on Strings

PRACTICAL

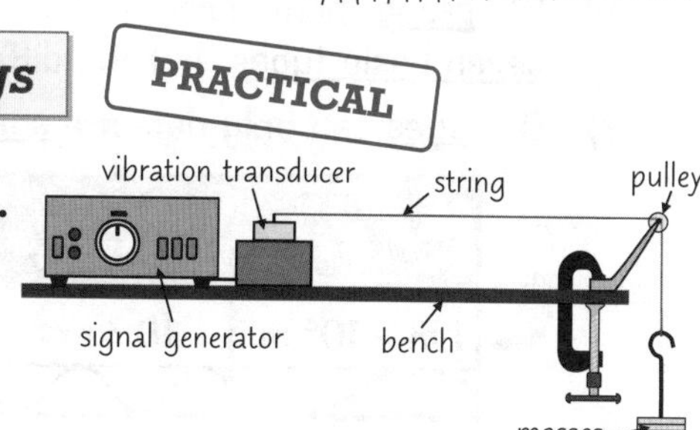

1) Set up the equipment shown on the right, then turn on the signal generator and vibration transducer. The string will start to vibrate.
2) Adjust the frequency of the signal generator until there's a clear wave on the string. The frequency you need will depend on the length of string between the pulley and the transducer, and the masses you've used.
3) You need to measure the wavelength of these waves. The best way to do this accurately is to measure the lengths of, say four or five half-wavelengths (as many as you can) in one go, then divide to get the mean half-wavelength (p.6). You can then double this mean to get a full wavelength.
4) The frequency of the wave is whatever the signal generator is set to (you could also measure it with a strobe, as in the experiment above).
5) You can find the speed of the wave using $v = f\lambda$.

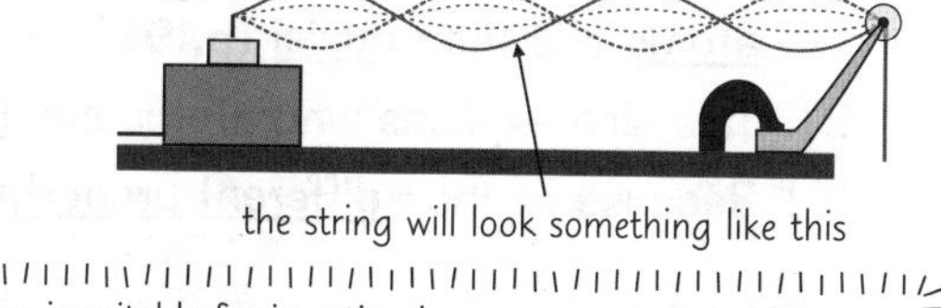

This set-up is suitable for investigating waves on a string because it's easy to see and measure the wavelength (and frequency).

Disco time in the physics lab...

Sound waves, ripples, and waves on strings are used as model waves because they're easy to work with.

Q1 Describe a suitable experiment to measure the wavelength of a water wave. [4 marks]

Wave Behaviour and Electromagnetic Waves

The differences between types of electromagnetic (EM) waves make them useful to us in different ways.

All Waves Can be Absorbed, Transmitted or Reflected

When a wave meets a boundary between two materials, three things can happen:

1) The wave is ABSORBED by the second material — the wave transfers energy to the material's energy stores. Often, the energy is transferred to a thermal energy store, which leads to heating (this is how a microwave works, see page 223).
2) The wave is TRANSMITTED through the second material — the wave carries on travelling through the new material. This often leads to refraction (see p.221). This can be used in communications (p.222) as well as in the lenses of glasses and cameras.
3) The wave is REFLECTED — this is where the incoming ray is neither absorbed or transmitted, but instead is 'sent back' away from the second material. This is how echoes are created.

What actually happens depends on the wavelength of the wave and the properties of the materials involved.

There's a Continuous Spectrum of EM Waves

1) Electromagnetic (EM) waves are transverse waves (p.218).
2) They transfer energy from a source to an absorber.

A camp fire transfers energy to its surroundings by emitting infrared radiation. These infrared waves are absorbed by objects and transfer energy to the object's thermal energy store, causing the object to warm up.	Radio waves transfer energy to the kinetic energy stores of electrons in radio receivers, which generates an electric current (see page 222).

3) All EM waves travel at the same speed through air or a vacuum (space). Electromagnetic waves aren't vibrations of particles, they're vibrations of electric and magnetic fields (p.227). This means they can travel through a vacuum.
4) They travel at different speeds in different materials (which can lead to refraction).
5) EM waves vary in wavelength from around 10^{-15} m to more than 10^{4} m.
6) We group them based on their wavelength and frequency — there are seven basic types, but the different groups merge to form a continuous spectrum.
7) Our eyes can only detect a small part of this spectrum — visible light.

	RADIO WAVES	MICRO WAVES	INFRA RED	VISIBLE LIGHT	ULTRA VIOLET	X-RAYS	GAMMA RAYS
wavelength	1 m – 10^{4} m	10^{-2} m	10^{-5} m	10^{-7} m	10^{-8} m	10^{-10} m	10^{-15} m

long wavelength, low frequency → short wavelength, high frequency

8) There is such a large range of frequencies because EM waves are generated by a variety of changes in atoms and their nuclei (p.195). E.g. changes in the nucleus of an atom creates gamma rays (p.196).
9) This also explains why atoms can absorb a range of frequencies — each one causes a different change.
10) Because of their different properties, different EM waves are used for different purposes.

Learn about the EM spectrum and wave goodbye to exam woe...

Nothing too difficult here, just a lot of facts to remember. Here's a handy mnemonic for the order of EM waves: 'Rock Music Is Very Useful for eXperiments with Goats'.

Q1 State the type of electromagnetic wave that has the lowest frequency. [1 mark]

Q2 Name the section of the electromagnetic spectrum that humans can see. [1 mark]

Refraction

Go and grab a glass of water a put a straw in it. The straw looks like it's bending — is it wizardry or refraction? Answer: refraction (unless you know something I don't).

Refraction — Waves Changing Direction at a Boundary

1) When a wave crosses a boundary between two materials it changes speed.
2) If the wave is travelling along the normal it will change speed, but it's NOT refracted.
3) If the wave hits the boundary at an angle it changes direction — it's refracted.
4) The wave bends towards the normal if it slows down. It bends away from the normal if it speeds up.
5) How much it's refracted by depends on how much the wave speeds up or slows down, which usually depends on the density of the two materials (usually the higher the density of a material, the slower a wave travels through it).
6) The optical density of a material is a measure of how quickly light can travel through it — the higher the optical density, the slower light waves travels through it.
7) The wavelength of a wave changes when it is refracted, but the frequency stays the same.

Ray Diagrams Show the Path of a Wave

Rays are straight lines that are perpendicular to wave fronts. They show the direction a wave is travelling in. You can construct a ray diagram for a refracted light ray.

1) First, start by drawing the boundary between your two materials and the normal. The normal is an imaginary line that's perpendicular (at right angles) to the point where the incoming wave hits the boundary.
2) Draw an incident ray that meets the normal at the boundary.
3) The angle between the incident ray and the normal is the angle of incidence. (If you're given this angle, make sure to draw it carefully with a protractor.)
4) Now draw the refracted ray on the other side of the boundary.
5) The angle of refraction is the angle between the refracted ray and the normal.
6) If the second material is optically denser than first, the refracted ray bends towards the normal (like on the right) and the angle of refraction is smaller than the angle of incidence. If the second material is less optically dense, the angle of refraction is larger than the angle of incidence.

incoming ray
angle of incidence
boundary
normal
angle of refraction
refracted ray

You can also Explain Refraction using Wave Front Diagrams

Wave travels this way

Each purple line is a wave front.

1) A wave front is a line showing all of the points on a wave that are in the same position as each other after a given number of wavelengths.
2) When a wave crosses a boundary at an angle, only part of a wave front crosses the boundary at first. If it's travelling into a denser material, that part travels slower than the rest of the wave front.
3) So by the time the whole wave front crosses the boundary, the faster part of the wave front will have travelled further than the slower part of the wave front.
4) This difference in distance travelled (caused by the difference in speed) by the wave front causes the wave to bend (refract).

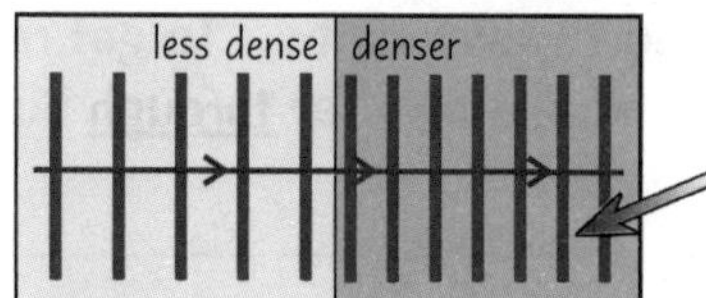

The wave fronts being closer together shows a change in wavelength (and so a change in velocity).

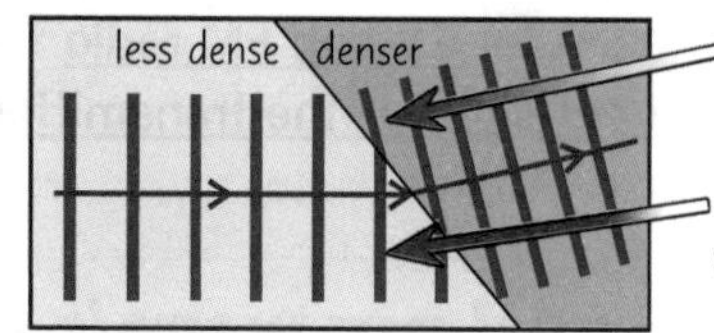

This part of the wave front travels slower than the rest.

So this part of the wave front will have travelled further by the time it crosses the boundary.

Lights, camera, refraction...

Refraction is a common behaviour of waves. so make sure you really understand it before moving on.

Q1 Draw a ray diagram for a light ray entering a less optically dense medium at 40° to the normal. [3 marks]

Radio Waves

EM waves are used for all sorts of stuff — and radio waves are definitely the most entertaining. They transfer energy to your car radio and your TV — what would you do without them?

Radio Waves are Made by Oscillating Charges

1) EM waves are made up of oscillating electric and magnetic fields.
2) Alternating currents (ac) (p.186) are made up of oscillating charges. As the charges oscillate, they produce oscillating electric and magnetic fields, i.e. electromagnetic waves.
3) The frequency of the waves produced will be equal to the frequency of the alternating current.
4) You can produce radio waves using an alternating current in an electrical circuit. The object in which charges (electrons) oscillate to create the radio waves is called a transmitter.
5) When transmitted radio waves reach a receiver, the radio waves are absorbed.
6) The energy carried by the waves is transferred to the electrons in the material of the receiver.
7) This energy causes the electrons to oscillate and, if the receiver is part of a complete electrical circuit, it generates an alternating current.
8) This current has the same frequency as the radio wave that generated it.

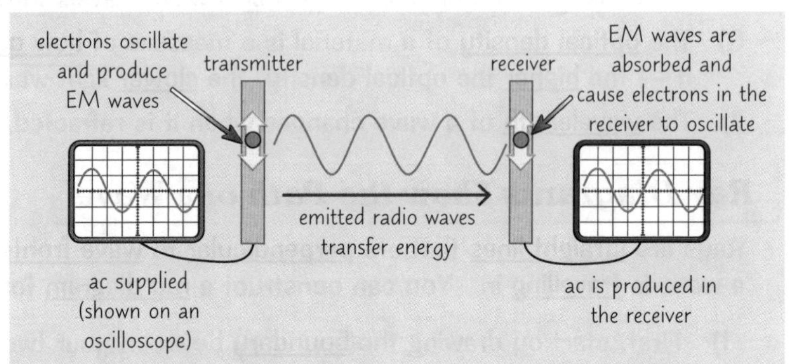

Radio Waves are Used Mainly for Communication

1) Radio waves are EM radiation with wavelengths longer than about 10 cm.
2) Long-wave radio (wavelengths of 1 – 10 km) can be transmitted from London, say, and received halfway round the world. That's because long wavelengths diffract (bend) around the curved surface of the Earth. Long-wave radio wavelengths can also diffract around hills, into tunnels and all sorts.
3) This makes it possible for radio signals to be received even if the receiver isn't in line of the sight of the transmitter.
4) Short-wave radio signals (wavelengths of about 10 m – 100 m) can, like long-wave, be received at long distances from the transmitter. That's because they are reflected (see p.220) from the ionosphere — an electrically charged layer in the Earth's upper atmosphere.
5) Bluetooth® uses short-wave radio waves to send data over short distances between devices without wires (e.g. wireless headsets so you can use your phone while driving a car).
6) Medium-wave signals (well, the shorter ones) can also reflect from the ionosphere, depending on atmospheric conditions and the time of day.
7) The radio waves used for TV and FM radio transmissions have very short wavelengths. To get reception, you must be in direct sight of the transmitter — the signal doesn't bend or travel far through buildings.

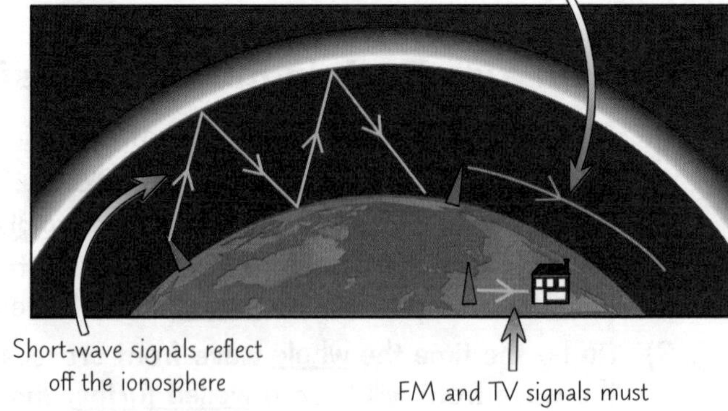

Size matters — and my wave's longer than yours...

Producing radio waves — who knew it was so tricky? It's worth it though — they're just so darn useful.

Q1 State one use of radio waves. [1 mark]

Q2 Describe how radio waves can be produced. [1 mark]

EM Waves and Their Uses

Radio waves aren't the only waves used for communication — other EM waves come in pretty handy too. The most important thing is to think about how the properties of a wave relate to its uses.

Microwaves are Used by Satellites

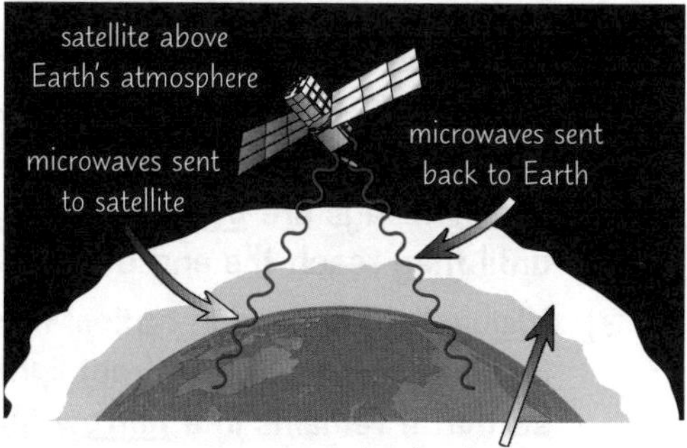

1) Communication to and from satellites (including satellite TV signals and satellite phones) uses microwaves. But you need to use microwaves which can pass easily through the Earth's watery atmosphere.
2) For satellite TV, the signal from a transmitter is transmitted into space...
3) ... where it's picked up by the satellite receiver dish orbiting thousands of kilometres above the Earth. The satellite transmits the signal back to Earth in a different direction...
4) ... where it's received by a satellite dish on the ground. There is a slight time delay between the signal being sent and received because of the long distance the signal has to travel.

Microwave Ovens Use a Different Wavelength from Satellites

1) In communications, the microwaves used need to pass through the Earth's watery atmosphere.
2) In microwave ovens, the microwaves need to be absorbed by water molecules in food — so they use a different wavelength to those used in satellite communications.
3) The microwaves penetrate up to a few centimetres into the food before being absorbed and transferring the energy they are carrying to the water molecules in the food, causing the water to heat up.
4) The water molecules then transfer this energy to the rest of the molecules in the food by heating — which quickly cooks the food.

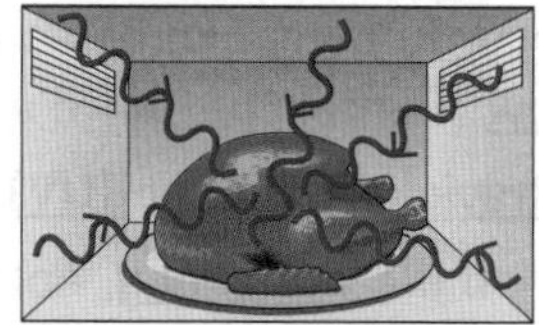

Infrared Radiation Can be Used to Increase or Monitor Temperature

1) Infrared (IR) radiation is given out by all objects — and the hotter the object, the more IR radiation it gives out.
2) Infrared cameras can be used to detect infrared radiation and monitor temperature. The camera detects the IR radiation and turns it into an electrical signal, which is displayed on a screen as a picture. The hotter an object is, the brighter it appears. E.g. energy transfer from a house's thermal energy store can be detected using infrared cameras.
3) Absorbing IR radiation causes objects to get hotter. Food can cooked using IR radiation — the temperature of the food increases when it absorbs IR radiation, e.g. from a toaster's heating element.

Different colours represent different amounts of IR radiation being detected. Here, the redder the colour, the more infrared radiation is being detected.

4) Electric heaters heat a room in the same way. Electric heaters contain a long piece of wire that heats up when a current flows through it. This wire then emits lots of infrared radiation (and a little visible light — the wire glows). The emitted IR radiation is absorbed by objects and the air in the room — energy is transferred by the IR waves to the thermal energy stores of the objects, causing their temperature to increase.

Revision time — adjust depending on brain wattage...

The next time you're feeling hungry and zap some food in the microwave, think of it as doing revision.

Q1 Explain why signals between satellites are transmitted as microwaves. [1 mark]

More Uses of EM Waves

Haven't had enough uses of EM waves? Good, because here are just a few more uses of those incredibly handy waves — complete with the all-important reasons for why they have been used. Get learning.

Fibre Optic Cables Use Visible Light to Transmit Data

1) Optical fibres are thin glass or plastic fibres that can carry data (e.g. from telephones or computers) over long distances as pulses of visible light.
2) They work because of reflection (p.220). The light rays are bounced back and forth until they reach the end of the fibre.
3) Visible light is used in optical fibres because it is easy to refract light enough so that it remains in a narrow fibre.
4) Light is also not easily absorbed or scattered as it travels along a fibre.

Ultraviolet Radiation Gives You a Suntan

1) Fluorescence is a property of certain chemicals, where ultra-violet (UV) radiation is absorbed and then visible light is emitted. That's why fluorescent colours look so bright — they actually emit light.
2) Fluorescent lights generate UV radiation, which is absorbed and re-emitted as visible light by a layer of phosphorus on the inside of the bulb. They're energy-efficient (p.172) so they're good to use when light is needed for long periods (like in your classroom).
3) Security pens can be used to mark property with your name (e.g. laptops). Under UV light the ink will glow (fluoresce), but it's invisible otherwise. This can help the police identify your property if it's stolen.
4) Ultraviolet radiation (UV) is produced by the Sun, and exposure to it is what gives people a suntan.
5) When it's not sunny, some people go to tanning salons where UV lamps are used to give them an artificial suntan. However, overexposure to UV radiation can be dangerous (fluorescent lights emit very little UV — they're totally safe).

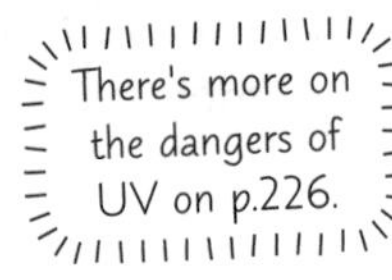

X-rays and Gamma Rays are Used in Medicine

1) Radiographers in hospitals take X-ray 'photographs' of people to see if they have any broken bones.
2) X-rays pass easily through flesh but not so easily through denser material like bones or metal. So it's the amount of radiation that's absorbed (or not absorbed) that gives you an X-ray image.
3) Radiographers use X-rays and gamma rays to treat people with cancer (radiotherapy). This is because high doses of these rays kill all living cells — so they are carefully directed towards cancer cells, to avoid killing too many normal, healthy cells.
4) Gamma radiation can also be used as a medical tracer — this is where a gamma-emitting source is injected into the patient, and its progress is followed around the body. Gamma radiation is well suited to this because it can pass out through the body to be detected.
5) Both X-rays and gamma rays can be harmful to people (p.226), so radiographers wear lead aprons and stand behind a lead screen or leave the room to keep their exposure to them to a minimum.

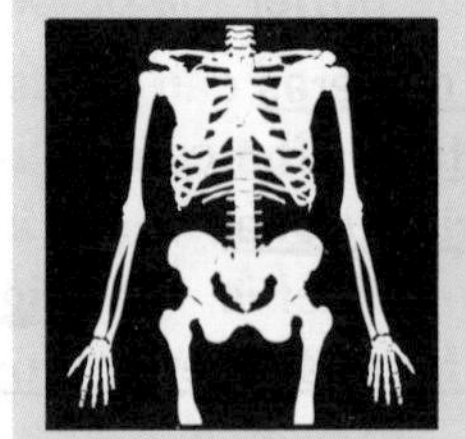

The brighter bits are where fewer X-rays get through. This is a negative image. The plate starts off all white.

There's more on gamma rays on p.196.

Don't lie to an X-ray — they can see right through you...

I hate to say it, but go back to page 222 and read all of the uses for EM waves again to really learn them.

Q1 State two uses of X-rays. [2 marks]

Q2 Explain why plastic optical fibres use pulses of visible light to transmit data. [2 marks]

Investigating Infrared Radiation

You saw on p.223 that all objects emit infrared radiation, but now it's time to see how the surface of the object affects how much it emits. I know, you can hardly contain your excitement. Neither can I.

You Can Investigate Emission With a Leslie Cube

PRACTICAL

The amount of infrared radiation emitted from an object is not just dependent on its temperature. It's also dependent on the material of its surface.

A Leslie cube is a hollow, watertight, metal cube made of e.g. aluminium, whose four vertical faces have different surfaces (for example, matt black paint, matt white paint, shiny metal and dull metal). You can use them to investigate IR emission by different surfaces:

1) Place an empty Leslie cube on a heat-proof mat.
2) Boil water in a kettle and fill the Leslie cube with boiling water.
3) Wait a while for the cube to warm up, then hold a thermometer against each of the four vertical faces of the cube. You should find that all four faces are the same temperature.
4) Hold an infrared detector a set distance (e.g. 10 cm) away from one of the cube's vertical faces, and record the amount of IR radiation it detects.
5) Repeat this measurement for each of the cube's vertical faces. Make sure you position the detector at the same distance from the cube each time.

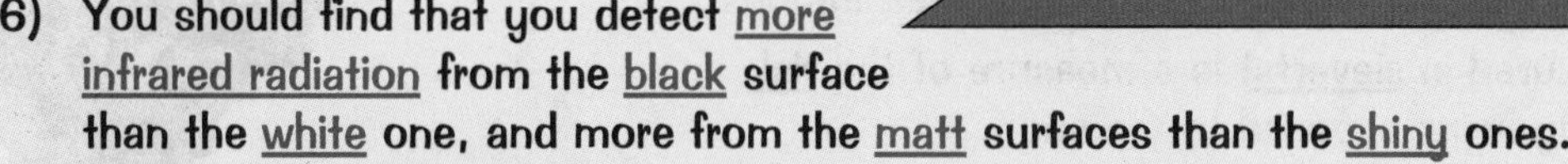

6) You should find that you detect more infrared radiation from the black surface than the white one, and more from the matt surfaces than the shiny ones.

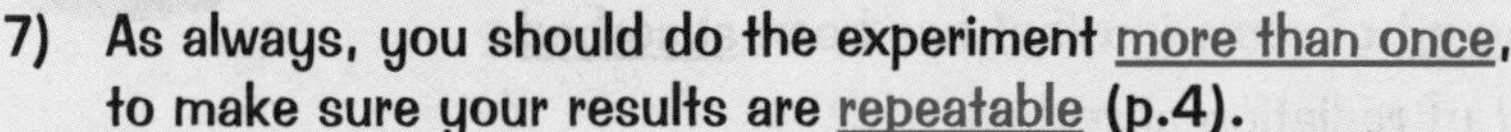

7) As always, you should do the experiment more than once, to make sure your results are repeatable (p.4).
8) It's important to be careful when you're doing this experiment. Don't try to move the cube when it's full of boiling water — you might burn your hands. And be careful if you're carrying a full kettle — your mate won't thank you if you spill boiling water into their bag (or down their back).

You Can Investigate Absorption with the Melting Wax Trick

PRACTICAL

The amount of infrared radiation absorbed by different materials also depends on the material. You can do an experiment to show this, using a bunsen burner and some candle wax.

1) Set up the equipment as shown on the right. Two ball bearings are each stuck to one side of a metal plate with solid pieces of candle wax. The other sides of these plates are then faced towards the flame.
2) The sides of the plates that are facing towards the flame each have a different surface colour — one is matt black and the other is silver.
3) The ball bearing on the black plate will fall first as the black surface absorbs more infrared radiation — transferring more energy to the thermal energy store of the wax. This means the wax on the black plate melts before the wax on the silver plate.

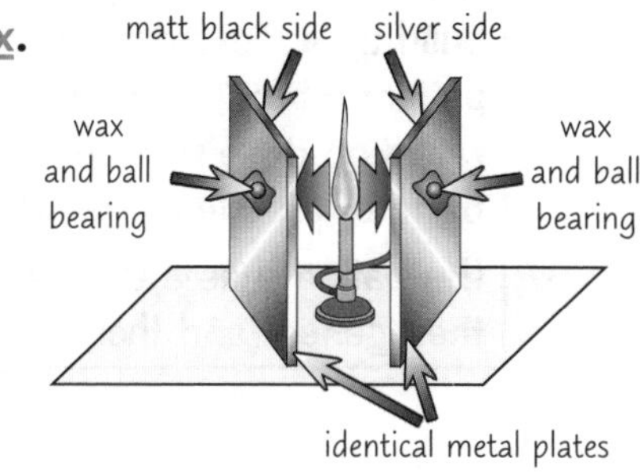

Feelin' hot hot hot...

When doing the experiment with the Leslie cube, you could also place your hand near each surface of the cube (but no touching, it'll be super hot) — you'll be able to feel which surface is emitting more infrared radiation.

Q1 A student makes two identical cups of tea in two mugs. The two mugs are the same, apart from their colour — one mug is black and the other is white. Explain which cup of tea will initially cool at a faster rate. [3 marks]

Dangers of Electromagnetic Waves

Okay, so you know how useful electromagnetic radiation can be — well, it can also be pretty dangerous.

Some EM Radiation Can be Harmful to People

1) When EM radiation enters living tissue — like you — it's often harmless, but sometimes it creates havoc. The effects of each type of radiation are based on how much energy the wave transfers.
2) Low frequency waves, like radio waves, don't transfer much energy and so mostly pass through soft tissue without being absorbed.
3) High frequency waves like UV, X-rays and gamma rays all transfer lots of energy and so can cause lots of damage.
4) UV radiation damages surface cells, which can lead to sunburn and cause skin to age prematurely. Some more serious effects are blindness and an increased risk of skin cancer.
5) X-rays and gamma rays are types of ionising radiation. (They carry enough energy to knock electrons off of atoms.) This can cause gene mutation or cell destruction, and cancer.

You Can Measure Risk Using the Radiation Dose in Sieverts

1) Whilst UV radiation, X-rays and gamma rays can all be harmful, they are also very useful (see pages 222-224). Before any of these types of EM radiation are used, people look at whether the benefits outweigh the health risks.
2) For example, the risk of a person involved in a car accident developing cancer from having an X-ray photograph taken is much smaller than the potential health risk of not finding and treating their injuries.
3) Radiation dose (measured in sieverts) is a measure of the risk of harm from the body being exposed to radiation.
4) This is not a measure of the total amount of radiation that has been absorbed.
5) The risk depends on the total amount of radiation absorbed and how harmful the type of radiation is.
6) A sievert is pretty big, so you'll often see doses in millisieverts (mSv), where 1000 mSv = 1 Sv.

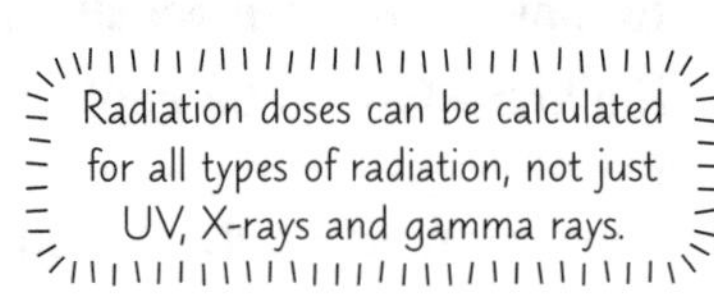

Risk can be Different for Different Parts of the Body

A CT scan uses X-rays and a computer to build up a picture of the inside of a patient's body. The table shows the radiation dose received by two different parts of a patient's body when having CT scans.

	Radiation dose (mSv)
Head	2.0
Chest	8.0

If a patient has a CT scan on their chest, they are four times more likely to suffer damage to their genes (and their added risk of harm is four times higher) than if they had a head scan.

This is not an excuse to stay in bed all day...

It's impossible to avoid all forms of harmful radiation, so it's all about balancing risks and reducing your exposure.

Q1 Give two effects of a person being exposed to too much UV radiation. [2 marks]

Q2 A patient's pelvis is being examined. It can either be examined with a single X-ray photograph or with a CT scan. An X-ray of the pelvis has a radiation dose of 0.7 mSv. A CT scan of the pelvis has a radiation dose of 7 mSv. How much larger is the added risk of harm if the patient has a CT scan? [1 mark]

Permanent and Induced Magnets

I think magnetism is an attractive subject, but don't get repelled by the exam — revise.

Magnets Produce Magnetic Fields

1) All magnets have two poles — north (or north seeking) and south (or south seeking).
2) All magnets produce a magnetic field — a region where other magnets or magnetic materials (e.g. iron, steel, nickel and cobalt) experience a non-contact force (p.201).
3) You can show a magnetic field by drawing magnetic field lines.

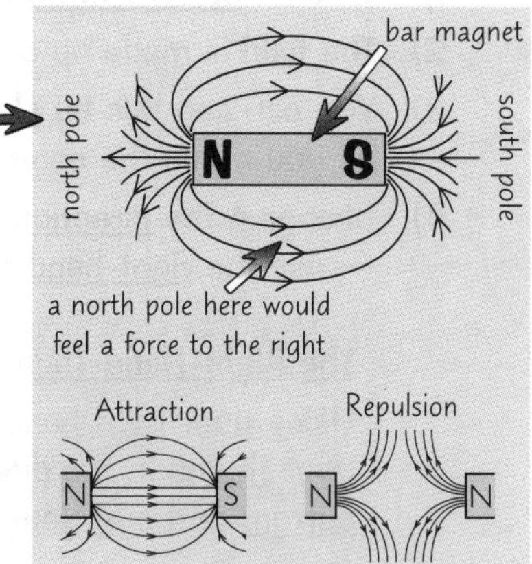

4) The lines always go from north to south and they show which way a force would act on a north pole if it was put at that point in the field.
5) The closer together the lines are, the stronger the magnetic field. The further away from a magnet you get, the weaker the field is.
6) The magnetic field is strongest at the poles of a magnet. This means that the magnetic forces are also strongest at the poles.
7) The force between a magnet and a magnetic material is always attractive, no matter the pole.
8) If two poles of a magnet are put near each other, they will each exert a force on each other. This force can be attractive or repulsive. Two poles that are the same (these are called like poles) will repel each other. Two unlike poles will attract each other.

Compasses Show the Directions of Magnetic Fields

1) Inside a compass is a tiny bar magnet. The north pole of this magnet is attracted to the south pole of any other magnet it is near. So the compass points in the direction of the magnetic field it is in.
2) You can move a compass around a magnet and trace its position on some paper to build up a picture of what the magnetic field looks like.
3) When they're not near a magnet, compasses always point north. This is because the Earth generates its own magnetic field, which shows the inside (core) of the Earth must be magnetic.

The north pole of the magnet in the compass points along the field line towards the south pole of the bar magnet.

N S NORTH POLE

Magnets Can be Permanent or Induced

1) There are two types of magnet — permanent magnets and induced magnets.
2) Permanent magnets produce their own magnetic field.
3) Induced magnets are magnetic materials that turn into a magnet when they're put into a magnetic field.
4) The force between permanent and induced magnets is always attractive (see magnetic materials above).
5) When you take away the magnetic field, induced magnets quickly lose their magnetism (or most of it) and stop producing a magnetic field.

N permanent magnet S — magnetic material

The magnetic material becomes magnetised when it is brought near the bar magnet. It has its own poles and magnetic field:

N permanent magnet S — N induced magnet S

induced poles

Magnets are like farmers — surrounded by fields...

Magnetism is one of those things that takes a while to make much sense. Learn these basics — you'll need them.

Q1 Draw the magnetic field lines for a bar magnet. Label the areas where the field is strongest. [2 marks]

Q2 Give two differences between permanent and induced magnets. [2 marks]

Electromagnetism

On this page you'll see that a magnetic field is also found around a wire that has a current passing through it. The strength of this field can be increased by wrapping the wire into a long coil called a solenoid. Fun.

A Moving Charge Creates a Magnetic Field

1) When a current flows through a wire, a magnetic field is created around the wire.
2) The field is made up of concentric circles perpendicular to the wire, with the wire in the centre.
3) You can see this by placing a compass near a wire that is carrying a current. As you move the compass, it will trace the direction of the magnetic field.
4) Changing the direction of the current changes the direction of the magnetic field — use the right-hand thumb rule to work out which way it goes.

The Right-Hand Thumb Rule

Using your right hand, point your thumb in the direction of current and curl your fingers.

The direction of your fingers is the direction of the field.

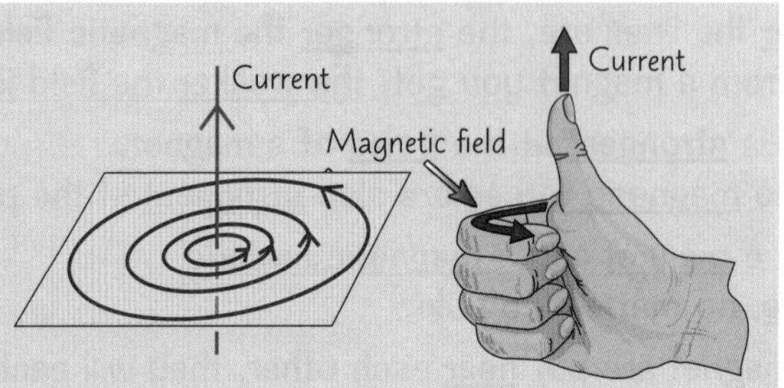

Don't get this confused with the left-hand rule that's over on page 230.

5) The strength of the magnetic field produced changes with the current and the distance from the wire. The larger the current through the wire, or the closer to the wire you are, the stronger the field is.

A Solenoid is a Coil of Wire

1) You can increase the strength of the magnetic field that a wire produces by wrapping the wire into a coil called a solenoid.
2) This happens because the field lines around each loop of wire line up with each other.
3) This results in lots of field lines pointing in the same direction that are very close to each other. As you saw on the last page, the closer together field lines are, the stronger the field is.

- The magnetic field inside a solenoid is strong and uniform (it has the same strength and direction at every point in that region).
- Outside the coil, the magnetic field is just like the one round a bar magnet.
- This means that the ends of a solenoid act like the north pole and south pole of a bar magnet. You can work out which end of the solenoid is the north pole and which is the south pole using the right-hand rule shown above.

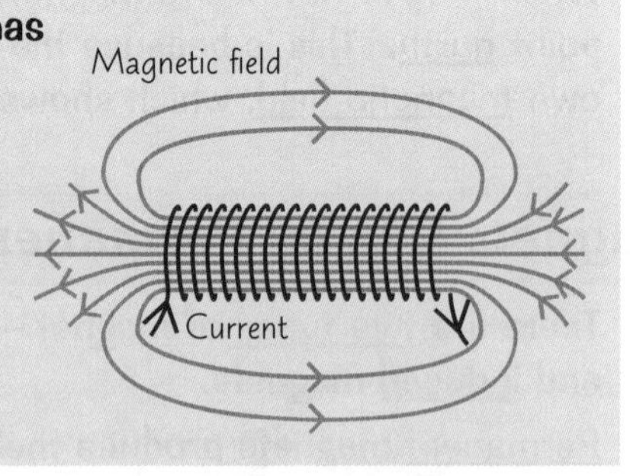

4) You can increase the field strength of the solenoid even more by putting a block of iron in the centre of the coil. This iron core becomes an induced magnet whenever current is flowing.
5) If you stop the current, the magnetic field disappears. A solenoid with an iron core (a magnet whose magnetic field can be turned on and off with an electric current) is called an **ELECTROMAGNET**.

Strong, in uniform and a magnetic personality — I'm a catch...

Electromagnets are used in loads of everyday things from alarms to trains, so you'd better learn how they work.

Q1 Draw the magnetic field for a current-carrying wire. [1 mark]

Q2 a) Draw the magnetic field for a current-carrying solenoid. [2 marks]
b) State one way that you can increase the field strength of a solenoid. [1 mark]

The Motor Effect

The motor effect can happen when you put a current-carrying wire in a magnetic field. It's really useful in stuff like... well... electric motors. If you want to know exactly what it is, you'll have to keep reading.

A Current in a Magnetic Field Experiences a Force

When a current-carrying wire (or any other conductor) is put between magnetic poles, the magnetic field around the wire interacts with the magnetic field it has been placed in. This causes the magnet and the conductor to exert a force on each other. This is called the motor effect and can cause the wire to move.

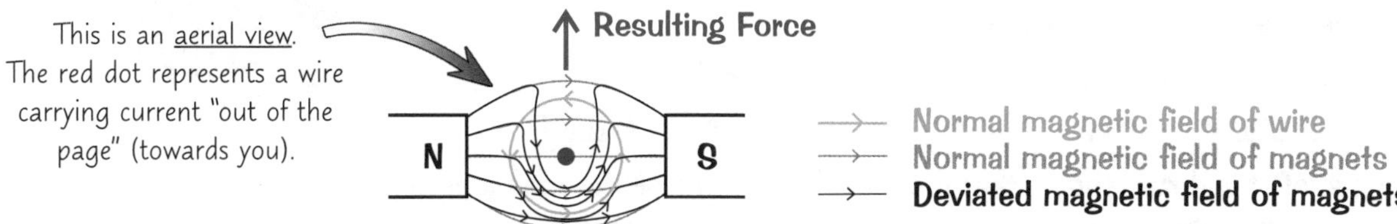

1) To experience the full force, the wire has to be at 90° to the magnetic field. If the wire runs parallel to the magnetic field, it won't experience any force at all. At angles in between, it'll feel some force.
2) The force always acts at right angles to the magnetic field of the magnets and the direction of the current in the wire.
3) A good way of showing the direction of the force is to apply a current to a set of rails inside a horseshoe magnet (shown opposite). A bar is placed on the rails, which completes the circuit. This generates a force that rolls the bar along the rails.

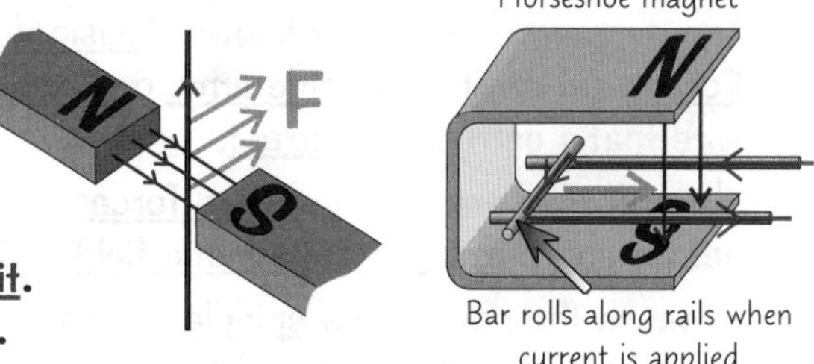

Bar rolls along rails when current is applied

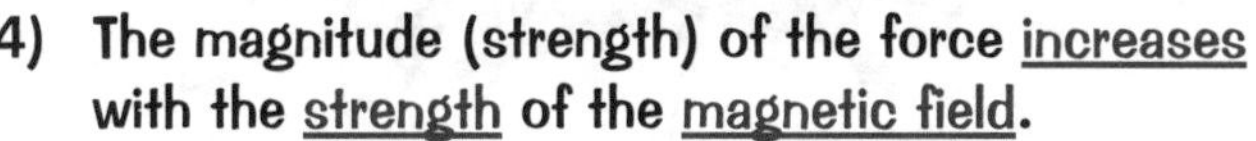

4) The magnitude (strength) of the force increases with the strength of the magnetic field.
5) The force also increases with the amount of current passing through the conductor.

You Can Find the Size of the Force Using F = BIl

The force acting on a conductor in a magnetic field depends on three things:

1) The magnetic flux density — how many field (flux) lines there are in a region. This shows the strength of the magnetic field (p.227).
2) The size of the current through the conductor.
3) The length of the conductor that's in the magnetic field.

When the current is at 90° to the magnetic field it is in, the force acting on it can be found using the equation on the right.

$$F = BIl$$

Force (N), Magnetic flux density (T, tesla), Current (A), Length (m)

An iron bar of length 0.20 m is connected in a circuit so a current of 15 A flows through it. If an external magnetic field of 0.18 T is placed at right angles to the direction of the current in the bar, calculate the force acting on the iron bar due to the presence of the magnetic field.

Force on the bar = magnetic flux density × current × bar length = 0.18 × 15 × 0.20 = 0.54 N

A current-carrying conductor — a ticket inspector eating sultanas...

You need to be comfortable rearranging and using that equation for force, so have a quick practise.

Q1 A 35 cm long piece of wire is at 90° to an external magnetic field. The wire experiences a force of 9.8 N when a current of 5.0 A is flowing through it. Calculate the magnetic flux density of the field. [4 marks]

Electric Motors

And now it's time to learn a silly hand gesture... and apply the stuff you read about on the last page... (sorry).

You Can Find the Direction of the Force Using the Left-hand Rule

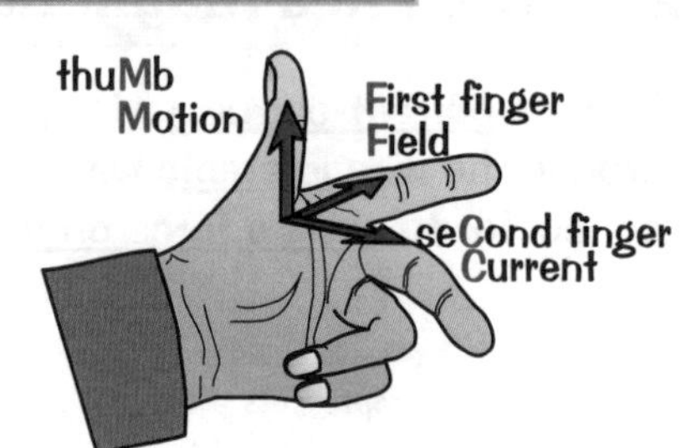

You learnt on the previous page that a force is exerted on any current-carrying conductor in a magnetic field.

You can find the direction of this force with Fleming's left-hand rule.

1) Using your left hand, point your First finger in the direction of the magnetic Field.
2) Point your seCond finger in the direction of the Current.
3) Your thuMb will then point in the direction of the force (Motion).

Fleming's left-hand rule shows that if either the current or the magnetic field is reversed, then the direction of the force will also be reversed.

This can be used for all sorts of things — like motors, shown below.

A Current-Carrying Coil of Wire Rotates in a Magnetic Field

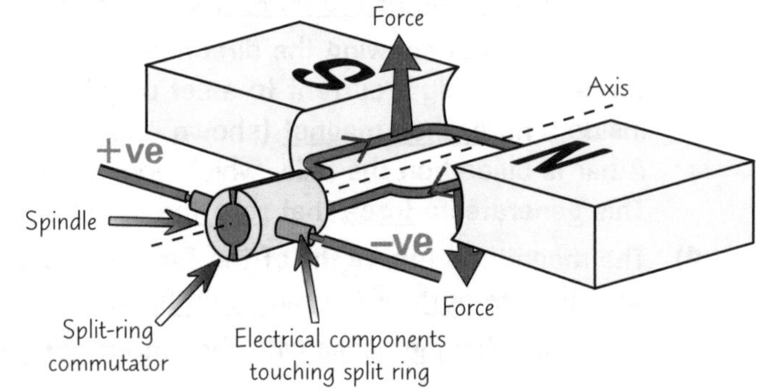

1) The diagram on the right shows a basic dc motor. Forces act on the two side arms of a coil of wire that's carrying a current.
2) These forces are just the usual forces which act on any current in a magnetic field (p.229).
3) Because the coil is on a spindle and the forces act one up and one down, it rotates.
4) The split-ring commutator is a clever way of swapping the contacts every half turn to keep the motor rotating in the same direction.
5) The direction of the motor can be reversed either by swapping the polarity of the dc supply (reversing the current) or swapping the magnetic poles over (reversing the field).
6) The speed of the motor can be increased by increasing the current, adding more turns to the coil or increasing the magnetic flux density.
7) You can use Fleming's left-hand rule to work out which way the coil will turn.

EXAMPLE: Is the coil turning clockwise or anticlockwise?

1) Draw in current arrows (from positive to negative, p.179).
2) Use Fleming's left-hand rule on one branch (here, I've picked the right-hand branch).
3) Point your first finger in the direction of the magnetic field (remember, this is north to south).
4) Point your second finger in the direction of the current.
5) Draw in the direction of motion (the direction your thumb is pointing in).

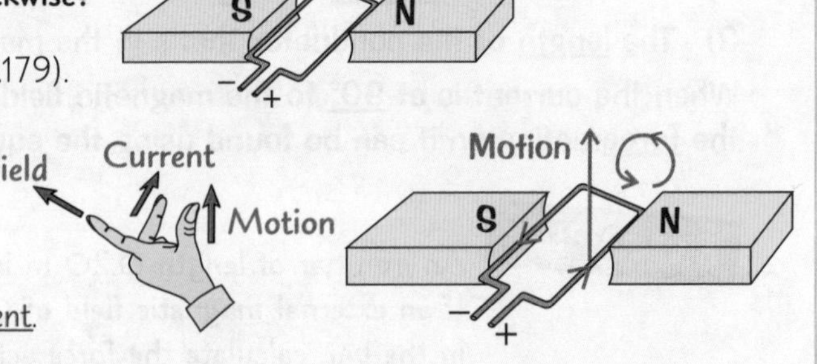

The coil is turning anticlockwise.

Left-hand rule for the motor effect — drive on the left...

Use the left-hand rule in the exam. You might look a bit silly, but it makes getting those marks so much easier.

Q1 A section of a current-carrying wire is in a magnetic field.
The wire is at 90° to the magnetic field.
Find the direction of the force acting on the wire. [1 mark]

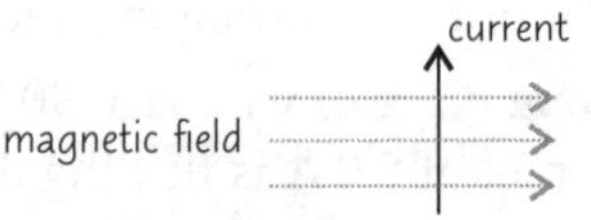

Revision Questions for Topics P6 & P7

Whew, the end of Topic P7 — time to see how much you can remember about the last two topics.

- Try these questions and tick off each one when you get it right.
- When you've done all the questions under a heading and are completely happy with it, tick it off.

Wave Properties (p.218-219)

1) What is the amplitude, wavelength, frequency and period of a wave?
2) Describe the difference between transverse and longitudinal waves and give an example of each kind.
3) Write down the equation that links wave speed, frequency and wavelength.
4) Describe an experiment you could do to measure:
   a) the speed of sound in air. b) the speed of waves on a string.

Electromagnetic Waves and Refraction (p.220-221)

5) Explain the terms absorption, transmission and reflection in terms of waves.
6) True or false? All electromagnetic waves are transverse.
7) Give an example of electromagnetic waves transferring energy from a source to an absorber.
8) Explain refraction and draw a ray diagram for a light ray entering a less optically dense material.
9) Draw a wave front diagram showing a wave entering a denser material.

Uses and Dangers of Electromagnetic Waves (p.222-226)

10) What kind of current is used to generate radio waves in an antenna?
11) Explain why microwaves are used for satellite communication and mobile phone signals.
12) Give an everyday use of infrared radiation.
13) What type of radiation is used to transmit a signal in an optical fibre?
14) What does the term 'ionising radiation' mean?
15) What does radiation dose in sieverts measure?
16) What is a Leslie cube? How could you use one to investigate IR emission by different surfaces?
17) True or false? The amount of infrared radiation absorbed by an object depends on the material of the object.

Magnets (p.227)

18) What is a magnetic field? In what direction do magnetic field lines point?
19) True or false? The force between two unlike poles is attractive.
20) Describe the behaviour of a compass that is far away from a magnet.
21) True or false? The force between a magnet and a magnetic material is always repulsive.

Basic Electromagnetism (p.228)

22) Describe the magnetic field around a current-carrying wire.
23) Why does adding more turns to a solenoid increase the strength of its magnetic field?
24) What is an electromagnet?

The Motor Effect (p.229-230)

25) Explain why a current-carrying conductor in a magnetic field experiences a force.
26) Name two ways you could increase the force on a current-carrying wire in a magnetic field.
27) What is Fleming's left-hand rule?
28) Explain how a basic dc motor works.

Measuring Techniques

Safety specs out and lab coats on, it's time to find out about the skills you'll need in experiments. Finally time to look like a real scientist... hurrah! But you also need to know about this stuff in your exams... boooo...

Mass Should Be Measured Using a Balance

1) To measure mass, start by putting the container you're measuring the substance into on the balance.
2) Set the balance to exactly zero and then start adding your substance.
3) It's no good carefully measuring out your substance if it's not all transferred to your reaction vessel — the amount in the reaction vessel won't be the same as your measurement. Here are a couple of methods you can use to make sure that none gets left in your weighing container...

- If you're dissolving a mass of a solid in a solvent to make a solution, you could wash any remaining solid into the new container using the solvent. This way you know that all the solid you weighed has been transferred.
- You could reweigh the weighing container after you've transferred the substance. This means you can work out exactly how much you added to your experiment.

Different Ways to Measure Liquids

There are a few methods you might use to measure the volume of a liquid. Whichever method you use, always read the volume from the bottom of the meniscus (the curved upper surface of the liquid) when it's at eye level.

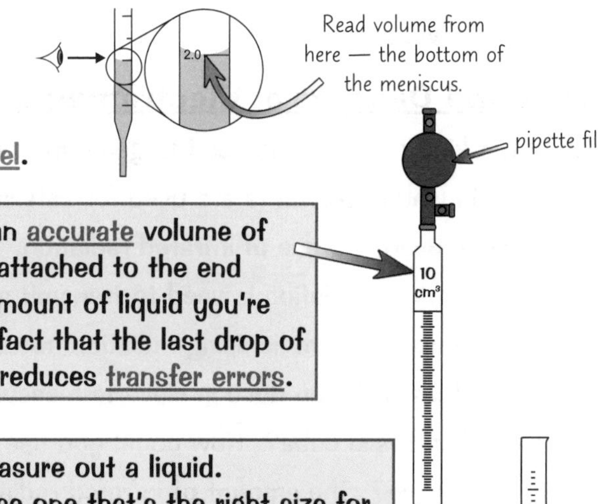

Pipettes are long, narrow tubes that are used to suck up an accurate volume of liquid and transfer it to another container. A pipette filler attached to the end of the pipette is used so that you can safely control the amount of liquid you're drawing up. Pipettes are often calibrated to allow for the fact that the last drop of liquid stays in the pipette when the liquid is ejected. This reduces transfer errors.

Measuring cylinders are the most common way to measure out a liquid. They come in all different sizes. Make sure you choose one that's the right size for the measurement you want to make. It's no good using a huge 1000 cm^3 cylinder to measure out 2 cm^3 of a liquid — the graduations will be too big, and you'll end up with massive errors. It'd be much better to use one that measures up to 10 cm^3.

If you only want a couple of drops of liquid, and don't need it to be accurately measured, you can use a dropping pipette to transfer it. For example, this is how you'd add a couple of drops of indicator into a mixture.

Gas Syringes Measure Gas Volumes

1) Gases can be measured with a gas syringe. They should be measured at room temperature and pressure as the volume of a gas changes with temperature and pressure. You should also use a gas syringe that's the right size for the measurement you're making. Before you use the syringe, you should make sure it's completely sealed and that the plunger moves smoothly.
2) Alternatively, you can use an upturned measuring cylinder filled with water. The gas will displace the water so you can read the volume off the scale — see page 237.
3) Other methods to measure the amount of gas include counting the bubbles produced or measuring the length of a gas bubble drawn along a tube (see p.52). These methods are less accurate, but will give you relative amounts of gas to compare results.
4) When you're measuring a gas, you need to make sure that the equipment is set up so that none of the gas can escape, otherwise your results won't be accurate.

Measuring Techniques

Eureka Cans Measure the Volumes of Solids

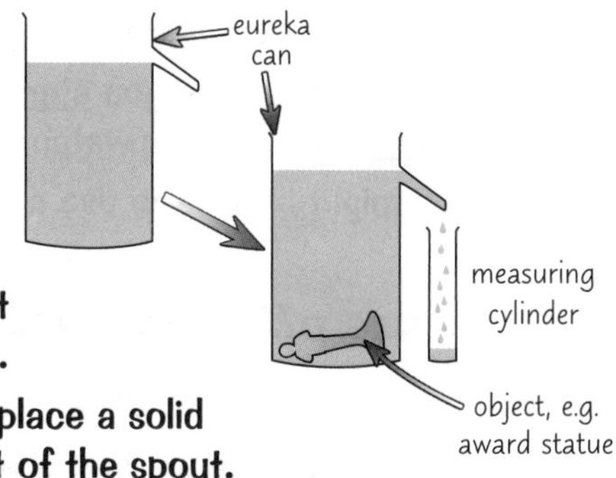

1) Eureka cans are used in combination with measuring cylinders to find the volumes of irregular solids (p.192).
2) They're essentially a beaker with a spout. To use them, fill them with water so the water level is above the spout.
3) Let the water drain from the spout, leaving the water level just below the start of the spout (so all the water displaced by an object goes into the measuring cylinder and gives you the correct volume).
4) Place a measuring cylinder below the end of the spout. When you place a solid in the beaker, it causes the water level to rise and water to flow out of the spout.
5) Make sure you wait until the spout has stopped dripping before you measure the volume of the water in the measuring cylinder. And eureka! You know the object's volume.

Measure Most Lengths with a Ruler

1) In most cases a bog-standard centimetre ruler can be used to measure length. It depends on what you're measuring though — metre rulers are handy for large distances, while micrometers are used for measuring tiny things like the diameter of a wire.
2) The ruler should always be parallel to what you want to measure.
3) If you're dealing with something where it's tricky to measure just one accurately (e.g. water ripples, p.219), you can measure the length of ten of them and then divide to find the length of one.
4) If you're taking multiple measurements of the same object (e.g. to measure changes in length) then make sure you always measure from the same point on the object. It can help to draw or stick small markers onto the object to line up your ruler against.

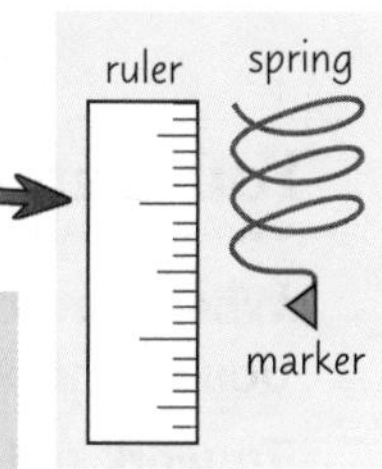

5) Make sure the ruler and the object are always at eye level when you take a reading. This stops parallax affecting your results.

Parallax is where a measurement appears to change based on where you're looking from. The blue line is the measurement taken when the spring is at eye level. It shows the correct length of the spring.

ruler
spring

Use a Protractor to Find Angles

1) First align the vertex (point) of the angle with the mark in the centre of the protractor.
2) Line up the base line of the protractor with one line that forms the angle and then measure the angle of the other line using the scale on the protractor.
3) If the lines creating the angle are very thick, align the protractor and measure the angle from the centre of the lines. Using a sharp pencil to trace light rays or draw diagrams helps to reduce errors when measuring angles.
4) If the lines are too short to measure easily, you may have to extend them. Again, make sure you use a sharp pencil to do this.

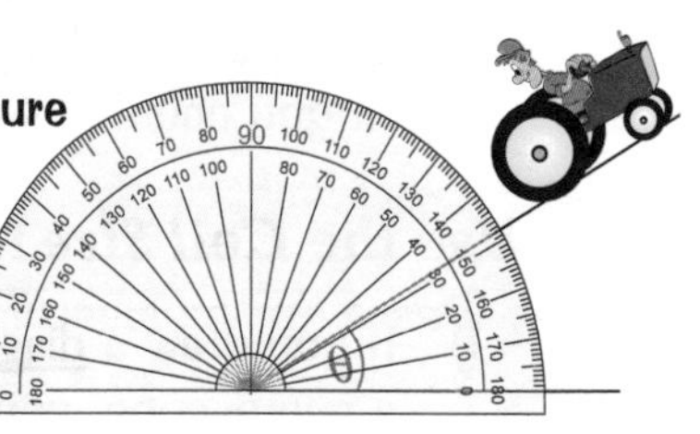

Measure Temperature Accurately

You can use a thermometer to measure the temperature of a substance:

1) Make sure the bulb of your thermometer is completely submerged in any mixture you're measuring.
2) If you're taking an initial reading, you should wait for the temperature to stabilise first.
3) Read your measurement off the scale on a thermometer at eye level to make sure it's correct.

Measuring Techniques

You May Have to Measure the Time Taken for a Change

1) You should use a stopwatch to time experiments. These measure to the nearest 0.1 s, so are sensitive.
2) Always make sure you start and stop the stopwatch at exactly the right time. Or alternatively, set an alarm on the stopwatch so you know exactly when to stop an experiment or take a reading.
3) You might be able to use a light gate instead (p.239). This will reduce the errors in your experiment.

Measure pH to Find Out How Acidic or Alkaline a Solution Is

You need to be able to decide the best method for measuring pH, depending on what your experiment is.

1) Indicators are dyes that change colour depending on whether they're in an acid or an alkali. You use them by adding a couple of drops of the indicator to the solution you're interested in.
2) Universal indicator is a mixture of indicators that changes colour gradually as pH changes. It doesn't show a sudden colour change. It's useful for estimating the pH of a solution based on its colour.
3) Indicators can be soaked into paper and strips of this paper can be used for testing pH. If you use a dropping pipette to spot a small amount of a solution onto some indicator paper, it will change colour depending on the pH of the solution.
4) Indicator paper is useful when you don't want to change the colour of all of the substance, or if the substance is already coloured so might obscure the colour of the indicator. You can also hold a piece of damp indicator paper in a gas sample to test its pH.
5) pH probes are attached to pH meters which have a digital display that gives a numerical value for the pH of a solution. They're used to give an accurate value of pH.

Litmus paper turns red in acidic conditions and blue in basic conditions. Universal indicator paper can be used to estimate the pH based on its colour.

You Can Measure the Size of a Single Cell

When viewing cells under a microscope, you might need to work out their size.

To work out the size of a single cell:

1) Place a clear, plastic ruler on top of your microscope slide. Clip the ruler and slide onto the stage.
2) Select the objective lens that gives an overall magnification of x 100.
3) Adjust the focus to get a clear image of the cells.
4) Move the ruler so that the cells are lined up along 1 mm. Then count the number of cells along this 1 mm sample.
5) 1 mm = 1000 μm. So to calculate the length of a single cell in μm, you just need to divide 1000 μm by the number of cells in the sample. E.g. if you counted 4 cells in 1 mm, the length of a single cell would be: 1000 ÷ 4 = 250 μm

You can read all about using a microscope on page 13.

View down the microscope

1 mm

cells

ruler marking

Use the Cell Size to Work out the Length of a Scale Bar

1) If you draw a diagram of a cell you've observed under a microscope, you might want to include a scale bar.
2) Once you know the size of one cell, you can use it to calculate how long your scale bar should be.
3) To draw a 500 μm scale bar, just use this formula:

scale bar

drawing of cell

500 μm

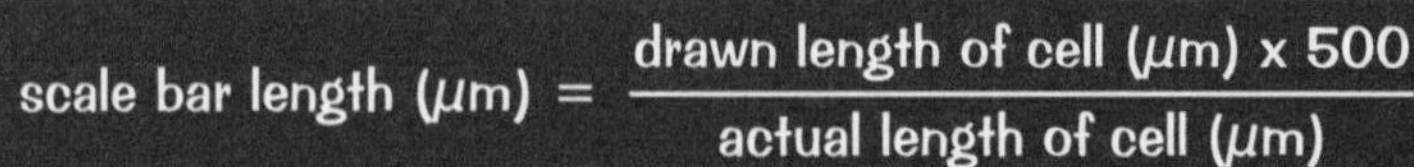
$$\text{scale bar length } (\mu m) = \frac{\text{drawn length of cell } (\mu m) \times 500}{\text{actual length of cell } (\mu m)}$$

Experimentus apparatus...

Wizardry won't help you here, unfortunately. Most of this'll be pretty familiar to you by now, but make sure you know these techniques inside out so they're second nature when it comes to any practicals.

Safety and Ethics

Before you start any experiment, you need to know what safety precautions you should be taking. And they depend on your method, your equipment, and the chemicals you're using.

Make Sure You're Working Safely in the Lab

1) Make sure that you're wearing sensible clothing when you're in the lab (e.g. open shoes won't protect your feet from spillages). When you're doing an experiment, you should wear a lab coat to protect your skin and clothing. Depending on the experiment, you may need to also wear safety goggles and gloves.
2) You also need to be aware of general safety in the lab, e.g. keep anything flammable away from lit Bunsen burners, don't directly touch any hot equipment, handle glassware carefully so it doesn't break, etc.
3) You should follow any instructions that your teacher gives you carefully. But here are some basic principles for dealing with chemicals and equipment...

Be Careful When You're Using Chemicals...

1) The chemicals you're using may be hazardous — for example, they might be flammable (catch fire easily), or they might irritate or burn your skin if it comes into contact with them.
2) Make sure you're working in an area that's well ventilated and if you're doing an experiment that might produce nasty gases (such as chlorine), you should carry out the experiment in a fume hood so that the gas can't escape out into the room you're working in.
3) Never directly touch any chemicals (even if you're wearing gloves). Use a spatula to transfer solids between containers. Carefully pour liquids between containers, using a funnel to avoid spillages.
4) Be careful when you're mixing chemicals, as a reaction might occur. If you're diluting a liquid, add the concentrated substance to the water (not the other way around) or the mixture could get very hot.

...and Equipment

1) Stop masses and equipment falling by using clamp stands. Make sure masses are of a sensible weight so they don't break the equipment they're used with, and use pulleys of a sensible length. That way, any hanging masses won't hit the floor during the experiment.
2) When heating materials, make sure to let them cool before moving them, or wear insulated gloves while handling them. If you're using an immersion heater to heat liquids, you should always let it dry out in air, just in case any liquid has leaked inside the heater.
3) If you're using a laser, there are a few safety rules you must follow. Always wear laser safety goggles and never look directly into the laser or shine it towards another person. Make sure you turn the laser off if it's not needed to avoid any accidents.
4) When working with electronics, make sure you use a low enough voltage and current to prevent wires overheating (and potentially melting) and avoid damage to components, like blowing a filament bulb.

You Need to Think About Ethical Issues In Your Experiments

1) Any organisms involved in your investigations need to be treated safely and ethically.
2) Animals need to be treated humanely — they should be handled carefully and any wild animals captured for studying (e.g. during an investigation of the distribution of an organism) should be returned to their original habitat.
3) Any animals kept in the lab should also be cared for in a humane way, e.g. they should not be kept in overcrowded conditions.
4) If you are carrying out an experiment involving other students (e.g. investigating the effect of caffeine on reaction time), they should not be forced to participate against their will or feel pressured to take part.

Safety first...

I know — lab safety isn't the most exciting topic. But it's mega important. Not only will it stop you from blowing your eyebrows off, it'll help you pick up more marks in the exam. And that IS worth getting excited about...

Setting Up Experiments

Setting up the equipment for an experiment correctly is important. These pages cover some of the experimental set-ups that you could be asked about in your exams. So you'd better get on and learn them.

You May Have to Identify the Products of Electrolysis

There's more about electrolysis on p.135-136.

1) When you electrolyse an aqueous solution, the products of electrolysis will depend on how reactive the ions in the solution are compared to the H^+ and OH^- ions that come from water.
2) At the cathode you'll either get a pure metal coating the electrode or bubbles of hydrogen gas.
3) At the anode, you'll get bubbles of oxygen gas unless a halide ion is present, when you'll get the halogen.
4) You may have to predict and identify what's been made in an electrolysis experiment. To do this, you need to be able to set up the equipment correctly so that you can collect any gas that's produced. The easiest way to collect the gas is in a test tube.
5) Here's how to set up the equipment...

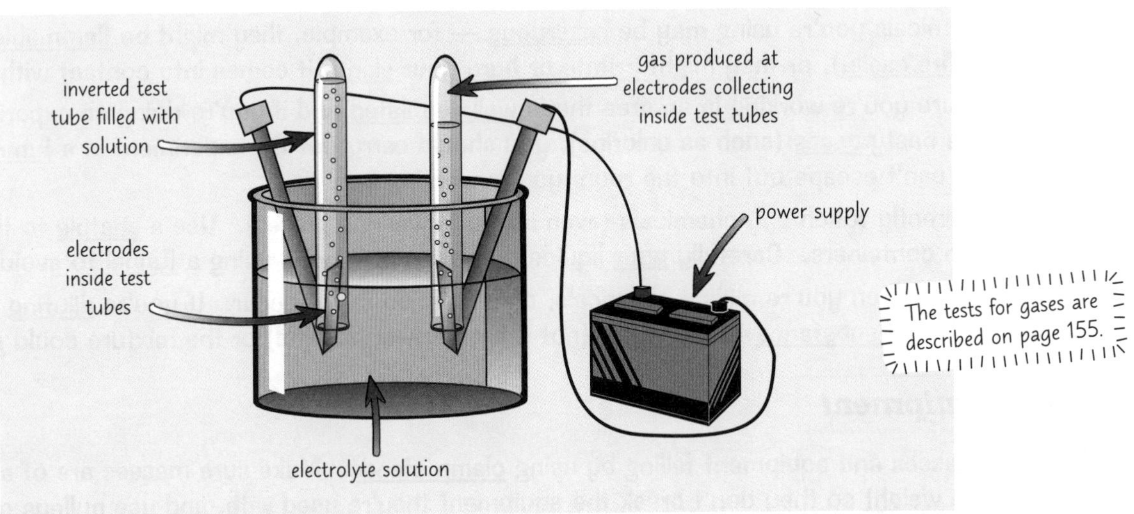

The tests for gases are described on page 155.

Potometers Should Be Set Up Underwater

A potometer is a special piece of apparatus used to measure the water uptake by a plant. Here's how to set one up:

If there are air bubbles in the apparatus or the plant's xylem it will affect your results.

1) Cut a shoot underwater to prevent air from entering the xylem. Cut it at a slant to increase the surface area available for water uptake.
2) Assemble the potometer in water and insert the shoot under water, so no air can enter.
3) Remove the apparatus from the water but keep the end of the capillary tube submerged in a beaker of water.
4) Check that the apparatus is watertight and airtight.
5) Dry the leaves, allow time for the shoot to acclimatise and then shut the tap.
6) Remove the end of the capillary tube from the beaker of water until one air bubble has formed, then put the end of the tube back into the water.
7) A potometer can be used to estimate the transpiration rate of a plant. There's more about this on page 41.

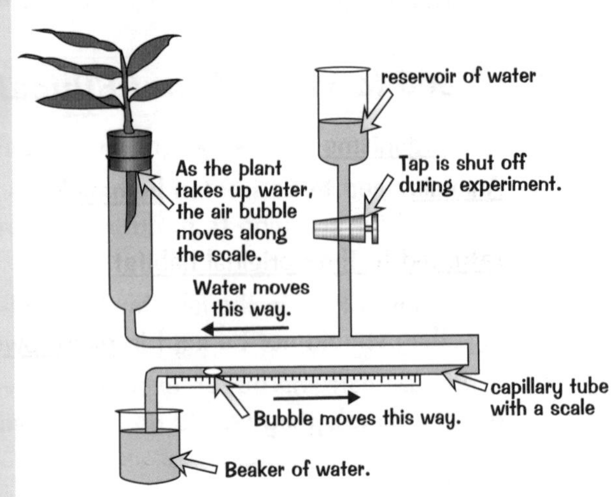

Setting Up Experiments

To Collect Gases, the System Needs to be Sealed

1) There are times when you might want to collect the gas produced by a reaction. For example, to investigate the rate of reaction.
2) The most accurate way to measure the volume of a gas that's been produced is to collect it in a gas syringe (see page 232).

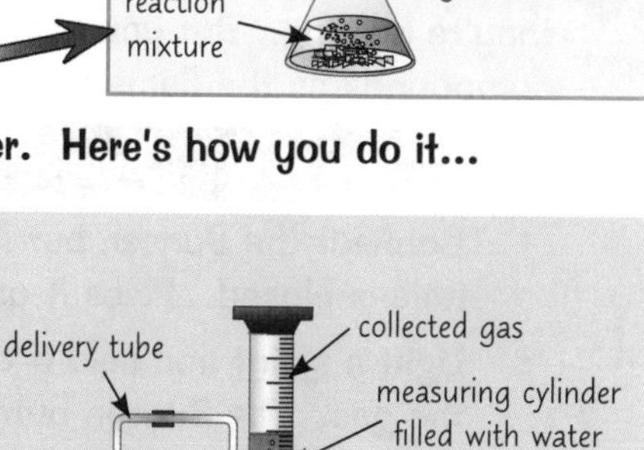

3) You could also collect it by displacing water from a measuring cylinder. Here's how you do it...

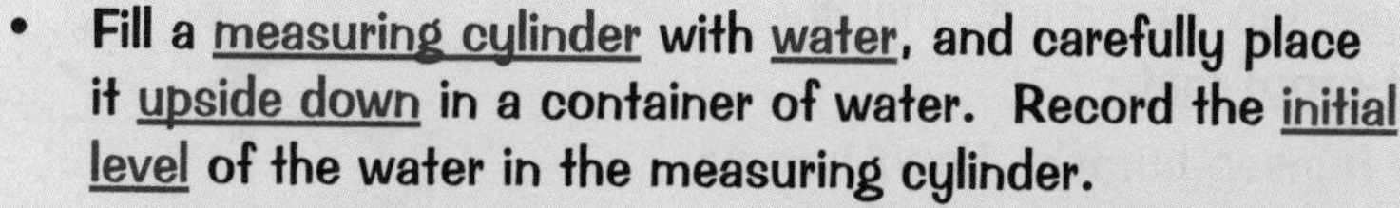

- Fill a measuring cylinder with water, and carefully place it upside down in a container of water. Record the initial level of the water in the measuring cylinder.
- Position a delivery tube coming from the reaction vessel so that it's inside the measuring cylinder, pointing upwards. Any gas that's produced will pass through the delivery tube and into the measuring cylinder. As the gas enters the measuring cylinder, the water is pushed out.
- Record the level of water in the measuring cylinder and use this value, along with your initial value, to calculate the volume of gas produced.

If the delivery tube is underneath the measuring cylinder rather than inside it then some of the gas might escape out into the air.

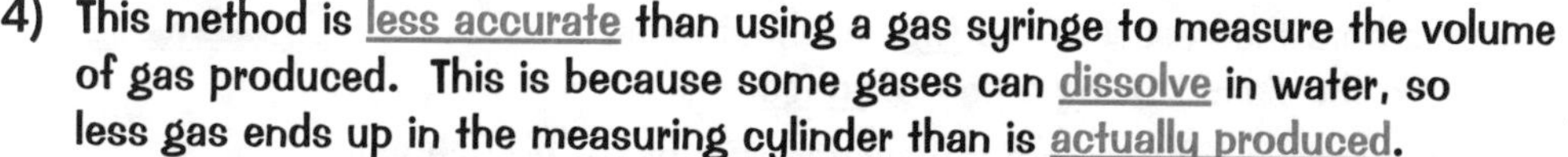

4) This method is less accurate than using a gas syringe to measure the volume of gas produced. This is because some gases can dissolve in water, so less gas ends up in the measuring cylinder than is actually produced.
5) If you just want to collect a sample to test (and don't need to measure a volume), you can collect it over water, as above, using a test tube. Once the test tube is full of gas, you can stopper it and store the gas for later.

Remember — when you're measuring a gas, your equipment has to be sealed or some gas could escape and your results wouldn't be accurate.

Make Sure You Can Draw Diagrams of Your Equipment

1) When you're writing out a method for your experiment, it's always a good idea to draw a labelled diagram showing how your apparatus will be set up.
2) The easiest way to do this is to use a scientific drawing, where each piece of apparatus is drawn as if you're looking at its cross-section.
3) For example:

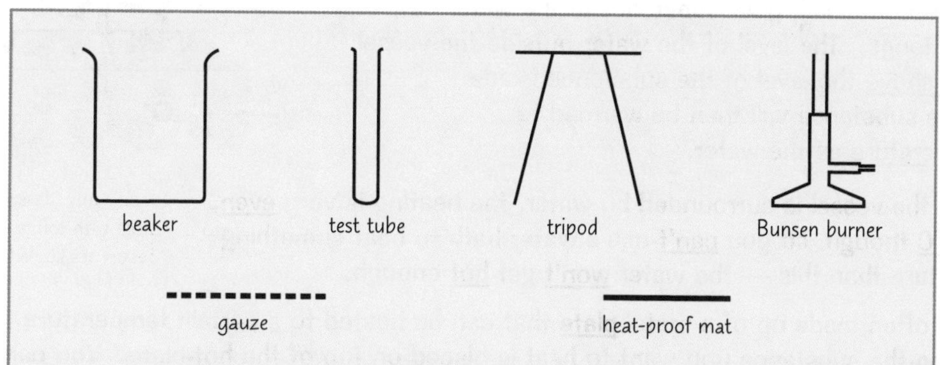

The pieces of glassware are drawn without tops so they aren't sealed. If you want to draw a closed system, remember to draw a bung in the top.

Science exams — they're a set-up...

It may seem like science exams are a devious ploy by the creatures of darkness to set you up for misery and heartache... and maybe they are. But whether they are or not, you need to know each of the experimental set-ups on these pages. It'll be worth it in the end, when you ace the exam and smite the evil ones with your top grades...

Heating Substances

Heating a reaction isn't as simple as wrapping it up in a lumpy wool jumper and a stripy scarf. There's more than one way to do it, and you need to be able to decide on the best, and the safest, method.

Bunsen Burners Have a Naked Flame

Bunsen burners are good for heating things quickly. You can easily adjust how strongly they're heating. But you need to be careful not to use them if you're heating flammable compounds as the flame means the substance would be at risk of catching fire.

Here's how to use a Bunsen burner...

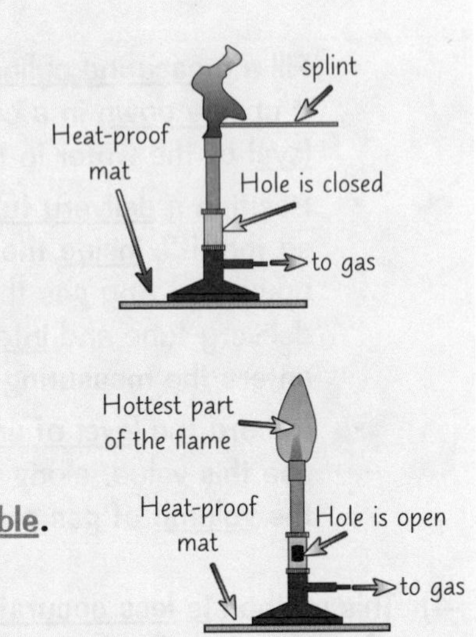

- Connect the Bunsen burner to a gas tap, and check that the hole is closed. Place it on a heat-proof mat.
- Light a splint and hold it over the Bunsen burner. Now, turn on the gas. The Bunsen burner should light with a yellow flame.
- The more open the hole is, the more strongly the Bunsen burner will heat your substance. Open the hole to the amount you want. As you open the hole more, the flame should turn more blue.
- The hottest part of the flame is just above the blue cone, so you should heat things here.
- If your Bunsen burner is alight but not heating anything, make sure you close the hole so that the flame becomes yellow and clearly visible.
- If you're heating something so that the container (e.g. a test tube) is in the flame, you should hold the vessel at the top, furthest away from the substance (and so the flame) using a pair of tongs.
- If you're heating something over the flame (e.g. an evaporating dish), you should put a tripod and gauze over the Bunsen burner before you light it, and place the vessel on this.

The Temperature of Water Baths & Electric Heaters Can Be Set

1) A water bath is a container filled with water that can be heated to a specific temperature. A simple water bath can be made by heating a beaker of water over a Bunsen burner and monitoring the temperature with a thermometer. However, it is difficult to keep the temperature of the water constant.
2) An electric water bath will monitor and adjust the temperature for you. Here's how you use one:
   - Set the temperature on the water bath, and allow the water to heat up.
   - Place the vessel containing your substance in the water bath using a pair of tongs. The level of the water outside the vessel should be just above the level of the substance inside the vessel. The substance will then be warmed to the same temperature as the water.

   rubber duck (optional)
   reaction vessel
   temperature control

   As the substance in the vessel is surrounded by water, the heating is very even. Water boils at 100 °C though, so you can't use a water bath to heat something to a higher temperature than this — the water won't get hot enough.

   Handle any glassware you've heated with tongs until you're sure it's cooled down.

3) Electric heaters are often made up of a metal plate that can be heated to a certain temperature. The vessel containing the substance you want to heat is placed on top of the hot plate. You can heat substances to higher temperatures than you can in a water bath but, as the vessel is only heated from below, you'll usually have to stir the substance inside to make sure it's heated evenly.

A bath and an electric heater — how I spend my January nights...

You know, I used to have a science teacher who'd play power ballads when the Bunsen burners were alight and sway at the front of the class like he was at a gig. You think I made that up, but it's true.

Working with Electronics

Electrical devices are used in a bunch of experiments, so make sure you know how to use them.

You Have to Interpret Circuit Diagrams

Before you get cracking on an experiment involving any kind of electrical devices, you have to plan and build your circuit using a circuit diagram. Make sure you know all of the circuit symbols on page 179 so you're not stumped before you've even started.

There Are a Couple of Ways to Measure Potential Difference and Current

Voltmeters Measure Potential Difference

1) If you're using an analogue voltmeter, choose the voltmeter with the most appropriate unit (e.g. V or mV). If you're using a digital voltmeter, you'll most likely be able to switch between them.
2) Connect the voltmeter in parallel (p.184) across the component you want to test. The wires that come with a voltmeter are usually red (positive) and black (negative). These go into the red and black coloured ports on the voltmeter. Funnily enough.
3) Then simply read the potential difference from the scale (or from the screen if it's digital).

Ammeters Measure Current

1) Just like with voltmeters, choose the ammeter with the most appropriate unit.
2) Connect the ammeter in series (p.183) with the component you want to test, making sure they're both on the same branch. Again, they usually have red and black ports to show you where to connect your wires.
3) Read off the current shown on the scale or by the screen.

Turn your circuit off between readings to prevent wires overheating and affecting your results (p.181).

Multimeters Measure Both

1) Instead of having a separate ammeter and voltmeter, many circuits use multimeters. These are devices that measure a range of properties — usually potential difference, current and resistance.
2) If you want to find potential difference, make sure the red wire is plugged into the port that has a 'V' (for volts).
3) To find the current, use the port labelled 'A' or 'mA' (for amps).
4) The dial on the multimeter should then be turned to the relevant section, e.g. to 'A' to measure current in amps. The screen will display the value you're measuring.

Light Gates Measure Speed and Acceleration

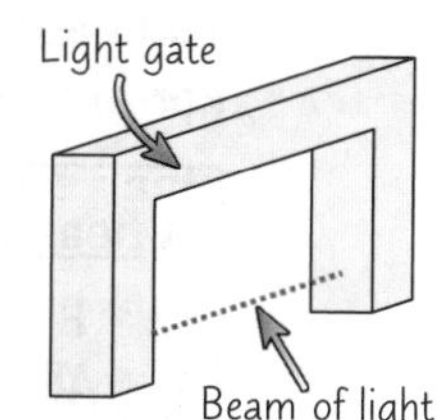

1) A light gate sends a beam of light from one side of the gate to a detector on the other side. When something passes through the gate, the beam of light is interrupted. The light gate then measures how long the beam was undetected.
2) To find the speed of an object, connect the light gate to a computer. Measure the length of the object and input this using the software. It will then automatically calculate the speed of the object as it passes through the beam.
3) To measure acceleration, use an object that interrupts the signal twice in a short period of time, e.g. a piece of card with a gap cut into the middle.
4) The light gate measures the speed for each section of the object and uses this to calculate its acceleration. This can then be read from the computer screen.

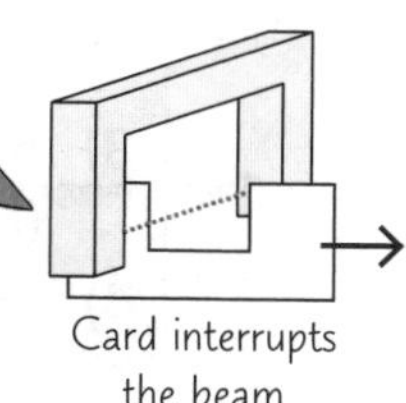

Have a look at page 213 for an example of a light gate being used.

A light gate is better than a heavy one...

After finishing this page, you should be able to take on any electrical experiment that they throw at you... ouch.

Sampling

I love samples... especially when I'm a bit peckish in the supermarket and they're handing out free cheese. Unfortunately, this page isn't about those samples. It's a lot more useful than that...

Sampling Should be Random

1) When you're investigating a population, it's generally not possible to study every single organism in the population. This means that you need to take samples of the population you're interested in.
2) The sample data will be used to draw conclusions about the whole population, so it's important that it accurately represents the whole population.
3) To make sure a sample represents the population, it should be random.

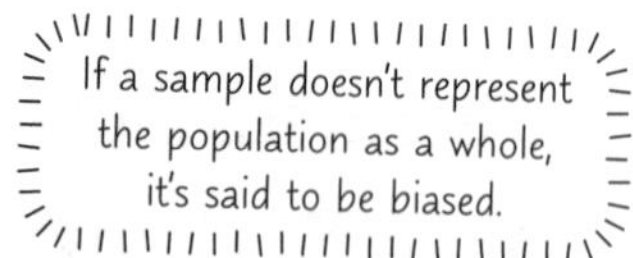

Organisms Should Be Sampled At Random Sites in an Area

1) If you're interested in the distribution of an organism in an area, or its population size, you can take population samples in the area you're interested in using quadrats or transects (see pages 87-88).
2) If you only take samples from one part of the area, your results will be biased — they may not give an accurate representation of the whole area.
3) To make sure that your sampling isn't biased, you need to use a method of choosing sampling sites in which every site has an equal chance of being chosen. For example:

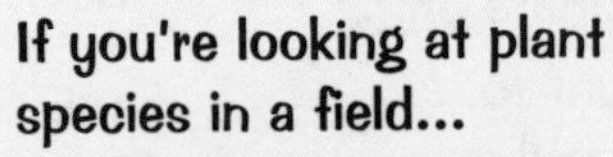

If you're looking at plant species in a field...

1) Divide the field into a grid.
2) Label the grid along the bottom and up the side with numbers.
3) Use a random number generator (on a computer or calculator) to select coordinates, e.g. (2,6).
4) Take your samples at these coordinates.

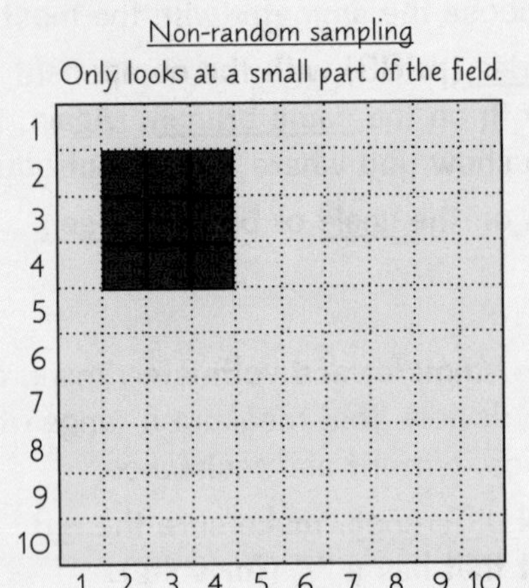

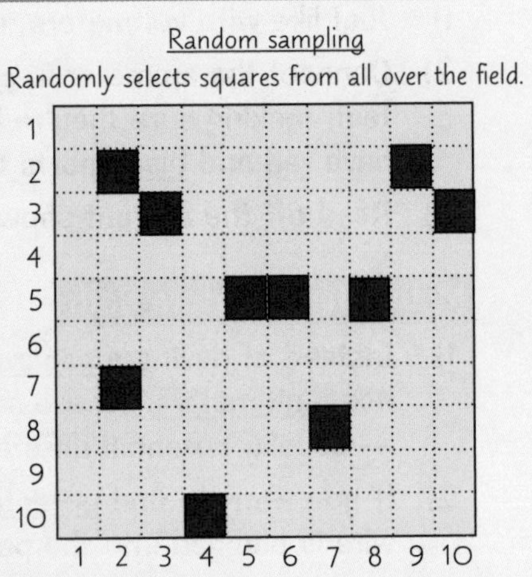

Health Data Should be Taken from Randomly Selected People

1) As mentioned above, it's not practical (or even possible) to study an entire human population.
2) You need to use random sampling to choose members of the population you're interested in. For example:

A health professional is investigating how many people diagnosed with Type 2 diabetes in a particular country also have heart disease:

1) All the people who have been diagnosed with Type 2 diabetes in the country of interest are identified by hospital records. In total, there are 270 196 people.
2) These people are assigned a number between 1 and 270 196.
3) A random number generator is used to choose the sample group (e.g. it selects the individuals #72 063, #11 822, #193 123, etc.)
4) The proportion of people in the sample that have heart disease can be used to estimate the total number of people with Type 2 diabetes that also have heart disease.

'Eeny, meeny, miny, moe' just doesn't cut it any more...

Sampling is an important part of an investigation. It needs to be done randomly, or the data won't be worth much.

Comparing Results

Being able to compare your results is really important. Here are some ways you might do it. I spoil you.

Percentage Change Allows you to Compare Results

1) When investigating the change in a variable, you may want to compare results that didn't have the same initial value. For example, you may want to compare the change in mass of potato cylinders left in different concentrations of sugar solution that had different initial masses (see page 18).
2) One way to do this is to calculate the percentage change. You work it out like this:

$$\text{percentage (\%) change} = \frac{\text{final value} - \text{original value}}{\text{original value}} \times 100$$

EXAMPLE: A student is investigating the effect of the concentration of sugar solution on potato cells. She records the mass of potato cylinders before and after placing them in sugar solutions of different concentrations. The table on the right shows some of her results. Which potato cylinder had the largest percentage change?

Potato cylinder	Concentration (mol/dm^3)	Mass at start (g)	Mass at end (g)
1	0.0	7.5	8.7
2	1.0	8.0	6.8

1) Stick each set of results into the equation:

$$\% \text{ change} = \frac{\text{final value} - \text{original value}}{\text{original value}} \times 100$$

1. $\frac{8.7 - 7.5}{7.5} \times 100 = 16\%$ — The mass at the start is the original value. The mass at the end is the final value.

2. $\frac{6.8 - 8.0}{8.0} \times 100 = -15\%$ — Here, the mass has decreased so the percentage change is negative.

2) Compare the results. 16% is greater than 15%, so the potato cylinder in the 0.0 mol/dm^3 sugar solution had the largest percentage change.

Percentiles Tell you Where in Your Data Set a Data Point Lies

1) Percentiles are useful if you want to compare the value of one data point to the rest of your data.
2) To find a percentile, you rank your data from smallest to largest, then divide it into one hundred equal chunks. Each chunk is one percentile.
3) This means that each percentile represents one percent of the data, and so the value of a percentile tells you what percentage of the data has a value lower than the data points in that percentile.

E.g. Mike the Meerkat is in the 90th percentile for height in his gang. This means that 90% of the gang are shorter than Mike.

4) Percentiles can be used to give a more realistic idea of the spread of data than the range (see p.6) — by finding the range between the 10th and 90th percentiles in a data set (the middle 80% of the data), you can look at the spread of the data while ignoring any outlying results.

An outlier is a value that's much larger or smaller than the rest of the values in a data set.

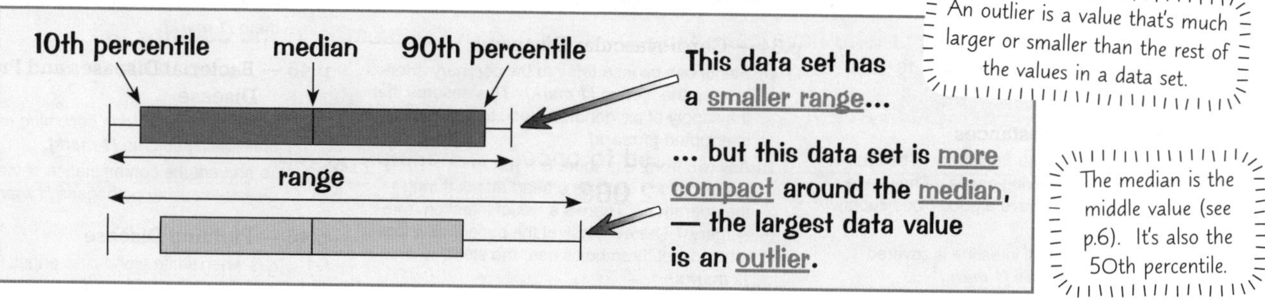

The median is the middle value (see p.6). It's also the 50th percentile.

Percentage change in how much I love maths after this page — 0%

Aaaand that's the end of Practical Skills, folks. Go forth, and science like you've never scienced before...

Answers

p.11 — Cells

Q1 Any two from: e.g. prokaryotic cells are smaller than eukaryotic cells ***[1 mark]***. / Prokaryotic cells don't have mitochondria but eukaryotic cells do ***[1 mark]***. / Prokaryotic cells don't have a true nucleus but eukaryotic cells do ***[1 mark]***. / Prokaryotic cells have circular DNA but eukaryotic cells don't ***[1 mark]***.

p.12 — Microscopy

Q1 real size = image size ÷ magnification
= 7.5 mm ÷ 100
= 0.075 mm ***[1 mark]***
0.075 × 1000 = 75 μm ***[1 mark]***

p.13 — More on Microscopy

Q1 To highlight objects within the sample by adding colour to them ***[1 mark]***.

p.14 — Cell Differentiation and Specialisation

Q1 E.g. they have few subcellular structures. / They're joined end to end. / They're long. ***[1 mark]***

Q2 The cell has a hair-like shape, which gives it a large surface area ***[1 mark]*** to absorb water and minerals from the soil ***[1 mark]***.

p.15 — Chromosomes and Mitosis

Q1 The cell has to increase the amount of its subcellular structures ***[1 mark]*** and duplicate its DNA ***[1 mark]***.

p.16 — Stem Cells

Q1 Copies of the plant can be made by taking stem cells from the meristem of the plant ***[1 mark]*** and growing them into new, genetically identical plants (clones) ***[1 mark]***.

p.17 — Diffusion

Q1 a) The ink will diffuse / spread out through the water ***[1 mark]***. This is because the ink particles will move from where is a higher concentration of them (the drop of ink) to where there is a lower concentration of them (the surrounding water) ***[1 mark]***.

b) The ink particles will diffuse / spread out faster ***[1 mark]***.

p.18 — Osmosis

Q1 Water will move out of the piece of potato by osmosis ***[1 mark]***, so its mass will decrease ***[1 mark]***.

p.19 — Active Transport

Q1 Active transport allows nutrients such as glucose to move from a lower concentration in the gut to a higher concentration in the blood (against the concentration gradient) ***[1 mark]***.

p.20 — Exchange Surfaces

Q1 Surface area:
(2 × 2) × 2 = 8
(2 × 1) × 4 = 8
8 + 8 = 16 μm² ***[1 mark]***
Volume:
2 × 2 × 1 = 4 μm³ ***[1 mark]***
So the surface area to volume ratio is 16 : 4, or 4 : 1 ***[1 mark]***.

p.21 — Exchanging Substances

Q1 E.g. they have a large surface area. / They have a moist lining for dissolving gases. / They have very thin walls. / They have a good blood supply. ***[1 mark]***

Q2 The surface of the small intestine is covered with small projections/villi ***[1 mark]***.

p.22 — More on Exchanging Substances

Q1 Any two from: e.g. it is made up of gill filaments which give a large surface area. / each gill filament is covered in lamellae, which further increases the surface area. / The lamellae have a thin surface layer of cells. / The lamellae have lots of capillaries. / A large concentration gradient is maintained between the water and the blood. ***[2 marks]***

p.24 — Cell Organisation

Q1 That it is made up of different tissues ***[1 mark]*** that work together to perform a particular function ***[1 mark]***.

p.25 — Enzymes

Q1 If the pH is too high or too low, it can interfere with the bonds holding the enzyme together. This changes the shape of the active site ***[1 mark]*** and denatures the enzyme ***[1 mark]***.

p.26 — Investigating Enzymatic Reactions

Q1 33 ÷ 60 = 0.55 cm³ s⁻¹ ***[1 mark]***

p.27 — Enzymes and Digestion

Q1 Bile is alkaline, so it neutralises the stomach acid and makes conditions in the small intestine alkaline ***[1 mark]***. The enzymes of the small intestine work best in these alkaline conditions ***[1 mark]***. It also emulsifies fats/breaks down fats into tiny droplets ***[1 mark]***. This gives a bigger surface area of fat for the enzyme lipase to work on, making digestion faster ***[1 mark]***.

p.28 — More on Enzymes and Digestion

Q1 Stomach ***[1 mark]***, pancreas ***[1 mark]*** and small intestine ***[1 mark]***.

p.29 — Food Tests

Q1 iodine solution ***[1 mark]***

p.30 — The Lungs

Q1 495 ÷ 12
= 41 breaths per minute. ***[1 mark]***

p.31 — Circulatory System — The Heart

Q1 The right ventricle ***[1 mark]***.

Q2 They supply oxygenated blood to the heart itself ***[1 mark]***.

p.32 — Circulatory System — Blood Vessels

Q1 They have a big lumen to help the blood flow despite the low pressure ***[1 mark]*** and they have valves to keep the blood flowing in the right direction ***[1 mark]***.

p.33 — Circulatory System — Blood

Q1 They help the blood to clot at a wound ***[1 mark]***.

Q2 They have a large surface area for absorbing oxygen ***[1 mark]***. They don't have a nucleus, which allows more room for carrying oxygen ***[1 mark]***. They contain haemoglobin, which can combine with oxygen in the lungs and release it in body tissues ***[1 mark]***.

p.34 — Cardiovascular Disease

Q1 a) Stents can be inserted into the coronary arteries to keep them open ***[1 mark]***. This ensures that the supply of oxygenated blood to the heart isn't interrupted ***[1 mark]***.

b) Any two from: e.g. there is a risk of complications such as a heart attack during the operation. / There's a risk of infection from surgery. / There's a risk of the patient developing a blood clot/thrombosis near the stent ***[2 marks]***.

p.35 — More on Cardiovascular Disease

Q1 a) The heart valves might not be able to open fully, meaning that less blood can flow through them ***[1 mark]***. They can also become leaky, meaning that blood is able to flow in both directions ***[1 mark]***.

b) By replacing the valve with a biological or mechanical valve ***[1 mark]***.

Q2 Any one from: e.g. surgery to fit an artificial heart can lead to bleeding and infection. / Parts of the artificial heart could wear out. / The electric motor could fail. / Blood doesn't flow through the heart as smoothly, which could cause clots and lead to strokes. / The patient has to take blood thinning drugs to prevent blood clots, which could cause problems with bleeding if they're hurt in an accident ***[1 mark]***.

p.36 — Health and Disease

Q1 The state of physical and mental wellbeing ***[1 mark]***.

Q2 It can be spread from person to person ***[1 mark]***.

p.37 — Risk Factors for Non-Communicable Diseases

Q1 The presence of certain substances in the body. / The presence of certain substances in the environment ***[1 mark]***.

p.38 — Cancer

Q1 Body cells dividing out of control ***[1 mark]***.

Q2 Any three from: e.g. smoking / obesity / UV exposure / viral infection ***[1 mark for each correct answer, up to 3 marks]***.

p.39 — Plant Cell Organisation

Q1 Meristem tissue is found at the growing tips of roots and shoots ***[1 mark]*** and is able to differentiate into lots of different types of plant cell ***[1 mark]***.

p.40 — Transpiration and Translocation

Q1 Xylem is made up of dead cells joined together end to end ***[1 mark]*** with no end walls between them and a hole down the middle ***[1 mark]***. It is strengthened by lignin ***[1 mark]***.

p.41 — Transpiration and Stomata

Q1 As it gets darker, the stomata begin to close ***[1 mark]***. This means that very little water can escape ***[1 mark]*** and the rate of transpiration decreases ***[1 mark]***.

p.43 — Communicable Disease

Q1 Viruses replicate themselves by using the machinery of the cell they live in to produce many copies of themselves ***[1 mark]***. The cell will usually then burst, releasing all the new viruses ***[1 mark]***.

p.44 — Viral, Fungal and Protist Diseases

Q1 a red skin rash ***[1 mark]***

Q2 Using a fungicide ***[1 mark]*** and by stripping the plants of the affected leaves and destroying them ***[1 mark]***.

p.45 — Bacterial Diseases and Preventing Disease

Q1 Strains of the bacteria becoming resistant to antibiotics/penicillin ***[1 mark]***.

Q2 To prevent the contamination of food by disease-causing pathogens ***[1 mark]***.

p.46 — Fighting Disease

Q1 It is when white blood cells engulf foreign cells and digest them ***[1 mark]***.

Q2 They secrete mucus to trap pathogens ***[1 mark]***. They have cilia ***[1 mark]***, which waft the mucus up to the back of the throat where it can be swallowed ***[1 mark]***.

p.47 — Fighting Disease — Vaccination

Q1 antibodies ***[1 mark]***

p.48 — Fighting Disease — Drugs

Q1 bacteria ***[1 mark]***

p.49 — Developing Drugs

Q1 Whether the drug works and produces the effect you're looking for ***[1 mark]***.

Q2 To make sure that the drug doesn't have any harmful side effects when the body is working normally ***[1 mark]***.

Q3 To help to prevent false claims about the results ***[1 mark]***.

p.50 — Photosynthesis and Limiting Factors

Q1 Glucose ***[1 mark]*** and oxygen ***[1 mark]***.

Q2 Light intensity ***[1 mark]***, volume of CO_2 ***[1 mark]*** and amount of chlorophyll ***[1 mark]***.

p.53 — The Rate of Photosynthesis

Q1 E.g. light intensity ***[1 mark]***, CO_2 ***[1 mark]***.

Q2 light intensity $\propto \frac{1}{\text{distance}^2}$ ***[1 mark]***

p.54 — Respiration and Metabolism

Q1 Any two from: e.g. to build up larger molecules from smaller ones. / To contract muscles. / To keep body temperature steady. ***[1 mark for each]***

Q2 The sum of all of the reactions that happen in a cell or the body ***[1 mark]***.

p.55 — Aerobic and Anaerobic Respiration

Q1 Glucose ***[1 mark]*** and oxygen ***[1 mark]***.

Q2 fermentation ***[1 mark]***

p.56 — Exercise

Q1 Long periods of exercise ***[1 mark]***.

Q2 An oxygen debt is the amount of extra oxygen your body needs to react with the build up of lactic acid and remove it from the cells ***[1 mark]***.

p.58 — Homeostasis

Q1 To maintain the right conditions for cells to function properly and for enzyme action ***[1 mark]***.

Q2 receptor (cell) ***[1 mark]***

p.59 — The Nervous System

Q1 Muscles ***[1 mark]***, glands ***[1 mark]***.

p.60 — Synapses and Reflexes

Q1 A rapid, automatic response to a stimulus that doesn't involve the conscious part of the brain ***[1 mark]***.

Q2 a) muscle ***[1 mark]***

b) The stimulus is detected by receptors ***[1 mark]***, which send impulses along a sensory neurone to the CNS ***[1 mark]***. The impulse is transferred to a relay neurone ***[1 mark]***. It is then transferred to a motor neurone and travels along it to the effector ***[1 mark]***.

p.61 — Investigating Reaction Time

Q1 242 + 256 + 253 + 249 + 235
= 1235 ***[1 mark]***
1235 ÷ 5 = 247 ms ***[1 mark]***

p.62 — The Endocrine System

Q1 Because it produces many hormones that act on other glands to regulate body conditions ***[1 mark]***.

p.63 — Controlling Blood Glucose

Q1 The pancreas secretes insulin ***[1 mark]***. Insulin causes glucose to move from the blood into liver and muscle cells ***[1 mark]***. In the cells, glucose is turned into glycogen for storage ***[1 mark]***.

p.64 — Puberty and the Menstrual Cycle

Q1 FSH/follicle-stimulating hormone ***[1 mark]***

Q2 testes ***[1 mark]***

p.65 — Controlling Fertility

Q1 The pill/oral contraceptives ***[1 mark]***.
The contraceptive patch ***[1 mark]***.

p.66 — More on Controlling Fertility

Q1 They stimulate several eggs to mature ***[1 mark]***.

Q2 E.g. it doesn't always work. / It can be expensive. / Too many eggs can be stimulated, resulting in unexpected multiple pregnancies. ***[1 mark]***

p.67 — Adrenaline and Thyroxine

Q1 thyroid gland ***[1 mark]***

Q2 When the high level of thyroxine is detected, the secretion of TSH from the pituitary gland is inhibited ***[1 mark]***. This reduces the amount of thyroxine released from the thyroid gland ***[1 mark]***, so the level in the blood falls back towards normal ***[1 mark]***.

p.68 — DNA

Q1 A small section of DNA found on a chromosome ***[1 mark]*** that codes for a particular sequence of amino acids ***[1 mark]*** that are put together to make a specific protein ***[1 mark]***.

Q2 The entire set of genetic material in an organism ***[1 mark]***.

p.69 — Reproduction

Q1 mitosis ***[1 mark]***

Q2 Because there are two parents, the offspring contain a mixture of their parents' genes ***[1 mark]***. This mixture of genetic information produces variation ***[1 mark]***.

p.70 — Meiosis

Q1 two ***[1 mark]***

p.71 — X and Y Chromosomes

Q1 XX ***[1 mark]***

p.72 — Genetic Diagrams

Q1 Your genotype is the combination of alleles you have ***[1 mark]***. Your phenotype is the characteristics you have ***[1 mark]***.

p.73 — More Genetic Diagrams

Q1

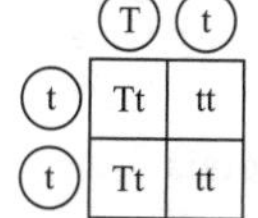

	T	t
t	Tt	tt
t	Tt	tt

long tailed : short tailed
1 : 1

[1 mark for correct gametes, 1 mark for correct offspring genotypes and 1 mark for correct ratio.]

p.74 — Inherited Disorders

Q1 Because the allele which causes cystic fibrosis is recessive ***[1 mark]***, so you have to have two recessive alleles to have the disorder ***[1 mark]***. Heterozygous people have one dominant and one recessive allele ***[1 mark]***.

p.75 — Variation

Q1 Differences between members of the same species ***[1 mark]*** that have been caused by the environment/conditions something lives in ***[1 mark]***.

p.76 — Evolution

Q1 Any three from: The environment changes too quickly. / A new predator kills all the individuals. / A new disease kills all the individuals. / They can't compete with another species for food. / A catastrophic event (e.g. a volcanic eruption or collision with an astroid) kills all the individuals. ***[1 mark for each correct answer, up to 3 marks]***

p.77 — Selective Breeding

Q1 E.g. to produce plants with large or unusual flowers ***[1 mark]***.

Q2 Selective breeding reduces the gene pool ***[1 mark]***. This causes an increased chance of organisms inheriting harmful genetic defects ***[1 mark]***. There is also an increased chance that a population could be wiped out by a new disease ***[1 mark]***.

p.78 — Genetic Engineering

Q1 Benefit — E.g. the characteristics chosen for GM crops can mean that they have an increased yield. / GM crops can be engineered to contain certain nutrients, which some people in developing nations may lack from their diets ***[1 mark]***.
Concern — E.g. some people are not convinced that GM crops are safe and are concerned that we might not fully understand the effects of eating them on human health. / Some people say that growing GM crops will affect the number of wild flowers and insects that live in and around the crops. / There is concern that the transplanted genes could get out into the natural environment, which could lead to the creation of 'superweeds' ***[1 mark]***.

p.79 — Fossils

Q1 The microbes that cause decay can't survive in low oxygen conditions ***[1 mark]***, so the dead organisms are preserved rather than decayed ***[1 mark]***.

p.80 — Antibiotic-Resistant Bacteria

Q1 Any one from: e.g. when the illness is only minor. / When the infection is being caused by a virus ***[1 mark]***.

Q2 Taking the complete course makes sure that all the bacteria are destroyed ***[1 mark]***. This means that there are none left to mutate and develop into antibiotic-resistant strains ***[1 mark]***.

p.81 — Classification

Q1 *Castor* ***[1 mark]***

p.83 — Competition

Q1 The interaction of a community of organisms with the abiotic parts of their environment ***[1 mark]***.

Q2 Any three from: light / space / water / mineral ions ***[1 mark for each correct answer, up to 3 marks]***.

Q3 A community where all the species and environmental factors are in balance so that the population sizes are roughly constant ***[1 mark]***.

p.84 — Abiotic and Biotic Factors

Q1 Any four from: moisture level / light intensity / temperature / carbon dioxide level / wind intensity / wind direction / soil pH / mineral content of soil ***[1 mark for each correct answer, up to 4 marks]***.

Q2 Any two from: availability of food / competition for resources / new pathogens ***[1 mark for each correct answer, up to 2 marks]***.

p.85 — Adaptations

Q1 a) A behavioural adaptation ***[1 mark]***.

b) E.g. it has flippers ***[1 mark]*** so it can swim for food ***[1 mark]***. / A thick layer of fat ***[1 mark]*** so it retains heat ***[1 mark]***. / A low surface area to volume ratio ***[1 mark]*** so it retains heat ***[1 mark]***.

p.86 — Food Chains

Q1 a) grass ***[1 mark]***

b) three ***[1 mark]***

c) grasshopper ***[1 mark]***

d) The population of grasshoppers could increase ***[1 mark]*** as there's nothing to eat them ***[1 mark]***. The population of snakes could decrease ***[1 mark]*** as there's nothing for them to eat ***[1 mark]***.

p.87 — Using Quadrats

Q1 0.75 × 4 = 3 buttercups per m^2 ***[1 mark]***.
3 × 1200 = 3600 buttercups in total ***[1 mark]***.

p.88 — Using Transects

Q1 A line used to help find out how organisms are distributed across an area ***[1 mark]***.

Q2 They could mark out a line across the field, from one corner to the other ***[1 mark]***. Then they could count all of the dandelions that touch the line ***[1 mark]***.

Q3 You could estimate the percentage of the quadrat covered by the organisms ***[1 mark]***.

p.89 — The Water Cycle

Q1 a) By evaporation / transpiration ***[1 mark]***.

b) By providing them with fresh water ***[1 mark]***.

p.90 — The Carbon Cycle

Q1 Microorganisms/detritus feeders break them down/digest them ***[1 mark]***.

Q2 By green plants and algae in photosynthesis ***[1 mark]***.

p.91 — Biodiversity and Waste Management

Q1 The variety of different species of organisms on Earth, or within an ecosystem ***[1 mark]***.

p.92 — Global Warming

Q1 Global warming causes higher temperatures, which cause ice to melt and seawater to expand ***[1 mark]***. This causes the sea level to rise ***[1 mark]***, which could lead to flooding of low-lying land and therefore the loss of habitats ***[1 mark]***.

p.93 — Deforestation and Land Use

Q1 Trees 'lock up' some of the carbon that they absorb during photosynthesis, so if lots of trees are removed, less carbon will be locked up from the atmosphere ***[1 mark]***. If the land is cleared by burning the trees, this means that lots of carbon dioxide is released ***[1 mark]***. Microorganisms feeding on leftover dead wood release carbon dioxide as a waste product of respiration ***[1 mark]***.

p.94 — Maintaining Ecosystems and Biodiversity

Q1 Hedgerows and field margins can be reintroduced around single-crop fields ***[1 mark]***. These provide a habitat for organisms that would otherwise be unable to live in the area ***[1 mark]***.

Q2 Breeding programmes breed endangered animals in captivity to make sure the species survives if they die out in the wild ***[1 mark]***. Individuals can sometimes be released into the wild to boost or re-establish a population ***[1 mark]***.

p.96 — Atoms

Q1 protons = atomic number = 7 ***[1 mark]***
electrons = protons = 7 ***[1 mark]***
neutrons = mass number – atomic number = 14 – 7 = 7 ***[1 mark]***

p.97 — Elements

Q1 E.g. it's the number of protons in an atom that determines what type of atom it is, so if all the atoms have the same number of protons then the substance is an element ***[1 mark]***.

Q2 protons = 26 ***[1 mark]***
neutrons = 56 – 26 = 30 ***[1 mark]***

p.98 — Compounds

Q1 (2 × Na) + (1 × C) + (3 × O) = 6 ***[1 mark]***

Q2 calcium chloride ***[1 mark]***
Calcium and chlorine ***[1 mark]***.

p.99— Chemical Equations

Q1 $2Fe + 3Cl_2 \rightarrow 2FeCl_3$ ***[1 mark]***

Q2 a) water → hydrogen + oxygen ***[1 mark]***

b) $2H_2O \rightarrow 2H_2 + O_2$
[1 mark for correct products and reactants, 1 mark for being balanced correctly]

p.100 — Mixtures and Chromatography

Q1 The pen ink might dissolve in the solvent and rise up the filter paper ***[1 mark]***.

p.101 — More Separation Techniques

Q1 Pour the copper sulfate solution into an evaporating dish and slowly heat the solution until crystals start to form or some of the solvent has evaporated ***[1 mark]***. Leave the dish to cool until crystals form ***[1 mark]***. Filter ***[1 mark]*** and then dry the crystals using a desiccator/ drying oven ***[1 mark]***.

p.102 — Distillation

Q1 Ethanol ***[1 mark]***. Ethanol has the second lowest boiling point and will be collected once all the methanol has been distilled off and the temperature increased ***[1 mark]***.

p.103 — The History of the Atom

Q1 In the plum pudding model, the atom is a ball of positive charge with electrons spread throughout it ***[1 mark]***.

Q2 If the plum pudding model was correct you would expect most of the alpha particles to have passed through the foil or only to have been deflected slightly ***[1 mark]***. The actual deflections of the particles suggests that atoms contain a small nucleus where the positive charge is concentrated ***[1 mark]***.

p.104 — Electronic Structure

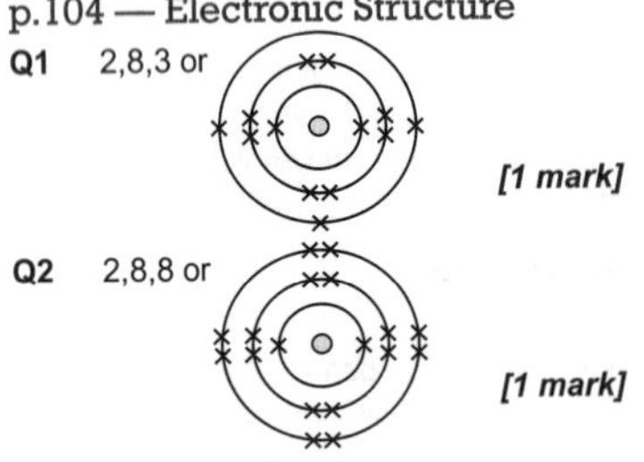

Q1 2,8,3 or ***[1 mark]***

Q2 2,8,8 or ***[1 mark]***

p.105 — Development of the Periodic Table

Q1 By relative atomic mass ***[1 mark]***.

Q2 E.g. he left gaps in order to keep elements with similar properties in the same group ***[1 mark]***. He switched the order of elements based on their properties, even if their atomic masses were no longer in order. ***[1 mark]***.

p.106 — The Modern Periodic Table

Q1 2 ***[1 mark]***

Q2 Both chlorine and bromine are in Group 7 and so have the same number of electrons in their outer shell ***[1 mark]***.

Q3 E.g. potassium forms 1+ ions as it's in the same group as sodium so will react in a similar way ***[1 mark]***.

p.107 — Metals and Non-Metals

Q1 non-metal ***[1 mark]***

Q2 Any three from: e.g. metals tend to be strong / good conductors of heat / good at conducting electricity / malleable / high melting/boiling temperatures ***[1 mark for each]***.

Q3 Positive ions ***[1 mark]***. Metals can be towards the left of the periodic table, where they don't have many electrons in their outer shell ***[1 mark]***, or they can be towards the bottom of the periodic table where the outer electrons are a long way from the nucleus so feel a weak attraction ***[1 mark]***. This means that not much energy is needed to remove the outer electrons and form a positive ion ***[1 mark]***.

p.108 — Group 1 Elements

Q1 As you go further down the group the outer electron is further away from the nucleus ***[1 mark]***. This means the attraction between the nucleus and the electron decreases so is more easily removed resulting in an increase in reactivity ***[1 mark]***.

Q2 $2K + 2H_2O \rightarrow 2KOH + H_2$ ***[1 mark for correct products and reactants, 1 mark for correctly balanced equation]***

p.109 — Group 7 Elements

Q1 Bromine would displace iodine in potassium iodide ***[1 mark]*** because bromine is more reactive than iodine ***[1 mark]***.

Q2 Halogens react by gaining electrons to make a full outer-shell ***[1 mark]***. As you go further down the group the outer electrons are further away so there is less attraction between them and the nucleus ***[1 mark]***. This means electrons are harder to gain so they become less reactive ***[1 mark]***.

p.110 — Group 0 Elements

Q1 Xenon has a higher boiling point than neon ***[1 mark]***.

Q2 Argon has a full outer-shell ***[1 mark]*** so is electronically stable and does not readily lose or gain electrons ***[1 mark]***.

p.112 — Formation of Ions

Q1 Noble gas electronic structures have a full shell of outer electrons ***[1 mark]***, which is a very stable structure ***[1 mark]***.

Q2 a) 1– ***[1 mark]***

b) 2+ ***[1 mark]***

c) 1+ ***[1 mark]***

p.113 — Ionic Bonding

Q1 Each sodium atom loses an electron to form an Na^+ ion ***[1 mark]***. Each chlorine atom gains an electron to form a Cl^- ion ***[1 mark]***. The oppositely charged ions are attracted to each other by electrostatic attraction ***[1 mark]***.

Q2

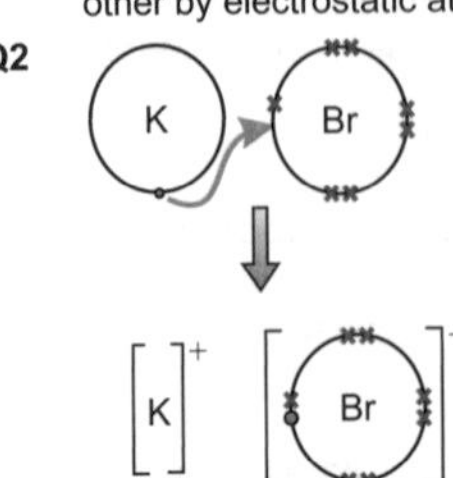

[1 mark for arrow showing electron transferred from potassium to bromine, 1 mark for correct outer shell electron configurations (with or without inner shells), 1 mark for correct charges]

p.114 — Ionic Compounds

Q1 a) It will have a high melting point ***[1 mark]*** because a lot of energy is needed to break the strong attraction between the ions/the strong ionic bonds ***[1 mark]***.

b) When melted, the ions are free to move, so they can carry an electric current ***[1 mark]***.

c) The compound contains caesium and chloride ions. Caesium is in Group 1 so forms 1+ ions ***[1 mark]***, and chlorine is in Group 7 so forms 1– ions ***[1 mark]***. The charges balance with one of each ion, so the empirical formula is CsCl ***[1 mark]***.

p.115 — Covalent Bonding

Q1

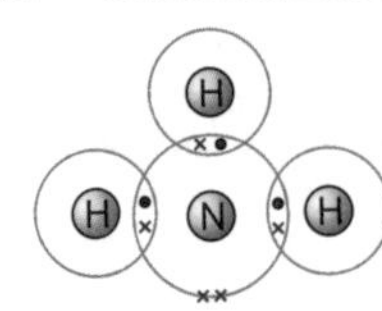

[1 mark for 3 shared pairs of electrons, 1 mark for correct number of electrons in outer shell of each atom (with our without inner shells on nitrogen)]

p.116 — Simple Molecular Substances

Q1 The intermolecular forces between molecules of O_2 are weak and don't need much energy to break ***[1 mark]***.

Q2 N_2 molecules aren't charged/There aren't any free electrons or ions ***[1 mark]***.

p.117 — Polymers and Giant Covalent Structures

Q1 $(C_2H_3Cl)_n$ ***[1 mark]***

Q2 To melt diamond you have to break the covalent bonds between atoms which are very strong ***[1 mark]*** but to melt poly(ethene) you only have to break the weaker intermolecular forces which needs less energy ***[1 mark]***. So diamond has a higher melting point ***[1 mark]***.

p.118 — Allotropes of Carbon

Q1 Any three from, e.g.: lubricants / catalysts / drug delivery / to strengthen materials ***[1 mark for each, up to 3 marks]***

p.119 — Metallic Bonding

Q1 Copper is a good electrical conductor ***[1 mark]*** as it contains delocalised electrons which are able to carry an electrical current through the whole structure ***[1 mark]***.

Q2 Pure copper would be too soft to use for a door hinge, but alloys are harder than pure metals, so are suitable ***[1 mark]***.

p.120 — States of Matter

Q1 The gaseous state ***[1 mark]***.

p.121 — Changing State

Q1 a) solid ***[1 mark]***
b) liquid ***[1 mark]***
c) liquid ***[1 mark]***
d) gas ***[1 mark]***

p.123 — Relative Formula Mass

Q1 a) A_r of H = 1 and A_r of O = 16
M_r of H_2O = (2 × 1) + 16 = 18 ***[1 mark]***
b) A_r of Li = 7, A_r of O = 16 and A_r of H = 1
So M_r of LiOH = 7 + 16 + 1 = 24 ***[1 mark]***
c) A_r of H = 1, A_r of S = 32 and A_r of O = 16
M_r of H_2SO_4 = (2 × 1) + 32 + (4 × 16) = 98 ***[1 mark]***

Q2 A_r of K = 39, A_r of O = 16 and A_r of H = 1
M_r of KOH = 39 + 16 + 1 = 56 ***[1 mark]***
$\frac{39}{56} \times 100 = 70\%$ ***[1 mark]***

p.124 — The Mole

Q1 M_r of H_2O = 16 + (2 × 1) = 18 ***[1 mark]***
number of moles = mass ÷ M_r
number of moles = 90 g ÷ 18 = 5 moles ***[1 mark]***

Q2 M_r of KBr = 39 + 80 = 119 ***[1 mark]***
mass = number of moles × M_r
mass = 0.20 × 119 = 24 g ***[1 mark]***

p.125 — Conservation of Mass

Q1 Total mass on the left hand side
= $M_r(H_2SO_4)$ + 2 × M_r(NaOH)
M_r of H_2SO_4 = (2 × 1) + 32 + (4 × 16) = 98
2 × M_r of NaOH = 2 × (23 + 16 + 1) = 80
So total mass on the left hand side = 98 + 80 = 178 ***[2 marks for 178, 1 mark for either 98 or 80]***
Total mass on right hand side
= $M_r(Na_2SO_4)$ + 2 × $M_r(H_2O)$
M_r of Na_2SO_4 = (2 × 23) + 32 + (4 × 16) = 142
2 × M_r of H_2O = 2 × [(2 × 1) + 16] = 36
142 + 36 = 178 ***[2 marks for 178, 1 mark for either 142 or 36]***
The total M_r on the left-hand side is equal to the total M_r on the right-hand side, so mass is conserved ***[1 mark]***.

p.126 — The Mole and Equations

Q1 a) N_2: $\frac{84}{28}$ = 3.0 mol ***[1 mark]***
H_2: $\frac{18}{2}$ = 9 mol ***[1 mark]***
NH_3: $\frac{102}{17}$ = 6.0 mol ***[1 mark]***
b) Divide by the smallest number of moles (3.0):
N_2: $\frac{3.0}{3.0}$ = 1 H_2: $\frac{9}{3.0}$ = 3 NH_3: $\frac{6.0}{3.0}$ = 2.0 ***[1 mark]***
The balanced symbol equation is:
$N_2 + 3H_2 \rightarrow 2NH_3$ ***[1 mark]***

p.127 — Limiting Reactants

Q1 M_r(KBr) = 119, M_r(KCl) = 74.5 ***[1 mark]***
No. of moles of KBr = 23.8 ÷ 119 = 0.200 mol ***[1 mark]***
From the reaction equation, 2 moles of KBr react to form 2 moles of KCl. So 0.200 moles of KBr reacts to form 0.200 moles of KCl ***[1 mark]***.
Mass KCl = 74.5 × 0.200 = 14.9 g ***[1 mark]***

p.128 — Concentrations of Solutions

Q1 mass = concentration × volume = 32 × 0.25 = 8 g ***[1 mark]***

Q2 volume = 15 ÷ 1000 = 0.015 dm^3 ***[1 mark]***
concentration = mass ÷ volume = 0.6 ÷ 0.015 = 40 g/dm^3 ***[1 mark]***

p.129 — Acids and Bases

Q1 red/orange ***[1 mark]***
Q2 alkaline ***[1 mark]***

p.130 — Strong Acids and Weak Acids

Q1 Any one of, e.g. sulfuric acid / nitric acid / hydrochloric acid ***[1 mark]***.

Q2 Change in pH = 3 – 6 = –3
Change in concentration of H^+ = $10^{-(-3)} = 10^3$ = 1000
So, the concentration of H^+ is 1000 times greater at pH = 3 than at pH = 6 ***[1 mark]***.

p.131 — Reactions of Acids

Q1 calcium carbonate + hydrochloric acid → calcium chloride + carbon dioxide + water
[1 mark for calcium chloride, 1 mark for carbon dioxide and water].

p.132 — The Reactivity Series

Q1 $2Na_{(s)} + 2H_2O_{(l)} \rightarrow 2NaOH_{(aq)} + H_{2(g)}$
[1 mark for correct reactants and products, 1 mark for balancing, 1 mark for state symbols]

p.133 — Separating Metals From Metal Oxides

Q1 $2ZnO + C \rightarrow 2Zn + CO_2$
[1 mark for the correct products, 1 mark for the correctly balanced equation]

Q2 Carbon is less reactive than calcium and therefore will not reduce calcium oxide / Calcium is more reactive than carbon, so calcium oxide won't be reduced by carbon ***[1 mark]***.

p.134 — Redox Reactions

Q1 a) $Zn_{(s)} + Fe^{2+}_{(aq)} \rightarrow Zn^{2+}_{(aq)} + Fe_{(s)}$ ***[1 mark]***
b) $Zn_{(s)}$ is being oxidised ***[1 mark]***. $Fe^{2+}_{(aq)}$ is being reduced ***[1 mark]***.

p.135 — Electrolysis

Q1 a) chlorine gas/Cl_2 ***[1 mark]***
b) sodium atoms/Na ***[1 mark]***

p.136 — Electrolysis of Aqueous Solutions

Q1 anode: $2Cl^- \rightarrow Cl_2 + 2e^-$ ***[1 mark]***
cathode: $Cu^{2+} + 2e^- \rightarrow Cu$ ***[1 mark]***

p.138 — Exothermic and Endothermic Reactions

Q1 exothermic ***[1 mark]***

p.139 — More Exothermic and Endothermic Reactions

Q1

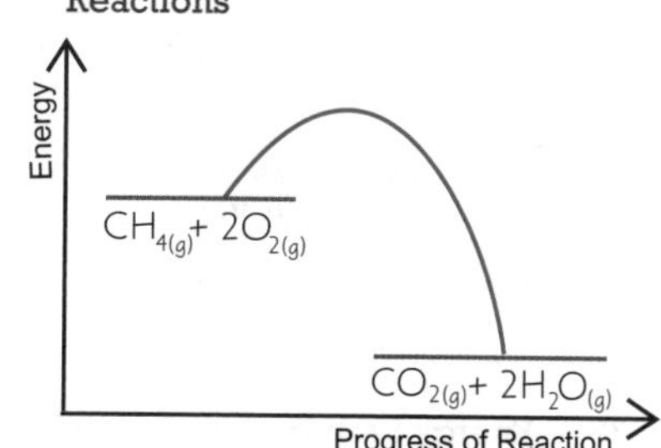

[1 mark for correct axes, 1 mark for correct energy levels of reactants and products, 1 mark for correct shape of curve linking the reactants to the products]

p.140 — Bond Energies

Q1 Energy required to break original bonds:
(1 × N≡N) + (3 × H–H)
= 941 kJ/mol + 1308 kJ/mol = 2249 kJ/mol ***[1 mark]***
Energy released by forming new bonds:
(6 × N–H)
= 2346 kJ/mol ***[1 mark]***
Overall energy change:
= 2249 kJ/mol – 2346 kJ/mol = –97 kJ/mol ***[1 mark]***

p.142 — Rates of Reaction

Q1 The activation energy for a reaction is the minimum amount of energy that particles need to react ***[1 mark]***.

p.143 — Factors Affecting Rates of Reaction

Q1 a) B ***[1 mark]***, because the powder has a higher surface area to volume ratio than the solid strip ***[1 mark]***.
b) B ***[1 mark]***, because the 4 mol/dm^3 HCl solution is more concentrated than the 2 mol/dm^3 solution ***[1 mark]***.

p.144 — Measuring Rates of Reaction

Q1 a) Add Na_2CO_3 to a flask containing HCl ***[1 mark]*** and take readings of the mass of the flask at regular intervals ***[1 mark]*** using a mass balance ***[1 mark]***. / Add Na_2CO_3 to a flask containing HCl ***[1 mark]*** and take regular readings of the volume of gas released ***[1 mark]*** using a gas syringe ***[1 mark]***. ***Maximum of 3 marks available.***
b) E.g. cm^3/s ***[1 mark]***

p.145 — Two Rates Experiments

Q1 E.g. volume of HCl added ***[1 mark]***, mass of magnesium used ***[1 mark]***.

p.146 — Finding Reaction Rates from Graphs

Q1 a) E.g.

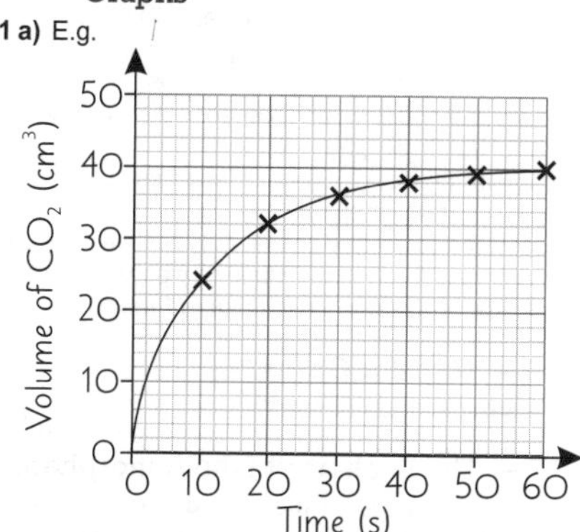

[1 mark for correctly marking on all 6 points, 1 mark for choosing a sensible scale for the axes, 1 mark for drawing a line of best fit.]

b) E.g.

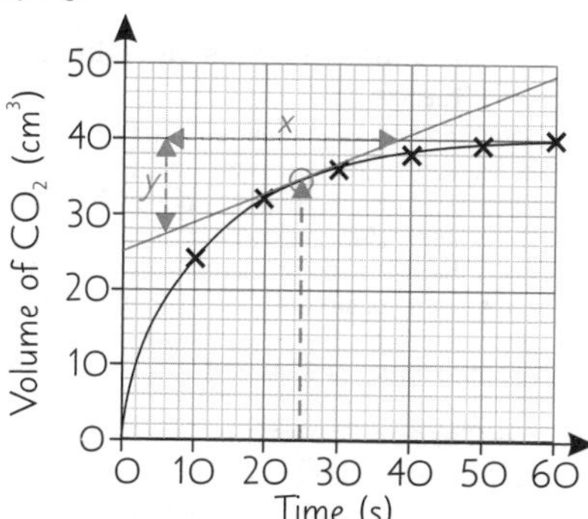

y = 40 – 27 = 13,
x = 38 – 6 = 32,
rate = y ÷ x = 13 ÷ 32 = 0.4 cm^3/s
[1 mark for drawing a tangent at 25 s, 1 mark for correctly calculating a change in y from the tangent, 1 mark for correctly calculating a change in x from the tangent and 1 mark for a rate between 0.3 cm³/s and 0.5 cm³/s]

p.147 — Reversible Reactions

Q1 A system is at equilibrium when both the forward and reverse reactions are happening at the same rate ***[1 mark]***.

p.148 — Le Chatelier's Principle

Q1 a) More $N_2O_{4(g)}$ produced ***[1 mark]***.
b) No effect ***[1 mark]***.
c) More CO_2 produced ***[1 mark]***.

p.150 — Hydrocarbons

Q1 a) $C_{10}H_{22}$ is more viscous than C_5H_{12} ***[1 mark]***.
b) $C_{10}H_{22}$ has a higher boiling point than C_5H_{12} ***[1 mark]***.
c) $C_{10}H_{22}$ is less flammable than C_5H_{12} ***[1 mark]***.

Q2 $C_3H_8 + 5O_2 \rightarrow 3CO_2 + 4H_2O$ ***[1 mark for correct reactants and products, 1 mark for correctly balancing]***

p.151 — Fractional Distillation

Q1 It suggests that the hydrocarbons in petrol have a lower boiling point than those in diesel ***[1 mark]***.

Q2 It's hot at the bottom and cooler at the top ***[1 mark]***.

p.152 — Uses and Cracking of Crude Oil

Q1 Number of C atoms = 5 – 2 = 3
Number of H atoms = 12 – 4 = 8
Formula = C_3H_8 ***[1 mark]***

p.153 — Purity and Formulations

Q1 a) The sample melts over a range of temperatures ***[1 mark]***. The melting point is lower than that of pure aspirin ***[1 mark]***.

b) Any range or single value within the range: 141-200 °C ***[1 mark]***

p.154 — Paper Chromatography

Q1 During paper chromatography, the molecules of each chemical in the sample move between the stationary phase and the mobile phase ***[1 mark]***. The mobile phase moves through the stationary phase over the course of the experiment, and anything that's dissolved in it will move with it ***[1 mark]***. The distance a compound moves through the stationary phase depends on how long it spends dissolved in the mobile phase compared to on the stationary phase ***[1 mark]***. Since different compounds will interact differently with the mobile phase and the stationary phase, they'll move different amounts through the stationary phase, and so be separated from each other ***[1 mark]***.

p.155 — Tests for Gases

Q1 carbon dioxide ***[1 mark]***

p.157 — The Evolution of the Atmosphere

Q1 Sedimentary rocks are formed when organic matter such as plant deposits or the shells and skeletons dead of marine animals fall to the seabed ***[1 mark]***. These become buried and compressed by sediments over millions of years forming rocks ***[1 mark]***.

p.158 — Greenhouse Gases and Climate Change

Q1 Any three from, e.g. polar ice caps melting / sea levels rising / costal erosion / changing rainfall patterns / some regions may have too much or too little water / it may be difficult to produce food / there may be an increase in the frequency and severity of storms. / the distribution of wild species may be affected ***[1 mark for each, up to a maximum of 3 marks]***.

p.159 — Carbon Footprints

Q1 E.g. governments can put a cap on the amount of greenhouse gases that a business can emit and issue licences for set amounts of emissions up to this point ***[1 mark]***. They can also impose taxes on companies according to the amount of greenhouse gases that they emit to encourage them to cut down on emissions ***[1 mark]***.

p.160 — Air Pollution

Q1 E.g. particulates (soot) ***[1 mark]***, unburnt fuels ***[1 mark]*** and carbon monoxide ***[1 mark]***.

p.161 — Finite and Renewable Resources

Q1 A finite resource, such as e.g. crude oil, will take a long time to replenish ***[1 mark]***. On the other hand, a renewable resource, such as e.g. timber, can be replaced within a relatively short time scale ***[1 mark]***.

p.162 — Reuse and Recycling

Q1 E.g. saves energy needed to extract metals from the earth / conserves limited supplies of metals from the earth / cuts down on the amount of waste going to landfill ***[1 mark for each]***.

p.163 — Life Cycle Assessments

Q1 Choice of material / manufacturing and packaging / using the product / product disposal ***[1 mark for each]***.

p.164 — Potable Water

Q1 E.g. filter the water first, using a wire mesh followed by sand and gravel beds ***[1 mark]***. Then sterilise the filtered water using chlorine / ozone / UV radiation ***[1 mark]***.

p.165 — Waste Water Treatment

Q1 Screening ***[1 mark]***, sedimentation ***[1 mark]***, digestion (aerobic / anaerobic) ***[1 mark]***.

p.167 — Energy Stores and Systems

Q1 Energy is transferred mechanically ***[1 mark]*** from the kinetic energy store of the wind ***[1 mark]*** to the kinetic energy store of the windmill ***[1 mark]***.

p.168 — Kinetic and Potential Energy Stores

Q1 The change in height is 5.0 m. So the energy transferred from the gravitational potential energy store is:
$E_p = mgh = 2.0 \times 9.8 \times 5.0 = 98$ J ***[1 mark]***
This is transferred to the kinetic energy store of the object, so $E_k = 98$ J ***[1 mark]***
$E_k = \frac{1}{2}mv^2$ so $v^2 = 2E_k \div m$ ***[1 mark]***
$= (2 \times 98) \div 2.0$ ***[1 mark]***
$= 98\ m^2/s^2$
$v = \sqrt{98} = 9.899...$
$= 9.9$ m/s (to 2 s.f.) ***[1 mark]***

p.169 — Specific Heat Capacity

Q1 $\Delta E = mc\Delta\theta$ so $\Delta\theta = \Delta E \div (m \times c)$ ***[1 mark]***
$= 50\ 000 \div (5 \times 4200) = 2.4$ °C ***[1 mark]***
So the new temperature
$= 5 + 2.4 = 7.4$ °C ***[1 mark]***

p.170 — Conservation of Energy and Power

Q1 $P = E \div t$
$t = 2 \times 60 = 120$ s ***[1 mark]***
$P = 4800 \div 120$ ***[1 mark]*** $= 40$ W ***[1 mark]***

p.171 — Reducing Unwanted Energy Transfers

Q1 Cavity wall insulation reduces energy transfer by convection ***[1 mark]***. It also reduces energy transfer by conduction ***[1 mark]*** because the insulating foam has a low thermal conductivity and so has a low rate of energy transfer from thermal energy stores ***[1 mark]***.

p.172 — Efficiency

Q1 efficiency = useful output energy transfer ÷ total input energy transfer
$= 225 \div 300$ ***[1 mark]*** $= 0.75$ ***[1 mark]***

Q2 efficiency = useful power output ÷ total power input
$= 900 \div 1200 = 0.75$ ***[1 mark]***
useful output energy transfer
= efficiency × total input energy transfer ***[1 mark]***
$= 0.75 \times 72\ 000$ ***[1 mark]*** $= 54\ 000$ J ***[1 mark]***

p.173 — Energy Resources and their Uses

Q1 a) renewable ***[1 mark]***

b) non-renewable ***[1 mark]***

c) non-renewable ***[1 mark]***

d) renewable ***[1 mark]***

p.174 — Wind, Solar and Geothermal

Q1 E.g. wind power can be unreliable as sometimes there's no wind or the turbines have to be stopped because the wind is too strong, so they don't provide a constant supply of energy ***[1 mark]***. Geothermal power plants can run continuously as they transfer energy from the thermal energy store of the ground ***[1 mark]***.

p.175 — Hydro-electricity, Waves and Tides

Q1 E.g. they disturb the seabed / they disturb the habitats of marine animals ***[1 mark]***

p.176 — Bio-fuels and Non-renewables

Q1 Any two from: e.g. they're reliable / they're comparatively cheap to run / they can respond quickly to changes in demand ***[2 marks]***

Q2 E.g. burning oil releases carbon dioxide, which contributes to global warming ***[1 mark]***. It also produces sulfur dioxide which causes acid rain, which is harmful to trees and animals and can have far-reaching effects in ecosystems ***[1 mark]***. Oil spills also occur when transporting oil, which can harm/kill animals that live in and around the sea ***[1 mark]***.

p.177 — Trends in Energy Resource Use

Q1 Any two from: e.g. building new power plants is expensive / people don't want to live near new power plants / renewable energy resources are less reliable than non-renewable energy resources / hybrid cars are more expensive than equivalent petrol cars ***[2 marks]***.

p.179 — Current and Circuit Symbols

Q1 $Q = It$ so $t = Q \div I$ ***[1 mark]***
$= 28\ 800 \div 8.0$ ***[1 mark]***
$= 3600$ s (= 1 hour) ***[1 mark]***

Q2 E.g.

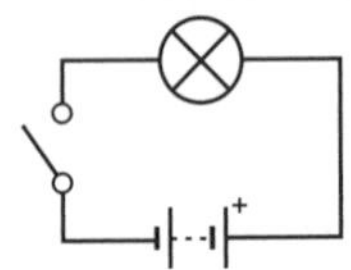

[1 mark for each correct symbol connected in a single loop, otherwise, award 2 marks for correct symbols in an incorrect loop]

p.180 — Resistance and V = IR

Q1 $V = IR$ so $R = V \div I$ ***[1 mark]***
$= 230 \div 5$ ***[1 mark]*** $= 46\ \Omega$ ***[1 mark]***

p.181 — Resistance and I-V Characteristics

Q1 a)

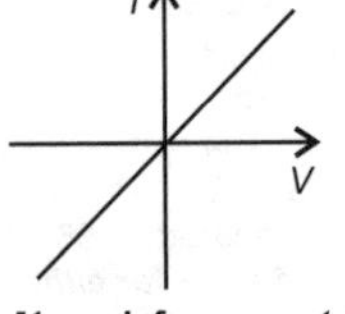

[1 mark for correct axes, 1 mark for a straight line through the origin]

b)

[1 mark for correct axes, 1 mark for correct shape]

p.182 — Circuit Devices

Q1 a) E.g. automatic night lights — a light automatically turns on when it gets dark ***[1 mark]***.

b) E.g. thermostats — the heating automatically turns on/off at a certain temperature ***[1 mark]***.

p.183 — Series Circuits

Q1 $V = 12 + 12 = 24$ V ***[1 mark]***
$R = 2 + 3 + 7 = 12\ \Omega$ ***[1 mark]***
$V = IR$ so $I = V \div R$ ***[1 mark]***
$= 24 \div 12$ ***[1 mark]*** $= 2$ A ***[1 mark]***

p.184 — Parallel Circuits

Q1 The current through the circuit increases ***[1 mark]*** and the total resistance of the circuit decreases to less than the resistance of the smallest resistor ***[1 mark]***.

Q2 E.g.

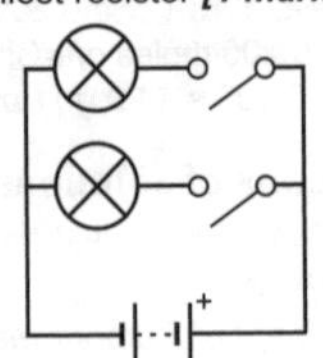

[1 mark for the correct circuit symbols, 1 mark for two bulbs connected in parallel, 1 mark for both switches being on the same branches as the lamps]

p.185 — Investigating Resistance

Q1

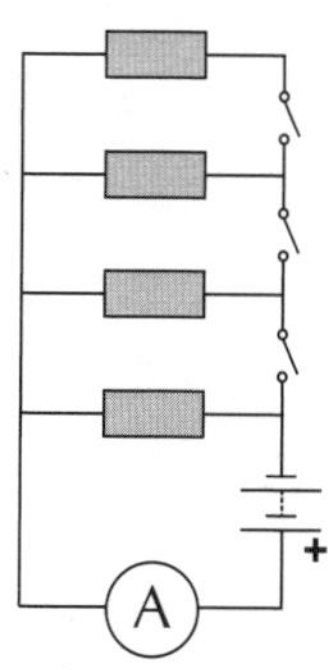

[1 mark for a circuit with several resistors connected in parallel and switches allowing one resistor to be added at a time.]

p.186 — Electricity in the Home

Q1 a) 230 V ***[1 mark]***

b) 0 V ***[1 mark]***

c) 0 V ***[1 mark]***

p.187 — Power of Electrical Appliances

Q1 $P = E \div t = 6000 \div 30$ ***[1 mark]***
$= 200$ W ***[1 mark]***

Q2 $P = E \div t$ so $E = P \times t$ ***[1 mark]***
$= 250 \times (2 \times 60 \times 60)$
$= 1\ 800\ 000$ J ***[1 mark]***
$E = 375 \times (2 \times 60 \times 60) = 2\ 700\ 000$ J ***[1 mark]***
So change in energy is
$2\ 700\ 000 - 1\ 800\ 000 = 900\ 000$ J ***[1 mark]***

p.188 — More on Power

Q1 $E = Q \times V = 10\ 000 \times 200$ ***[1 mark]***
$= 2\ 000\ 000$ J ***[1 mark]***

Q2 $P = V \times I = 12 \times 4.0$ ***[1 mark]*** $= 48$ W ***[1 mark]***

Q3 $P = V \times I = 230 \times 10.0 = 2300$ W ***[1 mark]***
This is equal to $P = I^2R$ ***[1 mark]***
$R = P \div I^2$ ***[1 mark]*** $= 2300 \div 10.0^2$ ***[1 mark]***
$= 23\ \Omega$ ***[1 mark]***

p.189 — The National Grid

Q1 The national grid distributes electricity at a high p.d. and a low current ***[1 marks]***. A high p.d. means that it can distribute lots of power per second (as power = p.d. × current) ***[1 mark]***. Using a low current reduces energy losses ***[1 mark]*** which makes the national grid efficient at transferring energy ***[1 mark]***.

p.191 — The Particle Model and Motion in Gases

Q1 Decreasing the temperature of the gas means that the gas particles have less energy in their kinetic energy stores ***[1 mark]***. They collide with the container less often ***[1 mark]*** and exert a smaller force when they do collide, meaning that the gas pressure is lower ***[1 mark]***.

p.192 — Density of Materials

Q1 First find the cube's volume:
$1.5 \times 1.5 \times 1.5 = 3.375$ cm^3 ***[1 mark]***
The cube's density is 3500 kg/m^3.
1 g/cm^3 = 1000 kg/m^3,
so this is $3500 \div 1000 = 3.5$ g/cm^3 ***[1 mark]***.
$\rho = m/V$ so $m = \rho \times V$ ***[1 mark]***
$= 3.5 \times 3.375 = 11.8125$ ***[1 mark]***
$= 11.8$ g (to 3 s.f.) ***[1 mark]***

p.193 — Internal Energy and Changes of State

Q1 Heating the solid transfers energy to the kinetic energy stores of the particles (increasing the internal energy) ***[1 mark]***. When the particles have enough energy in their kinetic energy stores, they can break the bonds holding them together ***[1 mark]***. The solid changes state and becomes liquid ***[1 mark]***.

p.194 — Specific Latent Heat

Q1 $E = m \times L = 0.25 \times 120\ 000$ ***[1 mark]***
$= 30\ 000$ J ***[1 mark]***

p.195 — Developing the Model of the Atom

Q1 a) The centre of an atom is a tiny, positively charged nucleus ***[1 mark]***. This is made up of protons and neutrons and is the source of most of the atom's mass ***[1 mark]***. Most of the atom is empty space ***[1 mark]***. Electrons orbit the nucleus at set energy levels ***[1 mark]***.

b) The radius of an atom is around 1×10^{-10} m ***[1 mark]***. The radius of a nucleus is 10 000 times smaller than this ***[1 mark]***.

p.196 — Isotopes and Nuclear Radiation

Q1 E.g. Alpha would not be suitable because it is stopped by a few cm of air or a sheet of paper ***[1 mark]***. It would not be able to pass through the packaging to sterilise the equipment ***[1 mark]***.

p.197 — Nuclear Equations

Q1 Beta particles ***[1 mark]***

Q2 ${}^{219}_{86}\text{Rn} \rightarrow {}^{215}_{84}\text{Po} + {}^{4}_{2}\text{He}$
[1 mark for correct layout, 1 mark for correct symbol for an alpha particle, 1 mark for total atomic and mass numbers being equal on both sides]

p.198 — Half-life

Q1 After one half-life the count-rate will be
$40 \div 2 = 20$ cps ***[1 mark]***
After a second: $20 \div 2 = 10$ cps
After a third: $10 \div 2 = 5$ cps ***[1 mark]***
So the ratio is 5:40 = 1:8 ***[1 mark]***

p.199 — Irradiation and Contamination

Q1 E.g. keeping sources in lead-lined boxes / standing behind shielding ***[1 mark]***

Q2 Irradiation ***[1 mark]***

p.201 — Contact and Non-Contact Forces

Q1 Contact force: air resistance ***[1 mark]***
Non-contact force: gravitational force ***[1 mark]***

Q2 a) Any two from: e.g. speed / distance / mass / temperature ***[2 marks]***

b) Any two from: e.g. displacement / momentum / force / acceleration / velocity ***[2 marks]***

p.202 — Weight, Mass and Gravity

Q1 a) $W = mg = 5 \times 9.8$ ***[1 mark]*** $= 49$ N ***[1 mark]***

b) $W = 5 \times 1.6$ ***[1 mark]*** $= 8$ N ***[1 mark]***

p.203 — Resultant Forces and Work Done

Q1 20 cm = 0.2 m ***[1 mark]***
$W = Fs = 20 \times 0.2$ ***[1 mark]*** $= 4$ J ***[1 mark]***

p.204 — Calculating Forces

Q1

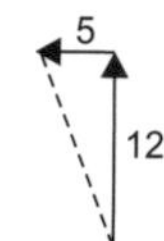

Resultant = 13 N
[1 mark for a correct scale drawing, 1 mark for correct resultant force]

p.205 — Forces and Elasticity

Q1 2 cm = 0.02 m ***[1 mark]***
$F = ke$ so $k = F \div e$ ***[1 mark]***
$= 1 \div 0.02$ ***[1 mark]***
$= 50$ N/m ***[1 mark]***

p.206 — Investigating Springs

Q1 2.5 cm = 0.025 m ***[1 mark]***
$E_e = \frac{1}{2}ke^2 = \frac{1}{2} \times 40 \times (0.025)^2$ ***[1 mark]***
$= 0.0125$ J ***[1 mark]***

p.207 — Distance, Displacement, Speed and Velocity

Q1 $s = vt$ so $v = s \div t$ ***[1 mark]***
$= 200 \div 25$ ***[1 mark]*** $= 8$ m/s ***[1 mark]***

Q2 a) Distance travelled = 1500 m ***[1 mark]***

b) Marie's journey ends at the same position as it started, so the displacement is 0 m ***[1 mark]***.

p.208 — Acceleration

Q1 $u = 0$ m/s, $v = 7$ m/s, $a = g = 9.8$ m/s^2,
$s = (v^2 - u^2) \div 2a$ ***[1 mark]***
$= (49 - 0) \div (2 \times 9.8)$ ***[1 mark]***
$= 2.5$ m ***[1 mark]***

p.209 — Distance-Time and Velocity-Time Graphs

Q1 E.g.

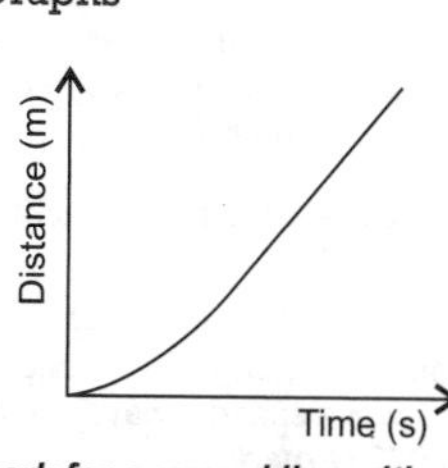

[1 mark for a curved line with an increasing positive gradient, 1 mark for the line becoming a straight line with a positive gradient]

Q2

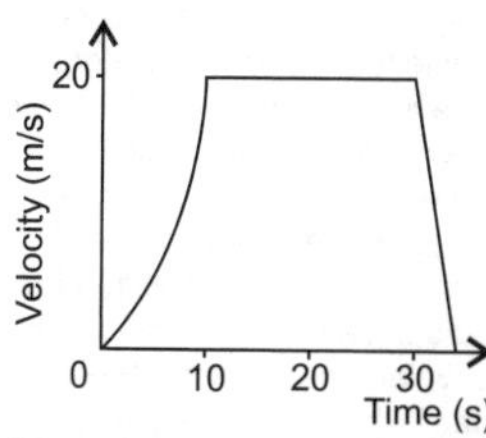

[1 mark for an upwards curved acceleration line to 20m/s, 1 mark for a straight line representing steady speed, 1 mark for a straight line representing deceleration]

p.210 — Terminal Velocity

Q1 As the ball falls, it accelerates towards earth due to the force of gravity ***[1 mark]***. Air resistance means that eventually the resultant force on the ball is zero ***[1 mark]***. The object cannot go any faster — this is its terminal velocity ***[1 mark]***.

p.211 — Newton's First and Second Laws

Q1 $F = ma = (80 + 10) \times 0.25$ ***[1 mark]***
$= 22.5$ N ***[1 mark]***

p.212 — Inertia and Newton's Third Law

Q1 When you lean on a wall, you exert a force on the wall. Due to Newton's Third Law, the wall also exerts an equal but opposite force (normal contact force) back on you ***[1 mark]***. You also exert a force on the ground and the ground exerts a force on you ***[1 mark]***. The resultant force is zero so you remain stationary ***[1 mark]***.

p.213 — Investigating Motion

Q1 A piece of card with a gap in the middle is attached to the trolley, so that two bits of card stick up and interrupt the light gate beam as it moves ***[1 mark]***. The length of each bit of card is input into the light gate software, and the light gate measures the velocity of each bit of card as the trolley moves ***[1 mark]***. It can use the two velocity values to find the acceleration ***[1 mark]***.

p.214 — Stopping Distances

Q1 Any one from: e.g. speed / road surface / condition of tyres / condition of brakes ***[1 mark]***

p.215 — Reaction Times

Q1 a) $v^2 - u^2 = 2as$
$v^2 = 2 \times 9.8 \times 0.162 + 0$ ***[1 mark]*** $= 3.1752$
$v = \sqrt{3.1752} = 1.781...$ m/s ***[1 mark]***
$a = \Delta v \div t$ so
$t = \Delta v \div a$ ***[1 mark]***
$= 1.781... \div 9.8$ ***[1 mark]*** $= 0.181...$ s
$= 0.18$ s (to 2 s.f.) ***[1 mark]***

b) His reaction time is longer in the evening ***[1 mark]*** so whilst driving, he may take longer to react to a hazard, meaning his thinking distance would be longer ***[1 mark]***.

p.216 — Momentum

Q1 $p = mv = 60 \times 3$ ***[1 mark]*** = 180 kg m/s ***[1 mark]***

Q2 Before the gun fires the bullet, the total momentum is zero (neither the gun nor the bullet are moving) ***[1 mark]***. When the bullet leaves the gun, it has momentum in one direction ***[1 mark]***. The gun moves backwards so it has momentum in the opposite direction ***[1 mark]***. This means that the total momentum after the bullet has been fired is zero. Momentum has been conserved ***[1 mark]***.

p.218 — Transverse and Longitudinal Waves

Q1 7.5 cm ÷ 100 = 0.075 m ***[1 mark]***
wave speed = frequency × wavelength, so
frequency = wave speed ÷ wavelength ***[1 mark]***
= 0.15 ÷ 0.075 ***[1 mark]***
= 2 Hz ***[1 mark]***

p.219 — Experiments With Waves

Q1 E.g. attach a signal generator to a dipper and place it in a ripple tank filled with water to create some waves ***[1 mark]***. Place a screen underneath the ripple tank, then turn on a strobe light and dim the other lights in the room ***[1 mark]***. Adjust the frequency of the strobe light until the ripples appear to freeze ***[1 mark]***. Measure the distance between shadow lines that are 10 wavelengths apart on the screen beneath the tank, then divide this number by 10 — this is equal to the wavelength of the ripples ***[1 mark]***.

p.220 — Wave Behaviour and Electromagnetic Waves

Q1 Radio waves ***[1 mark]***

Q2 Visible light spectrum ***[1 mark]***

p.221 — Refraction

Q1

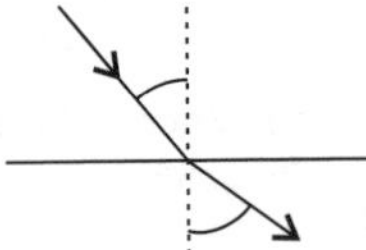

[1 mark for a correct diagram showing rays and the normal, 1 mark for an angle of incidence of 40°, 1 mark for an angle of refraction greater than 40°]

p.222 — Radio Waves

Q1 E.g. hands-free Bluetooth® headsets to use in the car ***[1 mark]***.

Q2 Radio waves can be produced by alternating currents / oscillations of charged particles in electrical circuits ***[1 mark]***.

p.223 — EM Waves and Their Uses

Q1 They can pass easily through the Earth's watery atmosphere without being absorbed ***[1 mark]***.

p.224 — More Uses of EM Waves

Q1 E.g. X-ray photographs ***[1 mark]***
treating cancer (radiotherapy) ***[1 mark]***

Q2 Visible light is easy to refract to the angles that are needed to trap the light ray inside the optical fibre ***[1 mark]***. Visible light is also not easily absorbed or scattered in a fibre ***[1 mark]***.

p.225 — Investigating Infrared Radiation

Q1 The black mug will initially cool at a faster rate ***[1 mark]***. This is because a black surface emits more infrared radiation than a white one ***[1 mark]***, so more energy is transferred away from the thermal energy store of the tea ***[1 mark]***.

p.226 — Dangers of Electromagnetic Waves

Q1 Any two from: e.g. UV radiation damages surface cells / cause sunburn / cause premature ageing of the skin / cause blindness / increase the risk of skin cancer.
[2 marks — 1 mark for each correct effect]

Q2 7 mSv ÷ 0.7 mSv = 10
So the added risk of harm from a CT scan is ten times higher than from an X-ray ***[1 mark]***.

p.227 — Permanent and Induced Magnets

Q1

field strongest

N S

[1 mark for a correct diagram, 1 mark for an indication of the field being strongest at the poles]

Q2 E.g. Permanent magnets produce their own magnetic fields but induced magnets become magnets when they're in a magnetic field ***[1 mark]***. The force between an induced magnet and a permanent magnet is always attractive, but between two permanent magnets it can be attractive or repulsive ***[1 mark]***.

p.228 — Electromagnetism

Q1 E.g. for current out of the page:

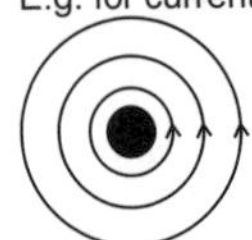

[1 mark for concentric circles with a correct direction]

Q2 a)

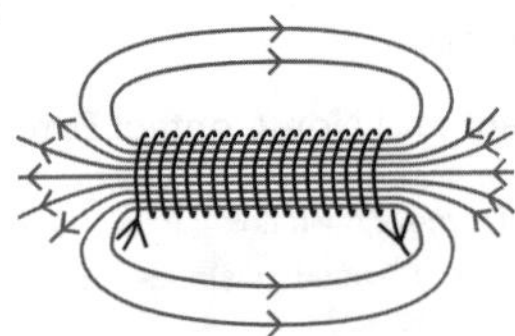

[1 mark for uniform field inside coil, 1 mark for field similar to a bar magnet outside of coil]

b) E.g. put a block of iron in the centre of the solenoid ***[1 mark]***.

p.229 — The Motor Effect

Q1 35 cm = 0.35 m ***[1 mark]***
Rearrange $F = B \times I \times l$
for the magnetic flux density, B:
$B = F \div (I \times l)$ ***[1 mark]***
= 9.8 ÷ (5.0 × 0.35) ***[1 mark]***
= 5.6 T ***[1 mark]***

p.230 — Electric Motors

Q1 Into the page ***[1 mark]***

Index

Index

Index

Index